TROPICAL SOILS

A COMPREHENSIVE STUDY OF THEIR GENESIS

TROPICAL SOILS

A COMPREHENSIVE STUDY OF THEIR GENESIS

by

E. C. J. MOHR
LATE PROFESSOR OF SOILS, UNIVERSITY OF UTRECHT

F. A. VAN BAREN
PROFESSOR OF SOILS, UNIVERSITY OF UTRECHT

J. VAN SCHUYLENBORGH
LECTURER IN SOIL CHEMISTRY AND PHYSICS,
UNIVERSITY OF AMSTERDAM

Third, revised and enlarged edition
1972

MOUTON – ICHTIAR BARU – VAN HOEVE
THE HAGUE – PARIS – DJAKARTA

Printed in The Netherlands by Geuze Dordrecht
Library of congress catalog card number 72-090087
ISBN 90 222 0229 1

PREFACE

It is with regret that this preface to a fully revised and, as far as the contents are concerned, enlarged new edition has to be started with stating that the senior author of the previous edition, Professor Dr E. C. J. Mohr died on January 22nd, 1970. Till the last weeks of his 96 years and 7 months of life he showed interest in the re-writing and re-shaping of Tropical Soils, which was in its former set-up so strongly related to our deceased colleague's standard work on the Soils of the Tropics, in particular to Indonesia. It indeed had been clear from the outset when a new edition of this textbook had to be considered that Professor Mohr, then 94 years old, could not participate actively in the preparation of the present volume. Therefore the writer of this preface sought the cooperation of a younger specialist in tropical soils. He was extremely content to find Dr J. van Schuylenborgh, former Professor of Soils, University of Indonesia, Bogor, now lecturer in Soil Chemistry and Soil Physics at the Laboratory of Physical Geography and Soil Science of the Amsterdam University, willing to undertake the job of assisting in making the textbook as up-to-date as possible. This new cooperation resulted in a full reorganisation of the text. The book is now composed of three parts. The first part is an only slightly revised and modernized version of the earlier introductory chapters on the soil forming factors climate, rocks, and rock minerals. The second part deals with the soils as they dominantly occur in tropical regions. A new approach is introduced as far as the genetical aspects of oxisols (laterite soils and latosols) are concerned, whereas new chapters on acid sulphate soils and paddy soils have been added. Part III finally contains a detailed discussion of experimental data and theoretical considerations of the basic dynamics of weathering and soil formation.

It is felt that the textbook in its modernized form will substantially contribute to a better understanding of pedogenesis in general and in tropical regions specifically.

Special thanks are due to Professor Dr E. G. Hallsworth who was so kind to provide us with the analyses of some laterite soils; to Dr L. v. d. Plas for many discussions of mineralogical problems in weathering and soil formation; to Mr N. van Breemen who collected and adapted the data for the chapters on paddy and acid sulphate soils; and to Mr W. A. Blokhuis, who commented the chapter on Vertisols.

We are very thankful to Mrs Van Schuylenborgh for the undertaking of typing the manuscript, to Mr G. Buurman and Mr Z. v. Druten for drawing and preparing the numerous graphs and pictures, to Mrs Koop-Nisbet for the careful correction of the English text, to Mrs G. Duvert for the final correction of the galley-proofs, and to the publishers for their willingness to fully meet the requirements of the authors notably with a view to the number of coloured photographs that illustrate the text.

F. A. VAN BAREN

AMSTERDAM, JANUARY 1970

CONTENTS

PART I

FUNDAMENTALS OF CLIMATE,
ROCKS AND MINERALS, WEATHERING,
AND ORGANIC MATTER TRANSFORMA-
TIONS

CHAPTER 1

ATMOSPHERIC CLIMATE
AND
SOIL CLIMATE

When considering climatic influences and climate – the latter conceived as the complex of climatological characteristics of any given place – a sharp distinction should be drawn between the climate in the atmosphere *above* the soil and the actual climate *in* the soil itself, i.e. the *soil climate*. Direct relationship with the soil and with soil forming or soil destroying processes is limited to the soil climate, the atmosphere above only being involved in so far as it exerts any influence on the aforementioned soil climate. Investigations and observations concerning these matters have led to a further distinction.

While meteorology is interested in the atmosphere as such, climatology concerns itself with the relations between the atmosphere and the earth's surface. These relations are generally studied on broad lines, as for example over the surface of the whole earth or at least that of one great continent. It is customary for meteorological records to be made, as far as possible, without taking into consideration incidental features of the earth's surface. As a result, the observations go no further and no deeper than an imaginary plane running at a tangent to the tops of vegetation, buildings, or whatever else may project above the earth's surface. Now, between that plane running over e.g. a forest, corn-field or meadow, and the surface of the soil, there is a relatively thin layer of atmosphere which is of the utmost importance, for it is the sphere in which plants, animals and human beings are living. Hence the name 'biosphere' which is sometimes given to it. Apparently climatic conditions within this region diverge to such an extent from those above the imaginary plane already mentioned, that it was deemed necessary to develop a specific climatic conception, called by some the 'microclimate', as opposed to the 'macroclimate' found at a higher level. The present authors do not consider that these expressions afford an adequate distinction since they give no indication of factual difference. There are indeed many differences between the two climates and this is not simply a question of dimensions. The essential feature is that in any particular landscape, taking the imaginary plane mentioned above as a dividing line, the 'macroclimate' is related to the free atmosphere above, and the 'microclimate' to the atmosphere below that line, i.e. within the vegetational cover or, in any case, quite close to the soil. This explains why a botanist favours speaking of the *'climat végétal'* (Scaëtta, 1937) whereas a pedologist prefers the expression *'near-the-soil climate'* as did Geiger (1927), when he spoke of 'das bodennahe Klima'. It is obvious that this climate requires its own exclusive observations and study.

In the same way, *soil climate* may be analysed. The soil is penetrated to a certain

4

depth, from the surface downwards, by the roots of vegetation. This part of the soil is also populated, however, by a flora of fungi and bacteria, and even by manifold soil fauna. All these forms of life are influenced by, and in their turn influence the climate of the soil, i.e. the nature of the air between the soil particles, water content and condition, etc. Further down – though this may not always be so – there is a part of the soil in which no form of life is to be detected, although organic matter, in a liquid or solid form, may be present. In these deeper soil layers, physical and chemical processes take place to the furthest extent reached by the soil solutions and gases, i.e. the underlying parent rock. But in the upper layers, offering shelter to animal and plant life, much more occurs, the transformations taking place in a very different way from those in the deeper lifeless layers. So we are inclined to divide the 'soil climate' ('pedoclimate') into two parts and to distinguish between a '*life-containing-soil climate*' and a '*lifeless-soil climate*'. The following summarizes the climate forms discussed above:

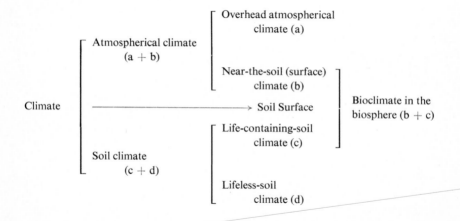

If a vegetation consists mostly of trees of some considerable height (as in a forest), it may be convenient, or indeed even necessary, to draw a further distinction between climatic conditions in the tree-tops (b-high) and those just above the soil (b-low), in the grass and shrub cover, or in field crops.

When compiling and elaborating observations regarding the overhead atmospherical climate (a), meteorologists and climatologists generally confine themselves to temperature, humidity, precipitation, wind velocity, etc. Consequently, information concerning the surface climate (b) is scarce, that relating to the life-containing-soil climate (c) is scarcer still, while information on the lifeless-soil climate (d) is practically non-existent. This is undoubtedly the explanation of why, up to the present, discussions on the differences between soils and soil properties have been based almost entirely on data concerning differences in the overhead climate (a), while the surface climate (b) has been almost completely disregarded.

Soil under forests, brushwood and dense crops has no direct contact with (a), but it has with (b). Now if it were possible, given a set of values for (a), to deduce, by a simple process, a corresponding set of values for (b), there would be no occasion to lay stress on the necessity for collecting observations regarding the near-the-soil climate (b). At present, however, the latter data is few and far between, with the result that the available information must suffice. It will be seen, that as the relation between (a) and (c) is dependent upon a prior knowledge of (b), and between (a), (b) and (d) upon a prior knowledge of (c), the greater the physical distance between the two extremes, the less reliable are conclusions based on a presumed direct inter-dependency. An essential consequence of this differentiation is the necessity, in so far as is possible, to investigate each distinct climate individually. Investigation carried out in that way would automatically prove their relationship, thereby leading to mutually beneficial results.

Climate is a complex conception, and as such it cannot be measured as an entity. It consists, however, of a number of *climatic factors*, each of which is measurable and consequently lends itself to scientific study. At this stage those various factors, known to have an influence on the soil and on what takes place within it, will be discussed. They are:

1) *Temperature:* – sunshine and cloudiness, – radiation.
2) *Water conditions:* – in atmosphere and soil.
3) *Humidity of the air:* – precipitation, – evaporation, and in addition to this
4) *The nature and state of vegetation:* – in so far as it affects the soil climate.

There may be other factors exercising an influence, but, if there are, they are as yet unknown.

1.1. TEMPERATURE

In the first place, a few brief comments on *radiation* should ensure a complete understanding of the problems attendant upon the temperature of the soil. The sun's rays directed to the earth, which are for the most part short-wave, shed only a part of their energy (in fact less than 50%) directly and unchanged on the surface of the earth. About 20% is absorbed in the atmosphere and transformed into heat. The rest, some 35%, is dispersed in the atmosphere as diffused radiation.

The direct radiation is absorbed by the soil and vegetation to a great extent, leaving a divergent fraction that is reflected, and which, when retracing its path, divides again, and is partially absorbed in the atmosphere as heat and partially lost in space. The short-wave rays absorbed by the soil raise the soil temperature. The soil in turn radiates energy into the atmosphere in the form of long-wave heat rays, and this radiation is, as we shall see, the principal means by which an increase in warmth is achieved in the lower atmospherical layers (b) as well as in several km of the overhead atmosphere (a). In addition, part of the heat generated at the soil surface is conducted to deeper soil layers, thereby influencing the temperature in (c). The 20% of sun-energy which is absorbed in the atmosphere is also converted into heat, thereby raising the air temperature. Half of the diffused radiation mentioned above serves to increase the effect of the direct radiation of the sun to the soil, while the other half is lost upwards into space.

This radiation, however, is diminished by further absorption into the atmosphere during its movement in both directions. After sunset, the irradiation of the sun is, naturally, nil, while that of the moon and stars may be ignored for all practical purposes. The irradiation upwards, from a more or less bare soil surface, or from vegetation and so on, continues however, and it increases markedly on clear nights when there is a very low water vapour-tension in the atmosphere. This results in an acute, rapid decline in the temperature of the soil surface. Since this radiation into interstellar space is not governed by the temperature of the atmosphere, the soil temperature can, in certain circumstances, fall several degrees below that of the atmosphere (as with night frosts). Quoting Geiger (1927), Zunker (1930, p. 209) says: 'It is not seldom that the air near the soil (about 30 cm) is 4–5 degrees C, and sometimes even more than 8 degrees, colder than that at a height of 2 metres.' As these observations were made in temperate regions of Europe, still greater deviations may be expected in the tropics, especially where the air is extremely dry.

Meanwhile, a continuous transference of heat takes place within the soil, downwards as well as upwards, depending on the differences in temperature between the successive soil layers. In a similar way, there is a continuous transfer of heat, due to convection, between the soil surface and the atmosphere (b) above it.

Summarizing the processes involving a change of energy, the soil gains heat mainly by the absorption of direct and indirect (diffuse) radiation from the sun, and to a far lesser degree by the transfer of heat from a warmer atmosphere. The soil loses heat by radiation into space, and by convection into a colder atmosphere. As a general rule, radiation is a far more important factor than convection in this respect, except in cases where the soil surface is covered by rather dense vegetation. In addition, vegetation consumes a certain amount of irradiated energy required for the photo-synthetic production of organic matter, and a much greater deal of heat for its transpiration, so that consequently the temperature of the surface atmosphere (b) is governed by whether the vegetation is high or low, although this process is rather complicated. Nevertheless, vegetation does lower the soil temperature (c) to a considerable extent.

The idea that sunshine is more constant in the tropics than in the temperate zone is a popular misconception, for in reality it is as variable as anywhere else on earth, due to the shifting of the rainbelt at annual periods, the monsoons, and especially the topography of the tropical regions. Thus in Java (Braak, 1928) the mean monthly sunshine – expressed as a percentage of an ideal figure, i.e. allowing for no clouds at all – varies between 90% and more, for stations on plains at sea-level, and 20% and less, in the case of several stations situated on mountain slopes. Yearly mean averages, therefore, are found to vary between 25% and 80%. There would be no purpose in attempting to calculate the mean values of these figures, but nevertheless it should be borne in mind that they are of greater significance in relation to soil temperature at places where the soil is not completely shaded by vegetation.

The actual hours of sunshine in any given period are more suitable for comparison when considering the temperate zones of the earth. De Bilt (in the centre of the Netherlands), for example, enjoys nearly 1600 hours sunshine a year while Djakarta has a mean annual total of more than 2300 hours. It is safe to say that the lowlands of Indo-

nesia receive a monthly average of 120–300 hours of sunshine, in other words 2000–
3000 hours annually. In the higher altitudes of mountain slopes, these figures occasionally drop to as little as 50 hours a month, or to 1300 hours a year, whereas in the
eastern part of the Archipelago (Makassar, Timur-Kupang) monthly figures of 300
hours and yearly ones of more than 3000 hours are no exception. It is impossible to
discuss the situation in other tropical countries in this respect, for in practically every
case relevant meteorological data is lacking, although it may be taken for granted that
similar differences will occur. It would appear to be imperative, therefore, that sunshine records be kept for the more important tropical countries, not only as an aid to
plant physiology and plant production, but especially to benefit the study of soil
temperature and soil processes.

The temperature of the overhead atmosphere (a) in the scheme on page 4 follows a
rather constant daily pattern. At sea-level, a minimum of about 20° C is reached just
before sunrise, followed by a steady increase in temperature to a maximum of 30–33°
at 12.30–14.30. This is followed by a drop in temperature which is regular or irregular
until the next morning, depending on current atmospherical conditions such as rain
showers and gusts of wind. The daily average is somewhere between 25 and 27° C.
As elevation increases, this figure drops by approximately 0.6° C for every 100 metres,
so that at a height of 1000 metres it will be about 20°, and at 2000 metres about 14°,
and so on. The yearly graduation of these figures is remarkably small for the equatorial
zone. In Djakarta for example, it amounts to no more than 1.5 degrees. As the distance
from the equator increases, however, while still remaining within the tropics, the annual
range of temperature increases correspondingly. When the sun is at its zenith and the
day at its longest, the mean daily temperature at sea-level in such areas often rises to
35° or more, yet six months later it may fall by as much as 20°.

Going a step further, the question arises of what influences the temperature of the
inter-vegetation, near-the-soil climate (b). There is a scarcity of available data, and
furthermore almost all that is available was recorded in the temperate zone (Germany:
Schubert, 1929). The observations made at Poona (Ramdas et al. 1934), therefore, are
more valuable in this respect for they brought to light important differences between
the overhead atmospheric climate of (a) and the surface layers of atmosphere (b), the
latter having been determined by a number of synchronous observations, made within
such crops as sugar-cane, jowar and wheat. Nevertheless, it still proved impossible to
draw any simple, general conclusions. 'The results,' it is stated, 'suggest that there is no
easily recognisable relationship between temperature within a crop and those in the
'open'. If it is desired to study the actual climatic conditions within a crop, therefore, it
may be necessary to measure the temperature there directly.'

Later investigations (Ramdas and Katti, 1934) into the near-the-soil climate (b)
above a bare black cotton soil (regur) provided remarkable results for the first metre.
It was discovered that when the soil surface – and here we are already in the realm of
the soil climate (c) – was heated intensely, say to 74° C, by radiation, then the atmosphere just above the soil (b) was also heated, and its temperature rose higher, especially during the afternoon, than that of the high level regions, even though it was only
by a few degrees. On the other hand, the temperature of (b), at night, fell below that of

(a). In fact, and this is very remarkable, the lowest temperature measured was at a height of 15–30 cm, shortly before sunrise.

Within a crop, whether it be grass or some other higher or denser vegetation, the temperature range between the maximum, in the afternoon, and the minimum, in the early morning, is of course smaller than that above a bare soil. The soil under grass receives less direct radiation, while that under forest receives practically none at all. Furthermore, evaporation from transpiring leaves reduces the temperature of the surrounding atmosphere still more. It is impossible, therefore, to predict the state or the tendency to change, at any given moment, of the course of a temperature curve for the near-the-soil atmosphere (b). This is due to the fact that this is governed to a great extent by such characteristic factors as the colour of the soil surface, the water content of the topsoil, and the state of cultivated or wild vegetation.

When considering the 'biosphere', which consists of the upper soil layers (c) together with (b), it is advisable at the outset to draw a distinction between conditions which promote, and those which prevent, sun radiation to the soil. In the latter case, in a dense tropical forest for example, the first few mm of the soil surface will, with slightly lesser deviations, follow the temperature of the air (b). In all other cases enormous differences in temperature, due to radiation, may be observed. The deeper one penetrates into the soil, the less these differences become noticeable until they cease to exist at all. This permits observations being made with regard to daily or yearly deviations, both of which are noticeable at their own, typical, individual depth. The daily deviation in the temperate zone is scarcely perceptible at a depth of more than half a metre, though the annual deviation assumes far greater importance, as it is measurable even to a depth of ten metres or more below soil level. It is probable that the figures for the interior of large continents are even more striking, since the difference between the two extremes of mean air temperatures for summer and winter are often greater than 50° C. The yearly deviation in the tropics, especially in the equatorial belt, is small, as is evident from the following data (Braak, 1928) for Djakarta:

TABLE I.I. *Soil temperature as related to depth, at Djakarta* (after Braak, 1928)

Depth cm	Yearly means	Monthly mean		Yearly mean of daily range	Absolute		Differ-ence
		Highest	Lowest		Maxima	Minima	
	°C	°C	°C	°C	°C	°C	°C
Atmosphere (a)	26.1	26.6	25.5	6.9	35.8	18.3	17.5
3	29.2	29.9	28.3	5.2	—	—	—
5	29.3	29.9	28.7	5.0	37.9	23.1	14.8
10	29.5	29.9	28.9	3.1	35.6	23.6	12.0
15	29.5	30.0	28.7	1.5	33.3	23.9	9.4
30	29.4	30.0	28.5	0.3	31.5	23.4	8.1
60	29.5	30.0	28.5	0.05	30.6	23.8	6.8
90	29.5	29.8	28.7	0.04	30.1	26.9	3.2
110	29.5	29.7	28.8	0.04	29.9	26.3	3.6

The figures for the daily amplitude of the temperature are amazing, the highest being recorded, naturally, at the surface of bare soils, and the highest of all on black soils, e.g. Poona black cotton soil. A maximum surface layer temperature of 74° C is quoted by Ramdas and Katti (1934). 'The temperature falls rapidly after sunset, and the minimum may be as low as 16° C. Thus the diurnal variation at the soil surface is in the region of 58° C, although of course this variation decreases rapidly with depth.' An enlightening graph (l.c. page 927) shows that the daily variation in black cotton soil diminishes to zero at a depth of no more than 15 cm. This depth is greater in other soils, but as already mentioned, it does not usually extend more than half a metre. Further, the following statement was made by Vageler: 'In fact, Pechuel-Loesche and Vageler have recorded temperatures of 84 to 86° C for the soil surface in the Congo and East Africa.' Similar figures have been recorded in other tropical and sub-tropical countries (Vageler, 1930). Other observations by the same author (Vageler, 1910) in East Africa have shown bare soil surface temperatures of 50 to 54°, while at a depth of only 5 cm below the surface, the temperature did not exceed 37°, and at a depth of 10 cm it was scarcely more than 30°.

On grass-covered ground (savanna), where the soil thermometers were placed under a short cut lawn, no more than 34° was registered, tallying with the above-mentioned observations made in Djakarta. At the same time, Vageler recorded no more than about 25° in an adjoining dense forest. In view of the fact that the air, at that moment, had a maximum temperature of from 26 to 30°, it appears that the surface of a bare soil may be as much as 20 to 25°, and in the case of Poona even higher than 30°; warmer, in fact, than the atmosphere several metres above that same surface. This only applies to the uppermost layer of the soil, and any form of vegetation whatsoever will reduce the difference.

These readings agree closely with the results of earlier investigations into soil temperatures at different depths, notably by Leather (1915) at Pusa, India, by Carton (1930) at Phu-Lien, Tonkin, and with later ones by Baeyens (1938) in the Congo.

There remain two features of general interest to be discussed here: 1) *the delay in reaching the maximum and minimum temperatures as one penetrates deeper*, and 2) *the mean temperature of the soil being higher than that of the surrounding atmosphere*.

When the soil surface is heated by radiation, heat is conveyed to the lower layers by conduction. The length of time which this conduction takes is dependent upon the composition and condition of the soil. In order to learn something about the different soil layers, therefore, it is essential that data should be recorded at different depths 24 hours of a day, and every day for at least one year. Observations on this comprehensive scale are seldom carried out, for the work involved would certainly be tedious. There is a chance, however, of the actual work involved being kept within reasonable limits. Carefully selected observations would guarantee that subsequent interpolations were simply and authentically derived.

The preceding remarks lead inevitably to the conclusion that all the information dealing with the temperature of air and soil available to date, is based on too sparse observations and is, therefore, of little value. That conclusion is confirmed by reference to the following example from Djakarta given bij Braak (1928). Near to the cabin where combined meteorological observations have been made since 1879, soil thermo-meters were placed under an open, closely cropped lawn at depths of 3, 5, 10, 15, 30, 60, 90 and 110 cm. Observations were recorded every hour during the day and night for more than two years (see table 1.2 on this page).

The following graph shows the curves for depths of from 3 to 30 cm. The readings at greater depths follow an almost straight line.

The curves demonstrate clearly the combined fluctuation of the maximum and minimum temperatures, as cited in table 1.2, columns 2 to 7.

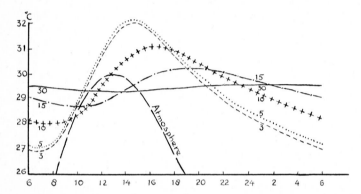

FIG. I. I. *Fluctuation of maximum and minimum temperature in relation to depth, as measured at Djakarta*

TABLE I.2. *Soil temperature at Djakarta (after Braak, 1928)*

I	2	3	4	5	6	7	8	9	10	11	12
Depth in cm	Mean daily maximum temperature	Time of the day	Retardation	Mean daily minimum temperature	Time of the day	Retardation	Yearly mean of temperature 24 hours	Yearly mean of daily amplitude	Absolute maxima of temperature	Absolute minima of temperature	Absolute amplitude of temperature
(Air)	29.97	1 pm	–	23.06	6 am	–	26.11	6.91	35.8	18.3	17.5
3[1]	32.12	2½pm	1½ h	26.92	7 am	1 h	29.20	5.20	–	–	–
5	32.11	3 pm	2 h	27.06	7 am	1 h	29.30	5.05	37.9	23.1	14.8
10	31.09	4½pm	3½ h	27.99	8 am	2 h	29.48	3.10	35.6	23.6	12.0
15	30.19	7½pm	6½ h	28.70	9½am	3½ h	29.46	1.49	33.3	23.9	9.4
30	29.56	1 am	12 h	29.28	2 pm	8 h	29.44	0.28	31.5	23.4	8.1
60	29.55	4 pm	27 h	29.50	5 pm	23 h	29.53	0.05	30.6	23.8	6.8
90	29.51	5 pm	52 h	29.47	4 pm	46 h	29.49	0.05	30.1	26.9	3.2
110	29.49	2 pm	73 h	29.45	4 am	68 h	29.47	0.04	29.9	26.3	3.6

[1] Braak mentions that this depth might be a little more, near to 4 cm.

From the data in table 1.2 it is possible to compute the retardation of the diurnal max-imum and minimum temperatures. Figures have been inserted which were computed in the same way from data for Poona (India) and Paulowsk (Eastern Germany), found in the publications of Ramdas and Katti (1934), and in those of E. Leyst (quoted by Schubert, 1930).

All these retardations follow the same pattern, although the soils and circumstances in which they were recorded differ considerably. The soil in Poona is a black cotton soil which is very heavy, in Djakarta it is oxic, while the Paulowsk soil is mostly quartz sand. The top layers in each of the three locations give almost identical results, although this is not the case with the subsoils. Quartz sand lends itself most readily to the conduction of heat, and black, heavy, clay soil the least.

TABLE I.3. *Retardation of diurnal temperature maxima and minima*

Depth in cm	Djakarta				Poona				Paulowsk	
	Retardation of maxima	Hours per 5 cm	Retardation of minima	Hours per 5 cm	Retardation of maxima	Hours per 5 cm	Retardation of minima	Hours per 5 cm	Retardation of maxima	Hours per 5 cm
5	2 h.	2.0 h.	1 h.	1.0 h.	2 h.	2.0 h.	1–2 h.	1–2 h.	2 h.	2.0 h.
10	3½	1.8	2	1.0	5½	2.7	2–4	1–2	–	–
15	6½	2.2	3½	1.2	10	3.3	10	3.3	–	–
20	8	2.0	4	1.0	–	–	–	–	6	1.5
30	12	2.0	8	1.3	–	–	–	–	–	–
40	17	2.1	12	1.5	–	–	–	–	11	1.4
60	27	2.2	23	1.9	–	–	–	–	–	–

It is safe to conclude that, with the exception of minor details, the maximum daily temperature follows that of the atmosphere with a retardation of 1 to 2 hours for every 5 cm of soil. When the air temperature is at its highest, between 11 a.m. and 3 p.m., the soil temperature at a depth of from 20 to 30 cm is at its lowest. The soil temperature reaches its maximum at a depth of 15 cm at 7 p.m., at 20 cm between 9 and 10 p.m., and at 30 cm after midnight. This is of importance in view of its influence and effects on all vegetation, especially the smaller crops.

Secondly, it follows from column 8 of table 1.2. that the mean temperature of the soil from the surface to a depth of at least 110 cm exceeds that of the atmosphere by about 3.4° C. This fact applies not only to Djakarta, but to many other tropical locations. In the majority of cases it is applicable mainly to bare soil, the difference decreasing with the density of vegetation. It is a remarkable point that the upper layers (from 3 to 5 cm below the surface) show a difference of 3°, whereas the deeper layers (from 15 to 110 cm) show one of 3.5°. At the Pasuruan Sugar Experimental Station (Eastern Java), Marr (1911) recorded 3.3° at a depth of 30 cm, and 3.7° at a depth of between 60 and 120 cm. A series of observations over several years at Bogor yielded a consistant figure of $3^{1}/_{3}$° C.

Carton (1930) quotes observations recorded in the shade at Tonkin. At a depth of

15 cm, the mean soil temperature was 2° C higher than the air temperature, while at a depth of 50 cm it was 4.5° higher. There is no corresponding data for bare soil in full sunshine, but the figure of 4.5° mentioned above is, nevertheless, remarkable. In full shade under a large Ficus-tree in Djakarta, at a depth of 30 cm, Braak (1928) observed a mean temperature almost equivalent to that of the air. Similar results were registered at other locations in Java, e.g. under a virginal forest at Tjibodas (at an elevation of 1450 m), and near the summit of the volcano Panggeranggo at a height of about 3000 m. Here, the difference between virgin forest and open grassland was 4°, and at the summit of Panggeranggo, 3°.

Up to the present there has been scarcely any investigation into whether, with increased altitudes, a scale of 0.6° C/100 m is valid for tropical soils at a depth of 1 m in all tropical regions. It appears to apply to the Panggeranggo summit. The surface temperature of the soil at greater altitudes is still unrecorded. It is safe to presume that as altitude increases, variations from the mean average towards the lower end of the scale are greater than is the case in the plains below. It is possible, therefore, that minima below freezing point (night frosts) may occur at lesser heights, e.g. 1500 m, than might be strictly anticipated in accordance with the scale.

In conclusion, attention should be devoted to the *colour of the soil surface* in so far as this is subject to radiation, in cases where there is no vegetation. The darker the colour, the greater the absorption and transformation into heat of the irradiated energy. For this reason where a number of soil samples of different colour are exposed to the sun, the lighter ones remain the coolest, while the darker ones become the hottest. There are all hues and shades of grey, yellow, red and brown soils between the two extremes. The highest excess of temperature over and above that of the air will therefore be evident in the darker soils.

Several interesting instances of this, based on experiments conducted at Poona (India), have been given by Ramdas and Dravid (1936). Of the total radiation from the sun and sun-lit sky (varying between roughly 900 cal. in summer and 200 cal. during the monsoon season), 86% is absorbed by the black cotton soil, 40% by the grey alluvial soil from the Indo-Gangetic plains, 60% by a grass-covered soil, and 94% by a surface covered with charcoal powder. On clear afternoons, during the summer, at Poona, the surface temperature often rises to 75° C. The experiments which yielded these results were carried out for one week, and consisted of observations made twice daily, at 6 a.m. and 2 p.m., at depths of 0–20 or 0–30 cm. In some of the experiments the original black cotton soil was covered by a thin layer (2 mm) of differently coloured soils. One series of tests was conducted between the 24th and the 28th of January, and another between the 30th of April and May the 6th, thus applying to the cool and hot seasons respectively (tables 1.4. and 1.5, p. 13).

It is an interesting fact that even a thin layer of covering soil affects the temperature in the soil to a depth of 15 cm. The diurnal fluctuations of temperature at a depth of 20 cm in the Poona soil are insignificant. Generally speaking, then, the influence of the surface colour is once again clearly evident.

In this connection it is worth mentioning a series of observations made by the Djakarta Observatory under the very dark-coloured surface of an asphalt layer. At a depth of 60 cm an average temperature was recorded of as much as 11° C above that of

TABLE I.4. *Mean soil temperature at different depths, in black cotton soil under cover of 2 mm of other soil, during the hot season* (after Ramdas and Dravid, 1936)

Depth in cm	6 am				2 pm			
	Pusa soil ash-coloured	Lyallpur soil light brown	Poona soil (uncovered) black	Sholapur soil slightly darker black	Pusa soil ash-coloured	Lyallpur soil light brown	Poona soil (uncovered) black	Sholapur soil slightly darker black
0	19.2	19.7	19.3	20.3	58.0	58.6	62.5	64.6
2	25.1	23.8	24.6	25.4	47.3	48.6	49.9	50.4
5	26.8	26.9	26.8	27.9	42.9	43.2	45.0	45.3
10	30.8	30.7	31.0	31.6	36.7	36.9	37.7	38.1
20	33.0	32.4	33.3	33.4	32.6	32.6	33.0	33.2

TABLE I.5. *Mean soil temperature at different depths, in black cotton soil under cover of 2 mm of other soil, during the cooler season* (after Ramdas and Dravid, 1936)

Depth in cm	6 am					2 pm				
	Trivandrum sea sand, white	Sakrand soil ash-coloured	Mekran soil yellowish brown	Bangalore soil red	Poona soil (uncovered) black	Trivandrum sea sand, white	Sakrand soil ash-coloured	Mekran soil yellowish brown	Bangalore soil red	Poona soil (uncovered) black
0	14.2	13.2	13.6	13.7	13.6	39.4	45.7	45.6	47.3	50.8
2	16.4	16.7	16.7	17.0	17.4	35.2	38.4	38.8	39.2	41.0
5	19.2	19.8	19.5	19.8	19.9	29.5	32.3	32.4	32.9	34.5
10	21.8	22.2	22.0	22.3	22.9	24.7	25.9	26.0	26.0	27.0
15	23.3	23.4	23.5	23.6	24.3	23.4	23.8	23.8	24.0	24.7
20	23.8	23.9	24.1	24.1	24.5	23.3	23.7	23.6	23.8	24.0

the air. Although no figures are available, the maximum surface temperature may be estimated as exceeding 70° C. While it is true that an asphalt soil cover is an artificial product, a maximum temperature of 74° C has been measured, as mentioned above, at the surface of black cotton soil in Poona, and this was by no means an exceptional case.

I.2. WATER CONDITIONS IN ATMOSPHERE AND SOIL

In the preceding pages consideration has been given to the manner in which atmospherical temperature, principally in the lower air layers, is governed by the temperature of the earth's surface. A discussion follows on how water conditions of the soil are principally dependent, although there are certain limitations, on water conditions in the atmosphere. To treat this subject in its logical sequence therefore, it would seem necessary to consider what takes place in the atmosphere, and then to see how that affects what takes place in the soil. The two are so closely inter-related, however, that individual treatment would be impractical. It is for this reason that they are discussed together. The details concerning the atmosphere will be taken as a starting point, but the extent to which they influence the soil-water conditions, especially in the tropics, will have to be borne constantly in mind.

Our ultimate objective is a study of the processes of weathering and soil formation, so that the movement of water in the soil, in any direction, be it rapid or slow, is of great interest.

This movement of the soil water is essential, so that there must also be a means of regress as well as a source of fresh supply. The soil or parent material must at the same time be such that water movement is possible by permeation and as a result of topographical conditions. The essential characteristic emerging from all this is the question of gain and loss of water. The diagram below illustrates the different ways in which these gains and losses may occur.

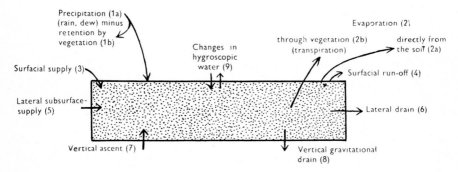

Five forms of gain are illustrated in the left half of the diagram and six forms of loss of water on the right. Since the principal means of gain is precipitation, this aspect may serve as a basis when discussing the factors involved in the water relationship of tropical soils.

I.2.I. PRECIPITATION

Provided that sufficient care is exercised, little difficulty is encountered in measuring rainfall. Rain-gauges are instruments to which reference is made almost as frequently as are the figures of 'mean annual rainfall' in publications covering the sciences, agriculture, geography, and other subjects for which a study of natural conditions is important. Popularity and common usage, however, do not necessarily imply maximum efficiency. This is clearly illustrated by the 'mean annual rainfall' figures quoted by numerous authorities in Indonesia. The Royal Magnetic and Meteorological Observatory in this former Netherlands overseas territory, published a number of publications on the subject of rainfall, based on observations made – in the later stages by 4000 stations – between 1879 and 1953. Such elaborate, well arranged and reliable rainfall statistics are probably available for but few tropical countries in the world. In the following pages, therefore, constant reference will be made to this vast treasure house of information.

First, a few general remarks on rainfall figures. In the tropics the amount of *total annual rainfall* varies not only from place to place, but it also fluctuates at the same station as well. If a mean annual figure is calculated for a period of between 20 and 60 years, the lowest and highest figures for such a series, as shown in the well-known handbook by Köppen and Geiger (1934), may be expressed as a percentage of the mean and the results obtained in this way will show an average of about 60% for the minimum and about 150% for the maximum. If the mean annual rainfall is 1000 mm, during some years it may be as low as 600 mm, yet during others, as high as 1500 mm for instance. The difference between the two extremes may increase proportionally beyond 60 and 150%; in the Netherlands Antilles, for example, extremes have been recorded which were between 20 and 250% of the mean.

No purpose would be served by the computation of a mean figure, for pedological aims, for the annual rainfall over the whole of the tropics. On the other hand, a few general considerations may assist when it comes to comparing different countries or special regions.

The accumulation of rainfall data for Indonesia, published by Berlage (1949), gives the following results (see table 1.6 below).

It appears that by far the greater number of stations (91%) fall between 1000 and 4000 mm, while if the group is extended to 5000 mm, it covers no less than 98%.

The divergence between the percentages mentioned above, for the various regions of Indonesia, is self-evident. Roughly speaking it may be said that Kalimantan and Sumatera get more rain ($\sim$ 2900 mm) than Java as a whole ($\sim$ 2600 mm), while the eastern part of the Archipelago receives much less: Sulawesi ($\sim$ 2300 mm) and the Little Sunda Islands ($<$ 1500 mm).

TABLE 1.6. *Mean annual rainfall in Indonesia*

Groups	Number of stations	Percentage		
< 1000 mm	26	0.6%		
1000–2000 ,,	1227	27.7 ,,		
2000–3000 ,,	1966	44.4 ,,	91%	
3000–4000 ,,	863	19.4 ,,		98%
4000–5000 ,,	293	6.6 ,,		
5000–6000 ,,	52	1.2 ,,		
> 6000 ,,	12	0.3 ,,		
	4439	100.0%		

These Indonesian figures are relatively high compared with those of other tropical regions. Although there are many tropical countries which receive much less rain, there are also some where the mean annual rainfall exceeds 8 m, and sometimes even 10 or 12 m (western coast of South America between 3° S and 8° N, a coastal area of Cameroon, a strip of coast along the north-eastern corner of the Gulf of Bengal).

Many stations in the Caribbean Archipelago, in the Western hemisphere, record figures similar to those for Indonesia, although many are much drier, especially in the northern parts of Venezuela and Colombia, where the rainfall is even less than 500 mm. The yearly mean average for Bengal, in India, is for the most part between 1200 and 2000 mm, though there are districts with a rainfall of over 2500 mm. Districts more to the West and in the centre of India receive less than 1000 mm.

According to Bayens (1938), the Congo Basin has about 1000–1500 mm rain; the equator belt gets more, but in the northern region of the tropics, which includes much of the Sahara and Arabia, less than 250 mm is recorded annually.

A. Vandenplas (1943) published a much more elaborate study of rainfall in the whole of the Congo territory. He described how the annual rainfall in some places near the coast and in the eastern part of the Congo is as low as 800 mm, while in other areas it exceeds 3000 mm. The central part, along the equator, receives considerably more than 2000 mm.

As far as the question in hand is concerned, the actual extent of rainfall is not of such great importance as is the amount of rain water actually absorbed by the soil. If the one were in direct relation to the other, it would be a simple matter to measure the rainfall and then deduce the amount actually taken in by the soil, but that relationship is, unfortunately, very complicated. This can best be explained by an analysis of the way in which the rain falls during the course of the year.

The first stage of this analysis is the division of the figures for the yearly rainfall into *monthly* quantities. The tremendous variation in distribution of the same yearly amount at different places over the 12 months becomes immediately apparent.

In table 1.7 which follows, a number of places with approximately the same mean annual rainfall have been selected from the data for Indonesia, and they have been arranged so that all the stations with a monthly rain minimum above about 100 mm are shown on the left, whilst on the right, opposite to them, are those which, for a considerable number of months, have a rain average of less than 60 mm. These limits of 100 and 60 mm will be explained in the following pages.

TABLE 1.7. *Variations in rainfall distribution in Indonesia*

Station	Mean annual rainfall mm	Lowest monthly mean mm	Station	Mean annual rainfall mm	Number of months under 60 mm
Tanang Talu (W. Sum.)	5008	260	Sadareke (Cheribon)	5018	2
Singkel (Sumatera)	4546	268	Malino (Sulawesi)	4230	3
Fakfak (West Irian)	3437	230	Pangkadjene (Sulawesi)	3545	3
Wakde (N. West Irian)	3008	207	Keling (Central Java)	3197	4
Sarmi (N. West Irian)	2590	202	Makassar (Sulawesi)	2577	5
Tobelo (Halmaheira)	2121	129	Pandean (E. Java)	2097	6
Palu (Sulawesi)	1579	111	Bojan (Lombok)	1567	7
Momi (N. West Irian)	1287	89	Reo (Flores)	1280	7

The graphs below illustrate the difference in question even better than the foregoing table, because they demonstrate clearly how the rainfall varies from month to month and how some places have a pronounced dry season during which the soil can dry out thoroughly, while in other places the soil is subjected to continual wetting (see fig. 1. 2, p. 17 and fig. 1. 3, p. 18).

Great differences in repartition of rainfall are also recorded in other parts of the tropics, e.g. the Caribbean Region. Although the climate of the islands as a whole seems to be drier, due to the greater distance from the equator, some stations on mountain slopes have recorded rainfall as high as that in Indonesia, some even with a lowest monthly mean of 244 mm, whereas other stations have records without a single wet month. This is illustrated in table 1.8 in which the number of 'wet' and 'dry' months have been placed after the relevant meteorological data (see table 1.8, p. 19).

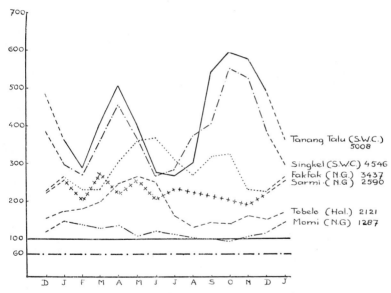

FIG. 1.2. *Monthly repartition of rainfall at stations with no month in which less than 100 mm is recorded*

This series ranges from *per-humid* and *humid* to really *arid* regions. Extremes, as in the right half of table 1.7., do not seem to occur in the Caribbean Region. A similar synopsis of rainfall figures for the Congo (see table 1.13, pages 26–27) shows that the monthly repartition of precipitation for that country is more in agreement with that for the Caribbean Region than with the records for Indonesia.

These monthly figures, however, do not tell the whole story. For the next stage of the analysis, it is necessary to go into greater detail concerning the intake of water into the soil. For example, suppose that a monthly rainfall has been recorded somewhere of say 150 mm. Now this may have been the result of three showers of 40, 80 and 30 mm on successive days, or on the other hand there may have been 25 rainy days in the month, each producing about 6 mm. In the first case in this hypothesis, it may be assumed that a great deal of the rain water could run off, while in the second case it is doubtful whether any of the rain would even moisten the top soil, especially if there were an appreciable amount of vegetation cover. It is therefore necessary to take into consideration the number of rainy days in the month and in the year.

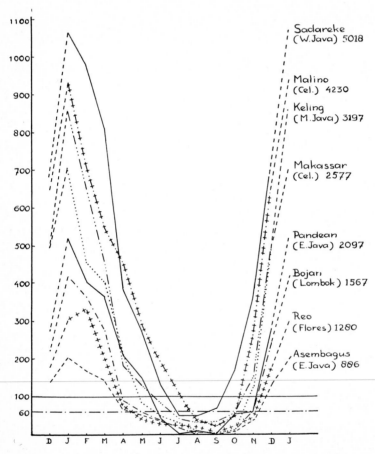

FIG. I.3. *Monthly repartition of rainfall at stations with 3 or more months with less than 60 mm*

Thus the next stage is the analysis of *the daily rains*. For instance, 20 mm may be the result of 10 hours drizzle or 10 minutes downpour, and this makes a great difference to the soil. It will be readily understood from this why the principal weather stations have set up, in the course of time, self-recording rain-gauges. The rain analysis may be read from their recordstrips as desired, although the more detailed the work is, the more tedious it becomes.

The ultimate stage in an ideal analysis would be the consideration of the effect upon the soil of each independent rain shower, although it is doubtful whether anyone would care to carry detail to that extent. Moreover, it would be virtually impossible to do so, since the other factors governing the water intake of the soil could not be measured with a similar degree of accuracy because of their great variability.

The development of this treatise may be aided by a few general remarks on types of rainfall.

TABLE I.8. *Rainfall data of stations in the Caribbean region grouped after the number of 'wet' months (> 100 mm) 'intermediate' months (100–60 mm) and 'dry' months (< 60 mm)*

Location	Yearly mean in mm	Highest monthly mean	Lowest monthly mean	Wet months	Inter-mediate months	Dry months
Moore Town, Jamaica	5638	893	244	12	0	0
Camp Jacob, Guadeloupe	3968	500	184	12	0	0
Morne des Cadets, Martinique . .	3035	380	157	12	0	0
Mazaruni, Guiana	2510	335	130	12	0	0
Comerio Falls, Puerto Rico	2016	225	121	12	0	0
Sanchez, Rep. San Domingo . . .	1963	248	95	11	1	0
Arecibo, Puerto Rico	1562	229	89	11	1	0
San Juan, Puerto Rico	1554	179	75	10	2	0
Cayey, Puerto Rico	1514	164	75	8	4	0
Jeremie, Rep. Haiti	1242	151	70	7	5	0
Bayeux, Rep. Haiti	2075	392	45	10	1	1
Mayaguez, Puerto Rico	2055	292	47	8	3	1
Batabano, Cuba.	1658	303	31	6	4	2
Saba, Neth. Antilles	1132	148	51	4	6	2
St. George, Grenada	1750	226	51	8	1	3
Negril Point, Jamaica	1396	200	47	7	2	3
St. Eustatius, Neth. Antilles . . .	1080	129	45	5	4	3
Pinar del Rio, Cuba	1609	267	31	6	2	4
Nueva Gerona, Isl. of Pines	1794	282	37	7	0	5
Preston, Cuba	1197	219	33	4	3	5
Cienfuegos, Cuba	984	150	18	6	0	6
Turks Island	761	127	29	2	3	7
Curaçao	572	136	9	1	3	8
Aruba	449	127	7	1	2	9
Azua, Rep. San Domingo	404	70	3	0	2	10

A mean yearly rainfall of 4000 mm does not necessarily mean that every month is a wet one with over 100 mm; there may be 2 or even 3 dry months with less than 60 mm. On the other hand there are places with a yearly mean of some 1500 mm, where each month yields a figure of over 100 mm.

Months of excessively high rainfall, say 800 mm, are generally recorded at places where there is less than 60 mm during other months. These areas occur mostly on mountain slopes where there are extremely constant monsoon winds; the direction changes after 6 months, so that the winds descend instead of ascending. The wind becomes warmer and dryer as it descends and can not, therefore, bring any rain.

An absolute maximum of over 1000 mm monthly often occurs; the total of 1534 mm recorded at Pangkadjene, South-Western Sulawesi, Indonesia, in February 1908 was, however, an exception.

On the other hand, there are some places where 1, 2 or even 3 absolutely rainless months have been recorded during 6, 7, 10 and even 20 successive years. Some stations in Indonesia have recorded 4, 5, 6 and 7 consecutive months without a single drop of rain in dry years, a fact of considerable importance with regard to vegetation. Natural vegetation that can not stand a drought of more than 100 days is not helped when the dry period terminates by heavy rains in the following months and only such vegetation as is adapted to drought will survive.

It is interesting to observe, with regard to the distribution of rainfall over a month, that when the total figure is very high there are always several days of very low rainfall, and in months with a very low total, there are always days with showers yielding 10 to 20 mm or more. The following results were obtained from an investigation into the daily rain tables of some 300 stations in Indonesia:

All months with   50 – 100 – 200 or more show at least
one shower of   10 –   15 –   20 mm or more.

Alternatively, all months *without*
showers of   10 –   15 –   20 mm or more show monthly
total *not* exceeding 50 – 100 – 200 mm.

There is, therefore, no single instance of the theoretically possible monthly figure of 75 mm with a daily maximum of 8 mm (10 or more rainy days), nor of the period of 20 rainy days totalling 250 mm with a daily maximum of 15 mm. These figures do serve to refute such suggestions as, for instance, the presumption that if a tropical forest with a monthly rainfall of some 70 mm, catches some 5 mm from every shower, then in 14 rain days with light showers of 5 mm each, not a single drop reaches the soil. This is untrue because the 70 mm in question never falls in this regular manner; it undoubtedly consists of some showers of more than 5 and even some of more than 10 mm, so that water does reach the soil.

The total rainfall in a given period divided by the number of rain days gives the *rainfall per day*. This figure for a year, as a mean of several decennia, ranges (for Indonesia) between 6 and 38 mm. In an exceptional month, of course, the extremes may be greater, e.g. 4 and 50 mm, and in rare instances even 100 mm may occur. The higher the rainfall per day, the less valuable it is to the soil. This is due to the fact that after the saturation point has been reached, most soils cannot absorb any more water within a short space of time, and a large proportion of heavy showers runs off.

Fig. 1.4 shows the relationship between yearly rainfall and rain days in Indonesia, the Caribbean Region and the Congo Kinshasa, and it includes demarcation lines inside which all of the registered rain stations could be located. Those stations situated between the 25- and 40-lines all have a pronounced monsoon rainfall, alternating with onger or shorter dry periods. The rain here falls mostly in heavy showers. All the

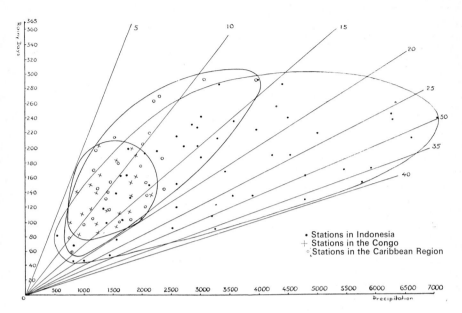

FIG. I.4. *Rainfall per day. Total yearly precipitation/rainy days*

stations between the 10- and 25-lines have neither dry nor excessively rainy months, and their soil is always wet.

The absolute daily maximum can be surprisingly high in Indonesia; 12 stations have recorded figures between 500 and 600 mm, 6 between 600 and 700, and one (Ambon) has even recorded 702 mm. Still higher amounts have been recorded in other tropical countries e.g. Charrapunji (India) 1036 mm. These figures are only of slight significance to the matter in hand at the moment; no more water will penetrate into the soil as a result of a daily rainfall of 1000 mm than from one of only 100 mm, unless there is a great difference in the number of hours during which the rain falls.

A few words on actual time taken for the rain to fall will serve to round the matter off.

The quotient rainfall (in mm): time (in hours) is called *rain intensity* – an important quantity in soil science, because of its influence on the intake of rain water into the soil and the erosive power of the surplus water.

In his excellent handbook on 'The Climate of the Dutch East Indies', Braak (1928) mentions some remarkable facts gleaned from the strips of self-recording rain-gauges, which record not only the quantity of rain, but also the length of time during which it fell.

The intensity may easily be calculated, therefore, from the following results which were recorded during a period of many years at a number of places, which may be considered representative of Indonesia. In table 1.9 several intensity figures are shown together with other corresponding data. The stations have been arranged in the order of their elevation above sea-level.

TABLE I.9. *Rain intensity data of Indonesian meteorological stations*

Elevation in m above sealevel	Station	Mean yearly rainfall in mm	Mean number of rain days per annum	Mean number of rain hours per annum	Mean number of rain hours per rain day	Mean rainfall in mm per rain day	Mean intensity per rain hour
2	Kupang (Timor)	1413	80	267	3.2	17.7	5.5
4	Menado (N. Sulawesi)	2697	164	529	3.2	16.4	5.1
5	Pasuruan (E. Java)	1316	87	263	3.0	15.2	5.0
7	Djakarta (W. Java)	1793	135	321	2.4	13.3	5.6
9	Pekalongan (Centr. Java)	2210	130	434	3.3	17.1	5.1
13	Karanganjer (Centr. Java)	3045	178	597	3.4	17.1	5.1
15	Kaliredjo (Centr. Java)	2981	173	539	3.1	16.2	5.2
24	Medan (NE. Sumatera)	2015	143	458	3.5	14.1	4.4
30	Manokwari (West Irian)	2391	143	547	3.8	16.7	4.2
35	Asembagus (E. Java)	886	72	197	2.7	12.2	4.5
83	Djember (E. Java)	2515	147	467	3.2	12.3	5.4
130	Kalisogra (Centr. Java)	3729	204	794	3.9	18.3	4.7
150	Wedi (Centr. Java)	1849	132	370	2.8	14.0	5.0
266	Bogor (W. Java)	4230	216	718	3.3	19.6	5.9
570	Tjipetir (W. Java)	2991	192	748	3.9	15.6	4.0
580	Salatiga (Centr. Java)	2689	164	572	3.5	16.4	4.7
730	Bandung (W. Java)	1949	144	557	3.9	13.5	3.5
920	Bukittinggi (Sumatera)	2248	194	776	4.0	11.6	2.9
1120	Gamblok Selong (W. Java)	4337	241	887	3.7	18.0	4.9
1400	Tjibodas (W. Java)	3380	229	824	3.6	14.7	4.1
1585	Tjinjiruan (W. Java)	2867	205	797	3.9	14.0	3.6
1735	Tosari (E. Java)	2025	147	494	3.4	13.8	4.1
1925	Kawa Tjiwideuj (W. Java)	3635	225	1101	4.9	16.2	3.3
3023	Panggerango (W. Java)	3324	283	1174	4.2	11.8	2.7

It appears that while the altitude increases from sea-level to 3023 m and the total rainfall varies between 886 and 4337 mm, the mean intensity per hour varies chiefly between 2.7 and 5.9 mm. There is a slight tendency for the intensity to be reduced by an increase of altitude; intensity is also less on mountain plains that are very enclosed (Bukittinggi, Bandung). On the other hand, a higher mean intensity is observed along the west coast of Sumatera, but this is due to a combination of a pronounced monsoon and the stowing effect of the rather high mountain ridge on the heavily waterloaded seawinds.

Djakarta's intensity records show that there the range of the *monthly* figures is even smaller.

It will be seen that the variability of rainfall is found, not in the intensity of that rainfall, but in the duration, i.e. the number of rain hours and rain days. The mean number of rain hours per rain day is rather constant over the entire Archipelago, being about $3\frac{1}{2}$. Djakarta shows the lowest mean of 2.4, and this is the figure resulting from the most conscientious registration of even the slightest rain, thereby recording a high

TABLE I.10. *Intensity-rainfall per hour at Djakarta*

Month	Mean monthly rainfall in mm	Mean number of rain days per month	Mean number of rain hours per month	Mean number of rain hours per rain day	Mean rainfall per rain day in mm	Mean intensity per rain hour in mm
January	300	19.4	60	3.1	15.5	5.0
February	299	18.3	53	2.9	16.3	5.6
March	210	16.3	41	2.5	12.9	5.1
April	147	12.0	26	2.2	12.2	5.6
May	113	9.2	20	2.1	12.3	5.8
June	96	7.7	15	2.0	12.5	6.5
July	63	5.5	12	2.2	11.5	5.2
August	42	4.0	7.5	1.9	10.5	5.7
September	66	5.7	9.5	1.7	11.6	6.9
October	111	8.8	16	1.8	13.9	4.7
November	142	12.6	30	2.5	11.3	4.7
December	204	15.8	40	2.5	12.9	5.2

number of rain days. The mean intensity per hour changes little, however, throughout the year.

To sum up, showers are more frequent and of longer duration at stations with a high total rainfall than at those with a small yearly amount, although their intensity is about the same.

It should be realised that the foregoing considerations give only an overall picture, and that deviations occasionally occur, sometimes quite extensive, for single months, single days and single hours.

For single months the mean intensity may rise to 8 or 9 mm per hour and for single days to as much as 17 mm per hour, although this only applies to particular hours of the day.

The table which follows, showing absolute rain maxima for a given short time, should prove interesting:

TABLE I.11. *Absolute rain maxima in very short periods*

During	5	15	30	60 min.
Rainfall in Indonesia[1] (6 stations)	17	39	64	87 mm
Rainfall in Germany[2]	15	34	47	55 ,,
Rain intensity in Indonesia (per minute)	3.4	2.6	2.1	1.5 ,,
Rain intensity in Germany (per minute)	2.9	2.3	1.6	0.9 ,,

[1] *J. Boerema* (1925)
[2] *Hellmann* in C. Hann – Lehrb. d. Meteor. 1915, p. 374

From this it may be seen that there is very little difference between the tropics and the temperate zones in so far as the highest intensities (15 minutes and shorter), the heaviest showers, thunderstorms and cloudbursts are concerned. The tropical figures are much higher, however, in cases where precipitation is of much longer duration, i.e. over 30 minutes.

The highest intensity per minute in Indonesia did not exceed 4 mm.

Still higher maxima have been observed per minute in Congo Kinshasa. A. Vandenplas (1943) stated: 'During short cloudbursts of a few minutes the maximum intensity surpasses 5 mm a minute, although it seems never to be in excess of 10 mm.' At Gazi, 14/3 1933, 23.5 mm was observed in five minutes, i.e. 4.7 mm a minute. And at Kinshasa, 6/5 1936, 30 mm in 7 minutes, i.e. 4.2 mm/min. The station at Tshofa had 123 mm in 45 minutes, i.e. 2.7 mm/min. for three quarters of an hour, a veritable deluge of rain.

A better idea of the intensity of tropical showers than is conveyed by these extreme figures can be derived from a special study of *cloudbursts*, that is showers having an intensity of at least 1 mm per minute for not less than 5 minutes. The total amount of rain resulting from such cloudbursts has been calculated by several stations and expressed in terms of percentages in the total rainfall during the same length of time. Corresponding values for Bavaria, originated by E. E. Brochier in Geiger (1927), have been added for the purpose of comparison with conditions in the temperate latitudes.

TABLE I.12. *Amount of rain, fallen as cloudbursts in % of total rainfall*

Stations in Indonesia	Cloudburst rain in % of total rainfall	Stations in Bavaria	Cloudburst rain in % of total rainfall
Tjinjiruan (W. Java)	8	Glasshütte	0.4
Ambon (Moluccas)	13	Oberjoch	0.7
Menado (N. Sulawesi)	14	Aschaffenburg	0.8
Bandung (W. Java)	17	Würzburg	0.9
Asembagus (E. Java)	19	Kempten	1.1
Padang (W. coast Sumatera) . .	19	Fällmühle	1.1
Djakarta (W. Java)	22	München	1.2
Medan (E. coast Sumatera) . .	24	Benediktbeuern	1.5
Djember (E. Java)	27	Bocklet	1.6
Bogor (W. Java)	29	Traunstein	1.7
Pasuruan (E. Java)	30	Schweinfurt	2.1
Bangelan (E. Java)	32	Augsburg	3.1
Sawahan (Centr. Java)	37	Nürnberg	3.7
Average	22	Average	1.5

This shows that the percentage of the total precipitation discharged in the form of cloudbursts in Indonesia is 10 to 15 times as great as that in Bavaria. If the much higher amounts of total rainfall for the tropics, as compared with those for the temperate regions (about 4 or 5 times the quantity) are taken into account, moreover, it seems no exaggeration to estimate the amount of water precipitated by tropical cloud-bursts as being 40 times more than that in temperate latitudes. Still higher figures result if all those showers of more than 10 mm, showing an intensity of less than 1 mm per minute, are added. Bogor is a case in point. Yearly amount 4230 mm: cloudburst rain 29% = 1240 mm. Allowing, though, for about 60 showers of 10 to 20 mm, amounting to some 900 mm, and for about 65 showers of from more than 20 to about 100 mm, amounting to some 2600 mm, adding up to 3500 mm, the smaller rainfalls contribute only about 700 mm to the yearly total.

Braak, under the title: 'Frequency of showers, classed according to duration and amount of rain' writes in his much quoted book: 'Statistics of the number of showers of different duration and amount, based on the records of self-recording rain-gauges, are being compiled and will be published in a separate paper.' It is a pity that this paper has never been published.

An investigation along the same lines as those proposed by Braak, although not so far-reaching, was carried out at many stations in Congo Kinshasa by Vandenplas (1943). He counted the mean monthly number of rain days of at least 0.1, < 1, < 10 or < 20 mm. By means of subtraction, the mean number of days with 0.1 to 0.9 mm, 1–4 mm, 5–9 mm, 10–19 mm, and 20 mm and more rain, are calculated. Al-though the publication does not mention how much rain fell in these 5 classes, an approximation can be computed. Assuming an average amount of rain per day for the lower four classes of 0.5, 2.5, 7, and 14.5 mm respectively, it is possible to calculate the total amount of rain for these four classes, and then by subtracting this amount from the total rainfall, the figure for the fifth class is found. By dividing the number of rain days for the fifth class on this amount, the mean daily intensity for this class may be obtained.

Table 1.13 shows the figures computed for several stations. Other values have been added: the mean yearly total rainfall R_f, the mean yearly number of rain days R_d, the mean rain intensity R_f/R_d, the percentage of rain days in the 5 classes and the number of dry months < 60 mm against the number of wet months > 100 mm. Finally, the amount of precipitation retained by the vegetation, although this is to be taken into consideration at a later stage.

All these are expressed as mean yearly figures. Monthly or even individual figures would be preferable, and this deficiency is not unappreciated, but there is neither time nor opportunity for such elaborate work (see table 1.13, pp. 26–27).

Approximate conclusions derived from this (incomplete) table are:

1. The range of figures for Congo Kinshasa is less extensive than those for Indonesia, e.g. the total yearly rainfall is between 3000 and 750 mm as against 7000 and 550 mm, the total number of rain days is between 200 and 80, as against 280 and 45, and the rain intensity per rain day is between 20 and 6 mm, as against 45 and 7 mm.
2. There is no simple correlation between the total yearly rainfall and the rain in-tensity per rain day, the mean intensity of the days with heavy showers (20 mm and more), nor with the occurrence of longer and shorter drought periods.

TABLE I.13. *Particulars of rainfall and rainwater retention by vegetation at various stations in Congo Kinshasa*

Stations	Mean yearly rainfall R_f in mm	Mean yearly number of rain days R_d	Mean daily rain intensity R_f/R_d in mm	Distribution of the rain days over 5 classes:									
				Number of yearly rain days of					Percentage of 100 rain days				
				0.1–0.9 mm	1–4 mm	5–9 mm	10–19 mm	20 and more mm	0.1–0.9 mm	1–4 mm	5–9 mm	10–19 mm	20 and more mm
A[1]-Bosondongo	1960	101	19.4	1	19	19	24	38	1	19	19	24	37
F -Yacoma	1617	86	18.8	1	16	18	19	32	1	19	21	22	37
B[1]-Inongo	1605	95	16.9	6	25	20	20	24	6	26	21	21	25
K[1]-Bendela	1549	91	16.5	6	23	17	19	26	7	25	19	21	29
A[1]-Boende	2160	134	16.1	11	39	16	27	41	8	29	12	20	31
F -Mologbwe	1663	94	17.7	1	21	19	22	31	1	22	20	23	33
C[1]-Albertville	1218	95	12.9	14	29	14	18	20	15	30	14	20	21
C[2]-Kamituga	2891	182	15.9	2	54	33	44	49	1	30	18	24	27
H -Tshela	1249	83	15.1	7	23	14	16	23	8	28	17	19	28
B[2]-Ebonda	1642	114	14.4	6	33	23	22	30	5	29	20	19	26
B[2]-Poko	1935	152	12.7	23	40	26	25	38	15	26	17	16	25
B[2]-Bambesa	1889	159	11.9	31	40	24	32	32	19	25	15	20	20
L -Kabwekatanda	1497	120	12.5	12	36	24	23	25	10	30	20	19	21
L -Kabondo Dianda	1346	107	12.6	8	33	20	23	23	8	31	19	21	22
E -Kasenyi	917	81	11.3	7	30	15	14	15	9	37	19	17	19
C[3]-Tshibinda	1883	185	10.2	29	58	35	37	26	16	31	19	20	14
M[2]-Elisabethville	1223	137	8.9	36	40	21	21	19	27	29	15	15	14
A[2]-Lula	1735	149	11.6	33	38	24	23	30	22	26	16	16	20
M[2]-Katentania	1140	116	9.9	13	39	23	24	17	11	33	20	21	15
C[3]-Ngweshe	1449	140	10.3	6	51	33	30	20	4	36	24	21	14
D[2]-Kabgaye	1125	118	9.6	5	48	26	24	15	4	41	22	20	13
D[1]-Kigali	989	109	9.5	11	38	25	23	12	10	35	23	21	11
E -Nioka	1193	143	8.4	24	47	30	26	16	17	33	21	18	11
C[2]-Lulenga	1825	196	9.3	9	75	47	38	27	5	38	24	19	14
D[2]-Nyanza Ruanda	1125	148	7.6	30	54	27	23	14	20	37	18	16	9
C[3]-Kissenyi	1228	152	8.1	13	61	38	27	13	8	40	25	18	9
M[1]-Lus.St.Jacques	769	96	8.1	7	39	22	19	9	7	41	23	20	9
D[2]-Nyundo	1263	200	6.3	43	78	39	27	13	22	39	19	14	7

3. The distribution of rain over the 5 classes bears little relation to the total yearly rainfall. This is clearly emphasized by a comparison of the following groupings, based on precipitations (see table 1.14, p. 28).

The variation in each of these groups remains constant, and there is no difference between the groups as a whole, whether the mean yearly rainfall is 1800, 1200 or 900.

4. In the 5 classes there is a fall of:

I   0.1–0.9 mm   0.025–1.7   % of the total rainfall
II   1–4   „   2.4–15.4   % „   „   „   „

Wet months: < 60 mm / > 100 mm	Distribution of the rain quantity:						Retention of rainwater by vegetation:							
	Yearly amount of rain in the 5 classes (mm)					Rain intensity of the 5th class R_f/R_d	Amount of rainwater, kept up by vegetation, if per rain day is adhering a maximum of							
	0.1-0.9 mm	1-4 mm	5-9 mm	10-19 mm	20 and more mm		5 mm	4 mm	3 mm	2 mm	5 mm	4 mm	3 mm	2 mm
							calculated in mm				in % of mean total rainfall			
-11	0.5	47.5	133	348	1431	38	453	372	286	214	23	19	14.5	10.5
-9	0.5	40	126	275.5	1175	37	386	316	243	166	24	19.5	14	10
-10	3	62	140	290	1110	46	385	321	251	175	24	20	15.5	11
-8	3	57	119	276	1094	42	370	308	241	167	24	20	15.5	11
-12	5.5	97.5	112	392	1553	38	523	439	345	241	24	20	16	11
-8	0.5	52.5	133	319	1158	37	413	341	264	181	25	20.5	16	11
-6	7	47	95	268	801	40	312	260	204	144	25.5	22	17	12
•-11	1	135	231	638	1886	38	766	640	498	347	26.5	22	17	12
•-7	3.5	57.5	98	232	858	37	326	273	214	150	26	22	17	12
-9	3	82	161	319	1077	36	450	385	302	211	27.5	23.5	18.5	13
-9	11.5	100	182	362	1279	34	557	467	369	260	29	24	19	13.5
-9	15.5	100	168	464	1152	36	556	467	370	262	29.5	25	19.5	14
•-7	6	90	168	333	900	36	456	384	303	213	30.5	25.5	20	13.5
•-6	4	82	140	334	786	34	416	350	276	193	31	26	20.5	14
•-2	3.5	75	105	203	530	35	298	255	203	144	33	28	22	15.5
•-9	14.5	145	245	536	942	36	650	551	439	312	34.5	29	23	16
•-5	18	100	147	305	653	35	420	360	290	209	34	29.5	24	17
)-10	16.5	95	168	333	1022	33	599	521	425	308	34.5	30	24.5	18
5-5	6.5	97.5	161	348	527	31	424	360	286	203	37	31.5	25	18
•-8	3	127	231	435	653	33	545	462	367	258	37.5	32	25.5	18
•-6	3	120	182	354	466	31	445	382	305	216	39.5	34	27	19
•-5	5.5	95	171	342	375	31	400	340	271	192	40.5	34.5	27.5	19.5
•-6	12	118	210	377	476	30	480	417	334	238	40	35	28	20
)-11	4.5	187.5	329	551	753	28	752	640	509	360	41	35	28	20
•-7	15	135	189	338	458	33	470	406	328	227	42	36	29	20
•-7	6.5	152	266	392	402	31	549	471	378	269	45	38	31	22
5-5	3.5	97	154	276	238	26	351	301	242	172	45	39	31	22
3-9	21.5	195	273	394	380	29	611	512	433	316	48.5	40.5	34.5	25

III   5-9   ,,   7-22   % of the total rainfall
IV   10-19 ,,   17-36   % ,, ,,   ,,   ,,
V   20 and more mm   30-70   % ,, ,,   ,,   ,,

It is possible that the very small rainfalls of less than 1 mm may be of some value for vegetation, but they are insignificant with regard to the soil and what happens in it.

Only rain and rainfall have been considered up to this point, but now the other forms of precipitation will be discussed.

Hail does occur in the tropics (Braak, 1928), even in the low lands, but it is a rare phenomenon and, as such, of no consequence with regard to the soil. Furthermore, as it melts, it is merely added to rain water in the rainfall records.

Snow is only encountered on the tops of very high mountains such as in New Guinea, Central Africa and Central and South America. No purpose would be served, therefore, by giving it any special attention in a book on tropical soils.

TABLE 1.14. *Distribution of the total quantity of rain over the 5 classes of rainfall stations of Congo Kinshasa* (after Vandenplas, 1943)

	Mean yearly rainfall	Percentage of the yearly rainfall in class				
		I	II	III	IV	V
Bambesa	1889	0.8	5	9	25	61
Tshibinda	1883	0.8	8	13	28	51
Lulenga	1825	0.2	10	18	30	41
Albertville	1218	0.6	4	8	22	66
Tshela.	1249	0.3	5	8	19	69
Elisabethville . .	1223	1.4	8	12	24	53
Kissenyi	1228	0.5	12	22	31	30
Nyundo	1263	1.7	15	22	31	30
Kasenyi	917	0.4	8	11	22	58
Kigali	989	0.6	10	17	35	38

Only a few records are available of investigations into *dew*. The subject was studied during a period of about one year in Djakarta by Visser (1928), and he gave a description of his own observations together with a critical survey of other literature on the same topic up to 1928. It appears that only two out of a dozen publications to which he made reference had any bearing on the tropics. The conclusions may be summarized as follows:

a. Very imperfect results were obtained for nearly all dew measurements made up to 1928, since until that time no infallible method had been devised. Visser even considered his own work and results only of value as approximations.
b. Only a small part of dew comes from the atmosphere, by far the greater amount originates from soil and particularly plant transpiration.
c. Visser gave the following preliminary average figures, still needing substantiation, for an open lawn at Djakarta:
   during the (dry) East Monsoon–0.15 mm dew per night of 13 hours,
   during the (wet) West Monsoon–0.20 mm dew per night of 11 hours.

Those figures are, in fact, much lower than had previously been estimated. Even if the amount of dew stated were to fall every night for a year, it would only mean about 60 mm per annum for Djakarta, i.e. about 1/40th of the rainfall. It is probable that the actual figure would be even lower.

Zunker (1930) gives a detailed study of dew, together whith figures obtained during experiments (in Central Europe). He estimates no more than 30 mm annually for Munich, in spite of a theoretical maximum of 0.24 mm per hour. Zunker's conclusion tends to confirm the results obtained by Visser. He emphasizes furthermore the opinion voiced by Visser that dew originates for the most part from the soil and only to a small extent from the atmosphere. It is easy to appreciate his contention, therefore, that dew has scarcely any significance from the point of view of increasing precipitation, although it is important as a means of protecting vegetation against too great a fall of temperature through the medium of what is termed by Zunker 'heat condensation', i.e. heat released by condensation of the water. This, however, has little effect upon the soil.

Bayens (1938) gives the following provisional scale of dew fall:

I slight	dew 0.0–0.2 mm per night	
II moderate	,, 0.2–0.5 ,, ,, ,,	
III ample	,, 0.5–1.0 ,, ,, ,,	
IV very plentiful	,, 1.0–1.5 ,, ,, ,,	
V excessive	,, 1.5–2.0 ,, ,, ,,	

Together with that scale, arrived at by deduction, he also computed the following figures for Kisantu (Congo Kinshasa) for the year 1935:

	J	F	M	A	M	J	J	A	S	O	N	D	Year
Rain (mm) . . .	109	55	327	223	298	–	–	15	12	150	325	86	1602
Dew (mm) . . .	19	14	20	23	22	22	12	10	2	9	14	18	185

Bayens concludes from these figures that the greater part of dew is supplied by the soil. A comparison, for instance, of the 3 months March to May, inclusive, with the 4 months June to September, inclusive, reveals considerable rain in the first case and practically none at all in the second. Dew apparently follows the same pattern allowing for a retardation of 1–2 months.

Although it is obvious in view of the results published by Bayens that he feels that dew is not a very important factor with regard to soil formation and should not be considered as an added source of water, its influence near the soil is, according to Walter (1964), not to be neglected. When studying the plant – water conditions in a stand of *Naratta-prothallieae* in Amani (East Africa) he observed heavy dew formation during rainless nights. The quantity varied from 0.26 mm (one measurement) to over 0.15 mm (14 times), between 0.15 and 0.1 mm 12 times and below 0.1 mm 11 times. Only during 3 nights no dew was formed. Taking into account that 0.1 mm of dew is equal to 100 ml per sq.m., sufficient water becomes available through dew formation to keep the air near the soil fairly moist. In his records Walter (1964, p. 92) described how the dew formed on top of the vegetation canopy, drips from leaf to leaf making the lower strata permanently humid. This contradicts the theory of Richards (1964) who maintains that it is unlikely that dew ever occurs in sufficient quantity to run down trunks of drip from leaves onto the soil. This is another subject for micro-climatologists. Taking Bayens' data and according to Richards it is obvious that dew is not an added source of water to the soil, but a partial replenishment for water lost by evaporation. From Walter's experience one might conclude that dew *is* an additional water source. It should be added, however, that in the deserts of the tropics and sub-tropics dew may be considered to be the main source of water for any soil formation, embryonic though it may be (Van Baren, 1964). Many observations and measurements will still have to be made before a satisfactory conclusion can be reached as to the differences in the total quantity of dew originating both from the soil and the atmosphere in various tropical countries.

There is a possibility that, in some locations, dew does play a part in the water supply of the soil, but, generally speaking, the amount of dew in relation to rainfall appears to be of subsidiary importance only, if not entirely negligible. This point is emphasized by the growing opinion that rainfall figures are attained in altogether too superficial a manner, as will be illustrated in the next section.

I.2.2. RETENTION OF RAIN BY VEGETATION

There is a part of the precipitation which never reaches the soil because it clings to the vegetation, and the quantity involved, naturally, increases with the density of the vegetation.

There is a scarcity of relevant information on this question. Only vague references are to be found relating to the tropics. Freise (1934), for example, writes: 'It was found (no figures resulting from experiments are given – Ref.) that where vegetation was dense, 30–55 % of the precipitation from soft rain showers, even of longer duration, found its way to the roots; about 20–30 % evaporated from the surface of the vegetation and the rest ran off.'

Coster (1937) says: 'As a rough estimation, the amount kept back by crowns of large forest trees together with that which evaporates directly from the forest soil, may account for $^1/_4$ to $^1/_3$ of the total precipitation.'

Japing (1930), in a paper on forest-hydrological work, quotes from Japanese investigations which revealed that from a total of more than 2000 mm of rainfall, in the case of a coniferous forest, 9–17 % was retained in the canopies, and in the case of a broad-leaved forest, a little less.

Geiger (1927) gives rather more comprehensive information with regard to Germany. He refers to investigations carried out by E. Hoppe (1896) with the aid of 20 rain-gauges, spaced diagonally through a spruce forest of about 60 years, and also in a forest of beeches which were 88 years old. His results were shown in 2 graphs on which table 1.15 has been based.

It is a remarkable fact that the spruce forest retained more than twice as much rain as the beech forest; this may be due to the retention of small drops between the needles. The leaves of beech trees would allow the water to flow down to the dripping-points of

TABLE I.15. *Rainwater retained in forest in Germany* (after Hoppe, in Geiger, 1927)

Rainfall	5 mm	10 mm	15 mm	20 mm	25 mm	Heaviest showers
Rainwater retained by the *spruce* forest .	65%	50%	36%	29%	23%	20%
or in mm	3.3	5.0	5.5	5.8	5.8	
Rainwater retained by the *beech* forest .	30%	21%	15%	11%	9%	
or in mm	1.5	2.1	2.2	2.2	2.2	

the leaves. It is also interesting to note that with a rainfall of 15 to 25 mm, the amount actually retained soon reached the maximum of 5.8 and 2.2 mm respectively.

Reviewing the data on rainfall interception up to 1962 Slavik (1965) mentions that research carried out in various typical stands in Czechoslovakia showed that an oak-beech stand intercepted 29%, a beech stand 40% and a winter oak stand 24% of a yearly precipitation of 540 mm. An interesting graph shows the relationship between precipitation amount, duration of rain and the interception by the vegetation canopy. This picture clearly shows that o.a. the interception is most directly related to the rain intensity, in this sense that fine rain is fully intercepted, whereas for instance with a rain intensity of 4 mm, more than 3 mm fall through. This fact tallies quite closely with the observations of Hoppe previously referred to.

It is only possible to guess at what the figures would be under tropical conditions; 4 mm per rain shower would seem to be a fair estimate for a dense virginal forest with a luxurious undergrowth of smaller trees, shrubs and weeds. If this surmise is correct, then it would be equally reasonable to conclude that 4 mm of the rainfall is held up on each rain day of the year by the vegetation, and subsequently evaporates before reaching the soil surface. Admittedly rainy days occur when less than 4 mm of rain is recorded, but there are also 24 hour periods in which there is more than one shower in excess of 4 mm, for example, one in the morning and one in the afternoon. It is beyond question that some of the water captured by the canopy flows along the stems and trunks, down to the soil, (see page 32) but no allowance is made for this either in Hoppe's calculation of 2 to 6 mm, nor in our own 4 mm. Finally it should be pointed out that tropical soils are far from being entirely covered by virginal jungle. They did originate, nevertheless, in periods when the earth's surface was only sparsely occupied by man. The earth's cover in tropical regions in those distant times, therefore, may be presumed to have consisted for the most part of jungles, or at least savannahs, with tall grasses, shrubs and isolated trees.

In view of all these, and perhaps other, considerations, it is rather difficult to arrive at an approximation of the real value of those 4 mm. The present authors concede that theirs is but a rough estimation. It does, nevertheless, consitute a starting point for further investigations and corrections. The following approximate figures for Indonesia show that research on this subject is of considerable value:

Rainfall	roughly on an average	2400 mm
Number of rain days. .	„ „ „ „	160
Rainfall per rainy day .	„ „ „ „	15 mm
Retained overground .	„ „ „ „ 160 × 4	= 640 mm

i.e. more than 23 % of the total rainfall, and the soil gets no more than 1760 mm.

Conclusion: we estimate that
under a cover of dense forest or jungle . 70–80% of the precipitation
under a cover of dense high grasses . . 80% „ „ „
„ „ „ „ cereals and other crops 80–85% „ „ „
and on bare soil . . . . 100% „ „ „
reaches the soil surface.

Another approximation may be made, based on the data published by Vandenplas (1943) as quoted and compiled in table 1.13 (pages 26–27). Starting from the rain distribution over the 5 classes mentioned by Vandenplas and comparing mean values of 5, 4, 3 or 2 mm as possible maxima retained in one rain day, the following quantities of rain water adhering to the vegetation may be computed:

5 classes of rain days	Average of one day's rain	Retained by (adhering to) the vegetation			
		5 mm	4 mm	3 mm	2 mm
I 0.1–0.9 mm	0.5 mm	all	all	all	all
II 1–4 „	2.5 „	all	all	n × 2.25	n × 1.75
III 5–9 „	7 „	n × 5	n × 4	n × 3	n × 2
IV 10–19 „	14.5 „	n × 5	n × 4	n × 3	n × 2
V 20 and more mm	x „	n × 5	n × 4	n × 3	n × 2

n = the number of rain days recorded in each class.
x = the mean daily intensity computed and entered in table 1.13.

So coming to the figures compiled in the last columns of table 1.13, it may be concluded that when the vegetation

is able to retain:	5 mm	4 mm	3 mm	2 mm
this means, that:	300–750 mm	250–650 mm	200–500 mm	150–350 mm
or:	23–48%	20–40%	15–35%	10–25%

of the total rainfall does not reach the soil and evaporates from the leaves, stems and branches. These figures are pretty much in agreement with those of Freise (1934) and Coster (1937) mentioned above and with Hoppe's results (in Geiger, 1927) for German conditions and the observations of Slavik (1965) for Czechoslovakia. Tropical conditions are represented in a hydrographic report from Surinam (1953) with the following figures:

During a rainfall, per day, of.	1	2.5	5	7.5	10	15	20	30	40	mm.
retained in the canopy . . .	0.8	1.2	1.6	2.0	2.5	3.2	4.2	6.0	7.8	,,
or in % of the rainfall. . . .	80	48	32	26	25	21	21	20	19.5	,,

These figures tally with those of the Congo and other tropical countries and are a confirmation of the theories given before.

From the foregoing it may be concluded that a great part of the rainfall may be lost to the soils, at least in certain circumstances. This is generally ignored in papers on soil processes and the present authors consequently feel justified in stating that detailed analyses of the character of the rainfall during the year merit full attention.

1.2.3. EVAPORATION AND TRANSPIRATION

Loss of water from the soil to the atmosphere may be subdivided as follows:
2a. loss directly from the soil itself, called *evaporation* and
2b. loss indirectly, via the roots and the leaves of the vegetation called *transpiration*.

1.2.3.1. *Evaporation*
It is extremely difficult to employ direct measurements as a means of gauging the evaporation from a soil surface. The quantity depends on a number of factors which differ from place to place, and from hour to hour. Some of these factors are:
1. the capacity of the atmosphere to absorb water vapour;
2. conditions of the soil surface;
3. the quantity of water present in the surface-layer, and subject to evaporation;
4. the velocity with which that quantity can be replenished from the subsoil to the surface-layer.

No purpose would be served by going into the matter of evaporation in too great detail here, because the question in hand is not one of evaporation for a surface measured in sq. cm, but for a surface of hectares or square kilometres; and similarly, not from hour to hour, but by the day, month or year.

Evaporation is considered exclusively as an atmospheric phenomenon by meteorological and climatological stations. They measure it with conventional fixed evaporimeters, which are mostly flat open vessels made of brass; the evaporation surface is pure water, maintained at a temperature approximating to that of the atmosphere. An implicit relationship is then assumed to exist between the evaporation thus determined and the evaporation of an entire landscape, and sometimes even greater regions.

The results of evaporimeters are not so very different from those of ponds and lakes, for instance, that they are of no use, as is shown by the following quotation of figures for Java stations (see tables 1.16 and 1.17, p. 34).

The annual amounts, therefore, vary between 500 and 1300 mm, and monthly amounts between 30 and 150 mm, measured by an evaporimeter the size of a letterbalance.

On the other hand, the evaporation from a water reservoir built for irrigation purposes (the Waduk Sumbersono at Lengkong, East Central Java), measured by the Irrigation Service over the period 1914–1923, averaged 4.5 mm per day (about 1650 mm p.a.). The lowest daily amount recorded was 3.8 mm in February (i.e. 114 mm for the month); the highest daily rate occurred in September, 5.5 mm (or 165 mm for the

TABLE I.16. *Evaporation of water from evaporimeters in Java* (after Braak, 1928)

Location	Evaporation in mm	
	Annual average per day	Average per year (previous column × 365)
Djakarta	1.5	550
Bogor	2.5	910
Patjet (garden)	0.9	330
Patjet (open meadow)	1.6	580
Kawa Tjiwideui	1.4	510
Bandung	2.8	1020
Pekalongan	1.7	690
Surabaia	3.2	1170
Pasuruan	3.6	1310
Tosari	2.0	730
Djember	3.1	1130

TABLE I.17. *Variations in mean monthly evaporation in different parts of Java* (after Braak, 1928)

	J	F	M	A	M	J	J	A	S	O	N	D	Year
Djakarta (W. Java)	36	36	38	38	39	40	48	57	60	57	48	45	542 mm
Surabaia (E. Java)	61	60	61	66	80	85	102	135	156	144	120	69	1139 mm

month); this clearly demonstrates the influence of the wet and dry monsoons. The amounts recorded are all similar to those given in table I.16 and table I.17 provided by the meteorological stations and coincide as a rule with some of the data obtained from the other countries.

TABLE I.18. *Mean annual evaporation from various free water surfaces in different countries* (after Braak, 1924 and Herman, 1932)

From a pond in Madras (very hot and dry) . . . . 2300 mm
From a water reservoir in Bombay (hot and dry) . . . . 1930 mm
From lakes in India (climatological data not given) . . . . 1600 mm
From a water reservoir in S. W. Africa (very dry) . . . . 2200 mm

Of a larger scope is the work of Cochrane (1956). He records that of all the rain that falls on Lake Nyasa (Tanzania) and its catchment – an area of 48.850 square miles –, only an average of $5\frac{1}{2}\%$ becomes available as free water to be stored in the lake or to flow down the river Shire. In other words $94\frac{1}{2}\%$ of the rainfall is lost, mainly by evaporation from land, vegetation and the lake. A more recent example of significant losses through evaporation is given by Stamm (1967) who mentions that the losses from Lake Mead on the Colorado River for the period 1953–1960 inclusive, averaged about $1,030 \times 10^6$ cubic meters per year. Extrapolating such a figure is a hazardous procedure. Riesbol et al. (1967) when summing up the factors that control evaporation, mention that they vary widely with altitude, latitude, topography and other climatic and physiographic conditions.

An interesting example is the detailed observation published by Freise (1936) of the water balance of the virginal evergreen forest in sub-tropical Brasil from the following data:

Rainfall 390 mm. Crown surface of 90 year old *Cedrella odorata Juss.* 428 sq.m. Crown recieved 167,000 liters of rainwater.

Measurements:

Running down trunk	61,360 liters	=	36.7%
Absorbed by bark	8,000 ,,	=	4.8%
Water in air below canopy	260 ,,	=	0.15%
Water in soil mass 500 m² to 0.5 m depth	41,000 ,,	=	24.55%
Water in litter on soil	810 ,,	=	0.5%
Total of water accounted for	111,430 liters	=	66.7%
Water evaporated	55,570 liters	=	33.3%

Richards (1964) using the same data, calculated that 27.6% of the total water flows to the base of the tree, 6.9% reaching the water table directly via cracks and 20.7% was absorbed by roots.

A formula to calculate evapotranspiration from meteorological data was introduced by Thornthwaite and Holzmann (1942). This reads as follows:

$$E = c \cdot (F - f) \cdot \frac{760}{P} \sqrt{W}$$

in which E is the evaporation, c is a constant, F is the maximum pressure of the water vapour at the point where evaporation is taking place, f is the real vapour pressure in the atmosphere, P is the atmospheric pressure in mm Hg, and W is the wind velocity.

A few comments may be made. As far as the soil surface is concerned, it makes a great difference whether the surface in question is smooth or rough, compact or broken up. The colour is important with regard to the effect which it exercises on the temperature of the soil, and evaporation from a black or dark red surface is much higher than it is from a light grey or white one.

Further, if evaporation is to take place, there must be water present at the soil surface.

It will be readily appreciated, therefore, that if all other conditions remain more or less the same, evaporation is greater during a month with many rainy days, than it is during a month with many dry ones, even though the total monthly rainfall remains the same. This is because the soil surface receives moisture from above on a greater number of occasions.

The principal factor governing the quantity of water supplied to the surface from below, is the velocity at which that quantity is restored from the lower layers. This velocity, in turn, depends on the permeability of all those layers. Another factor of importance is the quantity of water stored there, as well as the forces which raise the water from lower and damper layers, to higher and dryer ones, i.e. the capillary forces. The topographical features may also exercise a certain pressure in this respect. Finally, it should not be forgotten that the higher the temperature (as in the tropics), the lower the viscosity, and the higher the velocity of the soil water movement.

   In conclusion, we must bear in mind that all these conditions constantly change from spot to spot and from day to day. Taking all in all, this is enough to make the exact calculation of the evaporation over a greater soil surface or region, based on a synthesis of all the factors mentioned in the foregoing, an insoluble problem.

1.2.3.2. *Transpiration*

Not only in the temperate zones but also in the tropics investigators have paid considerable attention to the transpiration of single plants or whole areas of vegetation. Transpiration is, however, a physiological process which is affected by both environmental and plant factors. For a review and summary the reader is referred to Kramer et al. (1967) who state a.o. that solar radiation is the most important environmental factor, next to temperature, humidity and wind. As reliable plant factors regulating water loss are mentioned stomatal closure, leaf rolling, curling and orientation. An extensive study made by Coster (1937) in Java is also worth mentioning. He determined the transpiration of single leaves, whole branches and small trees on a weight basis.

'Luxuriant vegetation' means plenty of rain, sunshine and heat coupled with a high soil fertility. 'Poor' refers to a situation in which one or more of these favourable conditions is/are absent, e.g. a lengthy or prolonged dry monsoon or constant cloudiness of 80 %, etc.

The conclusions, arrived at by Coster, were to quote his own words: 'Our figures show how transpiration of the vegetation is the most important water consumer in the water economy of Java. In the low plains in many cases the whole precipitation evaporates through the plants. During the dry monsoon all available water, i.e. precipitation plus water stored in the soil, is used for transpiration. Even during the wet monsoon, when rainfall does not exceed 3000 mm a year or 250 mm a month, many types of vegetation use the total amount of water percolating into the soil. Reafforestation of the plains in the tropics is generally not conducive to the flow of springs.

   On the mountains (above 1000 m), the conditions are quite different. The transpiration of the vegetation is greatly reduced. The soil, mostly of good permeability, allows

TABLE I.19. *Transpiration as related to conditions of plant growth* (after Coster, 1937)

Plants (calculated over whole fields)	Conditions of plant growth		
	Luxuriant	Average	Poor
	mm	mm	mm
Imperata cylindrica Beauv.	1750	1000	300
Eupatorium pallescens D.C. . . .	2900	2000–1600	1000
Leucaena glauca Benth	4670!	4000–3000	
Acacia villosa	2400	1600	
Crotalaria anagyroïdes	2300	1500	
Tephrosia maxima	3100	2000	1000
Albizzia falcata	2300		
Thea assamica	900	500	
Hevea brasiliensis	1200		
Tectona grandis L.F. Teak forest . .	1200–1100	1000–800	500–400
Mountain forest; trees	740 ⎤ 870		
Mountain forest; undergrowth . . .	130 ⎦		
Bamboo forest	3000	1500	
Jungle ⎡ below 1000 m altitude . .		>1200	
⎢ on 1000 m altitude . .		1200–500	
⎣ on 2500 m altitude . .		600–500	

much rain water to percolate into the soil. The mixed forest, with a good soil cover of herbs and shrubs, has a relatively low rate of transpiration. Here is an important surplus of gain over loss of water, which is beneficial to irrigation in the plains.'

To Coster's we can add a few other tropical records. Both Van Raalte (1944) and Van de Goor (1950) found an average transpiration of 5 mm a day for rice, grown on wet paddy fields (sawahs), corresponding to 150 mm a month or 1800 mm a year. Kamerling (1906) investigated the transpiration of sugar cane. Cane, three months old, lost 28.6 m^3/ha/a day, while 5 months old cane lost 54.9 m^3/ha/a day, corresponding to 1030 and 1950 mm/a year respectively. In the fields, the amount of water required (rain plus irrigation) averaged 0.643 l/ha/sec. over a whole year, corresponding to 2060 mm/year.

All these figures tally well with Coster's records for Gramineae: Imperata cylindrica and bamboo.

Another way of roughly computing the transpiration of plants and plant associations is the determination of the organic matter built up by photosynthesis, and multiplying the quantities, obtained in this way, by the so-called '*transpiration ratio*' or '*water requirement*', i.e. water transpiration/organic matter formed. If this factor were constant for one plant species, or almost the same for different plants, it would prove very useful in this case. Unfortunately, it is not.

If we consider one particular species of plant, or even one single plant, the proportion water transpired/organic matter formed, is altered by all the factors affecting the numerator and the denominator.

The *first* group of factors (influencing transpiration) include:

1. the climatic conditions: the saturation deficiency of the air, the temperature, wind velocity and amount of sunshine;
2. the water supply to the leaves, which depends mostly on physical conditions of the soil and on weather conditions in previous days, weeks, months and even years;
3. the plant food supply to the roots, which is not only governed by the total quantity of plant food available, but also by the right proportions of desirable and undesirable ions in the soil moisture, necessary to the well-being of the plant.

The *second* group of factors (influencing the formation of organic matter) includes:

1. the climatic conditions: the amount of sunlight, the CO_2 supply from the air, and the temperature;
2. the water supply, to a much lesser degree than in the first group;
3. the plant food supply, in so far as there is no deficiency in the elements indispensable to assimilation (Fe–Mg–Mn).

A successful attempt to combine the factors mentioned into one concept has been made by Turc (1953) who devised a formula in which both the production of organic matter and soil water content, next to evaporation and transpiration, are taken into account. It reads:

$$E = \frac{P + a + V}{\sqrt{1 + \left(\dfrac{p+a}{L} + \dfrac{V}{2L}\right)^2}}, \text{ in which:}$$

E = evapotranspiration in mm of water per 10-day period;
P = precipitation in mm of water per 10-day period;
L = evaporation capacity of the air:

$$L = \frac{(t + 2)\sqrt{i}}{16}, \text{ in which:}$$

t = mean temperature of the air in a sheltered location during the 10-day period, in degrees centigrade;
i = total incoming radiant energy in cal./sq. cms per day;
a = column of water that may evaporate from a bare soil, disregarding precipitation, at the expense of the water contained in the soil, in mm per 10-day period;

  $a = 35 - \Delta$, with a maximum value of 10 mm;

  A = depletion of the soil moisture;
V = effect of the vegetation cover on the evapotranspiration, viz. further decrease of the soil moisture;
  for each 10-day period, V is the smaller of:

$$25\sqrt{\dfrac{Mc}{Z}} \text{ or } \left(30 + 1.5 \, Mc\dfrac{z}{Z}\right) - \Delta, \text{ in which:}$$

M = production of dry matter in 100 kg per ha (dried at $105°$ C);
Z = length of the growing season in 10-day periods;
z = the position of the 10-day period under consideration;
c = coefficient indicating the drying capacity of a given crop, in relation of the transpiration coefficient established for wheat.

This formula is used in a water deficiency study in European agriculture by Mohrmann and Kessler (1959) who, after considering Penman's formula (1956), Thornthwaite (1948) and a few others, arrived at the conclusion that Turc's formula may be expected to find universal application.

There are numerous early experiments as e.g. those carried out by Briggs and Shantz (1914), Shantz and Peimeisel (1927) and Dillman (1931), that although having other objects in view led to interesting results for the understanding of the water balance. Those of Shantz and Peimeisel will be mentioned in abbreviated form.

TABLE I.20. *Water requirements of different crops* (after Shantz and Peimeisel, 1927)

Crops	Water requirement on an average
Sorghums and millets	200–300
Corn – sugar beet	300–400
Common wheat	400–500
Barleys – buckwheat – cabbage – cotton	500–600
Rice – soy beans – flax	600–700
Several beans and peas	700–800
Alfalfas	800–1000
Western wheatgrass	1000–1400

The water requirements of all plants investigated (all of them annuals, no shrubs or trees being included) vary between 150 and approximately 1400 (1 : 9), although the range is much smaller for each individual plant species, say between 70% and 130% of the average, providing the measurements are carried out in the same area or at least under comparable climatic conditions. Change the climate and the results are very different, e.g. in the case of alfalfa: near the Canadian frontier – 518, in Akron (Col.) – 853, and in Texas – 1005!

There is a great paucity of records covering water requirements in the tropics. A few are available in respect of sugar cane. Experiments carried out by Kamerling (1906) in Java produced figures in the neighbourhood of 600 mm. In India, Khanna and Raheja (1947) arrived at figures of 190–330 mm for unmanured and 150–250 mm for manured cane. These figures are sufficient to make one hesitate before definitely concluding that the water requirement in the tropics is higher than in the temperate zones.

After all, plants are living organisms which adapt themselves readily to their environment, almost as though they had a sense of economics. If abundant water is available on a rather poor soil, the water requirement is high; if water is scarce on a rich soil, the water requirement decreases to less than half.

There are vast regions in the tropics with a very poor soil combined with a high rainfall throughout the whole year. The vegetation in this case will have a high water requirement and the corresponding water loss from the soil through transpiration, will be very high. There are also regions in the tropics which do have a rich soil (e.g. young volcanic ashes), while the rainfall is scanty. In areas like these the vegetation must develop with an extremely low water requirement. Natural vegetation has adapted itself of course, to these special conditions over a period of many years. Plants with low water requirement disappeared from the permanently wet tropical forests, and plants with a high water requirement were unable to survive in savannah and desert conditions. There are countless stages between these two extremes, so that it would appear practically impossible to calculate (via organic matter formed times water requirement) the amount of water transpired by a certain region, which is wholly or partially covered by vegetation consisting of all types of plants, both natural and cultivated. It would, therefore, be useless to attempt, in this way, to compute how much of the water entering the soil, remains for percolation deeper than the root zone, and other ways had to be found.

In the first place, experimental trials have been made with relatively small vessels or pots, filled with soil, as well as with lysimeters. We would have to go into too great detail, if we attempted to describe all these experiments. A few general remarks may suffice.

Such laboratory methods invariably possess the disadvantage that it is dangerous to extrapolate results, obtained with soil containers having a surface area of less than 1 sq. metre, to field surfaces of many hectares or even square km, or depths of a few decimetres, to the depth of the soil in the field, which often extends to more than 5 or 10 metres. The conditions in limited soil containers differ to an even greater extent from those in a field where vegetation has to be taken into account. A lysimeter, covering some square metres and overgrown with grass, may be compared reasonably accurately with pastureland adjoining it, but how can one compare a lysimeter, with perhaps only one tree on it, with an adjoining virginal forest?

Even though a more or less rough approximation is indeed better than nothing (and such experiments are certainly not without value for special purposes), we are of the opinion that certain other methods are to be preferred. Thornthwaite and Holzman (1942) worked out a method for the direct measurement of *evaporation plus transpiration* in the field which seemed to promise valuable results. Their method was based on the vertical distribution of moisture in the air and the intensity of turbulent mixing, calculated from appropriate data on the temperature, relative humidity and wind velocity at different heights.

Very detailed observations, made at Arlington, Va., in 1939, have been recorded in extensive tables. The results are produced in the following table, the original figures being converted into mm and arranged somewhat differently.

TABLE I.21. *Water balance based on field measurements by Thornthwaite and Holzman* (1942)

Months	Precip- itation	Condens- ation	Precipitation + Condensation		Evaporation + Transpiration		Run-off + Percolation	
	mm	mm	mm	%	mm	%	mm	%
January . .	81.6	2.0	83.6	100	13.4	16	70.2	84
February . .	–	–	–	–	–	–	–	–
March . . .	71.3	0.7	72.0	100	23.4	32.5	48.6	67.5
April	74.4	7.9	82.3	100	27.2	33	55.1	67
May	5.1	2.8	7.9	100	41.9	531	34.0	431
June	148.9	6.1	155.0	100	64.5	41.5	90.5	58.5
July	54.9	7.1	62.0	100	49.3	79.5	12.7	20.5
August . . .	75.7	4.7	80.4	100	37.1	46	43.3	54
September. .	–	–	–	–	–	–	–	–
October. . .	60.4	6.3	66.7	100	19.8	30	46.9	70
November. .	35.6	5.6	41.2	100	15.0	36.5	26.2	63.5
December . .	55.8	2.8	58.6	100	14.0	24	44.6	76
10 months. .	663.7	46.0	709.7	100	305.6	43	402.1	57

Like the original authors, we too regret the fact that records for February and September were unobtainable, as well as for several days during some of the other months, due to the pernicious habits of birds and numerous spiders, which damaged the recording apparatus. Precision instruments of this type, used in the open air, are always vulnerable, so that their usefulness in practice is rather limited.

We also regret that the sum total of the run-off and percolation was not split into its components. If the run-off could have been determined, even a rough approximation would have sufficed, we would most likely have obtained some interesting figures regarding percolation to layers deeper than the root zone.

Meanwhile, table 1.21 makes it sufficiently clear that there is no simple relation between monthly precipitation (P + C) and the amount of water lost by the soil to the atmosphere (E + T) again. The ratio of (E+T): (P+C) may be 80% or 16%, but it may also exceed 500%. This surplus of more than 400% of the small rainfall (during May) is, of course, water stored in the soil in previous months. It would, therefore, probably be better to name the last column of the table as 'run off + percolation + changes in moisture content of the soil'. And, as these changes may be very considerable, monthly figures tell us often very little about percolation. It is probable that useful results can only be obtained under protected conditions over a very protracted period, over years and decades.

1.2.3.3. *Evapotranspiration*
Some ten years later, Thornthwaite (1948), in a paper on the 'Rational Classification of Climate', proposed another method of measuring evaporation + transpiration, which he contracted to evapotranspiration. The present subject of research, however, is not the *actual evapotranspiration*, i.e. the amount of water that actually evaporates and

transpires, but the *potential evapotranspiration*, i.e. the amount of water which would evaporate and transpire if it were available.

Thornthwaite writes: 'We know very little about either actual ET_a or potential ET_p. We shall be able to measure ET_a as soon as existing methods are perfected.' (This obviously refers to the method mentioned in the foregoing pages.) 'But to determine ET_p is very difficult. It cannot be measured directly, but computed only from other experimental data. Besides meteorology, biology has to put in a word.'

Thornthwaite then developed a formula by which it was possible to compute a value for ET_p, based on its relation to the mean monthly temperature, corrected for variations in day length.

At times when the rainfall exceeds ET, water is stored in the soil and, on the other hand, when precipitation is less, the stored water is used up. This storage capacity, of course, is not constant but varies, according to Thornthwaite, around an average of about 100 mm. We, for our part, are very much inclined to doubt whether this figure of 100 mm a month is correct, or even approximately so. What about the tropics? Thornthwaite himself was also apparently not convinced of its general validity when he wrote: 'Whether or not the formula can be used without modification to determine ET_p in equatorial regions is uncertain. This question requires further study.' We should like to add: 'as well as the influence of the general properties of the most common tropical soils on the intake, storage and loss of water and, as a result, their influence on ET in tropical regions'.

He nevertheless made an attempt to apply his new method to some tropical experimental data by elaborating records from Bogor and Djakarta in Java, Port of Spain and Mon Plaisir Estate in Trinidad. He also added some figures obtained in Barahona, Dominican Republic, and the Congo Kinshasa. The following table has been constructed from this data:

TABLE I.22. *Potential evapotranspiration at a number of tropical locations* (after Thornthwaite, 1949)

	Mean monthly EvTr	Minimum	Maximum
	mm	mm	mm
Bogor, Java	112	96 (Febr.)	122 (Oct.)
Djakarta, Java	130	108 ,,	143 (May)
Port of Spain, Trinidad	119	91 ,,	144 ,,
Mon Plaisir Estate, Trinidad	109	81 ,,	134 ,,
Barahona			
Determination Irrigation Project . . .	123		
Thornthwaite's calculation	122		
Congo Kinshasa			
Bernhard's estimation	137 (130–145)		
Thornthwaite's calculation	122–135		

In connection with the figures for Java and Trinidad, Thornthwaite points out 'the monthly average values of potential ET are all near 100 mm'. It is a striking fact indeed that for all the tropical areas mentioned, spread out as they are over Asia, Africa and America, the amounts fall within such narrow limits.

Prescott (1949) published a paper at about the same time on a 'Climatic Index for the Leaching Factor in Soil Formation', in which he came to the conclusion that 'the most efficient single value climatic index is P/E^m', where P represents precipitation, E evaporation from a free water surface and m is a constant, varying from 0.67–0.80, with a probable mean of 0.73. A value for this index of 1.1–1.5 corresponds to the point where rainfall balances transpiration from the vegetation and evaporation of the soil.'

Prescott based this conclusion on 'evidence from the examination of soil boundaries in Australia, the records of drain-gauges all over the world, the use of water by field vegetation and the measurements of transpiration'. The first of these four starting points is the most interesting from a pedological point of view. The geographical boundaries of soil groups in Australia show a range of indices from 0.5 to 1.7, using a constant $m = 0.7$. The question is whether that constant, $m = 0.7$ or even 0.8, holds good for equatorial regions. No answer was given in the paper in question.

In a later paper by Prescott et al. (1952), a number of monthly values of the general index $P/E^{0.75}$ were established, as follows, for:

The break of the agricultural or pastoral season at the conclusion of the drought 0.4
Vegetation of low transpiration, or the start of drainage through the bare soil 0.8
Vegetation of average transpiration and catchment areas generally 1.2
High transpirations 1.6
Ricefields 2.0

Although the foregoing gives us a range from 0.4 to 2.0, we are still unaware of whether these values include essential tropical ones.

Assuming 'the relationship of the evaporation from a free water surface and atmospheric saturation deficit can be expressed by the approximate rule $E_w = 21$ s.d., where E_w is the evaporation expressed in inches per month and s.d. is the saturation deficit, expressed in inches of mercury', Prescott passes over from $P/E^{0.75}$ to a new index $P/\text{s.d.}^{0.75}$, which is about 10 times higher. The range of the new index varies, therefore, from 4 to 20.

Basing his considerations on experience gained in Australia, Prescott then assumed:

index < 4 – during all 12 months desert conditions prevail
index > 4 – the growth of vegetation is possible
index < 8 – seasonal cropping is possible during at least 5 months
index > 8 – perennial pasture is possible during at least 9 months
index = 12 – corresponds to the mean evapotranspiration from a full ground cover of vegetation and from soil reasonably continuously supplied with moisture.
index > 12 – associated with drainage through permeable soils and with run-off in catchment areas.

Prescott concludes his general considerations as follows: 'By using alternative estimates of evapotranspiration such as 10 s.d.$^{.75}$, 12 s.d.$^{.75}$ and 16 s.d.$^{.75}$, and by allowing for other levels of water storage in the soil, such as 2 and 6 inches, it should be possible to work out in detail the moisture conditions for different types of vegetations and for soils of different textures' (and different permeabilities! – Ref.), 'and thus place the science of edaphics on a more strictly quantitative foundation.'

Meanwhile at Rothamsted Penman (1948, 1949) worked out experimentally a simple system for the purpose of determining the maximum evaporation from a grass patch in comparison to the evaporation from open water:
$$E_T = f.E_o$$
Taking the year as a unit he calculated f to be about 0.75. This figure varies between 0.6 (winter) and 0.8 (summer) related to the hours of daylight.

Penman (1956) elaborated his original formula by using a combination of aero-dynamic and energy balance methods for a fully transpiring surface, assuming that the surface temperature of the plant cover is the same as the inner leaf temperature.

Next to the two or three formulae to calculate evapotranspiration viz. Penman, Prescott and Thornthwaite, many endeavours have been made to form the complex process of evapotranspiration into mathematical concepts. The index of A.S.A.'s monograph No. 11, 1967, lists no less than 14 different names attached to as many formulae. A critical comparison of procedures for computing evaporation and transpiration had already been made a few years earlier by Stephens and Stewart (1963) but the present authors agree more with Stanhill (1965) who states in the opening paragraph of his paper: 'Since the original publications in 1948 by Thornthwaite and Penman describing practical methods for the calculation of potential evaporation from climatic data many investigations have been described introducing new methods of calculation, comparing existing methods and listing them against measured values'. No attempt will be made to review or even list this vast literature, particularly as no method of approach dealt specifically with tropical soils as the main subject, but were directed to problems of irrigation or plant physiology.

The results of one classic research had, however, quite some influence on the understanding of climate as a factor in soil formation.

Observations were made during 1907 and thereafter at Bogor (Mohr, 1909), using cylinders about 0.5 m long and 0.5 m in diameter. The evaporation was determined indirectly by the direct measurement of the rainfall, the run-off from the surface and the percolation through the soil, with which these containers were filled:
Ev = Pr – (Ru + Pe), Evaporation equals Precipitation minus (Run-off plus Percolation). It appeared from the calculations that with an annual rainfall of approximately 4200 mm at Bogor, about 1100 mm ran off the surface of the bare soil, and 1900 mm percolated through it, so that altogether about 1200 mm evaporated.

One is immediately struck by the fact that this figure of 1200 mm coincides with the values derived from the recorded series of observations in respect of water surfaces (see page 34). Is there, then, so little difference between soil and water in this respect?

A 'Wild' evaporimeter, not mounted as suggested by meteorologists in the shade or under a meteorological shelter, but placed in the immediate vicinity of the soil cylinders, exposed to the wind and sunshine and only protected against rain, gave quite different values. Some of the results may be seen from table 1.23, which has been arranged in accordance with the evaporation figures.

TABLE I.23. *Water evaporation from an evaporimeter and from the soil*

Year 1908 Month	Rainfall R	Evaporation			
		E_w of the evaporimeter	E_s of the soil	E_s in % of E_w	E_s in % of R
	mm	mm	mm	%	%
October	625	151	139	92	22
January	528	141	136	97	26
April	576	140	134	96	24
February	373	108	103	95	28
March	189	147	102	69	54
December	242	149	95	64	39
November	371	121	94	78	25
August	272	147	92	63	34
May	242	145	91	63	38
July	261	135	86	64	33
June	392	145	85	59	22
September	135	152	81	53	60
Total	4206 mm	1681 mm	1238 mm	ave. 74%	ave. 29%

The evaporimeter, freely exposed to the weather, certainly showed a much higher rate of evaporation than its official counterpart, which has been placed in the shade under an appropriate shelter. The exposed evaporimeter also gave much higher readings than the soil cylinders did. An interesting fact which comes to light is the correlation of the mean figure for the relation $E_s/E_w = 0.74$, with Penman's figure of $f = 0.75$. Yet during four months, when the evaporation from the soil was at its highest, the soil being at its wettest, the readings correspond closely with those for evaporation from a free water surface (92–97% of the latter). These were the very months with the maximum number of rainy days viz. 17 to 21, whereas the other months had only between 7 to 14 rainy days.

It should be noted how evaporation increases with the increase in rainfall. As stated already on page 35, water must be present before it can evaporate. In the comparatively dry month of September, for instance, there was also, in addition to a maximum E_w of 152 mm, a minimum E_s of 81 mm. This was due to the fact that the soil remained dry for days, as there was no further moisture to evaporate. Heavy rains generally follow bright mornings, so that whenever water remains as the legacy of the day before, it also evaporates quite easily.

From the observations mentioned above (table 1.23), supplemented by similar observations made 6 months beforehand, as well as in subsequent years, it would appear that the relationships, sketched out roughly for the conditions under which the experiments were to be carried out, still hold good. After the data had been mapped out on a graph, it was found that the evaporation could be represented very approximately as a linear function of the rainfall:

$$E = C + f \cdot P$$

in which the constant C is about 60, and the factor 'f' about 1/8. This, of course, only applies to conclusions drawn from the Bogor experiments, i.e. for the cylinders used in making the measurements recorded above and for Bogor soil (brownish yellow oxic soil).

Naturally, it is scarcely permissible to generalize from such results. What else can one do, however, if one wishes to ascertain in how far these results apply to the area around Bogor, and the necessary data is not available? The only alternative, in view of the speculative and uncertain nature of the conclusions, is to continue one's investigations and see where they lead to.

According to the above formula, the evaporation in a climate with a rainfall of about 68 mm per month is of approximately the same magnitude as the rainfall. If the rainfall is less than 68, say 60 to 65 mm, a point is reached where the run-off and percolation both become practically zero, and all the rain water taken in evaporates again. If the rainfall is greater than 68 mm, however, the surplus may penetrate into the soil, although a portion of it is bound to run off the surface during heavy showers.

Whether this estimate also holds good for other places and other types of soil is another pertinent question. In cases where there is vegetation, whose foliage intercepts a certain quantity of the rain, thereby preventing it reaching the soil, as well as withdrawing considerable water from the soil which is later transpired, water may not penetrate deep into the soil. In the latter case the figure of 68 mm will certainly have to be raised. In addition, Bogor has a relatively moist climate. In dryer localities, even in the rainy season, one would hardly expect to strike a month like June 1908, when only 85 mm evaporated of the 392 mm rain which fell. As long as no experimental data are available, therefore, it appears that the limit should be increased to 90 or 100 mm of water evaporated every month in order to be on the safe side. We may assume with a reasonable amount of certainty that any surplus rainfall in excess of this amount will yield a certain quantity which soaks down into the soil.

We come therefore to the conclusion which although inadequately supported by facts at the present time does seem to be reasonable, namely that with P (precipitation) less than 60 to 65 mm a month, a climate in the tropics may be referred to as a *dry* (*arid*) one, while when P exceeds 90 to 100 mm, the climate may be classified as *wet* (*humid*).

This is why all the examples on the left-hand side of table 1.7 on page 16 were selected so that the rainfall throughout the year exceeds 100 mm a month in all cases with the exception of one as low as 90 mm. The examples cited on the right illustrate cases with the same annual rainfall, though where there are at least 4 months in the year where the rainfall is less than 60 mm. It may be taken for granted, therefore, that in the localities mentioned on the left the downward movement of water takes place throughout the whole year, whereas in the localities mentioned on the right the water movement pauses or even changes direction so that soil moisture moves upwards during several months of the year.

1.2.3.4. *Classification of climate*

If we compare the findings of other investigators, it appears that there is close agreement on some points, yet a marked discrepancy on others. It is a fact that the majority of those who drew up classifications for climates were either climatologists, geographers or biologists, so that their conclusions were based more on the vegetation and the river regimes than on the soil itself.

A. Penck (1910) drew a distinction between humid and arid climates according to the discharge of the rivers. If these flow regularly, the climate of the drainage basin was considered humid; if not, the basin was regarded as being periodically or permanently arid. Penck assumed about 1100 mm annually for Central America as the rainfall boundary at which rivers cease to flow. Such annual figures, however, are unsatisfactory as far as Indonesia is concerned.

E. de Martonne (1909) believed that an annual rainfall of at least 1500 mm is necessary in equatorial climates with no dry season. Months with less rain in mm than double the temperature in °C, are classified by him as being 'practically dry'; at least 8 such months were considered necessary to constitute a 'desert climate'. For places in Indonesia with a temperature of 25 to 27° C, this would mean a limit of 50 to 54 mm rainfall a month.

R. Lang (1915) suggests using his 'rain factor', the quotient R/t, in which R = total annual rainfall and t = the average temperature (in °C) during the year. It is clear that this is of purely meteorological value, determined with instruments in the atmosphere and without any special reference to the soil. Even so, Lang uses his factor under certain conditions for soil classification purposes. Thus according to Lang, 'where otherwise optimal soil forming conditions prevail', and given rain factors

above	160	'Raw humus soils' are formed,
from	160–100	'Black earths' are formed,
	100–60	'Brown earths' are formed,
	60–40	'Yellow earths, red earths and laterites' are formed and
below	40	'Soils of arid climates' are formed.

If the soil forming conditions, however, are not completely optimal in some respects, Lang considers that quite different types of soil may develop although they would be 'inferior' in every case and never 'superior'. It is as if such soil types belong to a higher R or a lower t; in other words when moving down the short table given above, one passes from less valuable to more valuable soil types. 'Nothing is to be expected', therefore, of the soil in all places with a RF (rain factor) in excess of 200. This group would include all areas in Indonesia, for example, having a temperature of 20° to 25° and an annual rainfall above 4000 to 5000 mm! If we add that there are a number of areas in Indonesia possessing 'red earths' and 'yellow earths', where the rain factors vary from about 35 (Asembagus, Eastern Java) to over 400 (on the slopes of the Slamat and in the Preanger), while 'black earths' occur in places with rain factors varying from 30 (near Waingapu on Sumba Island) to 90 (Modjo, Surakarta), it is obvious that Lang's rain factor loses all its significance when applied to a vast tropical region like Indonesia. This is probably also the case as far as many other tropical countries are concerned.

Alfred Meyer (1926) proposed a quite different system: the quotient N : S, where N = the precipitation, and S = the saturation deficit. This is also a meteorological quantity or, if one wishes, a climatic factor, but it is in any case quite independent of all soil characteristics. This, after all, is the main objection which can be raised from our point of view with regard to all such systems.

This opinion is shared by several other soil workers. Ramann (1918) summarizes his experiences and opinion in a few words when he says, 'application of the climatic formulae of Lang and Meyer revealed their insufficiency'. Stremme (1917) too, finds himself unable to agree with Lang's rain factor, and Scaëtta (1936) states, 'during the last time pedologists have given vote to the existence of a soil climate, be it, then, subordinate to the last named. Thus one could understand how with the same factor of Lang or the Meyer quotient two soils may have quite another soil climate and develop in quite different way.'

Köppen (1916) worked out other relationships. Originally (1901) he took at least two dry months with less than 6 rainy days per month as a limit between an 'almost moist rain forest climate' and a 'savannah climate', a limit under which all Central and Eastern Java would fall into the savannah climate. Subsequently (1916), he developed the following conclusive scheme:

Tropical rain climates (A) have:
with an average annual temperature of about 25°C t about 20°C
an average annual rainfall of . . . . at least 700 mm to at least 600 mm.
They are further to be divided into:
(A.f.): continuously moist, having in the least rainy month at least 60 mm.
(A.m.): monsoon rain climates, with moderate dry periods.
(A.s.) and (A.w.); combined to (A.d.): periodically dry savannah climates,

with an annual rainfall of	1500	2000	1500	1000 mm
and the month poorest in rain at the most	0	20	40	60 mm

Dry climates (B) are subdivided into:
(B.s.): steppe climate having:

with an annual temperature of	25°	20°	15°	10°C
an annual rainfall smaller than	700	600	500	400 mm

(B.w.): desert climates with rainfall maxima equal to half that of the steppe climates.

(B.w.) does not occur in Indonesia, for there are no annual rainfall figures under 350 mm. Even (B.s.) occurs very seldom. Palu (Sulawesi) at sea level shows an average of 547 mm over a period of more than 33 years. Types (A.f.), (A.m.) and (A.d.) occur extensively in Indonesia, although (A.f.) applies to the greater part of the Archipelago.

It should be noted that Köppen also uses a limit of 60 mm for (A.f.); below that, he considers a month 'dry'. He does not mention a limit of about 100 mm.

Plotting the foregoing data in graph form, we get figure 1.5.

We can easily find in the records for Djakarta (Berlage, 1949) a series of stations corresponding to the points *a* to *l* in the graph, and it appears that there is hardly any difference in rain character between *b*, *c* and *d* or between *k* and *l*, although there is a great difference between *f*, *a*, *b*, *g* and *k*, all (A.f.), or between *d*, *e* and *i*, all (A.d.).

In short, Köppen's criteria (A.f.), (A.m.) and (A.d.) are unsatisfactory for calculating soil moisture conditions in tropical countries such as Indonesia, and it is obviously desirable that a change be made to a system better suited to such regions.

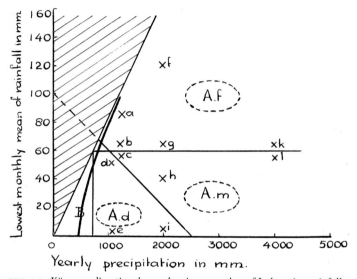

FIG. I.5. *Köppens climatic scheme showing a number of Indonesian rainfall stations*

Starting with the question of how rainfall figures may be used to determine the possible occurrence and intensity of a dry period in the soil, an answer must be found which tallies as closely as possible with reality and one which lends itself to application in practice. After various attempts, yielding less satisfactory results, it was decided, therefore, to use the following system:

1. Both on account of the limit of 60 to 65 mm, found in Mohr's experiments and because Köppen assumed the same limit of 60 mm for 'continuous moist', while de Martonne also approached that same limit fairly closely in his differentiation between 'moist' and 'dry' months, *60 mm of rain are taken as the limit* above which a month is considered to be more or less moist, and beneath which a month is considered more or less dry.

2. It does, of course, make a great difference whether there are one or two of these dry months, or seven or eight, at a given station. The *number of months*, therefore, is of great importance.

3. Another important factor is whether the dry months are preceded or followed by moderately moist months (with P between 60 and 100 mm), or by quite wet months (with P greater than 100 mm). In the first case, the first of these dry months may be

counted among those which are fully 'dry'; in the latter event, a residual effect is obtained from the preceding very wet season, so that as far as the soil and vegetation in many places are concerned, the 'dry period' really begins to take effect later. Similarly, the effects of the drought will be relieved earlier when the month which follows brings more rain than a month with only moderate rainfall (with P between 60 and 100 mm). For example, 3 dry months and 9 wet ones mean a quite sharp though not prolonged dry period, preceded and followed by heavy rains; 3 dry months and 5 wet ones mean 4 transitional months. If 2 transitional months precede the dry period and 2 follow it, the dry period will be felt much more intensively by the soil and vegetation.

On the basis of these considerations, the stations, for which monthly rainfall figures were available over sufficiently long periods, were grouped according to the number of 'dry' and 'wet' months, while the number of 'moist' months (between 60 and 100 mm) can be ascertained simply from the consideration that 'moist' $= 12 - (\text{dry} + \text{wet})$.

TABLE I.24. *Number of rain stations in Indonesia grouped after number of 'wet' and 'dry' months*

Number of 'dry' months (each with less than 60 mm rainfall)	2	3	4	5	6	7	8	9	10	11	12
0	–	–	–	–	3	8	33	155	202	235	750
1	–	–	3	1	2	15	71	142	48	8	
2	–	–	1	1	2	33	145	133	11		
3	–	–	2	7	30	237	298	98			
4	–	1	–	9	78	215	67				
5	–	–	18	38	51	56					
6	2	1	20	20	8						
7	–	–	23	2							
8	–	2	3								

Header spanning columns: Number of 'wet' months (each with more than 100 mm rainfall). Diagonal group labels I, II, III, IV, V, GROUPS.

As it is obvious that we cannot show all the 45 groups which may occur on a single map, they must be combined into larger units.

The numbers given in this graph for stations in Indonesia have been calculated on data available for the years up to 1928. It did not seem necessary to correct them up to 1941, as this would not have changed the character of the graph, which has, moreover, been very ably corrected by Schmidt and Ferguson (1952) (see page 52).

If we take into consideration what was said under 3 above, the 'drought' will increase in the graph, not only vertically downwards, but also horizontally from right to left, forming 5 or rather 6 larger groups, as indicated by the broken lines on the graph.

The following additional remarks may serve for further elucidation:

Group I The continuously wet or at least moist stations where (on an average) the rainfall never falls below 60 mm in any single month. There are very many of these stations and there are vast differences between them. There are, for example, those in which the rainfall in no single month exceeds 200 mm, yet here are others where this never falls below 300 mm in any single month. In addition to stations where there is little variation in rainfall during the wettest and the dryest months, there are others where the monsoons make themselves felt, either more strongly or more weakly, on account of the noticeable differences in rainfall. Even so, all the stations of this group have the following characteristics in common, namely that there will be a *surplus of rain above evaporation*, during practically *the whole 12 months of the year*, which is important from the point of view of the soil and vegetation. If we differentiate between the stations with a minimum monthly rainfall never falling below 100 mm, we find the places having a continuously 'wet' climate and, ipso facto, wet soil. These areas are distinctly separate from the places where one or more (with a maximum of 6) months occur which are only 'moist' (60 to 100 mm rainfall).

Group II The places in Indonesia where only one 'dry' month is observed would be considered to have a weak dry period. This means quite weak; for in those regions the soil does not really dry out, or at most, only the uppermost surface soil on bare land. Where 9 to 10 'wet' months follow 2 'dry' ones as in groups (2–9) and (2–10), there is really a sharp dry period, but given the prelude and the postlude, droughts of long duration certainly do not occur; therefore, these 2 groups are added to II.

Group III Obviously, a frequent type with maxima of (3–8), (3–7), and (4–7) is very widely distributed, especially on Java. Here there is observed a marked dry season, during which the soil can dry out quite thoroughly to a considerable depth. Consequently, during a part of the year, the evaporation exceeds the moisture supply.

Group IV In this group, that phenomenon of a dry season comes more clearly into the foreground. It is self-evident that the groups (4–3) and (4–8) do not belong in one larger group, but (4–3) goes along better with (6–6) in IV, and (4–8) better with III.

Group V Finally, a few places with a long and fierce drought are best placed together into a separate group.

On this basis, a map of Java and Madura was drawn 35 years ago. The number of stations with an adequate number of years of observation has since increased considerably, not only in Java and Madura, but also on the other islands of the Archipelago. Therefore, it was possible to prepare a similar map of Indonesia as a whole, with the addition of Western New Guinea.

In his book on the soils of the Netherlands Indies (1938), the senior present author mentioned (pt. II, p. 167, 274, and 284) the often unsatisfying result of calculating the average monthly rain figures over a great number of years. This is because such a computation always leads to a flattening of the yearly curve. The dry monsoon, never failing, may set in earlier or later, with a variance of 1, 2 or even 3 months. Hence, the monthly figures over many years cannot give more than a blurred and indecisive answer in regard to the question of the occurrence and length of periods of drought. We cite from the English translation by Pendleton (Mohr, 1944): 'instead of the method of presentation used in this book, it would be better to go into the duration of the dry period or periods, for each year, and to work out their length statistically. However, I have neither the time nor the opportunity to do this.' Fortunately, at the Observatory at Djakarta Schmidt and Ferguson (1952) executed this tedious work and published two maps: one for Java and Madura, one for the whole of the Archipelago. Indeed, this is an important corrective improvement and enlargement of previous work. Although, for weather stations, where the change of the wet season into the dry one, and vice versa, is very constant at the same point of time in the course of the year, the difference between the two kinds of maps cannot be very important. On the other hand, where that change moves up in either direction in one, two or more months from one year to the other, the difference is notable, and maps of Schmidt and Ferguson's system are preferable.

Nevertheless, it must be stated, that a careful study of the map gives the impression of the old arbitratiness in the drawing of the boundaries of the groups. But in view of the practical problems in map drawings and reproductions, this arbitratiness can seldom be avoided. This becomes certain when, as here, there are differences which gradually merge one into the other.

In the preceding discussion, the limit of 60 mm rainfall was rightly held to denote the minimum below which arid conditions in the soil would certainly appear, and above which the soil climate would be more humid. However, it is not as simple as that.

In the first place, the temperature (in Indonesia, the elevation) has an influence: the higher one goes the cooler it is. This in turn also reduces the evaporation. On the other hand, a stronger radiation in the higher tracts will heat the soil surface intensively, and in this way further the evaporation. But a great deal depends on the saturation deficit of the air, which is locally very variable. On the outer slopes of the mountains, the saturation deficit in rising currents of air will, of course, become small (cloud formation), and the evaporation will diminish; but whenever a descending Föhn wind sets in upon the slopes or upon high plains, then the wind, at the higher elevation levels, may already be dry. However, the Föhn wind in Switzerland is not so drying as is the 'Kumbang' wind in the low plains of Cheribon, or the 'Bohorok' on Sumatera's East Coast. In short, a general formula cannot be so simply conceived. Besides, there are high mountain stations such as on the Idjen Plateau, where definitely 'dry' months occur.

It is clear that a different approach is necessary. This has been undertaken by Papadakis (1961) who introduced the concept *leaching index*. As a basis he used the climatological data of 2400 stations spread all over the world. Arriving at the conclusion that Thornthwaite's formula did not meet the requirements of a range of diverging climatic conditions he developed a new formula:

$$E = 0.5625 \, (e_{ma} - e_d)$$

where E is the monthly evapotranspiration in centimetres,

e_{ma} the saturation vapour pressure corresponding to the average daily maximum temperature of the month, and

e_d the atmospheric water vapour pressure of the month corresponding to the dew point, both in millibars.

The author computed the E-values for the 2400 metereologic stations with the aim of evaluating derived regional information on crop growing possibilities. Papadakis also dealt with climate as a factor in soil formation (see Papadakis, 1964). He based his research on water surplus data; that is the quantity of rain over evaporation, intro-ducing the concept 'normal' and 'maximum' leaching rainfall, Ln and Lm respectively, the humidity index, H.I., is given by the ratio: available water/evapotranspiration.

When studying the water-balance Papadakis also takes into account the amount of available water which is the quantity of stored water in the preceding month plus additional rainfall in mm, with as a maximum the total rainfall for a given month. As an example the results of the averages of the months of December, January, February and March of the station Tucuman in Argentina are reproduced.

TABLE I.25. *Climatic data of Tucuman, Argentina* (after Papadakis, 1961)

	December	January	February	March
T_{ma}	31,6	32,2	31,0	28,5
e_{ma}	46,5	48,1	44,9	38,9
e_d	21,5	22,7	21,9	21,3
$e_{ma} - e_d$	25,0	25,4	23,0	17,6
E	14,1	14,3	12,9	9,9
R	15,3	17,8	15,3	15,2
R–E	+ 1,2	+ 3,5	+ 2,4	+ 5,3
St.W.	1,2	4,7	7,1	10,0
Av.W.	15,3	17,8	14,3	15,2
H.I.	1,09	1,24	1,19	1,54
2 R	30,6	35,6	30,6	30,4
2 R–E	+16,5	+21,3	+17,7	+20,5

From these data it follows that the 'normal' leaching rainfall, Ln, for Tucuman amounts to 1,2 + 3,5 + 2,4 + 4,3 = 12,4 as the algebraic sum of the difference between rainfall and evapotranspiration, for the other months E being larger than R. The Lm value calculated by adding up the 2R-E values is 88.4. 6.6 should be added to the figures reproduced in the table as the 2R-E value for November. This month, the only one with 2R > E, has not been included in the set of data for the sake of brevity.
Papadakis went on to classify the climates in ten great groups each being subdivided into divisions and sub-divisions. The first group is the 'Tropical Great Group' which is split up in 8 divisions viz.:

1.1 humid semi-hot equatorial (4)
1.2 humid semi-hot tropical (8)
1.3 dry semi-hot equatorial (7)
1.4 hot equatorial tropical (8)
1.5 semi-hot equatorial tropical (8)
1.6 cool tropical (2)

54

1.7 humid frostless highland (4)
1.8 dry frostless highland (4)

The figures between brackets indicate the number of sub-divisions. As will be seen from the names of the divisions the classification is based on temperature and on rainfall, also in the form of the resulting evaporation and leaching indices. Length of humid and dry seasons, if any, and the humidity and temperature regimes are taken into account, being factors which influence the classification of a given region of observation in the system. A few examples may clarify the system (see p. 55).

This section may be concluded with a method of representing a type of climate in a graph, which at one look shows length and intensity of rainfall as well as of aridity. The climate diagrams which follow have been developed by Walter (1958) who published a map with numerous weather stations of Africa. A few years later a climate diagram world atlas was edited by Walter and Lieth (1960). The diagrams below give a few examples from observation stations in Ghana.

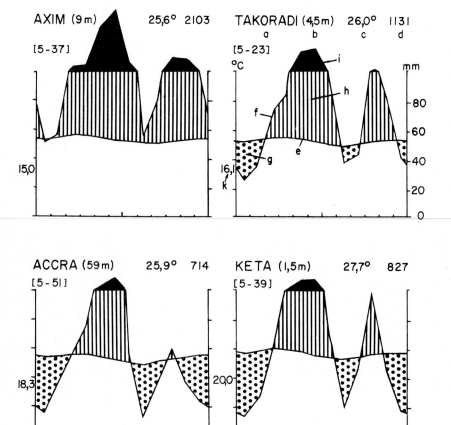

FIG. I.6. *Climate diagrams of various stations in Ghana, Africa (after Walter, 1958)*

TABLE 1.26. *Classification of climate after Papadakis* (1961)

| Evapotranspiration in cm | | | | | | | | | | | | | Stations | HI | Ln cm | Lm cm | HS be | DS be | HRTR | Clim. type |
J	F	M	A	M	J	J	A	S	O	N	D	An								
8	8	9	10	11	11	12	13	13	12	11	9	127	Bogor (Indonesia)	3.24	282	M	8–7	0	EqHU	1.11
11	11	11	7	6	6	6	7	8	9	10	10	102	Chukwani (Zanzibar)	1.38	54	M	11–12	0	EqHu	1.12
10	9	9	10	9	7	6	6	6	8	9	10	99	Accra (Ghana)	0.74	47	M	3–5	12–2	EqMo	1.31
11	12	13	15	20	18	17	17	17	11	11	11	176	Madras (India)	0.72	47	M	10–12	2–6	EqMO	1.46
11	13	13	10	9	11	10	11	13	12	9	9	131	Kitui (Kenya)	0.74	31	M	11–12; 4	6–9	Tt,MO	1.73

In this table evapotranspiration is equivalent to potential evapotranspiration (water evaporated and transpired by a vegetation covered surface when growth is not limited by water shortage). It is computed with the formula on page 53. *HI* is the annual humidity index, that is the ratio annual rainfall/annual evapotranspiration; *Ln*, the normal leaching rainfall, i.e. the difference rainfall minus evapotranspiration during the humid season, given in centimeters; *Lm*, the maximum leaching rainfall, i.e. the difference between two times rainfall minus evapotranspiration during the non-dry season, given in centimeters; *M* means rainfall above 99 cm. The humid season, *HS*, includes all months in which rainfall is greater than evapotranspiration. *be* means the beginning and end of the humid and dry season. If there are two humid seasons this is indicated by two sets of figures. For instance the Chukwani climate is characterized by two humid seasons, one beginning in November to the end of December and another one from beginning of March to the end of May. The *DS* or dry season includes the months in which rainfall plus the water stored in the soil from previous rains cover less than half of the evapotranspiration. *O* means that such a season does not occur. The symbols for the humidity and temperature have the following meaning: *Eq* is semi-hot equatorial. Average maximum temperature below 33.5° C. *EQ* is hot equatorial. T above 33.5° C. *Hu* indicates humid with 1 or more not humid months. *HU* means all months humid. Humid means that *Ln* is greater than 20% of annual evapotranspiration. *Mo* is dry monsoon. *Ln* is less than 20% annual evapotranspiration. *MO* is moist monsoon. *Ln* is greater than 20% annual evapotranspiration.

56

The following explanation of the parameters and additional information will facilitate the reading of the diagrams on page 54.

On the abscissa the twelve months of a year are given. North of the equator January to December, south of the equator July to June. The ordinate gives the temperature in °C or the rainfall in mm. One division mark indicates 10°C or 20 mm of precipitation.

a – name of the station
b – elevation of same
c – mean annual temperature
d – mean yearly rainfall
e – curve of mean monthly temperatures
f – curve of mean monthly precipitation

g – period of drought (pointed area)
h – humid season (hatched area)
i – with precipitation over 100 mm per month the scale is reduced to 1/10 (black area).
k – mean minimum temperature

1.2.4. SURFACIAL SUPPLY AND RUN-OFF; INFILTRATION AND PERMEABILITY

Surfacial supply and surfacial run-off are in nature only of significance in connection with the slope and occurrence of ridges and separate hills and mountains on the one hand, and of valleys and depressions on the other.

Whether there will be any water movement over the surface depends, in addition to the slopes of the land, on three factors:

a. the *intensity of the rainfall*,
b. the *infiltration capacity*, i.e. the ability of the surface layer of the soil to soak up water, measurable in mm per time unit,
c. the ability to conduct this water downward to the lower layers of the soil profile, i.e. the *permeability* of the different soil layers.

If the infiltration capacity and the permeability are large – as for example on dunes – the intensity of the rain may be great and the slope steep, yet no water will flow off over the surface; instead it is all soaked up and carried downward at once. If as a contrast infiltration capacity and/or permeability are small, then even with a modest rain shower, considerable amounts of water are likely to move over the surface.

Thus, besides the permeability, the *infiltration capacity* is of great importance. This is largely dependent on vegetation, litter, etc., left on the soil surface. In general, vegetation facilitates the intake of rain water into the soil, so that the infiltration exceeds the losses of water by transpiration of that same vegetation, especially upon slightly undulating land. But often vegetation has the opposite effect; for instance, in pine forests, also occurring in the tropics, on slopes where the ground is covered with fallen needles, facilitating rapid flowing off and so reducing infiltration.

As a rule – and this may be admitted with hesitation – luxuriant vegetation (such as in tropical forests of to-day, and likely in ancient times to a much larger extent) extracts the moisture out of the rooted subsoil. Consequently, this promotes water movement from the surface layer by suction towards the subsoil, and thus increases the infiltration capacity, but not the percolation to deeper soil layers.

To consider infiltration in the right way, we shall have to divide into two parts the water taken in by the soil from the moment it moistens the soil:

a. the water increasing the moisture content of the toplayer(s) of the soil itself, and
b. the water taken up, but transported to the depth.

The first part (a), is sucked in with more eagerness than the second part (b). The soil endeavours to be saturated first before it is disposed to let further quantities of water pass to the deeper layers. So it is understandable that the dryer the soil is before moistening, the greater is the rate of infiltration, i.e. the infiltration capacity in the first time, decreasing thereafter until the topsoil is saturated and transport downwards starts. From that time, it is no longer the infiltration capacity that dominates, but the permeability.

It is an interesting investigation by Free, Browning, and Musgrave (1940), which corroborates these considerations. The relative infiltration of soil in situ was determined by the tube method on 68 sites, spread all over the U.S.A. on some 54 soil types.

Galvanized-steel tubes, 20 cm in diameter were inserted into the soil. The tubes are 45–60 cm long, depending on the length of the tube required to penetrate the subsoil. After the tubes were sunk, up to about 5–7 cm of the top, a head of water about 6 mm deep was maintained on the soil surface enclosed by each tube by means of a self-dispensing calibrated burette.

After sampling at 3 depths: 0–17,5 cm, 17.5–37.5 cm, and 37.5–62.5 cm, followed by a determination of the water content at these depths, the rates of infiltration were recorded as the cumulative amounts during 0–15, 0–30, 0–60, 0–120 and 0–180 minutes. The first day started at the initial field moisture and subsequently 24 hours later, the soil still being wet from the water supplied the preceding day.

From these records (table 12 of the paper of Free, Browning, and Musgrave), the rates of infiltration in mm per hour during the five times of observation were computed. A selection of the 68 plots, including the extremes on both sides, is given in table 1.27, see page 58.

In view of these figures, the following may be stated:
1. A decrease of infiltration from the first quarter till the last one of three hours.

2. The lower the initial moisture content, the greater the difference between the infiltration at the start of the experiment and that at the finish. This means that the principal reason for a great and quick infiltration is not the permeability, but the initial deficiency of soil moisture. First the topsoil and the next layer(s) saturate themselves eagerly before allowing any appreciable percolation.

3. Only in a few of these experiments the infiltration in the third hour of the first and the next day was similar. So it is doubtful whether the soil was saturated as far as 60 cm in the three hours for the majority of the experiment plots. Indeed, comparing the soil moisture figures at the three depths mentioned above on the first and second days, we see at many plots that the water has penetrated not further than about 40 cm in 24 hours.

4. The amounts of infiltration observed range between 12 cm and nil for the first quarter of an hour. The first figure corresponds with 8 mm/min. As we saw before

58

TABLE I.27. *Rate of infiltration in different soil types of the U.S.A.* (after Free et al., 1940)

Site nr	Soil type		Rate of infiltration in mm per during the...					%-Soil moisture before run, at depth of		
			first quarter	second quarter	3rd and 4th quarter	second hour	third hour	9 cm	28 cm	51 cm
24	Honeoye gravelly silt loam (sod)	I	478	306	224	170	146	15	15	14
		II	230	177	163	145	121	32	24	22
123	Austin clay	I	208	85	69	63	61	17	18	18
		II	134	48	45	45	45	28	22	21
142	Athena silt loam	I	174	63	48	41	37	12	13	13
		II	71	44	28	23	21	27	25	22
127	Bates very fine sandy loam	I	79	52	46	44	43	25	24	22
		II	31	11	11	10	10	26	24	23
106	Fayette silt loam	I	139	28	13	7	6	10	10	11
		II	18	7	6	6	6	30	23	16
37	Muscingum silt loam	I	17	12	9	8	9	23	21	23
		II	16	10	10	9	10	27	21	19
133	Buell clay loam	I	150	45	22	12	10	15	16	19
		II	30	6	4	4	3	24	22	21
119	Austin clay	I	81	10	7	6	7	24	23	21
		II	22	2	3	2	2	35	27	23
131	Crown light clay	I	106	30	14	4	2	16	12	8
		II	0	0	0	0	0	34	24	16
112	Westmoreland clayey silt loam	I	2	1	0.5	0	0.5	30	32	32
		II	0	0	0	0	0	29	30	31

(see page 22), the heaviest rainfall ever recorded does not exceed 4 mm/min. Such a downpour – supposing it came down on the 68 experiment plots in question here – would be swallowed only in 5 of them.

Taking the highest quantities of rain, recorded in Indonesia (Braak, 1928), for more than one min. viz.:

for	15 min	30 min	60 min
	45 mm	75 mm	120 mm

again the same 5 plots can absorb all the rainwater. Some other plots can stand it for the first quarter, but run-off begins during the second.

5. When the toplayer of a soil, wherever it may be, is saturated to its maximum water capacity, and the rain continues, there will be a run-off. This does not mean at all, that the whole soil to any depth is wet to its maximum. That wet toplayer may be 30 cm, or even no more than 2.5 cm, while below it the soil may be unsaturated or even dry. Indeed, it will take the water rather a long time to penetrate to greater depth. In the experiments considered here, on 8 of the 68 plots, the soil moisture at a depth of 38–64 cm did not increase, but even decreased during the 2 days of intensive water supply from above. The conclusion is that during those two days the abundant quantity of water from the toplayer did not reach that depth. On 5 or 6 plots, the water content at a depth of 18–38 cm did not rise more than 1 %. If we had an accelerated film at our disposal, running through a whole year or even longer, of a graph showing water content of the soil at various depths from 1 cm to many metres and above, the corresponding line of precipitation would show the water moving through the soil in waves very incongruent to what a superficial look at the rainfall data and the soil surface would lead us to expect.

6. Especially the reducing influence of the vegetation, natural or agricultural, with a more or less extensive root system, on the form of the waves mentioned above, would assumedly be demonstrated.

7. Penetration of some importance will be observed only on very permeable soil profiles, and with much rain of long duration, causing considerable infiltration. When the rain consists of short heavy showers or of prolonged drizzly rain only not much water will penetrate to any appreciable depth, even through a permeable soil profile. Too much water returns into the atmosphere by evaporation and transpiration. On soils with minute permeability, infiltration is great only after a long drought, and then only until the saturation of the topsoil. Transport of the water to greater depths, however, takes years.

8. Penetration of the rainwater to a depth from where there is no more drought back to the surface, requires passing of the root zone. If this zone is 30–90 cm thick, with an average water capacity of 40–60 vol. %, the root zone can store a quantity of water corresponding with 120–540 mm of rain. After a long and severe drought, this quantity has to be filled up first before penetration downward will start. Of course, this stock almost never will be fully exhausted, and on the other hand, only in special conditions will it reach 100 %. Supposing that the water content in the toplayer decreases to perhaps 10 % of the storage capacity, while at a depth of about 1 m it will not change very much and will stop decreasing at about 60–70 % of full capacity, the necessary supply at the beginning of a rainy season corresponds to about 50–60 % of those 120–540 mm, i.e. 60–300 mm, roughly estimated.

Conclusion: as long as the rainfall does not supply more than 60 mm to the root zone, this zone never gets sufficiently saturated, and penetration of water to a greater depth is improbable. But if the rainy season sets in with more than 300 mm infiltration, in a relatively short time (e.g. 2 or even 1 month), drainage to greater depth will certainly take place.

If the dry period or season is less severe than supposed above, the replenishment of the moisture will be proportionately less, of course, and drainage to deeper layers will start earlier. An infiltration of 300 mm is not necessary, and 200 or 100 mm may be sufficient.

Now it is necessary to scrutinize the *permeability* a little more, because it is one of the most prominent properties of soil. It is enormously divergent for different soils and, it may be said, especially for tropical soils.

The following table, quoted after a study of Zunker (1930), shows some theoretically calculated permeability figures:

TABLE I.28. *Theoretical permeability as related to grain size* (after Zunker, 1930)

Grain size	Permeability		
	cm/sec.	mm/min.	mm/hour
5 – 2 mm	5.0	3000	180000
2 – 1 ,,	1.06	636	38050
1 – 0.5 ,,	0.297	178	10700
0.5– 0.2 ,,	0.051	30.6	1836
0.2– 0.1 ,,	0.0106	6.36	380
0.1– 0.05 ,,	0.00278	1.67 [1]	102 [2]
50 –20 μ^3	0.00054	0.32	1.9
20 –10 ,,	0.000124	0.075	4.5
10 – 5 ,,	0.000032	0.019	1.14
5 – 2 ,,	0.0000061	0.0037	0.22
2 – 1 ,,	0.0000013	0.0008	0.047

[1] 1 mm/min. = cloudburst
[2] 20 mm/hour = heavy showers
[3] For reasons of convenience and lack of space in tables, μ stands for μm in all following pages.

A natural soil, however, never consists of only one of these grain sizes. Therefore another table with experimental results on natural soils given by Zunker (1930), may do better for comparison:

TABLE I.29. *Permeability of soils as related to texture* (after Zunker, 1930)

Soil types	Specific surface U	Permeability		
		mm/min.	mm/hour	1 mm during
Sands	1–20	60–0.3	3600–18	3 min.
Silty sands ⎤ Loamy sands ⎦	20–300	0.3–0.0012	18–0.072	3 min.–14 hours
Sandy loams ⎤ Loams ⎦	300–400	0.0012–0.000006	0.072–0.00036	14 hours–120 days
Heavy loams ⎤ Clays ⎦	> 4000	< 0.000006	< 0.00036	> 4 months

The inadequacy of these two tables is that permeability is treated as a single value, dependent only on the texture of the soil. Indeed, this is insufficient, and in practice not right. It is well-known that the degree of aggregation of single soil grains to crumbs, the porosity in the form of cracks, channels and root tubes, organic matter, etc., can increase the permeability of the soil in the field immensely, while impervious pans can fully impede it. So the theoretical and laboratory figures have a relative value only. This is proven again if one compares the infiltration figures of Free, Browning, and Musgrave (1940) with the data on the granulometric analysis of the surface soil and the subsoil of the same 68 sites. Experience in the field seems to be the only means to arrive at useful information regarding permeability of soil layers and soil profiles.

I.2.5. LATERAL SUB-SURFACIAL SUPPLY AND LATERAL DRAIN

Lateral sub-surfacial supply and lateral drain from the soil are generally of little significance. Movements of water are mainly dependent upon the permeability of the soil material; since the forces that give rise to the replacing of the water have, as a rule, only very small horizontal components, any appreciable lateral movement of water takes place only in pervious soils. This movement occurs mostly in soil close to the ground water table, or below the ground water level.

Small differences in this respect are sometimes clearly perceptible in the vegetation. For example, when a road-cut runs through a tuff formation which is a complex of layers of earth of varying degrees of perviousness, we can see very clearly – from horizontal strips of mosses, little ferns and certain grasses – just which layers exhibit lateral water movement, and which do not.

Also, beside water channels, rivers or canals with a water level higher than the surrounding land, one can observe – in prolonged dry times – a better growth of vegetation nearer the natural or artificial dikes along the channel. However, this phenomenon occurs only in cases of relatively pervious material, i.e. rich in sand or coarse volcanic ash.

1.2.6. VERTICAL ASCENT AND VERTICAL GRAVITATIONAL DRAIN

Vertical ascent and vertical gravitational drain bring us directly to still another important phenomenon in the soil, namely, the ground-water and the *ground-water level*. If the ground-water level is many metres deep, it has little influence on surface soil moisture. On the other hand, if the ground-water level stands close to or at the soil surface, one would seldom consider the possibility that the water would still move downward.

First, let us consider the case of a water table very deep below the surface. As far as the upper portions of the soil are concerned, the water table is practically non-existent. If the soil is uniform and permeable, then gravity will be able to manifest itself fully. The rainwater penetrates downward from the surface, filling the capillaries, saturating the surface soil, and in case there is much water available, it penetrates further and further. If the air below can only find a way out somewhere, the water acts as a suction agent that is, as it sinks further, it sucks air from above into the cracks and capillaries freed from water, while beneath new capillaries and cracks constantly fill up. Finally, the ground-water is reached and fed. This process continues until the descending water stands in equilibrium with the ground-water. Apart from the hygroscopic moisture, there is then in the soil adhering water, angular water, and water remaining in the fine capillaries, besides the water in the capillaries in connection with the ground-water.

One realizes instantly that permeability is of great significance for the progress of this process. The less pervious the soil, the more slowly the process advances. At a certain limit, it will practically come to a standstill. Indeed, heavy clay and loam soils frequently occur in Indonesia, with a permeability of practically zero. In such soils, there is no question of flowing through (8), nor of ascent (7), nor lateral movements (5 and 6).

Let us now consider the case of a pervious soil with a high ground-water level, i.e. just below the surface of the soil.

Whenever a heavy shower falls, the penetrating water will soon unite with the ground-water and raise its level. If the ground-water can escape laterally, nothing changes. But if it cannot get away, the water rises closer to, or even stands on, the surface. The soil then becomes oversaturated with water, and is without air. Only through evaporation can the soil emerge again, for example, in the next dry season.

Under what conditions is there a definite capillary ascent of water? Immediately after the rains cease and the dry period begins? By no means everywhere, and only in certain circumstances. In a soil, homogeneous of texture and structure, the ascending water comes from ground-water, and will only rise in proportion to the rate of water removal from the higher capillaries. In soils which are particularly suited for drawing up water, the greatest rise which has been actually observed, is from 2 to 2.5 m. To move that distance, the water requires about a month. If the ground-water level lies 2.5 m or below the level from which the water is taken up, then ascent is practically out of the question. Is it not true that those soils with the greatest capacity for drawing up water always consist for the greater part of coarse silt of 20 to 50μ? When you come across soils with a larger proportion of fine grains – for example lutum of 1 to 2 μ, commonly called clay – then the theoretical height to which water can ascend is almost 50 m, but the time that is needed for even one metre rise is about two years.

By that time the entire 'dry' season – even though it continues for 8 months – is long past.

The removal of water may occur: a) through evaporation or b) through plant roots.

For a) it is essential that the capillary passages connected with the ground-water continue to, or come close to, the surface of the soil. If one is dealing with soil that draws up water very strongly, then the ground-water must certainly not stand deeper than about 2.5 m, especially if one is to notice anything of the ascent on the surface. In more sandy types of soil this distance must be much smaller. And in the heavier loam and clay soils, there is no need to have any illusion that the water lost from the surface during heavy droughts can be replaced through capillary rise.

For b) – that is to say water loss via the plant roots – the ground-water level may, from the nature of the case, lie deeper than for a). The roots of many plants go down 1 to 2 m deep, and those of many trees descend as much as 8 m or more. For example, even if the ground water level is 10 m below the surface, it is possible that forest on this land – even in the driest time – does not suffer for lack of water. On the other hand, the water table may stand at 5 m, and if the forest is chopped down to make the land available for permanent crops, the roots of these crop plants generally cannot go deeper than 2 m, and hence cannot survive the dry period. Capillary ascent does not bring the water nearer than about 3 metres below the surface.

Now, there is still another complication which should not be neglected. If water rises by capillarity, the ground-water must, at the same time, be replenished from below or laterally. If that does not occur, a vacuum would develop somewhere beneath, and that is impossible. Under such conditions, therefore, the capillary rise cannot occur.

1.2.7. HYGROSCOPIC WATER

The variation in content of hygroscopic water 9 of the scheme on page 14 remains to be discussed. Whenever the relative humidity of the atmospheric air drops appreciably below 100%, the soil – although already 'dry' – will still lose moisture, namely, the hygroscopic moisture. This happens more especially when the soil is heated by radiation from the sun, and the soil temperature rises to far above that of the atmosphere (see also page 13). For example when there is an air temperature of 30° C and a relative humidity (RH) of 40 percent, the actual water vapour tension is $0.4 \times 31.5 = 12.6$ mm. If, in addition to this, the surface of the soil is warmed up to, say 45° C, then the RH is $12.6 : 71.4 = 17.7$ per cent for the immediate proximity of the soil particles. With such a 'drought', these particles will lose almost all their hygroscopic water. There are soils in Indonesia with a hygroscopicity exceeding 20 percent. With the dryness mentioned, they may lose nearly 20% of their weight in the form of water vapour. If, during the night, the temperature of the nearby air falls, sufficiently saturating the air, the loss of hygroscopic moisture is forthwith made up. Then the cooling off through radiation from the soil is already sufficient for the soil particles on the surface to take up hygroscopic moisture from the atmosphere again, though this moisture be imperceptible for the eye.

Interesting figures are accredited by Ramdas and Katti (1934), already referred to on page 11. In an experiment of some 20 days, they recorded with Poona soil a mean loss of 4.56% of the topsoil during the daytime, and during the corresponding nights a mean gain of 4.28%. In another experiment in the field, not with prepared soil samples, loss as well as gain ranges between 1.1 and 4.3, on an average of 2.25%. Certainly, amounts not to be neglected.

On account of this result, the writers give a hint well worth remembering: 'In taking samples from the upper layers of the soil for measurement of soil moisture, due consideration has to be given to the time of day at which the samples are removed from the field.'

Regarding water movements in the soil in the form of *water vapour*, the following may be briefly mentioned: the principal factors of movement of water vapour are differences in pressure and in temperature. These movements are, in comparison to water movements in the liquid form, small and insignificant. In the tropics the differences in pressure are relatively small, and the differences in temperature are not reflected markedly beyond a depth of more than 1 m. Consequently, it may be expected that, in general in the tropics, soil water movements in the form of water vapour are of no great importance.

Now, if we review what has been said under headings 1 to 10, then it appears that all factors which contribute to the water relationships, are subjected to continual variation. The result is an equally variable amount of water in the soil. In order to be able to say more about this subject, the conception 'water capacity' has been introduced. But at the same time, the necessity was realized in defining this conception.

If, by exposure to rain for example, water is added to 'dry' soil – which may already contain hygroscopic water – then the hygroscopicity is first raised to its maximum, then the capillary pores and spaces are filled until the maximum water capacity is reached. Then the soil is 'wet'. Under continuously 'humid conditions', the water content is always close to the ultimate water capacity. But under 'arid conditions' the water capacity lies continually near the 'dry' point, close to the so-called hygroscopicity, or even below it.

So if nothing else happened, the matter would be quite simple. Certainly it is so for a coarse sandy soil, for example. The hygroscopic water is of no principal significance, while the water in capillary pores and other cavities is what the plant lives on in sandy soils.

But in heavy soils, such as clay, other factors prevail. Clay particles do not behave as sand grains; that is, in the presence of water, the latter remain the same as they were without water. If a heavy clay soil were like that, then one would have this case: the clay is dry, hard, impervious; rain falls on it and the surface becomes moistened, then the rest of the water cannot penetrate and runs off. In short, a behaviour as if only a stone layer were there. But the conditions are really otherwise, as will be clear from the following considerations:

If 1 dm³ of dry sand weighs 1600 grams and the specific weight is 2.67, then the volume of the sand grains is 1600 : 2.67 = 600 cc. Hence the volume of the pores is 400 cc. Now, if the sand takes up 400 gm of water in those pores, then the volume of the wet sand is still 1 dm³, and the maximum water capacity is 400 : 1600 = 25% (calculated according to weight).

Let us contrast this with a clay such as is often found in Indonesia. At the maximum water capacity, 42 grams of such a clay have a volume of 27 cc. When thoroughly dried out and, in addition, kneaded and weakly pressed (with the hand only), the final weight is 24 grams. Thus the 9 cc $+$ 1 cc (10%) air space $=$ 10 cc. With the intake of water, these 10 cc swell tot 27 cc, thus to 270% of their dry volume.

It is of importance to keep clearly in view that this signifies in nature: a *swelling* of the soil, when completely wetted from, say, 1 to 3, or a shrinking from 3 to 1 when dried out! Various conditions, however, prevent such extremes. In the *first* place, many soils are not really clay soils, and thus have a lower capacity for swelling and shrinking. *Secondly*, soils in nature do not so frequently become saturated to their maximum water capacity, and on the other hand are but seldom dried out to their minimum moisture content. A little moisture invariably remains behind. *Thirdly*, in nature gravity acts on great quantities of *wet, plastic* clay, so that the whole mass sinks or rises vertically. This is not so easily observed. If we do not use suitable instruments, or do not have bench marks anchored deep in the unchanging subsoil at our disposal, a rising or sinking of even 30 to 60 cm of a large level field escapes detection. A great deal of the cubic swelling or shrinking really does take place in a vertical direction, and is more or less imperceptible to the eye. *Fourthly, cracking* together with the shrinking, comes in as a factor, sometimes as single big cracks in not too fine grained loam soils. Sometimes, with very colloidal clay soils, this takes place as an endless cracking and granulation of the soil down to very fine cubes, to sharp-edged 'sand', or even to a fine 'sand' which may blow about in the wind. Interesting observations and conclusions regarding cracks, are given by Hardy and Derraugh (1947).

It is a good thing to keep in mind that it is just the heaviest soils, those richest in colloidal clay, that are the most plastic and impervious when moist and wet, and which, upon drying, crack, break down, and granulate. If such a soil did not crack, then after a long drought it could hardly become moistened afresh. Actually it becomes moist again because it is broken up by wide – sometimes metres deep – channels and fissures, as well as minute cracks. Whenever the rains fall, the points of contact for water are legion, and the thorough moistening of the soil material – practically impervious to water – need take only months, weeks, sometimes days, instead of years. Similarly, the water loss at first takes place from the surface, and increases as the smaller and larger cracks originate, thus exposing new surfaces for evaporation. Nevertheless, drying out in this way may continue for months, though it extends to only 25 or 50 cm in depth.

So there is a great and principal difference with respect to the manner in which the water economy regulates itself in pervious and impervious soils. The difference is something like that between the human traffic in a great railway station and that in a concert hall. In the one case, the traffic is flowing through; in the other, the hall fills, the doors close, later open again and then the hall empties.

For the impervious soil types, this signifies that when once they are fully saturated by a quantity of water which is, for example, till some depth 300 mm rain, any further rainfall cannot be absorbed anymore. So it makes no difference whether 500 mm or 2000 mm falls in the rainy season, the surplus still runs off over the surface.

Meanwhile, it is desirable to emphasize once more that, from the point of view of

66

soil science, it is exactly not enough to say: with a monthly rainfall of 100 mm or more, a downward movement will occur; and with a monthly rainfall of less than 60 mm, the reserve will occur. Such a statement applies to rather permeable soil material, and as far as upward movement is concerned, it is further limited by those restrictions which have been spoken of under 'ascent'. But for impervious soil material, descending and ascending movements of water are practically of no consequence. With these soil types, one is confronted with other processes.

1.3. SOIL AIR

Beside solid constituents and soil water, there is more or less soil air. If a definite volume of soil be taken as an unit, $(V_s + V_w + V_a = 1)$, the volume of the solid parts (V_s), calculated over a certain time, is quite constant, also that of water plus air, the total pore space is constant: $V_w + V_a = 1 - V_s$. From this, it follows that V_a becomes the greatest when the soil is as dry as possible (V_w is at a minimum), and that V_a becomes the smallest when the soil is saturated with water (V_w is at a maximum).

From the many figures which are given in the literature, we record here only that V_s seldom goes below 26% or above 60%, so that $V_w + V_a$ then varies between 74% and 40%. By way of exception in very dry soil, V_a can be more than $\frac{3}{4}$ of the whole volume, in dried out peat, for example, 84%. But as a rule, it does not exceed 40 to 55%. In soil saturated with water, the water never occupies the entire space $V_w + V_a$ (the pore space or porosity), but always allows a little air to remain. In other words, the maximum water capacity, calculated volumetrically, remains always less than the pore space. That difference is sometimes quite considerable: 15%, but it can also be very small: to almost 0. In the latter case, nearly all of the soil air is gone, but as a soil is hardly ever saturated to the maximum, the minimum of V_a, approaching 0, very seldom occurs in nature. As a rule, the air content ranges between 5% and 40% of the pore space.

If a soil is practically saturated after a few hours of continuous, fairly heavy rain, some air still remains in it. This is sometimes called the minimum air capacity. This quantity is of great importance to the vegetation. For various cultivated European crops Kopecky (1914) determined the optimum to be between 5 and 20%.

In Java Kerbosch and Spruyt (1929) came to the conclusion that the air capacity of Cinchona soils (brown, lateritic mountain soils) varies between 16 and 13%, and has an optimum of about 27%.

From data of Vriens and Tijmstra (1906–1909), wherein figures relating to the porosity and to the water capacity of many Deli soils – though air capacity is not mentioned – the figures may be calculated as follows:

TABLE I.30. *Mean air capacity of 'Deli soils'* (after Vriens and Tijmstra, 1906)

In % of the total volume	Minimum	Maximum	Approximate
Porosity	48.9	87.3	50 to 75%
Water capacity	33.9	55.3	35 to 55%
Air capacity	8.5	39.2	10 to 40%

Most of the figures of Vriens and Tijmstra, for the air content of soils on the East Coast of Sumatera, lie between 14 and 27%. As regards the order of magnitude, they are in good agreement with the above-mentioned results relating to the Cinchona soils of Java, and with the values of European soils.

In a detailed treatise on tea and rubber soils of Indonesia, Vageler (1928) discussed soil-air relationships. He remarked at that time that data on these relationships, concerning undisturbed virginal soils, were lacking. As far as we know they are not yet amplified till to-day.

Soil gas investigations in the temperate zone on earth are mainly limited to the constituents: nitrogen, oxygen, and carbon dioxide. Most of the research deals with the variations of the CO_2 content. The ratio $N_2:O_2$ being about 78:21 in the normal atmosphere, was found to diverge but little in the uppermost layers of the soil. At 15 cm depth the O_2 content may drop occasionally to 10%, and at 70 cm depth to 3%. Yet, it always remains quite considerable.

Whenever the soil contains specious open capillaries, air can easily penetrate the soil and no essential differences between soil air and atmosphere are to be expected. The CO_2 content in the free atmosphere is about 0.03% by volume. Close to the soil surface – for example 2 cm above it – it is at calm usually 2 to 3 times as much. If a breeze strikes over the soil, the difference is of course wiped out. In forests – especially early in the morning after a calm night – the CO_2 content is higher at an even greater height; for example 1 m above the soil surface it is double or more than that outside the forest.

In a soil with low permeability the CO_2 content increases considerably, for example, at 30 cm depth, to 0.05–0.10% CO_2 by volume; at 100 cm depth to 0.4–2.0% CO_2 by volume, and even to 5% or more. Not only the CO_2 content varies, but also the O_2 content. The following table gives relevant data of cacao soils of Trinidad quoted after Vines et al. (1942), but slightly differently arranged (see table 1.29, p. 61).

In the wet season the oxygen content decreases rather suddenly between depths of 45 and 90 cm. The content of CO_2 first increases from 6.5 to about 10%, and then remains constant. In the dry season, there seems to be a constant production of CO_2 at the cost of the O_2 content in all layers. But the nearer to the surface, the more the CO_2 appears to be replaced again by O_2 as a result of diffusion. Nevertheless, the O_2 content remains rather conspicuous to a depth of one metre or more. In order to obtain O_2-free soil air, it will consequently be necessary to deprive it from communication with the atmosphere, namely by a water layer.

The concept 'anaerobic weathering' is, therefore, almost equivalent to the conception of weathering under water. But this may not be complete as in certain circumstances the water may hold a marked quantity of oxygen in solution, so that 'under water' is not quite synonymous with 'oxygen-free'.

Secondarily, the results obtained in Pusa, India are interesting. Harrison and Subramania (1913, 1916) studied the gases of paddy (wet rice) fields there. Their work was completed by Leather (1915). The latter found that, in different determinations, in the dry season – thus not under submerged conditions – the water content in the Pusa

TABLE I.31. *Volume percentages of oxygen and carbon dioxide in soil air of cacao soils of River Estate, Trinidad* (after Vines et al., 1942)

Depth in cm	Wet season Oct.-Jan.		Dry season Febr.-March	
	O_2	CO_2	O_2	CO_2
Atmosphere	21.0	0.03	21.0	0.03
10	13.7	6.5	20.6	0.5
25	12.7	8.5	19.8	1.6
45	12.2	9.7	18.8	3.2
90	7.6	10.0	17.3	5.2
120	7.8	9.7	16.4	6.8

soil, to about a depth of 1 m, varied from 16 to 6% by volume, and the corresponding air volume was between 30 and 45%. In the following rainy season the water content increased to 25 to 33%, while the air (gas) content decreased to between 30 and 15% by volume. Only in a deeper layer (1.25 m) lower figures were found, namely from 10% to 4% by volume. Yet, even these amounts are not so very low.

Now, it is remarkable that the Indian experiments – carried out under real tropical conditions at a temperature of 30° C – showed that the soil air is sometimes not 'air' in the common sense of the world, but an entirely different mixture of gases.

This is most clearly demonstrated by the investigations of Harrison and Aiyer (1916), who found in the water-free soil air from rice (paddy) fields:

Nitrogen	N_2	between	75	and	11%	by volume
Oxygen	O_2	,,	2.8	,,	0%	,, ,,
Carbon dioxide . .	CO_2	,,	2	,,	20%	,, ,,
Methane.	CH_4	,,	17	,,	73%	,, ,,
Hydrogen	H_2	,,	0	,,	2.2%	,, ,,

Here we see that oxygen almost entirely disappears, whereas the content of nitrogen strongly decreases. Their places are taken by carbon-dioxide, and more especially, by methane and hydrogen. In other similar investigations nitrogen was even found to have disappeared, while hydrogen increased to more than 11%.

Leather (1915) refined the method of investigation still more by determining in addition to the nitrogen also the argon. This latter element occurs in the atmosphere in approximately 1/80th of the quantity of nitrogen. In this way Leather studied – with the aid of the $N_2:A_2$ ratio – whether the so-called 'nitrogen' of the earlier determinations (actually $N_2 + A_2$) remained present and inactive as such, or whether, through the microflora, N was added to the system or used up. Actually, he found that the ratio (under rice field conditions), which is about 75 to 81.5 in normal surface soil, can run up to 92 or 98. This can only be explained by assuming there is a production of free N_2, owing to the action of bacteria.

Also noteworthy is Leather's observation that in the immediate proximity of the roots of various plants growing in 'normal' soils, the constituents of the 'soil air' showed the following percentages:

Temperature about 30°C	Nitrogen	73–85 % by volume
	Oxygen	2.2–13.8% ,, ,,
	Carbon dioxide . .	3.3–17.0% ,, ,,
Air content 5.5–25.0% by	Methane	none
volume	Hydrogen	0.0–1.4 % ,, ,,
	Argon	0.9–1.1 % ,, ,,
	$N_2 : A_2$	76–83 % ,, ,,

Even though the sampling was done at a depth of 30 cm or less, and even though there is always some oxygen in such dry soils, the low content of O_2 is striking. Methane was never found in this zone, but hydrogen regularly, which is quite remarkable. It seems unlikely that the roots exhale hydrogen; this gas is probably produced by micro-organisms. But then, likewise, the micro-organisms may have produced CO_2, and it becomes uncertain as to how much of a part the roots have played in CO_2 production. Here, we refer to the interesting results of De Gee (1950), relating to the determination of the redox-potential in an irrigated rice soil (sawah) profile near Bogor, Java. The following values were recorded (see table 1. 32).

Thus, immediately below the brown soil surface, in the blue-grey mud, the redox-potential fell suddenly from 600 mV to below 100 mV. At 10 cm depth a minimum was reached, and below 17 cm depth, the redox-potential increased again very suddenly over as short a distance as 3 cm. Finally, at 30 cm depth, below the sawah-mud – in the dryer subsoil – the initial value of 600 mV was re-reached.

The soil gases at the different depths were not investigated, but it may be assumed that enormous differences in composition at very short distances in depth would have been found.

TABLE 1.32. *Redox-potentials at different depths in a rice soil profile in Bogor, Java* (after De Gee, 1950)

Depth	Millivolts measured
At the surface	400–600 mV
1–3 cm	50–100 ,,
10 ,,	0–50 ,,
17 ,,	0–200 ,,
20 ,,	400–500 ,,
30 ,,	nearly 600 mV

Finally, we may call attention to some results of investigations concerning the solid matter-water-air content and relationships, because these include a factor of the greatest importance. That is *time*!

In the southern tropical parts of Vietnam Y. Henry (1931) has recorded some observations by F. Auriol on two plots of the Giaray experiment station: one plot of red, uncultivated soil, devoid of all vegetation; the other plot of the same red soil, covered with heavy, second-growth forest. Each month the plots were sampled, and in these samples the water content was determined. The results, recorded in graphs, are

TABLE I.33. *Soil moisture under bare and forested land in Vietnam* (after Henry, 1931)

	Layer	1929				1930							
		Sept.	Oct.	Nov.	Dec.	Jan.	Feb.	Mar.	Apr.	May	June	July	Aug.
		%	%	%	%	%	%	%	%	%	%	%	%
Bare land	0–15 cm	26.4	24.5	27.5	20.3	20.6	19.4	16.7	23.9	25.9	27.6	24.5	27.5
	15–30 ,,	27.2	26.1	28.2	22.6	22.7	22.3	20.3	24.9	27.3	28.6	26.1	28.0
	30–60 ,,	29.3	28.7	29.4	26.2	25.7	23.9	22.6	22.7	29.0	30.0	28.9	29.4
	100–130 ,,	29.6	30.0	29.8	27.4	26.0	25.6	26.0	25.4	30.4	30.5	30.3	30.6
Forested land	0–30 ,,	28.5	27.0	27.1	22.7	22.8	21.7	21.2	25.2	27.3	27.5	28.3	29.1
	30–60 ,,	27.6	26.4	25.6	23.4	22.6	21.9	21.4	22.2	26.9	24.1	28.3	28.6
	100–130 ,,	27.6	26.3	25.4	24.4	23.7	22.0	21.6	21.4	26.3	24.0	27.2	28.2
Rainfall in mm		425	195	147	28	16	32	13	80	321	229	336	346

stated in figures here, corresponding rainfall figures having been added (see table 1.33).

In this two things stand out: first, under the forest, the different layers of the soil vary much less in moisture content than those of the bare plot; second, the subsoil of the forest soil shows a smaller water content than that of the deforested soil. The author explains this in the following way: first, considerable rain is intercepted by the leaves and evaporates; hence, less water reaches the soil (conf. table 1.13). The second and main reason is that the vegetation takes by its roots an important part of its water from the deeper layers of the soil. This explanation is admittedly quite correct, but it is probably not yet complete. We know that elsewhere in his paper Henry recorded that bare soil had a clay content of about 62 %, while the soil under the forest yielded values of 52-52-38 %. In this connection we might call attention to what N. Beumé-Nieuwland (1922) writes:

'If in soils of that kind, with a high content of fine constituents but in crumb structure, there are influences at work which do not favour that structure or even work against it, then the rainwater penetrating into the soil can take away from the seed-shaped soil particles a part of the clay. In deeper layers the narrowing capillaries or the presence of flocculating agents precipitate this clay... Also the crumb structure of the surface layer is in part destroyed by the tropical rains beating upon unprotected soils; ...crumbs which are present become beaten to bits, washed away in the rainwater, and are carried into the pores of the soil. Proofs of this are to be found in the results of the 19th century investigations of Pitsch, Wollny, Fesca, Ramann, and others. For the Indies J. Beumé calls attention to this.'

Thus, it is quite conceivable that in Tonkin, on bare soils, an infiltration of clay from upper to lower layers has taken place. By this means, the intake of water of the upper layers was increased, and consequently a higher water content was found in deeper horizons.

Returning to the outcome of the investigation in Vietnam, it must be pointed out that in many localities of Central Europe a distinct difference of ground water level was established. This was after comparing adjoining plots of the same sort of soil, partly occupied by forest, partly bare or at most carrying some thin grass. In short, let the conclusion be stated thus: under forests and, in general, under all kinds of intensive vegetative cover, a lower ground water level may be expected and is, indeed, found.

Rawitscher (1946) reports on the important role of the vegetation in the process of the downward and upward movement of water in the soil. He studied, amongst many others, the moisture profile of a soil near Emas, south-east Ribeirâo Preta, Sao Paulo, Brazil, and found very interesting facts related to the water content of the soil downwards to the ground water level in the middle of the dry season. The monthly precipitation, as measured in Ribeirâo Preta, is shown in the following graph:

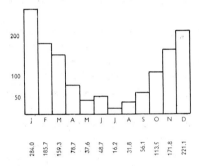

FIG. I.7. *Curve of precipitation at Ribeirâo Preta, Sao Paulo, Brazil, 1910–1922 (after Rawitscher, 1946)*

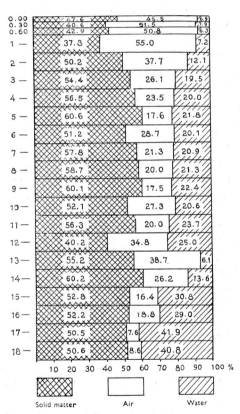

FIG. I.8. *Soil moisture profile of Emas Sao Paulo, Brazil, date of observation 27.7.42 (after Rawitscher, 1946)*

Profile: Homogeneous fine loam without any gravel or rock fragments. First 10 to 12 metres: red-yellow colour of lateritic soils. At greater depth buff coloured (pale brownish-yellow). Near the ground water at 17 to 18 m: sandy layers.

From these observations can be concluded that even at the height of the dry season the (total) water content below 1 m appeared to be considerable. Rawitscher computes that a column of 1 square metre from top to bottom, contained 3771 l water, which is certainly more than the threefold of the mean annual precipitation at Emas, totalling about 1200 mm. Taking into account the dense forest vegetation, some 200 mm will never reach the ground, and at least some 600 mm will be lost by transpiration. Thus, no more than about 400 mm may penetrate to deeper layers than the root zone, perhaps still less. This is emphasized by the observations given by Rawitscher, who mentions that in the forest area of the Rio Doce (North Minas Geraes), the rivers and brooks are dry in the dry season, but in the adjacent deforestated area they contain water throughout the whole year.

It depends, therefore, upon the state of the vegetation as to whether a great or small part of the water infiltrating the soil will move downward to the ground water, meanwhile leaching the soil to a great depth. And so it is possible to consider a certain climate in relation to the soil as semi-arid or still humid, depending upon the vegetation standing on it.

Chenery and Hardy (1945) studied the moisture profile in some forest and cacao soils of Trinidad. They mention that one of the sites studied – covered by a red clay soil type (Talparo clay) – carried a distinctly 'dry' forest type, although the rainfall would justify a wet tropical forest. The reason for this discrepancy was found in the fact that the soil at this particular site of steep slopes showed scarcely any water penetration at all, because the soil surface was 'un-infilterable', being devoid of litter and crumb, and hard and glazed through erosion. Consequently, the land supports a dry type of forest, even though it occurs in a belt of high rainfall of about 2000 mm a year, with 3 dry season months of less than 40 mm rain each. This demonstration of the failure of heavy tropical rainfall to penetrate and to wet certain kinds of clay soils – merely because of their unsuitable surface and situation – is particularly noteworthy.

Here may be inserted a personal experience of the senior present author on a rubber plantation in Indragiri (Eastern Sumatera). It is established on slightly rolling land, the soil being a light brownish rather heavy silt loam. The whole plantation was conscientiously clean-weeded. Although the yearly rainfall was nearly 3000 mm – equally distributed over the whole year – the easily-satisfied rubber trees would not thrive, and showed poor foliage on thin stems. Diseases or plagues could not be ascertained, but the soil surface was as smooth and even as a tennis court, without any infilterability. Every heavy shower immediately ran off to the well-maintained drains. The result was that the rubber trees suffered from water deficiency. Breaking up the top soil by deep forking and digging, followed by the planting of a low but dense green manure cover changed the water condition in the soil so radically that the rubber plantation changed into a very prosperous one in less than two years.

However, it may occur that the rain penetrates only a few centimetres under less anthropogenetically provoked circumstances. This follows from Milne's description of soils, derived from marls in Tanzania (1947).

Next to these anthropogenetic and topographic factors, texture is of even greater importance as Chenery and Hardy (1945) show. They prove this by comparing the moisture profiles of the Marper silt, the L'Ebranche clay-silt, and the Brasso clay – while, for the sake of completeness, the profile of the Talparo clay discussed above is also reproduced – together with a rainfall diagram.

EXAMPLES OF MOISTURE PROFILES

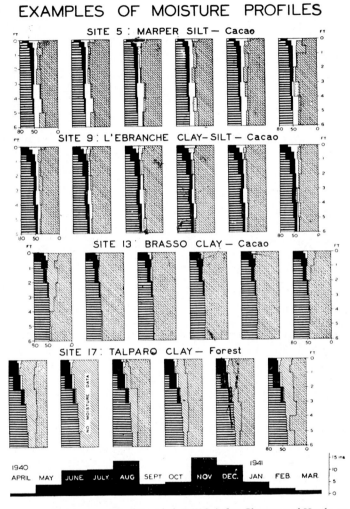

FIG. I.9. *Moisture profile of Trinidad, B.W.I. (after Chenery and Hardy, 1945)*

The diagram depicts the moisture status at different depths, down to 2 m, at different times of the year. Each profile shows the porosity characteristics of the soil. The thick horizontally shaded area on the left represents the percentage volume of solid soil matter. The cross-hatched area on the right represents the percentage volume of the capillary pore spaces; that is, those that can store water but are too small to store air, being mostly micro-reticulate and colloidal. The unshaded area represents the percentage volume of the non-capillary pore spaces; that is, those through which water can pass readily under gravity, and which can store air and permit root penetration. The blackened area represents soil organic matter content. The dotted area represents the total percentage volume occupied by water at the time of sampling. Thus, the percentage volume of the free air space (or degree of unsaturation by water), derived by the difference between total porosity and volume of water content, can at once be observed. This measures the amount of aeration.

Chenery and Hardy call this representation a 'diagram', but it is really a 'triagram' because besides the soil depth and soil-water-air relation, the *time* is also taken up in it. It is then in the simple form of 6 profiles for a year. Yet, this is real progress, and the line is marked.

There followed, soon after, a study of the water and air relations of some Trinidad sugar cane soils by Hardy and Derraugh (1947). In part I of their paper, the main results obtained are pictured in graphs, showing soil moisture and soil air fluctuations in sandy and clay soils. Here not only a greater frequency (e.g. four day's rainfall) is put into practice, but also a 'moving average' through the whole year. One of these graphs is reproduced below (see fig. 1.10 p. 75).

1. The white unshaded upper area, bounded by the zigzag line, indicates the volume of free air contained in the pore spaces of the soil, as determined weekly for 5 dry season and 3 wet season months. The change in seasons is shown by a vertical black line.
2. The horizontal dotted line at the 10% level, marks the arbitrary lower limit of adequacy for soil aeration.
3. The shaded area marks the corresponding volume of water, noncapillary water being represented by vertical stripes and capillary water (field capacity or index of texture water) by inclined stripes.
4. The white horizontal line marks the wilting coefficient level, or the lower limit of available water.
5. The thick black horizontal stripe at the bottom of the graph, represents the beginning of solid-soil volume which, if continued downwards, would make up a total of 100%.
6. The black vertical columns ('chimney stacks') at the bottom of the figure represent 4-daily rainfalls in inches.
7. The rolling zigzag line above the rainfall columns gives the monthly (28-day) rainfall, expressed as a 4-day moving average, in inches. The critical value denoting 'soaking' rains appears to be 4 inches (100 mm); it is indicated by the fine dotted horizontal line.

In part II of their paper, the rainfall is analysed in a somewhat similar way as in the previous pages of this present book. Special attention is given to the 'effective rainfall', i.e. the rain that penetrates the soil and percolates downwards, and is absorbed into the rooting zone. Experimental evidence indicates that penetrating and percolating rain consists of medium showers, having an intensity of 10 to 18 mm per hour. Torrential showers, having an intensity of 20 mm and more, are wholly or partly 'effective' only when the soil is dry and cracked, or otherwise highly infiltrable. They are 'ineffective' when the soil is already saturated with water, or when its surface is compacted, puddled or crusted. Light showers (i.e. showers having an intensity of 10 mm an hour or less) are 'ineffective' because they evaporate without any penetration into the soil worth mentioning. Thus, effective rainfall may be evaluated as the difference between total rainfall and the sum of the fractions which evaporate, run off and penetrate beyond the rooting zone.

It may be pointed out that if the lower limit of 10 mm is split like this: 4 mm retained in the vegetation and 6 mm returned to the atmosphere by evaporation, then there is sufficient agreement with figures given in the preceding pages of this book. Also, the limit of 20 mm agrees fairly well with the observations in the Congo and in Indonesia.

We may conclude the review of this interesting investigation by drawing attention to

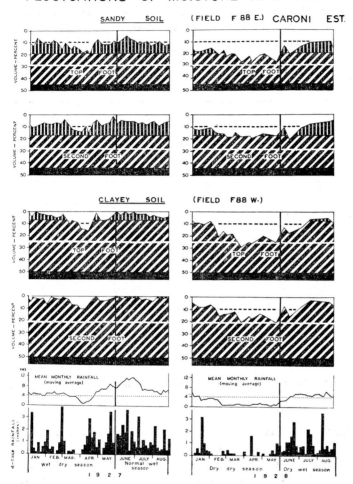

FIG. I.I0. *Soil moisture profiles of Trinidad (after Hardy and Derraugh, 1947)*

the fact that in the diagrams the frequency of the rainfall data is increased again from 4-day to 3-day totals. This raises the accuracy and value of the moving average curves over the whole year. By inverting the effective rainfall diagrams, some idea of the theoretical depth of penetration of rainwater may be obtained – be it only approximately.

This chapter may be concluded with a few general considerations.

In the first place an interesting study from Ecuador on the relationship climate: vegetation: soils merits attention. Frei (1958) describes nine important soil groups belonging to the classes of desert soils, black and brown tropical soils, oxic soils and andosols. Climatic differences have been recognized as the main reason for these widely varying soil formations. These reflect clearly the differences in annual precipitation and monthly rain distribution. The soil profiles and vegetation cover also seem to be greatly influenced by the differences in the mean annual temperature, depending on the altitude above sealevel.

The geographic profile through Ecuador in fig. 1.11, clearly shows the relationship mentioned above.

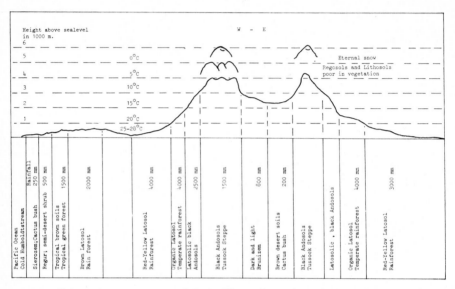

FIG. 1.11. *Schematic representation of the landform of Ecuador and relation between soil type, vegetation and climate (after Frei, 1958)*

Opposing this fine present-day example is the fact that climatic influences different from and preceding those presently active, may have affected what is now visible. It has been notably Kubiena (1963) who, by studying the micromorphology of soils, clearly exposed paleoclimatic influences in present-day soils. In his contribution to the Symposium on Changes in Climate organized by UNESCO and the World Meteorological Organisation Kubiena presented numerous examples of the consistency of the original structural habit under climatic conditions which differ markedly from those now effective. To quote one example, the red loams of the Island of São Tiago (Cape Verde Islands) which were formed under tropical forest occur in a region where the forest has now completely disappeared owing to a continuous decrease in precipitation and an increase in the length and intensity of the dry season. This observation is supported by Stephens' paper on climate as a factor of soil formation through the Quaternary (Stephens, 1965). This well-known Australian soil scientist discusses clearly the meaning of changes in climate for landscape development and soil formation, pointing to the 'differences in the component elements which make up the pedological and geomorphic record of Quaternary events in the different continents'. Africa, Australia and South India are stable ancient landmasses whereas the other continents have been shaped by glacial and volcanic activities and orogenic earth crust deforming dynamics. This difference in geological history is reflected in the climate and its influence on the nature and progress of soil formation. In a sense these considerations hold a warning that the climatic context should be handled as a whole and not too narrowly as a sum of particular events, however important these may be as indications of an expected course of current soil forming processes.

LITERATURE CITED

BAEYENS, J. 1938 Les sols de l'Afrique Centrale, spécialement du Congo Belge. Tome I – Le Bas-Congo. *Publ. I.N.E.A.C.* Brussels. pp. 375.

BERLAGE jr, H. P. 1949 Rainfall in Indonesia; Mean rainfall figures for 4399 rainfall stations in Indonesia, 1879–1941. *Verh. Kon. Magn. Meteor. Observ. Batavia*, nr 37, pp. 212.

BEUMEE-NIEUWLAND, N. 1922 Onderzoekingen van djati-boschgronden op Java. *Meded. Proefsta. Boschwezen, Buitenzorg*, 8 : 1–91.

BOEREMA, J. 1925 Mean rainfall figures for 2715 rainfall-stations in the Netherlands East Indies, calculated from observations made during the period 1879–1922. *Verh. Kon. Magn. Meteor. Observ. Batavia*, nr 14, pp. 192.

— 1926 Typen van den regenval in Ned. Indië. *Verh. Kon. Magn. Meteor. Observ. Batavia*, nr 18, pp. 103.

BRAAK C. 1928 The climate of the Netherlands Indies. *Proc. Royal Magn. Meteorol. Observ. Batavia*, No. 8, pp. 272.

BRIGGS, L. J. and SHANTZ, H. L. 1914 Relative water requirement of plants. *J. Agric. Res.*, 3 : 1–64.

CARTON, P. 1930 Température du sol à Phu Lien (Tonkin). *Bull. Econ. Indochine*, 33: 688B–707B.

CHENERY, E. M. and HARDY, F. 1945 The moisture profile in some Trinidad forest and cacao soils. *Trop. Agric.* (Trinidad), 22 :100–115.

COCHRANE, N. J. 1956 The cyclic behaviour of Lakes Victoria and Nyasa. *Col. Geol. & Min. Resources*, 6 nr 2 :169–175.

COSTER, CH. 1937 De verdamping van verschillende vegetatievormen op Java. *Tectona* (Buitenzorg), 30 : 1–102.

DILLMAN, A. C. 1931 The water requirement of certain crop plants and weeds in the northern great plains. *J. Agric. Res.*, 42 : 187–238.

FREE, G. R., BROWNING, G. M. and MUSGRAVE, G. W. 1940 Relative infiltration and related physical characteristics of certain soils. *U.S.D.A. Techn. Bull.*, No. 729, pp. 51.

FREI, E. 1958 Eine Studie über den Zusammenhang zwischen Bodentyp, Klima und Vegetation in Ecuador. *Plant and Soil*, 9 : 215–235.

FREISE, F. W. 1934 Beobachtungen über den Verbleib von Niederschlägen im Urwald und den Einfluss von Waldbestand auf den Wasserhaushalt der Umgebung. *Forstwiss. Zentr. Blatt*, 56 : 231–245.

FREISE, F. 1936 Das Binnenklima von Urwäldern im subtropischen Brasilien. *Peterm. Mitt.*, 82 : 302–307.

GEE, J. C. DE 1950 Preliminary oxydation potential determinations in a 'sawah'-profile near Bogor (Java). *Trans. 4th. Internat. Congr. Soil Sci. Amsterdam*, I : 300–303.

GEIGER, R. 1927 Das Klima der bodennahen Luftschicht. Braunschweig, pp. 246.

— 1930 Mikroklima und Pflanzenklima. Handb. d. Klimatologie, Band I. Part D, pp. 47.

HANN, J. V. 1915 Lehrbuch der Meteorologie.

78

HARDY, F. 1946 The evaluation of soil moisture. *Trop. Agric.* (Trinidad), 23 : 66–75.
— 1947 Effective rainfall and soil moisture in Trinidad. *Trop. Agric.* (Trinidad), 24 : 45–51.
— and DERRAUGH, L. F. 1947 The water and air relations of some Trinidad sugarcane soils. Part I and II. *Trop. Agric.* (Trinidad), 24 : 76–87, 111–121.
HARRISON, W. H. and SUBRAMANIA AIYER, P. A. 1913, 1916 The gases of swamp rice soils. *Mem. Dept. Agr. India* (Pusa), III, 3 : 65–106; IV, 1, 4 : 1–18, 135–149.
HENRY, Y. 1931 Terres rouges et terres noires basaltiques d'Indochine. *Gouvern. Gén. Indochine* Hanoi, pp. 210.
HOPPE, E. 1896 Regenmessung unter Baumkronen. *Mitt. Oesterr. Vers. Stat.*
HYDROGRAPHIC REPORT from Surinam, 1952. *Rapport no. 5 Sticht. Planbureau Suriname.*
JAPING, H. W. 1930 Bosch-hydrologisch onderzoek van den laatsten tijd. *Tectona*, 23 : 919–953.
KAMERLING, Z. 1906 De verdamping van de rietplant. *Arch. Java Suik. Ind.*, 14 : 18–39.
KERBOSCH, M. and SPRUIT Pzn, P. 1929 Beoordeeling van kinagronden. *Cinchona*, 6 : 34–111.
KHANNA, K. L. and RAHEJA, P. C. 1947 The relative efficiency of water requirements in relation to manurial experiments. *Indian Journ. Agric. Sci.*, 17 : 371–376.
KOPECKY, J. 1914 Die physikalischen Eigenschaften des Bodens. *Intern. Mitt. Bodenk.*, 4 : 138–198.
KÖPPEN, W. 1916 Klassifikation der Klimate nach Temperatur, Niederschlag und Jahreslauf. *Peterm. Mitteil.*, 62 : 197–203.
KRAMER, P. J., BIDDULPH, O. and NAKAYAMA, F. S. 1967 Water Absorption, Conduction and Transpiration. In: Irrigation of Agricultural Lands. *A.S.A. Monograph*, nr 11, Chapt. 17 : p. 332.
KUBIENA, W. L., 1963. Paleosols as indicators of paleoclimates. *Arid Zone Res.* nr 20 : 207–209.
LANG, R. 1915 Versuch einer exacten Klassifikation der Böden in klimatologischer und geologischer Hinsicht. *Int. Mitt. Bodenk.*, 5 : 312–346.
LEATHER, J. W. 1915 Soil temperatures. *Mem. Dept. Agr. India (Chem. Ser.)*, IV, 2 : 19–49.
MARR, TH. 1911 Bodemtemperaturen. Meteorologische waarnemingen verricht te Pasuruan gedurende het tijdvak 1901–1910. *Arch. Java Suik. Ind.*, 1 : 541–594.
MARTONNE, E. DE 1909 Traité de géographie physique. Paris, vol. I : 205–225.
MEYER, A. 1926 Ueber einen Zusammenhang zwischen Klima und Boden in Europa. *Chem. der Erde*, 2 : 209–342.
MILNE, G. 1947 A soil reconnaissance journey through parts of Tanganyika Territory, December 1935–February 1936. *J. Ecol.*, 35 : 192–265.
MOHR, E. C. J. 1909 Ueber Verdunstung von Wasser- und Bodenoberflächen. *Bull. Dept. Agric. Buitenzorg* (Java), nr XXIX, pp. 12.
— 1909 Kleine bijdrage ter beoordeeling van het waterhuishoudingsvraagstuk. *Teysmannia* (Batavia), 20 : 151–166.
MOHRMANN, J. C. J. and KESSLER, J. 1959 Waterdeficiencies in European Agriculture. *Int. Inst. Land Reclamation and Improvement*, Wageningen, Publ. 5, pp. 60.
PAPADAKIS, J. 1961 Climatic Tables for the World. *Av. Cordoba*, 4564, Buenos Aires. pp. 160.
PENCK, A. 1910 Versuch einer Klimaklassifikation auf physiogeographischer Grundlage. *Sitz. ber. Preuss. Acad. Wiss.-Phys. Math. Kl.*,: 236–246. In: Blanck–Handb. d. Bodenlehre, II (1929) : 28–29.
PENMAN, H. L. 1948 Natural evaporation from open water, bare soil, and grass. *Proc. Roy. Soc.*, 193A: 120–145.
— 1949 The dependence of transpiration on weather and soil conditions. *J. Soil Sci.*, 1 : 74–89.

PENMAN, H. L. 1956 Evaporation: an introductory survey. *Neth. J. Agric. Sci.*, 4 : 9–29.

PRESCOTT, J. A. 1949 A climatic index for the leaching factor in soil formation. *J. Soil Sci.*, 1 : 9–19.

—, COLLINS, JOYCE, A. and SHIRPURKAR, G. R. 1952 The comparative climatology of Australia and Argentina. *Geogr. Review*, 42 : 118–133.

RAMANN, E. 1918 Bodenbildung und Bodeneinteilung. Berlin.

RAMDAS, L. A. and DRAVID, R. K. 1936 Soil temperatures in relation to other factors controlling the disposal of solar radiation at the earth's surface. *Proc. Nat. Inst. Sci. India*, 2 : 131–143.

— and KATTI, M. S. 1936 Agricultural meteorology: Preliminary studies on soil moisture in relation to moisture in the surface layers of the atmosphere during the clear season at Poona. *Indian J. Agr. Sci.*, 4 : 923–937; 6 : 1163–1200.

—, KALAMKAR, R. J. and GADRE, K. M. 1934 Agricultural meteorology: Studies in microclimatology. Part I. *Indian J. Agric. Sci.*, 4 : 451–467.

RAWITSCHER, F. 1946 Die Erschöpfung tropischer Böden infolge der Entwaldung. *Acta Tropica*, 3 : 211–241.

— 1948 The water economy of the vegetation of the 'Campos Cerrados' in Southern Brazil. *J. Ecology*, 36 : 237–268.

RICHARDS, P. W. 1964 The Tropical Rainforest. *Cambridge Univ. Press.*, pp. 450.

RIESBOL, H. S., MILLIGAN, C. H., SHARP, A. L. and KELLY, L. L. 1967 Surface Water Supply and Development. In: Irrigation of Agricultural Lands. *A.S.A. Monograph*, nr. 11, Chapt. 6 : 58–59.

SCAËTTA, H. 1936 Contribution à l'étude des climats des sols tropicaux. *Météorologie*, 12 : 531–546.

— 1937 La genèse climatique des sols montagnards de l'Afrique centrale. *Mém. Inst. Roy. Col. Belge, Sect. Sci. Natur. Méd. Coll.*, 4/5 : 7–340.

SHANTZ, H. L. and PEIMEISEL, L. 1927 The water requirement of plants at Akron. *J. Agric. Res.*, 34 : 1093–1190.

SCHMIDT, F. H. and FERGUSON, J. H. A. 1952 Rainfall types based on wet and dry period ratios for Indonesia with Western New Guinea. *Verh. Kement. Perhub. Djaw. Meteorol. dan Geofis.*, nr 42, pp. 77.

SCHUBERT, J. 1929 Das Klima der Bodenoberfläche und der unteren Luftschicht in Mitteleuropa. In: Blanck – Handb. d. Bodenlehre, II : 54–91.

— 1930 Das Verhalten des Bodens gegen Wärme. In: Blanck – Handb. d. Bodenlehre, VI : 342–375.

SLAVIK, B. 1965 Rain interception in decidious forests. *Arid Zone Res.*, nr 25 : 193–199.

STAMM, G. G. 1967 Problems and Procedures in determining Water Supply Requirements for Irrigation Projects. In: Irrigation of Agricultural Lands. *A.S.A. Monograph*, nr 11, Chapt. 40: 771–785.

STANHILL, G. 1965 The concept of potential evapotranspiration in arid zone agriculture. *Arid Zone Research*, 25 : 109–117.

STEPHENS, C. G. 1965 Climate as a Factor of Soil Formation through the Quaternary. *Soil Sci.*, 99 : 9–15.

STEPHENS, J. C. and STEWART, E. H. 1963 A comparison of the procedures for computing evaporation and evapotranspiration. *Int. Ass. Sci. Hydr. (Gen. Ass. of Berkeley)*, Publ. 22: 123–133.

STREMME, H. 1917 Zur Kenntnis der Bodentypen. *Geol. Rundschau*, 7 : 330.

THORNTHWAITE, C. W. 1948 An approach toward a rational classification of climate. *Geogr. Review*, 38 : 55–94.

— 1949 Climate and soil moisture in the tropics. *Geogr. Review*, 39 : 498–501.
— and HOLZMAN, B. 1942 Measurement of evaporation from land and water surfaces. *U.S.D.A. Techn. Bull.*, No. 817, pp. 143.
TURC, L. 1953 The soil water balance: Interrelations of rainfall, evaporation and run-off. *African Soils*, III : 139–172.
VAGELER, P. 1910 Die Mkatta-Ebene. *Beih. z. Tropenpfl.*, IX, 4/5 : 251–395.
— 1928 De analysemethoden van het Agrogeologisch Laboratorium van het Proefstation voor Thee, Buitenzorg. (2) Water- en luchthuishouding en bewerkbaarheid. *Arch. v. d. Theecult. in Ned. Ind.*, 1 : 87–89.
— 1930 Grundriss der tropischen und subtropischen Bodenkunde. Berlin, pp. 210.
— 1940 Die Vegetationszonen Zentralbrasiliens als Ergebnis von Klima, Boden und Geschichte. *Zeitschr. Weltforstwirtsch.*, 7 : 813–854.
VAN BAREN, F. A. 1964 Physical-Geographical Aspects of Arid and Semi-arid Regions (Summary). *Tijdschr. Kon. Ned. Aardr. Gen.* 80 : 182–195.
VAN DE GOOR, G. A. W. 1950 Research on irrigating rice. *Landbouw* (Bogor), 22 : 195–220.
VANDENPLAS, A. 1943 La pluie au Congo Belge. *Mém. Inst. Roy. Météorol. d. Belg.*, XVI, pp. 127.
VAN RAALTE, M. H. 1944 Experiments on the water household of tropical plants. II. A method for the determination of the water consumption of a swamp vegetation. *Ann. Bot. Gardens, Buitenzorg*, vol. Hors Série : 1–14.
VINE, H. 1949 Nigerian soils in relation to parent materials. *Comm. Bur. Soil Sci. Techn. Comm.*, 46 : 22–29.
VISSER, S. W. 1928 Dauwmetingen te Batavia. *Natuurk. Tijdschr. v. Ned. Ind.*, 88 : 229–251.
VRIENS, J. G. C. and TIJMSTRA Bzn, S. 1906–1910 Deligronden. *Meded. Deliproefst.* 2 : 175–233; 4 : 155–172; 5 : 115–168; 6 : 293–297.
WALTER, H. 1958 Klimadiagramm-Karte von Afrika. *Deutsche Afr. Ges.*, Bonn, Schriftenreihe nr 4, pp. 27.
— and LIETH, H. 1960 Klimadiagramm-Weltatlas. *Gustav Fischer Verlag*, Jena.
ZUNKER, F. 1930 Das Verhalten des Bodens zum Wasser. In: Blanck – Handb. d. Bodenlehre, VI : 66–220.

CHAPTER 2

ROCKS AND ROCK MINERALS
An Introductory Chapter on Petrography

2.1. ROCKS

For a complete appreciation of the problems concerning soil genesis, some knowledge of petrography is indispensable. Whatever their locality all soils are either directly or indirectly derived from rocks, and therefore from rock-forming minerals. This is particularly important to the study of weathering processes in tropical regions, since it is a well-known fact that in areas with high temperatures and often high rainfall, the chemical disintegration of rocks and the end-product of the processes of alteration and decomposition, i.e. soil, are directly dependent on the properties and features of the parent material. Both the rock and its mineral ingredients are important. Considerations should be given to the rock as a whole because its structure, texture and hardness together determine its physical resistance to weathering. The significance of the minerals is that their chemical composition, crystal structure and susceptibility to alteration and decomposition are all important factors from both pedologic and agricultural points of view.

A few brief comments on the fundamentals of earth science may facilitate an understanding of what is further written. The earth is one of the planets which revolve round the sun. It possesses two fluid spheres, one of which, the atmosphere, consists of gases and completely envelops the earth to a height of about 150 km. The second, the hydrosphere, includes the waters of seas, lakes, and streams and to a lesser degree, the vast quantity of subterranean water. Under these lies the lithosphere, or hard crust of the earth, and it is this crust which consists of rocks and their mineral ingredients.

Five billion years ago the earth flew from the sun in a gaseous state, cooled and contracted to a fluid, then to a body enveloped by a solid crust. The surface of our planet was moulded by all manner of physical forces which must have been active during the processes of cooling and solidification. The situation still can not be called static. The dynamism underlying the physical phenomena which aroused such a keen interest in naturalists in the distant past is certainly not extinct today. The fact that diverse forces are active below the thin solidified outer shell is most clearly emphasized by such manifestations as earthquakes and volcanism. The form of the earth as we know it today, with its oceans and continents, its deep basins and high mountain complexes, was brought about by dynamic, inward or endogenic forces functioning closely with the exogenic or outward forces of the atmosphere and the hydrosphere. It is clear that the material which solidified in the very early stages of cooling has seldom, if ever,

82

retained its original shape and position. Rocks which crystallized at a great depth have been brought to the surface by the intricate mechanisms of folding and thrusting. Quantities of molten substance (magma) are often located near enough to the surface for the magma to escape in whichever direction affords the least resistance, i.e. to lower depths, flowing out as lava, or in cases where the inward pressure is sufficiently high, outwards into the atmosphere in the form of a volcanic eruption.

From a chemical point of view, the composition of rocks, whether they crystallized at great depth or not, or in the free atmosphere, must be dependent on the chemical composition of the original molten material. These rocks may be termed primary rocks. On arrival at the earth's surface, however, these rocks were subjected to the exogenic forces of atmosphere and hydrosphere. They altered chemically and physically, or, in one word, they weathered to secondary products. These secondary products were carried off by winds and surface water from higher places and transported to lower regions, terminating in ocean basins or other depressions. There, in the course of time, they probably hardened when covered with successive layers of the same or other material, due to pressures and temperatures which increase with depth. These deposits, sands and clays, which in some cases have hardened to a certain extent, are classified together as sedimentary rocks. Both igneous and sedimentary rocks may be transformed into metamorphic rocks by means of endogenic forces, including high temperature, high pressure, folding, etc. If no chemical compounds in gaseous or fluid form add to or detract from the composition of the original rock then the total chemical composition will be either that of the magmatic rock or of the sedimentary rock, but the mineral ingredients will adapt themselves to the new circumstances and may be quite different in both chemical and physical properties from the original compounds.

More detailed consideration will now be given to the rocks within the lithosphere. The result of the process of crystallization has always been the same, so that the geologic age of a rock is of no significance from a petrographic or pedogenetic point of view.

There are three distinct divisions of rocks:
Igneous rocks, forming on solidification of the glowing, molten mass called magma.[1]
Sedimentary rocks, formed by consolidation of deposits from wind or water.
Metamorphic rocks, transformations from either igneous or sedimentary rocks.
Igneous and metamorphic rocks are, in general, crystalline rocks; that is to say they are composed of whole crystals, whereas sedimentary rocks are very often composed of fragments of crystals or rocks. The chemical composition of the molten fluid,

[1] Attention should here be drawn to the fact that there are substantial reasons for doubting whether all rocks classified as 'igneous' are indeed directly derived from molten magma. One of the commonest 'igneous' rocks, granite, is now known in many cases not to have originated from magma, but is the result of a pneumatolitic process by which sedimentary rocks such as clay and claystone were transformed by vapours rich in silica emanating from a great depth; and there is no difference between this granite and the genuine plutonic type. Petrologists and geologists have accorded considerable attention to this form of granite during recent years.

magma, determines the composition of its crystallization products. A change in chemical composition is influenced by the presence or absence of groups of minerals which are characteristic of a special type of igneous rock. The same magma may give birth to rocks with different mineral composition, even if this is only slight, due to a divergence in the pressure and temperature conditions prevailing during any period of crystallization.

A mean composition of igneous rocks may be computed from the different chemical analyses. This very elaborate work was carried out by Clarke and Washington (1924) and reviewed by the Geophysical Laboratory of the Carnegie Institute of Washington in 1955 with the following result:

TABLE I.34. *Mean chemical composition of igneous rocks* (after Yearbook Carnegie Institute 1955)

Silicon oxide	SiO_2	59.1
Aluminium oxide	Al_2O_3	15.3
Ferric oxide	Fe_2O_3	0.2
Ferrous oxide	FeO	3.8
Magnesium oxide	MgO	3.5
Calcium oxide	CaO	6.1
Sodium oxide	Na_2O	5.8
Potassium oxide	K_2O	3.1
Water	H_2O	1.1^5
Titanium oxide	TiO_2	1.0^5
Phosphorus oxide	P_2O_5	0.3
Manganese oxide	MnO	0.1
Other elements		0.5
		100.0

Although all the known elements are present in magma, there is a residue totalling only 0.5% of the mean of igneous rocks consisting of all the other elements not tabulated here. It does not follow from this that minerals containing zirconium (Zr) for example, do not occur as rock forming constituents. Zircon ($ZrSiO_4$) is, on the contrary, a common mineral in many types of rocks, although ZrO_2 forms only 0.04% in the average composition. This also applies to borium (B) which is prominent in the well known complex silicate, tourmaline. On the average, however, these elements do not play an important part.

Another remarkable fact which emerged from the work of Clarke and Washington was that the average composition of the whole lithosphere to a thickness of 16 km, was similar to the average composition of igneous rocks. This fact supports the assumption that all rocks originated from the igneous material.

Only averages have been mentioned thus far, and this suggests that the chemical composition of rocks of different magmatic origin may be different. This is so, and it has been found that the most satifactory classification of rocks is that based on their chemical composition.

2.1.1. IGNEOUS ROCKS

This section of petrology was studied in great detail by Niggli (1923) who developed a system of classification based on the molecular ratios determined by total analysis, of the most important oxides. The most prominent of these is silicon dioxide and this is of particular importance since the percentage present determines whether minerals rich in silica, with a low percentage of silica, will crystallize, or whether it is in sufficient excess of other elements to allow quartz to crystallize.

A comparison of two very common igneous rocks, a granite and a basalt, clearly demonstrates this. The first solidified at great depth below the surface of the earth and the second very near to or even on the surface, so a different type of formation is evident in each case, and this will be discussed later.

TABLE 1.35. *Chemical composition of a granite of Guiana* (after Harrison, 1934) *and a basalt of Java* (after Mohr, 1944)

	Granite	Basalt
SiO_2	70.8	52.9
Al_2O_3	14.4	18.9
Fe_2O_3	2.3	4.1
FeO	1.0	4.8
MnO	tr	0.4
MgO	0.9	3.7
CaO	1.4^5	8.6
NA_2O	2.8	4.0
K_2O	5.3	0.9
H_2O^+	0.7^5	0.6
H_2O^-	–	0.8
TiO_2	0.4	1.0
P_2O_5	–	0.2
	100.1	100.9

One or two important points are immediately obvious. Firstly the high SiO_2 and alkali ($Na_2O + K_2O$) content of the granite compared with the basalt, and the high content of iron-oxides, manganese and alkaline earths of the basalt compared with the granite. This is emphasized if the molecular quantities are computed, as they were by Niggli, and then grouped under *si* for SiO_2, *al* for Al_2O_3, *fm* for the iron-oxides, manganese-oxide and magnesium-oxide, *ca* for CaO and *alk* for the alkalies ($Na_2O +$ - K_2O). The reason for this grouping is that the dark coloured iron-magnesium minerals, often containing manganese, contrast with the important group of the feldspars, i.e. the calcium and/or sodium or potash bearing light coloured silicates. The process of calculating the so-called Niggli-values is quite simple and is briefly as follows.

The percentages by weight, obtained by total analysis, are converted into molecular quantities by dividing each percentage by the molecular weight of the oxide concerned and multiplying the result by 1000. The molecular values of Al_2O_3; $FeO + Fe_2O_3$ (one molecule of Fe_2O_3 being calculated as 2 mol FeO) $+ MgO + MnO$; CaO; and $Na_2O + K_2O$ are now added and calculated again on a basis of mutual percentages, the total thus adding up to 100 and giving the Niggli-value *al* for Al_2O_3; *fm* for $Fe_2O_3 + FeO + MnO + MgO$; *ca* for CaO and *alk* for $Na_2O + K_2O$. The factor used to co-ordinate the total of the molecular values on a percentage basis of 100 is also used to convert the molecular value of SiO_2 into a comparable figure *si*. Other oxides such as TiO_2, P_2O_5 and so on, may also be converted to Niggli-values, *ti*, *p*, etc. These will not be included in the present discussion since they are of no direct importance for rock-classification purposes. If the procedure mentioned above is carried out on the two analyses given on page 84, the following results are achieved:

TABLE I.36. *Calculation of Niggli-values of a granite and a basalt*

	Granite				Basalt			
	percentage by weight (a)	molecular weight (b)	molecular value (a:b) × 1000	Niggli-values	percentage by weight (a)	molecular weight (b)	molecular value (a:b) × 1000	Niggli-values
SiO$_2$	70.8	60	1181	si 351	52.9	60	881	si 140
Al$_2$O$_3$	14.4	102	141	al 42	18.9	102	186	al 30
Fe$_2$O$_3$	2.3	160	15 × 2 ⎫		4.1	160	25 × 2 ⎫	
FeO	1.0	72	13.5 ⎬ 67.5		4.8	72	66 ⎬ 217	
MnO	tr	71	– ⎪	fm 20	0.4	71	6 ⎪	fm 34
MgO	0.9	39	24 ⎭		3.7	39	95 ⎭	
CaO	1.4^5	56	26	ca 8	8.6	56	153	ca 24
Na$_2$O	2.8	62	45 ⎫ 101.5	alk 30	4.0	62	64 ⎫ 74	alk 12
K$_2$O	5.3	94	56.5 ⎭		0.9	94	10 ⎭	
			336				630	

Now a comparison of the two rocks produces the following:

Niggli-values	si	al	fm	ca	alk
granite	351	42	20	8	30
basalt	140	30	34	24	12

More information is obtained from these figures by further computing the amount of SiO_2 bound as silicate, *si'*, to the other elements and the free SiO_2, *qz*, or quartz. The simple formula $si' = 100 + 4\,alk$ gives the combined silica and $si - si' = qz$ or the free quartz. This *si'* value is found by using the method for petrographic calculation, which is based on the following standard mineral composition:

alkali-feldspars $(K_2O, Na_2O) : Al_2O_3 : 6SiO_2$
plagioclase $CaO : Al_2O_3 : 2SiO_2$
dark minerals $(FeO, MnO, MgO, CaO) : SiO_2$
The amount of SiO_2 combined as silicate can now easily be computed:

SiO_2 used for the formation of feldspar	$6\ alk$
,, ,, ,, ,, ,, ,, plagioclase	$2\ (al - alk)$
,, ,, ,, ,, ,, ,, dark minerals	$c - (al - alk) + fm$
	$si' = 100 + 4\ alk$

Applying this formula to the two rocks under discussion gives the following results for granite:

$si' = 100 + 120 = 220$
$qz = si - si' = 351 - 220 = 131$
and for basalt:
$si' = 100 + 52 = 152$
$qz = si - si' = 155 - 152 = 3$

This shows by a single figure that the granite has a considerable excess of SiO_2 and is consequently very rich in quartz, while basalt contains little free silica.

This method of representing the results of chemical analyses will now be expanded for some of the commonest igneous rocks.

TABLE I.37. *Grouping of some igneous rocks after their Niggli values*

Type of rock	Location	Niggli-value						Author
		si	al	fm	c	alk	qz	
granite	Guiana	351	42	20	8	30	+131	Harrison (1934)
rhyolite	Sumatera	483	55	6	3	36	+239	Idenburg (1937)
diorite	California	171	34	29	24	13	+ 19	Niggli (1923)
andesite	Java	156	31	33	25	11	+ 12	Mohr (1944)
gabbro	Surinam	115	19	47	26	7	− 15	Yzerman (1931)
basalt	Sumatera	118	22	48	21	9	− 18	Idenburg (1937)

The difference in silica content is the most outstanding feature of this table, but a perceptive study of the data also reveals that a high SiO_2 content is accompanied by a high content of aluminium oxide and alkali oxides, while a low silica content coincides with high contents of the oxides of iron, magnesium, and calcium. This is clearly illustrated by means of a simple graph, indicating the *si*-value on the abscissa, and the percentage of *al, fm, c* and *alk*, on the ordinate.

It is fairly obvious that since the chemical composition of a rock is a reflection of the constituent minerals, different appearance of the rock will result from a different mineralogical composition.

Another difference in outward appearance, depending on the mode of formation, should be mentioned before going into this mineralogical aspect of petrology. The igneous rocks, as has been mentioned in the foregoing pages, are products of the

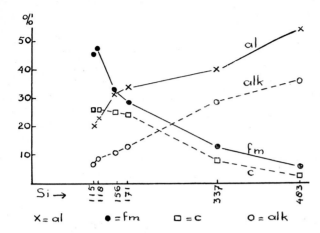

FIG. I.12 *Relation between SiO₂ and other oxides in rock composition*

crystallization of magma. It does not necessarily follow that solidification occurred under identical physical conditions of pressure and temperature. On the contrary there are three distinct main groups:

   I. those which solidified in the magma itself at a great depth: the *plutonic rocks*;
  II. those which solidified at moderate depths, such as dikes; a dike being a mass of igneous rock that fills a fissure in pre-existant rocks: the *intrusive or dike rocks*;
 III. those which solidified on the surface of the earth, as a result of volcanic activity which caused the magma to erupt: the *extrusive or effusive rocks*.

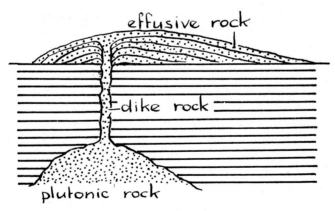

FIG. I.13. *Scheme of the genetic relations between the three groups of igneous rocks (after Escher, 1948)*

The process of crystallization occurred in a different way in each of the cases mentioned due to differences in both the pressure and temperature between magma and its surroundings, and consequently in the rate of cooling.

   In I there was high pressure, and the temperature difference between hearth and hearth surface must have been small. Crystallization therefore proceeded slowly and this type of rock was ultimately built up from large crystals of the different minerals. The cooling took place much more quickly in the case of II. A few large minerals belonging to the early generation will still occur, but there was a preponderance of small-sized constituents. The interstices were filled up with glass existing as an amorphous undercooled fluid. Cooling occurred almost instantaneously in III, at least in cases where the flow of liquid magma was not too thick. A few crystallized minerals, in most cases brought from below by the rising magma, were embedded in a vitreous mass. The result was the optimum porphyric structure, as it is called, as opposed to the coarse-grained or holocrystalline structure of the plutonic rocks.

The characteristic structural features of a typical plutonic rock and a typical effusive rock are illustrated in the figures 1.14 and 15.

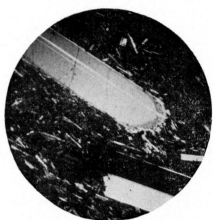

FIG. I.14. *Structure of a plutonic rock (granite, N. E. Timor) 38 x, crossed nicols*

FIG. I.15. *Structure of an effusive rock (trachite, Ethiopia) 38 x, crossed nicols*

There is still one interesting fact that should be mentioned about the distribution of the different types of igneous rocks, and which is equally applicable whether the rocks belong to the plutonic or the effusive group, and whether they are rich (as is the case with acid rocks) or poor in silica (as are basic rocks). If the cause of the different types of magma is regarded as a specific petrological problem and is therefore left out of the present discussion, it is purely a question of observation to realize that by far the most abundant types of igneous rocks are granite and basalt. Furthermore, if Daly's findings for North America are extrapolated to the total surface of the earth, it may be estimated that among the plutonic rocks the granites and granodiorites together occupy more than twenty times the total area covered by all the other intrusive rocks combined. Basalt probably has a volume at least five times greater than all the extrusives put together.[1] Pyroxene-andesite, next to the rhyolitic types, is the most abundant among the other extrusive forms.

[1] Only the area of the plutonic rocks can be estimated since the depth, and therefore the volume is not known. Both surface and thickness are known for the extrusive rocks so that the volume can be calculated approximately.

These petrological facts may be summarized: differences in the structure of the igneous rocks depend on the mode of formation, and differences in their chemical composition depend on the type of magma from which they originated. This also determines the mineralogical composition, so that the main rock types may be grouped according to their most important minerals (see table 1.38).

It should be pointed out that the grouping in table 1.38 is not exclusive, i.e. the minerals listed as being characteristic of a certain type of rock may also be found in one or more of the other types. If such is the case, however, they are not predominant, occur only in small quantities, and may therefore be listed as 'accessory', as e.g. the calcium-phosphate mineral apatite.

TABLE I.38. *Synopsis of the principal igneous rocks and their characteristic constituent minerals*

Magma	Mode of origin	Name of rock	Quartz	Orthoclase	Microcline	Sanidine	Albite-oligoclase	Andesine	Labradorite-Anorthite	Muscovite	Biotite	Hornblende	Hypersthene	Augite	Olivine	Volcanic glass
Granitic	P	granite	×	×	×		×			×	×	×				
Granitic	E	rhyolite	×			×	×				×	×				×
Grano-dioritic	P	quartz-diorite	×				×	×			×	×				
Grano-dioritic	E	dacite	×				×	×			×	×				×
Dioritic	P	diorite						×	×		×	×	×	×		
Dioritic	E	andesite						×	×		×	×	×	×		×
Gabbroid	P	gabbro							×					×	×	
Gabbroid	E	basalt							×					×	×	×

P = plutonic   E = effusive

There are further interesting examples of minerals of the plutonic type such as orthoclase for example, also formed as low temperature authigenic minerals. An example of this is to be found in Berg's description (1952) of a feldspatized sandstone consisting of 48% pure orthoclase. Iron minerals such as magnetite (Fe_3O_4) and ilmenite ($FeTiO_3$) have also been omitted because they are not characteristic. As far as the relative importance of the listed minerals is concerned, the mutual percentages of these constituents, as calculated by Clarke and Washington, may be found in any textbook on petrology. According to these geologists, the average mineralogical composition of all igneous rocks is as follows:

Feldspar	59.5%
Hornblende and augite	16.8%
Quartz	12.0%
Biotite	3.8%
Other minerals	7.9%

It must be added that there are groups of igneous rocks in which the average composition diverges widely from those quoted here. They are the rocks, for example, which are composed for the most part of feldspatoids such as nepheline or leucite, or of the mafic mineral olivine. They are specific cases which will have to be left out of this discussion.

2.1.2. SEDIMENTARY ROCKS

The sedimentary rocks may be subdivided into two groups:
A. those formed from deposits transported by flowing water or by the wind – the so called clastic sedimentary rocks;
B. those formed by the precipitation of compounds dissolved in an aqueous solution; and therefore of chemical origin.

The first group (A) is characterized by minerals falling into two classes: a) the insoluble residues of rock decomposition and b) the comparatively resistent minerals such as kaolinite, illite, etc., oxides of aluminium and of iron and similar products of rock weathering. It is possible that all known rock forming minerals will be found in the second class; obviously there will only be occasional instances of minerals strongly susceptible to weathering, while there will be an abundance of the resistant rock constituents. Quartz is the most important of these followed by other minerals such as zircon, rutile, tourmaline, magnetite, ilmenite and so on. Examples with an abundance of plagioclases are rarely found among the most important rock components. In marine deposits, as the sea water is rich in Na and Ca, they have a better chance of survival than the potash feldspars; these being more resistent to decomposition in fresh water. Compared with quartz all the feldspars show a higher degree of susceptibility to weathering. Since the minerals which compose these rocks are either secondary or else a random accumulation, it is obvious that a subdivision in accordance with their mineralogical composition would be useless. The most satisfactory basis for classification is by the grain size. The clastic rocks can then be subdivided into three groups:
I. *psephitic* rocks, consisting chiefly of gravel, pebbles, and boulders. If these materials, rounded by transportation, become cemented to a secondary rock after being deposited then the whole is called conglomerate. If the fragments are sharp, the resulting rock is called breccia.
II. *psammitic* rocks, consisting chiefly of material of sandy texture. When consolidated they form sandstones which may be more specifically defined, for example, as:
quartz-sandstone, if the minerals are exclusively or mainly quartz;
graywacke, if the minerals are feldspars and mafic components, often with an argillaceous binding;

arkose, if the rock contains a high percentage of feldspar which has suffered little, if any, alteration from weathering.

III. *pelitic* rocks, consisting of the finest materials of rock decay, and therefore of clay texture. When indurated they form:

mudstone, if composed of clay minerals and other constituents of mud consistency, most generally finely divided quartz; it is non-laminated;

shale, composed of the same minerals, but now a laminated rock.

The second group (B) of sedimentary rocks may be subdivided logically in accordance with the nature of the chemical compound which constitutes them. Since rocks formed from the deposits of calcium carbonate are widely distributed and are known to be the parent material of important soil types, they will be the only ones considered here. Organic agencies are frequently active in the depositing of calcium carbonate, although purely chemical deposits may occur as the CO_2 content of the sea water decreases, causing decreased solubility of the calcium carbonate. If precipitation occurs without interference from anorganic sediments, the result will be a pure carbonaceous rock in which the remains of sea-borne organisms may frequently be recognized. This type of rock is formed mostly in seas which do not border directly on continental regions. When this does occur, a certain mixing with fluvio-transported or air-borne mineral sediments will be inevitable, and a series of rocks will be formed which may be classified according to their contents of calcium carbonate and clay. In such cases distinction is made between:

limestone	100% of $CaCO_3$,		no	clay
clayey limestone	90% ,,	,,	10%	,,
carbonaceous marl	70% ,,	,,	30%	,,
marl	50% ,,	,,	50%	,,
clayey marl	30% ,,	,,	70%	,,
carbonaceous mudstone	10% ,,	,,	90%	,,
mudstone	no	,,	100%	,,

$MgCO_3$ may also be present to a large extent. Dolomite or dolomitic limestones may replace the limestones in the scheme above. The result may possibly be the predominance of Mg. Since $CaCO_3$ is more soluble than dolomite, a progressive increase in dolomite-formation may take place by interchange. This is probably important for agriculture, since a Ca : Mg ratio > 1 is the most preferable. It is not considered to have any direct bearing on the process of soil formation and the pure calcium carbonate rocks are definitely the more common.

The rocks mentioned will, of course, be built up from minerals of the carbonate group, with calcite as the predominant constituent followed by dolomite, gypsum ($CaSO_4.2H_2O$) and many amorphous or cryptocrystalline silica in the form of opal or chalcedony. The characteristic compounds of the pelitic rocks are montmorillonite and beidellite. Any other mineral occurring in the limestone and its derivatives is of detrital origin, with the possible though rare exception of the adular variety of orthoclase or of an authigenic species of tourmaline.

TABLE I.39. *Chemical composition, weatherability and origin
of the common rock-forming minerals*

COLOURLESS MINERALS

Name	S.G.	Chemical composition
Quartz	< 2.9	SiO_2
Orthoclase	< 2.9	$KAlSi_3O_8$
Microcline	< 2.9	$KAlSi_3O_8$
Sanidine	< 2.9	$KAlSi_3O_8$
Albite	< 2.9	$NaAlSi_3O_8$ (= Ab)
Oligoclase	< 2.9	$Ab_{80} - An_{20}$
Andesine	< 2.9	$Ab_{50} - An_{50}$
Bytownite	< 2.9	$Ab_{20} - An_{80}$
Anorthite	< 2.9	$CaAl_2Si_2O_8$ (= An)
Muscovite	$\gtrless$ 2.9	$KAl_2 (AlSi_3O_{10}) (OH)_2$
Calcite	> 2.9	$CaCO_3$
Zircon	> 2.9	$ZrSiO_4$
Apatite	> 2.9	$Ca_4 (PO_4)_3 (CaF, Cl)$
Kyanite	> 2.9	Al_2SiO_5
Serpentine	< 2.9	$Mg_3Si_2O_5 (OH)_4$

COLOURED MINERALS

Name	S.G.	Chemical composition
Rutile	> 2.9	TiO_2
Anatase	> 2.9	TiO_2
Brookite	> 2.9	TiO_2
Titanite	> 2.9	$CaTiSiO_5$
Tourmaline	> 2.9	$NaFe_2Al_4B_2Si_4O_{19} (OH)$
Grossularite (Garnet)	> 2.9	$Ca_3Al_2 (SiO_4)_3$
Andalusite	> 2.9	Al_2SiO_5
Staurolite	> 2.9	$2Al_2SiO_5 . Fe(OH)_2$
Epidote	> 2.9	$Ca_2 (Al, Fe)_3 Si_3O_{12} (OH)$
Hornblende	> 2.9	$Ca_3Na (Mg, Fe)_6 (Al, Fe)_3 (Si_4O_{11})_4 (OH)_4$
Augite	> 2.9	$Ca (Mg, Fe)_3 (Al, Fe)_4 (SiO_3)_{10}$
Hypersthene	> 2.9	$(Mg, Fe) SiO_3$
Olivine	> 2.9	$(Mg, Fe)_2 SiO_4$
Biotite	> 2.9	$K (Fe, Mg)_2 (Al, Fe) (AlSi_3O_{10}) (OH)$
Magnetite	> 2.9	Fe_3O_4
Ilmenite	> 2.9	$FeTiO_3$

This section on sedimentary rocks may be concluded by referring to a concept of Erhart (1956) who postulated that a complete profile of sedimentary deposits as it could occur in the epicontinental seas or oceans would reflect the pedogenetic and morphologic history of the hinterland. In the first stage of development a vegetation

Weatherability	Most common source of derivation
very low	Acid igneous and metamorphic rocks
low	ibid.
low	ibid.
low	Acid plutonic rocks
low	Acid igneous and metamorphic rocks
medium	ibid.
high	Intermediate ⎤
very high	Basic
very high	Ultra-basic ⎬ igneous and metamorphic rocks
low	Acid ⎦
soluble	Limestone
very low	Acid igneous and metamorphic rocks
medium	Acid and alkali and metamorphic rocks
low	Metamorphic rocks
medium	Basic metamorphic rocks

very low	Acid igneous and metamorphic rocks
very low	Acid igneous and metamorphic rocks
very low	ibid.
low	Acid and interm. igneous and metam. rocks, alt. limest.
low	Pneumatolytic rocks
low	Metamorphosed limestones, schists.
low	Contact metamorphic rocks
low	ibid.
low	Metamorphic rocks, altered impure limestones
medium	Acid and interm. igneous rocks
medium	⎤ Intermediate igneous rocks
medium	⎦
very high	Basic and ultrabasic igneous rocks
very high	Acid and intermediate igneous and metam. rocks
very low	Basic and ultrabasic igneous rocks
very low	ibid.

cover would protect the surface of the earth and only easily soluble components resulting from the process of weathering would be transported to the sea giving rise to the formation of calcareous and/or magnesium-rich sediments and ultimately carbonate rocks. As this process is strongly related to biological phenomena he named the period during which this was dominant 'période de biostasie' indicating that some 'biological' equilibrium prevailed. Then this equilibrium was disturbed by a change of climate, or by orogenesis or any other exogenic dynamism and the vegetation was destroyed. Erosion started, causing the transportation of fine sediments from land to sea as clay and silt firstly, then sand and finally, related to the progress of weathering in the hinterland, of metal oxides, iron-concretions, and even boulders of appreciable dimensions. This period was called 'période de rhexistasie' indicating the rupture of the equilibrium.

2.2. MINERALS

Some knowledge of the most outstanding features, the chemical composition, weatherability, and common mode of occurrence, is indispensable for a real understanding of the part played by the rock-forming minerals in soil-forming processes, and also of the value of the minerals as detrital components.

The most outstanding characteristic of the minerals is their colour. It would appear that they could satisfactorily be subdivided as coloured and colourless, bearing in mind that in the mineralogical sense colourless is synonymous with white. It should also be emphasized that several minerals exist in both colourless (white) and coloured varieties. These common features form the basis of the summary in table 1.39. The specific gravity has also been given because, although it is of no importance here, in soil mineralogical analysis the minerals are often grouped as light minerals (s.g. < 2.9) and heavy minerals (s.g. > 2.9), 2.9 being the specific gravity of bromoform, which is the liquid normally used for heavy mineral separation. This division is employed due to the fact that there is much wider variety of heavy minerals than light ones. In fact the same light mineral may often be found in conjunction with any of the several different heavy species. Andesine, the intermediate type of the plagioclases for example, may be the dominant mineral next to augite, hornblende or hypersthene. If this is the case, the diagnostic value lies in the dark coloured heavy minerals and not in the andesine. This situation is common in volcanic areas. This phenomenon is of importance in feldspar bearing metamorphic rocks. The same feldspar may occur associated with such metamorphic minerals as epidote, kyanite, andalusite or staurolite, and in such cases it has, of course, no diagnostic value at all. Since the light minerals form the great majority of the rock-forming species, they are of the greatest importance from a soil forming point of view (see p. 119). Clay minerals as newly formed compounds will be discussed in several of the following chapters.

To eliminate any misunderstanding, it should be stated that the data on minerals as listed in table 1.39 is of no value for determinative purposes. The reader interested in the features and properties of minerals which are essential for their microscopic determination is referred to any one of the existing text-books on mineralogy.

I. The plagioclase group is an isomorphous series of calcium-sodium feldspar ranging from pure $NaAlSi_3O_8$ (albite) to $CaAl_2Si_2O_8$ (anorthite). The intermediate forms are composed of a certain ratio of albite units (Ab) and anorthite units (An). An example is the formula of andesine which consists of half albite and half anorthite units, and is consequently $Ab_{50}An_{50}$.

II. If two bivalent or trivalent ions are cited in brackets, the symbols separated by a comma, this means that the two ions are isomorphically interchangeable and occur in the same mineral next to another in an undefined ratio. The formula for olivine (Mg, Fe)$_2$SiO$_4$, for instance, indicates that the mineral consists of units Mg$_2$SiO$_4$ and Fe$_2$SiO$_4$ in unfixed quantities. Another example of this is hornblende, in which mineral (Al, Fe)$_3$ is included in the seemingly complicated formula, indicating, as previously explained, that aluminium and ferric iron occur next to some other item in an irregular mixture.

III. It will be observed that the silicon-oxygen groups are often placed in brackets, with Al enclosed in some cases. This method of writing a silicate formula is based on the modern concept of silicate structures, the basic silicon-oxygen groups being

nesosilicates: (SiO$_4$)$^{-4}$ as for example in   olivine

inosilicates: $\begin{cases} (SiO_3)^{-2} & ,, \;\; ,, \qquad ,, \qquad ,, \quad \text{hypersthene and augite} \\ (Si_4O_{11})^{-6} & ,, \;\; ,, \qquad ,, \qquad ,, \quad \text{hornblende} \end{cases}$

phyllosilicates: (Si$_2$O$_5$)$^{-2}$,, ,,   ,,   ,,   mica-minerals

tectosilicates: (SiO$_2$)$^{\circ}$,, ,,   ,,   ,,   feldspars and quartz

The mica-minerals, muscovite and biotite, and the potash-feldspars and plagioclases are examples of the isomorphous replacement of Si^{+4} by Al^{+3} leaving one valency to be saturated by a monovalent cation such as K or Na. Anorthite provides an illustration of the fact that of the original (Si$_4$O$_8$)$^{\circ}$ two Si^{+4} are replaced by two Al^{+3} resulting in (Al$_2$Si$_2$O$_8$)$^{-2}$. If these few points are borne in mind, table 1.39 should be readily understood. Only stoichiometric formulae have been given for the minerals listed in the foregoing table, but it has been mentioned before that many minerals contain the composing cations in variable quantities. From hundreds of analyses, Mohr (1944) calculated the limits between which the cation-oxides and SiO$_2$ may vary in the principal rock building minerals. The results of his calculations are incorporated in table 1.40.

TABLE 1.40. *Limits between which the metal-oxide and SiO$_2$ content in percentage by weight of the principal rockforming minerals may vary*

	SiO$_2$	Al$_2$O$_3$	Fe$_2$O$_3$	FeO	MgO	CaO	Na$_2$O	K$_2$O	H$_2$O	TiO$_2$	MnO	P$_2$O$_5$	F$_2$, Cl
Quartz	~100	–	–	–	–	–	–	–	–	–	–	–	–
Potash-feldspar	62–66	18–20	–	–	–	0–3	0–4	9–15	–	–	–	–	–
Plagioclase													
Acid	61–70	19–26	–	–	–	0–9	6–11	0–4	–	–	–	–	–
Basic	50–60	27–35	–	–	–	10–20	0–5	0–2	–	–	–	–	–
Leucite	~55	~23	–	–	–	–	–	19–21	–	–	–	–	–
Mica													
Muscovite	44–46	34–37	0–2	0–4	0–3	–	0–2	8–11	3–6	–	–	–	0–7
Biotite	33–36	13–30	3–17	5–17	2–20	0–2	–	6–9	3–11	1–3	0–2	–	0–3
Hornblende	38–58	0–19	0–6	0–22	2–26	0–15	1–3	0–2	–	0–2	0–2	–	–
Pyroxene													
Augite	45–55	3–10	0–6	1–14	6–20	16–26	–	–	–	0–5	0–9	–	–
Hypersthene	48–54	1–8	1–8	0–2	13–21	19–25	1–7	–	–	–	0–2	–	–
Olivine	35–43	–	0–3	5–34	27–51	–	–	–	–	–	–	–	–
Magnetite	–	–	~69	~31	–	–	–	–	–	–	–	–	–
Ilmenite	–	–	0–10	~50	–	–	–	–	–	~49	–	–	–
Apatite	–	–	–	–	–	~48	–	–	–	–	–	~40	~7
Volcanic glass													
Acid	70–80	12–15	0–2	0–2	–	0–2	2–4	3–5	0–4	–	–	–	–
Basic	46–60	14–20		0–2	2–3	2–6	3–4	0–2	–	0–2	–	–	

After studying this chapter, the reader may arrive at the conclusion that its contents are rather detailed and specialized. It is the conviction of the present authors that weathering phenomena and soil development, especially in the tropics, are so closely related with rocks and rock minerals that a complete understanding of the processes involved can only be achieved by giving due consideration to the parent rock and its components, as well as to the mineral constituents found in the soil. This concept will be developed still further in the next section which deals with applied soil mineralogy.

2.3. APPLIED SOIL MINERALOGY

For details on the history of this specialized method of research the interested reader is referred to one of the earlier editions of the present volume (1954, 1959). At that time the mineralogy of soils from volcanic rocks, lahar flows and ash deposits, received particular attention as they occur widely in Indonesia and in most of the islands of the Indonesian Archipelago where volcanism has been the dominant landscape-forming factor. As this also applies to other tropical areas a few examples have been inserted in the present volume.

After earlier qualitative work Druif (1934–1936) started a regional semi-quantitative mineralogical study of the Deli (Sumatera) tobacco area. He investigated a number of soils derived from different tuffaceous parent material. The following mean composition of five Deli tuffs of different origin are summarized (table 1.41):

TABLE 1.41. *Synopsis of the mineralogical composition of typical Deli tuffs* (after Druif, 1936)

	Volcanic glass	Quartz, volcanic	Sanidine	Albite	Oligoclase	Andesine	Magnetite	Ilmenite	Biotite	Green hornblende	Brown hornblende	Hypersthene	Diopsidic pyroxene	Augite	Apatite	Zircon	Spinel	Orthite	Garnet	Perowskite[1]
Liparite tuff	□	○	□	×	×		+	+	○	×		+			+	○		×		
Dacite-liparite tuff	□	○	×	+	□			□	□	□	+	×			+	□				
Young dacite tuff	□	□	+		□	×	○	○	×	○	×	○			+	×	+		×		
Old dacite tuff	□	×	+		□	□	□	□	□	○	+	×	+		×	×	+		+		
Andesite-dacite tuff	□	+			○	○	□	□	□	□	□	○	+	+	+	+			+	+

[1] Perowskite is the calcium titanate $CaTiO_3$

Legenda: abundant ○   much □   moderate ×   rare +   trace |

Although this mode of presentation of quantitative data is considered to be rather subjective and allows only a comparison per single mineral in vertical direction, the difference in mineralogical composition of the distinguished types of the tuffs is clearly revealed.

Quartz and zirkon characterize the liparite tuff. They are of decreasing importance with decreasing acidity of the parent material. Here, acidity is meant in the petrographic sense of the word: decrease in silica content, and increase in alkaline earths. Biotite is most conspicuous in the liparitic material, but is still of importance in most other tuff types. Sanidine, in the liparite-andesite range, drops to a very low level, whereas the plagioclase increases in quantity. The cerium-epidote orthite is only found in the liparitic tuffs and as such, may be used as a guide mineral for distinguishing Deli liparite tuff soils.

As well as the soils directly derived from the Quaternary tuffs mentioned, soils derived from Tertiary material and marine soils have been analysed. Quaternary soils are a.o. those alluvial soils transported by the Deli rivers and deposited along the banks (river levee soils). Each of these groups of soils has a characteristic mineral association, the most conspicuously different being the Tertiary soils. Granitic quartz, coloured zircon and tourmaline are the dominant constituents. Brookite is scarce, and in alternating but always very small quantities the metamorphic minerals occur: staurolite, andalusite, and sillimanite. Epidote is sometimes prevalent.

Any mixture of Quaternary tuff soils with soil material of the Tertiary age is easily recognized. The river levee soils are typical examples of this. As the natural fertility of the Tertiary soils is much lower than that of the young volcanic ones, differences in productivity will occur when a river cuts or has cut through Tertiary deposits. This would cause a mixing of soil material of different origin and age and a consequent change in fertility. Druif gives several examples of the Deli tobacco area, where seemingly similar soils showed great differences in quality. The solution to this problem was easily found after mineralogical examination of the soils, which revealed the presence of Tertiary material in the liparitic tuff soils. It is also important to know whether the soil is derived from liparitic tuff or from andesitic parent material. These differences are easily seen under a microscope.

No less than 37 minerals were found in the Tertiary marine deposits in the hinterland, viz. in alphabetic order:
actinolite, amphibole, anatase, andalusite, apatite, brookite, calcite, chalcedony, chloritoid, corundum, diaspore, dumortierite, epidote, garnet, glauconite, hematite, ilmenite, kaolinite, kyanite, magnetite, microcline, monazite, muscovite, orthoclase, plagioclase, quartz, rutile, sillimanite, staurolite, titanite, topaze, tourmaline, zircon, zoisite, and locally: gypsum, limonite, pyrite.

It will be understood that any difference in origin may be easily established by studying the mineral association of a soil. Further within a certain species, several different characteristics can often be recognized. For instance, 'garnet' occurs in yellow, green, brown and pink forms. Pink garnet occurs only in the older nonvolcanic sediments and the others have never been encountered in these sediments.

The zircon of the volcanic tuff soils is always colourless and strictly idiomorphic. On the other hand coloured, often rounded zircons characterize the Tertiary sediments. Similar differences in habit and colour are common for minerals like quartz, amphibole, etc.

About the same time as Druif, Neeb (1935) published her observations that soils of the

TABLE 1.42. *Mineralogical compositions of soils of different origin (total mineral content in % of the sandy fractions)*

Location and number of soil sample	Fraction	Ore	Tourmaline	Zircon	Garnet	Rutile	Chloritoid	Epidote	Green hornblende	Basaltic hornblende	Glaucophane	Augite	Hypersthene	Apatite	Albite	Oligoclase	Intermediate plagioclase	Basic plagioclase	Orthoclase	Sanidine	Quartz (turbid)	Quartz (transparent)	Organic silica	Muscovite	Biotite	Iron oxide concretions	Rock fragments	Miscellanea	Remarks
Residency Surakarta (Java) No. 2426	I	—										20					14			53	—	2	—	1	—		66	—	Andesitic parent material. Rock fragments: andesitic. Vitrophyric groundmass with feldspar and pyroxene phenocrysts. Miscellanea: weathered rock fragments
	II	—										8	1				30	2		42	tr		—	—	—		64	2	
	III	3							tr¹	tr		10	2				21			36	—		—	—	—		50	3	
	IV	9							—	tr		16	1				27	—		16	—		—	—	—		58	—	
	V	3							—	—		15	—				19	—		29	—		tr	tr	—		58	—	
	A²	3		tr													22				—		—	—	—			1	
Residency Japara-Rembang (Java) No. 6867	II	3						1	—							—	—			53	7		—	1	—		25	9	Latitic³ parent material. Rock fragments: non determinable porphyric fragments. Miscellanea: non determinable weathered fragments
	III	6			tr			—	1							5	6		8	42	6		1	tr	1		2	4	
	IV	5		1				5	6	tr			2	tr		5	2		10	36	11		tr	tr	5		2	tr	
	V	6		1				6	—	tr			1			5	—			16	13	2	—	2	24		—	tr	
	A	6						—	—				—			—	2		10	29	tr		—	3	tr		3	—	
Residency South and E. Kalimant. No. 73132	I/II															—					53		tr		tr	17		9	Granitic parent material. Fractions I/II consist mainly of organic material. Miscellanea: non determinable material and gibbsite
	III															5			10		56			2	24	29		6	
	IV/V															5			8		53			3	5	41		9	
	A															5			10		56			tr	7	70		9	
Masamba (Sulawesi) No. 64827	II		2			2	5	5	1		2										53			47		17	8	2	Schistose parent material. Fraction I not present. Rock fragments: schistose
	III						3	3	3												34		3	70		29			
	IV										15										30			30		41			
	V										9										29			61		70			
	A		1	1		1																	1	45		53			

¹ trace
² A: average content based on weight percentages of fractions
³ Latite is synonymous with trachy-andesite.

same colour, texture and, generally speaking the same morphologic features, may be of different origin. In some cases this difference in origin meant a difference in agricultural potentiality.

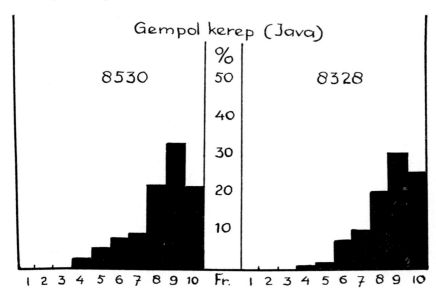

FIG. I.16. *Histograms of two sugar-cane soils of Java of different agricultural value*

Figure 1.16 is the histograms of two soils very much alike in general appearance but quite opposite in fertility. Soil 8328 contained only basic plagioclases, whereas sodium plagioclase and zirkon dominated soil 8530 indicating a rather acid character of the parent material. This soil was very deficient in phosphate, in contrast to No. 8328 which is rich in this plant nutrient.

These two examples have only a very local importance. Large-scale mineralogical research had been begun in the Soil Research Institute at Bogor (Java, Indonesia) with the analysis of many thousands of samples. The object of this work was firstly the determination of the petrographic origin, an important factor in the early classification of Indonesian soils; secondly the evaluation of the stage of weathering and the mineral reserve of the soils. For the last purpose the sandy fractions which were isolated by the granulometric analyses (see p. 156) were separately studied for their total mineral content. The data collected was also indicative of the origin of the material.

A study of the heavy mineral association is indispensable for a detailed sedimentary-petrological research, as this association allows a much more detailed grouping of the soils because the heavy fraction shows greater diversity in minerals than the light fraction.

A few examples, taken at random from thousands of mineralogical analyses carried out under the supervision of the second author, are given here as tables 1.42 and 43, as an illustration of the way in which the results of microscopical investigations are registered. This is done for the purpose of estimating the mineral reserve, qualitatively and quantitatively, and for classification based on the heavy mineral association.

TABLE I.43. *Mineralogical composition of the heavy mineral residue of soils of different origin* (in percentages of non-opaque minerals)

Sample location	Sample number	Opaque	Tourmaline	Zircon	Garnet	Rutile	Anatase	Brookite	Titanite	Staurolite	Kyanite	Andalusite	Chloritoid	Epidote	Green hornblende	Basaltic hornblende	Augite	Hypersthene	Glaucophane	Lawsonite	Remarks
Residency Jogjakarta (Java)	16993	–													1		98	1			volcanic soils
	20048	2													94		4	2			
	20018	–													15		–	85			
	20378	13													71	20	8	1			volcanic soil mixed with metamorphic material
	22195	84		9	6					4				21	51	1	5	3			
Residency Bodjonegoro (Java)	64973	55	2	84	4								2				1	7			metamorphic material
	64974	63	3	75	2					2			6	5			2	5			
	64975	6	6	37	3					8			32	10	4						
Island of Muna (Sulawesi)	60895	55	5	13	2	10	1	1	1	1	3			4	1			1	40	17	schistose material

Although the data presented gives a clear picture of the characteristic mineral associations, one factor of enormous importance tends to complicate matters: i.e. the activity of several volcanoes which built up such a great part of Java and Sumatera.

FIG. I.17. *The eruption of the Gunung Kelut of August 31st, 1951 (photo Mrs. Stam-Brandsma)*

Distribution in ash deposits. A most unique study of volcanic ashes, their spreading, and their mineralogical and chemical composition has been carried out by Baak (1949). He made a detailed study of the recent ashes of the Java volcanoes Smeru, Kelut and Merapi and a mineralogical study of the ashes of Krakatao, Galunggung, Tjirimai, Bromo, and Lamongan (1948). The 1949 paper will be discussed in detail as the data demonstrates explicitly the great value of mineralogical research for soil scientific purposes.

One of the most notorious volcanoes of the Indonesian Archipelago is the Gunung Kelut, situated in the eastern part of Central Java. The highest elevation of the Kelut is 1731 m above sea level; therefore we may consider this volcano to be a dwarf among such giants as the Smeru, Merapi and others, which rise up from the plains of Java to an elevation of about 3000 m or more. The notoriety of the Kelut is due to the many recent catastrophic eruptions which have claimed thousands of lives, while the damage is difficult to express in terms of money. The catastrophic character of the eruptions is mostly due to the lake in the crater of the volcano, as enormous volumes of water have been ejected on many occasions. The lava forms thick, hot mudstreams with this water (called lahars), which flow down the ravines at great speed. The lahar phenomena of the Kelut were studied in detail by Kemmerling (1921) after the last but one devastating eruption which took place during the night of May 19th–20th, 1919. The lake, containing 38 million m^3 of volcanic boulders, pumice, ash, etc., calculated on the basis of water was completely ejected together with almost 40 million m^3 of solid andesitic rock material. In 45 minutes, 5110 human lives were lost, 104 villages were partly or totally destroyed, flowering plantations were seriously damaged or totally destroyed by a thick cover of hot volcanic ash.

FIG. I.18. *Ash layer on coffee trees (Robusta) after the eruption of the Gunung Kelut on May 20th, 1919 (photo Hartjens)*

Kemmerling arrives at the following conclusion with regard to the lahar phenomena (compiled by Baak): the eruption starts with the formation of a kind of steam pillow at the bottom of the crater lake produced by the increasing heat which does not raise the temperature of the water mass above. When the eruption itself takes place, the whole lake is ejected. First a cold mud stream will run down through the ravines along the mountain slopes, soon followed by a hot mudstream which is formed by the lower waters of the lake mixed with ejected hot clasmatic products. This mudstream possesses an enormous erosive power, and makes deep incisions in the existing ravines. Even when the tail of the mudstream is no longer fed by new material from the crater, the lahar continues to grow due to the material eroded from the ravines. The specific gravity of this turbulent mud is very high, and large boulders will be transported, either floating in or drifting on top of the lahar. During the downward flow of the hot mudstream the enclosed water will try to escape into the atmosphere; this is partly prevented by the rain of efflata blown out of the crater. Finally, when all the steam has escaped from the lahar, only dry material will remain, consisting of debris from the slope of the volcano, sand and boulders from the ravines, mixed with material eroded from the ravine by the lahar. Near the top of the volcano, the lahar consists of a real mudstream, but by the increase of the amount of material taken up in the ravines and the decrease of the amount of water – which escapes as steam – it will gradually change into a sand and gravel stream, mixed with little water. The remaining water of this sandstream is reduced due to the internal friction.

After the crater lake has been thrown out, the debris of the inner slopes of the crater is erupted. This debris, together with the material derived from the disintegrated

FIG. I.19. *Subsided lahar, with volcanic boulders, at a distance of 20 km from point of eruption, Gunung Kelut, May 1919 (photo J. H. Coert)*

pumice dome, is mixed with ash, steam, and volcanic gas. This material forms glowing clouds above and around the crater, and they roll down like a hot stream of air without being hampered by surface obstacles, carrying pumice and rock-fragments, destroying all on their path downwards.

The finest ash particles are blown to a height of many kilometers, and fall slowly as an ash rain covering extensive areas. Their shape and extension are determined by the prevailing wind. From earlier descriptions it is evident that the phenomena described have occurred at every eruption.

In 1901 a violent eruption was also recorded. The ash which was blown out moved mainly westward, owing to the prevailing monsoon, and was distributed over the total area of Western Java. The ash of the 1919 eruption showed a quite different distribution, covering 3/4 of Java west of the G. Kelut, all Eastern Java and practically the whole of the island of Bali.

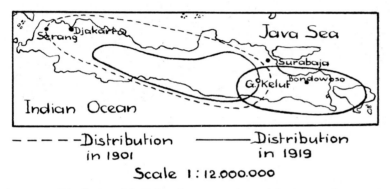

FIG. I.20. *Distribution of the Kelut ash in 1901 and 1919 (after Kemmerling, 1921)*

The reason for the distribution in opposite direction has to be found in the system of the winds which prevail in this region. It is a well-known fact that at an elevation of about $6\frac{1}{2}$ km over Java, the wind is permanently from the east (passate and anti-passate, Van Bemmelen, 1911).

During the eruption of the Kelut the lower monsoon wind was from the west, but above $6\frac{1}{2}$ km the permanent easterly trade wind prevailed. The ash which had not reached the elevation of $6\frac{1}{2}$ km had been blown directly to the east by the monsoon wind; but the ash which had reached that elevation was blown first to the west. After falling below the lower limit of the trade winds, it will have been blown back by the monsoon wind, and this meant that the main distribution was to the west.

The amount of ash (and pumice) deposited depends on the distance from the eruption point. Near the crater the ash layer was 45 cm thick. Kemmerling supplies the following data on the slopes of the volcano at several elevations:

Locality	Elevation	Thickness ash-layer
Margomulio	800 m	250 mm
Sumberpetung	700 m	200 mm
Sumberlumbu	350 m	130 mm

FIG. I.21. *Volcanic complex of Tengger Mountains. In the background, periodical eruptions of the Smeru volcano are to be seen. The influence of different wind directions at different heights is clearly demonstrated by ash-clouds (photo W. Roepke)*

At greater distances from the eruption point (for example Bandung, which is situated 500 km west of the Kelut), only a very thin layer was perceptible. However, the volcanic ash reached enormous elevations in the atmosphere, and was observed as far away as Paris, and in Germany (Kemmerling, 1921).

To stress still more the importance of the volcanic activities described, a synopsis is given below of the amount of ash deposited, and the surface area involved.

TABLE I.44. *Amounts of volcanic material blown out by the G. Kelut in the night of may 19th–20th, 1919 (after Kemmerling, 1921)*

Zones / Size-grades	Surface area involved in square kilometres	Mean thickness of ash-layers in metres	Volume of ash in millions of cubic metres	Weight by volume of freshly deposited ash	Weight of ash in millions of tons of 1000 kilograms
450–50 mm	500	0.25	125	1.250	156.25
50–15 mm	2250	0.0325	73	0.840	61.25
15–3 mm	5450	0.009	49	0.367	81.50
3–1/5 mm	16700	0.0016	27	0.260	7.00
1/5–1/20 mm	42000	0.00013	6	0.150	0.90
hardly perceptible . . .	34000	0.0001	3.4	0.100	0.34

It will be clear that this tremendous amount of volcanic material of andesitic origin will exert its influence on soil-forming processes, and will raise the fertility of the arable soil. This is because it carries important soil-forming minerals and all sorts of elements contained in the volcanic glass. To evaluate this influence, a detailed study of the fresh ash is most necessary. For this reason, Baak has undertaken investigation of the ash collected at the time of eruption in several locations at different distances. The samples were separated in the usual way into 10 fractions of which the sand and coarse silt grades were subjected to microscopic analysis. A selection of the data shows the composition of the ash at various distances from the eruption point (table 1.45).

TABLE 1.45. *Mineralogical composition of the sandy fractions of some samples of volcanic ash of the G. Kelut* (after Baak, 1949)

Sample No.	Fraction[1]	Mutual percentages of minerals								Km from crater — = West + = East
		Opaque	Volcanic glass	Rock fragments	Plagioclase	Augite	Hyper-sthene	Green Hornblende	Oxy-hornblende	
7046	III	5	7	27	46	7	8	–	–	—9
	IV	3	20	16	46	7	8	–	–	
	V	4	35	10	49	1	–	–	1	
	VI	1	85	4	10	–	–	–	–	
8501	IV	3	84	–	11	1	1	–	–	—92
	V	1	52	1	35	3	7	1	–	
	VI	2	82	–	12	1	3	–	–	
8271	V	12	46	2	38	–	2	–	–	—360
	VI	4	86	–	9	1	–	–	–	
7049	III	4	–	23	47	9	17	–	–	+36
	IV	17	15	8	45	8	7	–	–	
	V	9	25	14	42	3	7	–	–	
	VI	4	73	7	14	–	2	–	–	
7050	III	–	56	7	35	1	1	–	–	+66
	IV	1	39	14	41	4	1	–	–	
	V	8	47	5	37	–	3	–	–	
	VI	1	84	–	15	–	–	–	–	
7039	IV	10	80	–	7	1	2	–	–	+166
	V	4	42	2	45	2	5	–	–	
	VI	1	84	–	13	1	1	–	–	

[1] fraction III: 500–200μ   fraction V: 100–50μ
   „   IV: 200–100μ   „   VI: 50–20μ

It may be concluded from this table that:
a. fraction VI contains hardly any opaque grains (magnetite, ilmenite, ore),
b. rock fragments are more abundant in fraction III than in the finer fractions,
c. fraction VI consists mainly of volcanic glass,
d. plagioclase is most abundant in fraction V,
e. pyroxenes are generally confined to the coarser fractions,
f. volcanic glass tends to be the main component in the ash deposited farthest from the volcano.

The analysis shows further that the material is of augite-hypersthene andesitic origin. Microscopic investigation revealed the presence of three different types of volcanic glass: small translucent pumice fragments with round holes resulting from gas inclusions; translucent glass splinters with concave facets, probably fragments of larger pumice particles; elongated glass splinters with brownish-black parallel striae, causing a hairy appearance like pulled glass threads.

A distinct increase in content of SiO_2 with increasing distance from the volcano, is seen from the chemical data. In table 1.46, the results of total chemical analyses of several ashes (sampled at increasing distances W as well as E of the crater), are reproduced, and the chemical composition of the solid andesitic rock of the G. Kelut is included for comparison. The Niggli-values have been calculated to facilitate the comparison (see table 1.46).

Location:
1. Tjilatjap. Analyst: J. V. Shields, 1919. Sample No. 8271, Inst. Soil Res., Bogor.
2. Suaru Buluroto. Analyst: J. V. Shields, 1919. Sample No. 7043, Inst. Soil Res., Bogor.
3. White ash, Lahar Badak. Analyst: R. G. Reiber (vide Stehn, 1929).
4. Augite-hypersthene-hornblende andesite G. Kelut. Analyst: R. Djokojuwono (vide Jaarb. Mijnwezen, 1935-36).
5. Malang. Analyst: J. V. Shields, 1919. Sample No. 7049, Inst. Soil Res., Bogor.
6. Sumber Asin. Analyst: R. G. Reiber (vide Stehn, 1929).
7. Bondowoso. Analyst: J. V. Shields, 1919. Sample No. 7039, Inst. Soil Res., Bogor.

This data confirms the results of the mineralogical analysis and reveals that the material which travelled the farthest is lowest in specific gravity. Nearer to the volcano the plagioclase is probably richer in calcium and poorer in sodium than at more remote locations. The *fm*-value of Niggli (representing iron and magnesium oxides) is highest when nearest to the volcano, and lowest at the greatest distances. This is in agreement with the observation that the content of dark-coloured magnesium-iron silicates decreases with increasing distance.

The ash samples have also been treated with strong hydrochloric acid and with a 2% solution of citric acid: a method for determining acid-soluble contents used for routine analysis in the Institute for Soil Research at Bogor, Indonesia (see table 1.47). The results showed little or no difference between samples close to the volcano and samples taken farther away. This is remarkable as the material close to the volcano is much

TABLE I.46. *Total chemical analysis of volcanic ash of the G. Kelut* (after Baak, 1949)

Distance from crater (— = W; + = E)	1 −36	2 −9	3 −5	4 rock	5 +36	6 +56	7 +166
SiO_2	60.8	54.8	52.6	57.6	54.3	57.0	59.9
TiO_2	0.6	0.6	0.9	0.6	0.7	0.9	0.6
P_2O_5	0.2[5]	0.2	0.2	0.1	0.2	0.2	0.3
Al_2O_3	18.3	20.6	17.2	18.0	20.7	17.8	18.6
Fe_2O_3	3.9	4.5	3.9	3.9	4.9	4.3	3.7
FeO	2.4	3.8	5.9	3.9	3.3	4.1	2.2
MnO	0.2[1]	n.d.	0.1	0.2	0.3[1]	0.1	0.3[1]
MgO	1.9	3.3	4.4	3.1	3.2	2.6	2.0
CaO	6.0	8.5	10.2	8.5	8.8	7.8	6.4
Na_2O	5.9	3.0	3.1	3.1	2.9	3.6	3.9
K_2O	1.0	0.5	1.1	0.8	0.5	1.1	1.0
H_2O^+	1.0	n.d.	0.4	tr	0.6	0.5	1.5
H_2O^-	n.d.	n.d.	0.1	0.3	n.d.	0.1	n.d.
SO_3	0.2	0.2[5]	0.2	n.d.	0.2	0.3	0.4
Niggli values							
si	206.0	153.0	134.0	168.0	150.0	172.0	200.0
al	36.5	33.5	26.0	31.0	33.5	31.5	36.5
fm	26.5	32.0	37.0	32.0	31.5	30.5	26.0
c	22.0	25.5	27.5	26.5	26.0	25.5	23.0
alk	15.0	9.0	9.5	10.5	9.0	12.5	14.5
qz	+46	+17	−4	+26	+14	+22	+42

[1] = Mn_3O_4

coarser, and it was expected that a finer material would be more easily attacked by the acid than the coarse particles. This result is possibly due to the fact that the ash is

TABLE I.47. *Extraction values of volcanic ash of the G. Kelut*

Sample No.	Organic matter in %	Extraction values in percentages						Distance in km — = W + = E
		P_2O_5		K_2O		CaO	MgO	
		25% HCl	2% citric acid	25% HCl	2% citric acid	25% HCl	25% HCl	
8505	0.00	0.054	0.044	0.024	0.010	1.115	0.024	+ 36
8561	0.05	0.060	0.048	0.020	0.012	1.049	0.026	+ 56
8272	tr	0.066	0.052	0.029	0.021	1.059	0.023	+154
7039	0.66	0.062	0.039	0.029	0.015	1.276	0.029	+166
7042	0.04	0.055	0.034	0.038	0.010	0.920	0.034	− 4
7043	0.13	0.068	0.043	0.031	0.016	1.014	0.024	− 8
8501	0.12	0.061	0.046	0.022	0.011	1.253	0.024	− 92
Average	–	0.062	0.044	0.028	0.014	1.100	0.023	

composed for the greater part of pumice. Probably, being a porous material, it will react similarly on contact with acid whether it is fine or coarse.

If the average weights in kilograms of P_2O_5, K_2O, CaO, and MgO are calculated, on the basis of the amount of material blown out in one night, taking – for practical purposes – only that part of the ash which has been spread out sufficiently thinly to be in direct contact with the soil, i.e. a mean thickness of less than 10 mm, the following figures result (table 1.48).

TABLE 1.48. *Weight of phosphate, potash, calcium, and magnesium supplied by one eruption of the volcano G. Kelut*

Area involved in hectares	Mean thickness of ash-layer in mm	Total amount of oxides supplied in millions of kilograms					
		P_2O_5		K_2O		CaO HCl	MgO HCl
		HCl	citric acid	HCl	citric acid		
545,000	9	50.5	35.8	22.8	11.4	896.5	18.6
1,670,000	1.6	4.34	3.08	1.96	0.98	77.0	1.62
4,200,000	0.13	0.56	0.39	0.25	0.13	9.9	0.26
3,400,000	0.1	0.21	0.15	0.09	0.04	3.7	0.08
		Amount of oxides supplied in kg/ha					
545,000	9	93	66	42	21	1640	33
1,670,000	1.6	2.6	1.9	1.2	0.6	46.1	1
4,200,000	0.13	0.13	0.09	0.06	0.03	2.3	0.06
3,400,000	0.1	0.09	0.04	0.03	0.01	1.4	0.02

Apart from the influence which such a supply of chemicals will exert on pedogenetic processes, volcanic ash has also a definite fertilizing value. This is confirmed by the investigations of De Peralta and Decena (1940), who report on the beneficial influence of volcanic ash ejected from the Mayon volcano (Luzon, Philippines) to the growth of the tobacco crop.

In the same way Baak investigated the ashes of eight other volcanoes in Java (1948). It was found that each of these was characterized by a specific mineralogical association, although different eruptions were sometimes found to produce lava in which different but allied minerals might be dominant as e.g. augite and hornblende, this being directly related to the P-T ranges prevailing at the onset of the eruption.

Although volcanic ash soils are most instructive from the point of view of soil mineralogy, other instances are also known of direct relationships established between mineralogy and soil quality. An example is the study published by Van Baren and Kiel (1956) on soils from Kolombangara (Solomon Islands). Four fertility classes were established based on the content of available Ca, Mg, K, and PO_4, and the high level of Al and Mn. It was found that the mineralogical composition in table 1.58 neatly correlated with these classes. This is shown by fig. 1.28.

In exceptional cases it may occur that a rare mineral strongly dominates the heavy fraction of the soil. Such a phenomenon is recorded by Reynders (1964) in his pedo-ecological study of soil genesis in the tropics. This author gives the following mineralogical composition of an intergrade between a rendzina and a brown podzolic soil developed on limestone (table 1.49). The profile studied occurred in the Mol Mountains (West Irian) at an elevation of 2150 metres.

TABLE I.49. *Mineralogical composition of the sand fraction of a rendzina/brown podzolic intergrade; Mol Mountains, West Irian*

Sample Nr.	Depth in cm.	Opaque	Tourmaline	Zircon	Garnet	Monazite	Vesuvianite	Rutile	Anatase	Brookite	Titanite	Staurolite	Kyanite	Andalusite	Epidote	Hornblende	Oxy-hornblende	Augite	Hypersthene	Glaucophane
422	20– 0	–	–	–	–	–		–			–				–	–	–	–	–	–
23	0–10	97	20	12	4			13			35				I	12	I	–	–	
24	10–15	97	17	13	2			11			46				4	7	I	–	–	
25	15–60	93	11	14	4			7			50				I	30	–	–	–	

The high content of titanite is striking and is formed during the weathering of schistous rocks with Ti-bearing chlorite in the presence of excess lime. The high content in titanite appears not to be reflected in a high content of titanium in the soil. In the area studied, soils occur developed on slates and shales and on other types of limestones, which show a higher level of TiO_2 both in the soil and in the clay fraction. Microscopic examination does not help to explain certain details of the chemical composition in this case; its value here is purely diagnostic. This is understandable if it is realized that the heavy fraction contained only 3% non-opaque minerals and of these 30–50% is titanite. Also the sand fraction, which is the basic material for the mineralogical analysis, is made up of 3–4% heavy fraction, and this fraction constitutes in the present case only 4% of the soil. Still a specific mineral may determine the chemistry of a soil. This is to be seen in the investigation of Koch (1946) who reports that the manganese content of Ceylon soils, notably in the hill country, is closely related to the content of the Mn-garnet spessartite, which occurs as an important constituent in the widely distributed metamorphic rock khondalite[1].

The relationship between mineralogy of the soil and of the rocks from which they are derived was investigated by Van Baren (1941). Special attention was given to the potash-bearing minerals biotite, muscovite, the potash-feldspars, leucite and the phosphate mineral apatite.

---

[1] Khondalite, type locality the Khonds of India, is a garnetquartz-sillimanite rock.

The potash minerals. The common, rock-forming potash-minerals, have the following chemical compositions (table 1.50).

TABLE 1.50. *Chemical composition of the most common potash-minerals*

Mineral species	Theoretical composition	Mean % K_2O	Mean % MgO	Number of analyses
Micas				
Biotite	$K_2(Mg_4Fe)Al(Al_3Si_5O_{20})(OH)_4$	7.01	18.9	20
Muscovite	$KAl_2(AlSi_3O_{10})(OH)_2$	9.01	1.2	20
Feldspars				
Orthoclase	$KAlSi_3O_8$	14.81	–	20
Sanidine	$KAlSi_3O_8$	11.61	–	2
Feldspathoïd				
Leucite	$K_2(Al_2Si_2)O_8$	19.48	–	20

If these minerals should be classified according to their importance as a potash-mineral the following order would result: 1. leucite; 2. orthoclase; 3. sanidine; 4. muscovite; and 5. biotite. In reality, only leucite and biotite are important, being direct sources of potash for plant growth; the latter mineral is also an important natural source of magnesium. Although there are several volcanoes of the mediterranean alkaline magma-type, for example, G. Muriah, G. Lurus, and G. Ringgit on Java, and some on the Little Sunda Islands, Sulawesi, and Kalimantan, there is no quantitative data available concerning the occurrence of leucite in relation to the potash content of the soil. The reason for this is the very great susceptibility of this mineral to weathering which causes its disappearance in a very early stage of soil formation. It is never encountered in the soil. However, the abundance of leucite in the tephritic parent rocks causes the presence of a high content of potash in the soil which is derived from these rocks. This abundance of leucite is clearly seen in the photographs which represent a thin section of a leucite-phonolite (fig. 1.22), and a polished hand-specimen of a leucite-tephrite (fig. 1.23). Percentages of K_2O which are soluble in HCl to as high as 0.15%, and soluble in citric acid up to 0.03%, are no exception, even if no potash-bearing minerals are present.

Interesting is the correlation of the content of K_2O and MgO to the content of biotite in percentages of the sand fractions of the soil.

Table 1.51 shows the content of potash-bearing minerals in soils from Sumatera and Sulawesi, as compared with K_2O and MgO soluble in HCl, and K_2O soluble in citric acid.

As it has to be taken into account that in routine mineralogical analysis only the fractions > 50 µ are investigated, so far the correlation between content of minerals and content of plant feeding minerals is very satisfactory. The liparite soils of Dairi (Sumatera) show a very close relationship to biotite-MgO content. The potash supply is undoubtedly dependent upon the mica content. It is clearly pointed out that

FIG. I.22. *Thin section of a leucite phono-lite, Gunung Muriah, Java*

FIG. I.23. *A polished hand-specimen of leucite tephrite, Gunung Muriah, Java*

sanidine is much less important than biotite as a source of potash. Orthoclase and muscovite are also less susceptible to weathering and do not easily release their potash in an acid-soluble form.

The data for magnesium of the soils derived from schist deserves further consideration. Soils 75018, 75173 and 75193 are derived from metamorphic rocks, among which are not only mica-schists, but also amphibolites and related dynamomorphic altered diabases. The latter rock type was found to have a very high content of magnesium: 4 or 5 times the amount compared with the other rocks involved. It will be clear that contamination with only a small amount of weathered material of the diabase will cause a substantial increase in magnesium content of a soil. In samples 75018 and 75193 this could be microscopically proved by the occurrence of picotite and enstatite.

A second possibility is the influence of marine material. For example, sample No. 75173 contained 10.1 % CO_2, proof of contamination by limestone-detritus. The mineralogical analysis revealed the presence of no less than 40 % of calcium carbonate concretions in the sand fractions.

The phosphate minerals. Although there is only one common rock forming phosphate mineral, i.e. apatite, composition $Ca_5 (PO_4)_3 (F, Cl)$, it is difficult to detect the source of phosphorus in the soil, for organic bound phosphate can also be of great importance. It must be added that apatite only seldom occurs in large enough crystals or crystal fragments for microscopic detection. Nevertheless, soil mineralogical research has given ample indications of importance of the natural phosphate supply.

TABLE 1.51. *Correlation between content of potash minerals and potash and magnesium content of some Indonesian soils*

Soil sample No.	Soil description	Sand fraction in %	Org. matter in %	Orthoclase	Sanidine	Muscovite	Biotite	K₂O HCl	K₂O Citric acid	MgO HCl
				in % of the sand				in % of the soil		
Daïri-lands Sumatera										
	Soils derived from liparite									
78523	Brown liparite mountain soil	82.5	5.1	—	2.6	—	9.3	0.155	0.033	0.314
78657	Id.	65.5	4.6	—	3.4	—	5.5	0.163	0.025	0.279
78655	Id.	54.1	12.1	—	0.8	—	9.2	0.111	0.021	0.301
78398	As above, weakly podzolized	74.2	4.0	—	1.0	—	1.0	0.031	n.d.	0.043
78888	Yellowish grey, strongly podzolized, liparite tuff loam	19.8	25.4	—	0.9	—	—	0.027	0.018	0.008
78580	Id.	67.2	6.3	—	9.1	—	0.3	0.031	0.012	0.008
78545	Yellowish grey liparite tuff loam	71.2	10.5	—	0.5	—	1.3	0.045	0.031	0.092
78736	Brown liparite mountain soil	79.9	2.7	—	6.2	—	0.6	0.045	0.020	0.135
Palopo-Malili Sulawesi										
	Soils derived from granite									
74948	Brownish yellow to yellowish pink	18.7	n.d.	—	—	—	0.5	0.015	n.d.	0.038
75031	Granite lateritic soil	44.9	n.d.	0.7	2.7	—	1.7	0.046	n.d.	0.172
75066	Id.	39.5	n.d.	2.7	—	—	2.3	0.046	n.d.	0.231
75045	Id.	57.0	n.d.	10.7	9.2	—	18.6	0.368	n.d.	0.719
75040	Id.	59.3	n.d.	4.6	4.8	0.73	30.0	0.563	n.d.	0.816
	Soils derived from schist									
75018	Brownish grey sandy soil	42.5	n.d.	—	—	8.45	—	0.015	n.d.	0.596
75173	Yellowish grey fine sandy loam	2.77	n.d.	—	—	12.05	—	0.036	n.d.	0.747
75193	Bluish grey bog soil	5.9	1.8	4.5	—	49.90	4.0	0.062	n.d.	0.694

Apatite is a mineral which occurs as an accessory component in plutonic and effusive rocks of different magmatic origin. If during the process of rock formation pneumatolitic processes are dominantly active – that is, if the magma has a high content of volatiles – a concentration of apatite in the solidified rock is one of the results. This is typically the case in the rocks of the G. Muriah, already discussed in relation to the occurrence of leucite. Photographs show the apatite in thin sections of some of the more important alkali rocks of this volcano.

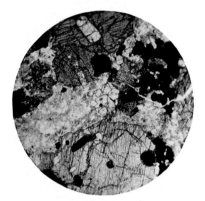
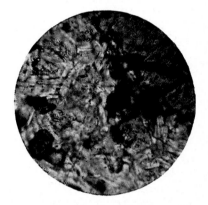

FIG. I.24. *Some large apatite crystals in leucite-tephrite, Gunung Muriah, Java*

FIG. I.25. *Abundant tiny rods of apatite in leucite-tephrite, Gunung Muriah, Java*

Photograph 1.25 is particularly interesting as it shows very abundant tiny needles of apatite in the groundmass of the leucite-tephrite. If such a rock is weathered to a soil, these tiny needles can hardly survive the leaching which goes with weathering. If it does survive, it will not be found by microscopical analysis of the sand fraction, as it has dimensions of the silt or clay size. Nevertheless, it may be expected that the soil which is derived from such rocks is high in phosphate. This has already been discussed by several soil investigators in Java (Beumée-Nieuwland, 1922; Marr, 1912).

Table 1.52 shows the content of P_2O_5 soluble in HCl and citric acid of soils of the G. Muriah as compared with soils of Sulawesi.

Volcanic glass. Volcanic glass very often comprises 80% or more of the sandy fractions (see table 1.45, p. 105), but its importance cannot be expressed as exactly as that of the rock-forming minerals of known chemical composition. This glass is the rest-magma remains which take part in the building up of a rock as the last solidified product after the crystallization of the minerals. It will consist of the surplus of elements that have not crystallized into one or other minerals of a given chemical composition. Consequently, a great difference in the composition of glasses is to be expected. In one case it may be composed of almost pure SiO_2, but in other cases it may contain appreciable quantities of such elements as phosphorus, calcium, magnesium, potash etc. The susceptibility to weathering will depend on the composition of the glass, a.o. on its SiO_2 content. The only generalization that can be made is that glasses of basaltic

TABLE I.52. *Relation between content of apatite and P_2O_5 of some Indonesian soils*

Sample No.	Description of soils	Sand fraction in %	Org. matter in %	Apatite in % of sand	P_2O_5 % in HCl	P_2O_5 % in Citric acid
G. Muriah (Java)	*Soils derived from tephrite-tuff and apatite*					
68842	Greyish brown tephrite tuff soil	49.7	1.9	0.71	0.366	0.128
71046	Bright red tephrite tuff soil	32.6	6.5	0.74	0.379	0.148
68844	Greyish brown tephrite tuff soil	36.6	0.8	2.16	0.391	0.138
61767	Old, brown tephrite tuff soil	11.7	9.2	–	0.157	0.011
61766	Old, brown tephrite tuff soil	20.9	18.2	–	0.167	0.006
71367	Old, brown tephrite tuff soil	14.7	5.0	–	0.236	0.014
71362	Old, brown tephrite tuff soil	23.7	3.5	–	0.283	0.026
Masamba (Sulawesi)	*Soils derived from granite*					
75077	Yellowish grey sandy soil	85.2	n.d.	–	0.039	n.d.
75097	Greyish, fine loamy sand	73.1	2.1	–	0.061	n.d.
75095	Bluish grey loam	18.5	n.d.	–	0.072	n.d.
75069	Dirty yellow sandy soil	84.4	2.4	tr	0.079	n.d.

origin will contain less SiO_2 and more alkaline earths and iron than glasses of liparitic origin. They will also weather more easily. Acid glass is always colourless; basic glass has, more likely, a brownish hue, owing to a certain amount of iron. The glass of the Bromo volcano is one of the typical examples of a glass which rates high as a source of plant nutrition. It will be easily understood that if appreciable quantities of volcanic glass are added to a soil the soil-forming processes will be influenced by this material. Therefore mineralogical analysis is a necessary part of chemical research into the processes of weathering, which is carried out mostly on several layers of horizons of a profile. A very interesting example is given by Kiel and Rachmad (1948) of the Institute for Soil Research at Bogor. In order to investigate the influence of weathering on the content of minerals in different horizons of a profile, one has to be certain that the profile to be studied is homogeneous. Kiel and Rachmad studied the 'lateritic' weathering of a liparite tuff of Lake Toba (Sumatera), and they compared it with the podzolic weathering of material of the same origin. They selected two profiles: one of a 'lateritic' soil developed on liparite tuff, occurring at an elevation of 50 m, one of a podzolic soil of the same origin, occurring at an elevation of 1600 m above sea level.

The profile description reads as follows:

I. Yellowish-brown liparite tuff Ultisol

Location: 1 km W of Aekkuo (East coast Sumatera) along the main road from Udjung Padang to Rantauprapat.

Physiography: undulating, severely eroded hilly country.

Elevation: 50 m above sea level.

Vegetation: secondary shrubs (blukar).

Horizon	Depth (cm)	
A1	0– 10	Grey-brown humic surface soil; abrupt boundary to brown
A2	10– 30	quartz sandy clay; rather compact; abrupt boundary to
A3	30– 55	yellow-brown quartz sandy clay, more compact than A2, merging into

B₁	55–120	pale red friable clay with a few small iron-concretions and some quartz grains, merging into
B₂	120–270	brown-grey, red mottled, friable clay with quartz grains, biotite flakes and some tuff fragments, merging into
B₃	270–500	yellow-grey friable clay, less red mottled than B₂; increasing content of tuff fragments with increasing depth, merging into
C	500–600	grey weathered liparite tuff, merging into
R	600+	grey non-weathered liparite tuff.

II. Shallow liparite tuff Podzol, rich in quartz

Location: Daïri-lands (residency Tapanuli, Sumatera); 7 km SSW of Silalahi
Physiography: mountain plain
Elevation: 1600 m above sea level
Vegetation: virgin rain forest

Horizon	Depth (cm)	
A₁	0–30	brown, spongy raw-humus layer with some translucent quartz grains, abrupt boundary to
A₂	30–35	light-grey, single-grained podzolic quartz sand, abrupt boundary to
B₂ₕ	35–40	black-brown, humic luted quartz sand, abrupt on
B₂ᵢᵣ	40–45	yellowbrown, humic iron hard pan, nearly impervious to tree roots, abrupt on
C	45–75	yellow-grey weathered liparite tuff, merging into
R	75– ?	light grey unweathered liparite tuff, rich in pumice

These two profiles have been analysed microscopically, and both the heavy mineral fractions of the total sand and the mineral content of the sand fractions have been investigated. The first method is a qualitative study of the homogeneity of the soil material, the second a quantitative study of the soil minerals for diagnostic purposes. The results obtained are listed in table 1.53, p. 116.

It may be inferred from this data that the Ultisol profile is indeed homogeneous, though the occurrence of rounded tourmaline and rutile indicates a slight contamination with non-volcanic material. The increase in the upper layers of the rare earths (cerium, yttrium, etc.) silicate, orthite, with the simultaneous decrease of green hornblende, is an indication of selective weathering of the hornblende, as orthite is very resistant.

The Podzol is distinctly less homogeneous. The abundance of zircon in A₂ and B₂ₕ, next to the large amounts of garnet (variety andadrite) in the upper two horizons of the profile, and the ratio green hornblende: hypersthene: orthite indicate various sources of the material.

As mentioned above, the increase in orthite may be explained by its greater resistance to weathering, but this is hardly an acceptable explanation for the increase from 1 % in R to 15 % in C, especially as the content drops again to the very low level of 1 % in B₂ᵢᵣ. Also, 34 % hypersthene in C, as compared with 2 % in R, indicates that the profile is not homogeneous. It seems quite possible that the C and B₂ᵢᵣ horizons

TABLE I.53. *Mineralogical composition of the heavy fractions of two soil types of Sumatera* (after Kiel and Rachmad, 1948)

Horizon	Depth in cm	Opaque	Non-opaque minerals in mutual percentages							
			Tourmaline	Zircon	Garnet	Rutile	Green Hornblende	Augite	Hypersthene	Orthite
Ultisol										
A$_1$	0–10	35	–	7	–	tr	54	–	tr	39
A$_2$	10–30	17	tr	4	–	1	64	tr	–	31
A$_3$	30–55	73	–	4	–	1	42	tr	–	53
B$_1$	55–120	86	tr	10	–	tr	55	–	tr	35
B$_2$	120–270	67	tr	16	–	–	46	tr	tr	38
B$_3$	270–500	10	–	4	–	–	80	tr	–	16
C	500–600	12	tr	2	–	–	88	–	–	10
R	> 600	1	tr	3	–	–	90	2	1	4
Podzol										
A$_1$	0–30	not investigated								
A$_2$	30–35	62	1	71	8	–	2	tr	1	17
B$_{2h}$	35–40	55	–	63	3	–	14	2	6	12
B$_{2ir}$	40–45	1	–	3	–	–	76	–	20	1
C	45–75	3	–	13	–	–	38	–	34	15
R	> 75	–	–	1	–	–	95	1	2	1

(distinguished as such by macroscopical study of the profile in the field) have been deposited during the later phases of volcanic eruption which also built up the tremendously thick layers of liparite tuff. It is questionable whether this variety in mineral content is important with regard to the development of the profile by weathering influences, but it will be clear that in such a case it is hardly possible to establish the weathering sequence. Also, the value of chemical research is limited if such irregularities occur in the make-up of the profile.

Nevertheless, the total mineralogical analysis of the sand fractions revealed some interesting points. This is shown by the results of microscopic investigations of the two soils (table 1.54).

With regard to the weathering process, the most interesting mineral is biotite which is fairly easily dissolved and decreases sharply in the top layers of the profile. The percentages of the resistant minerals (quartz and sanidine) then increase from parent rock to surface horizon. The oligoclase seems to remain constant, but microscopic examination revealed that etchings on the crystallographic planes of this plagioclase were more frequent and conspicuous with the crystals in the top layers, than with those of the lower horizons.

A typical example of weathering of biotite is found in horizon C of the liparite tuff Podzol (table 1.55). No conclusions can be made from the absence of biotite in the

TABLE 1.54. *Mineralogical composition of the sand fractions* > 50µ *of Ultisol from Sumatera* (after Kiel and Rachmad, 1948)

Horizon	Depth in cm	Minerals in mutual percentages												
		Ore	Zircon	Green Hornblende	Hypersthene	Orthite	Oligoclase	Sanidine	Quartz (translucent)	Quartz (turbid)	Volcanic glass	Biotite	Iron-stained weathered fragments	Organic SiO$_2$	Sericite
A$_1$	0–10	tr	tr	tr	–	–	12	31	49	2	2	3	tr	tr	I
A$_2$	10–30	tr	tr	–	–	–	13	31	43	2	3	6	I	tr	I
A$_3$	30–55	tr	tr	tr	–	tr	10	31	45	3	I	8	I	tr	I
B$_1$	55–120	–	–	–	–	–	12	26	38	I	tr	20	I	–	2
B$_2$	120–270	–	–	–	–	–	8	17	26	I	3	42	tr	–	3
B$_3$	270–500	tr	tr	I	–	–	13	21	22	tr	4	37	I	–	I
C	500–600	tr	tr	tr	–	–	11	12	9	tr	46	22	–	–	tr

horizons A to C, as it is not finally proved that C and R have been deposited contemporaneously. The amorphous biotite as found in horizon C gives a clear picture of the weathering process involved. Biotite occurs mainly in small pseudo-hexagonal piles of flakes. In such a pile, totally bleached flakes often alternate with dark brown, supposedly fresh flakes, giving the crystal alternating dark and light layers. The very thin flakes in such a pile are easily detached from one another, and it can then be seen that all different stadia from almost unchanged biotite to totally bleached amorphous remainders occur. From a photograph showing the weathering of biotite in liparitic soils from Daïri, Sumatera, it will be seen that this is a normal phenomenon (fig. 1.26).

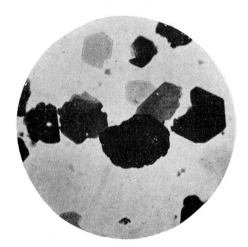

FIG. 1.26. *Weathering of biotite in a liparitic soil from Sumatera*

Mineralogical soil research, as was formerly carried out in Indonesia, has been treated extensively because the various aspects of soil mineralogy in relation to the pedology of the tropics are most clearly established. As has been mentioned in the introductory remarks of this chapter, soil scientists in a few other tropical countries have also realized the value of mineralogical investigations when studying soil problems. So Ballou (1934) mentions in his paper on geology and soils of the Dutch Leeward Islands, that the difference in geological origin of the soils is reflected in the mineralogical composition. Some typical examples were soils from Saba and St. Eustatius compared with soils of St. Martin. St. Eustatius and Saba have a consolidated base of old volcanic rocks – probably of Cretaceous or early Tertiary age – covered with layers of recent volcanic material of hypersthene andesitic composition. In St. Martin a similar volcanic base is covered by marine sediments of aqueous tuffs, cherts, and conglomerates which are in turn overlain by massive Oligocene limestones.

The mineral components of the Saba and St. Eustatius soils occur in fresh or only slightly decomposed grains. About half of these are soda-lime feldspar, the rest mainly of ferro-magnesian minerals with little or no magnetite. The St. Martin soils on the other hand, contain abundant red-coloured ferruginous products of the weathering of ferro-magnesian minerals, which occur together with partly altered cloudy feldspar and certain fresh minerals such as zircon and secondary chlorite.

A similar difference in mineralogical composition which is directly related to the age of the soils, is reported by Hardy, Robinson, and Rodriguez (1934) on the soils of Grenada and St. Vincent, also in the Caribbean region. The ochre-yellow, brown or black soils from St. Vincent consist almost entirely of unaltered fresh mineral grains viz. soda-lime feldspar, hypersthene, augite, olivine, and magnetite. But the red soils of Grenada, of similar andesitic and basaltic origin, generally contain no more than 7% unaltered mineral grains. The cause of this difference is to be found in the volcanic history of St. Vincent. The northern part of the island was covered by volcanic ash which was blown out during the eruption of Soufrière Mountain in 1902 and 1903; the soil-forming rocks of Grenada are, on the other hand, mainly much older, compact, igneous lavas.

From Niue Island (Pacific Ocean) Grange (1948) reports an interesting case of the contamination of soil developed on limestone with airborne volcanic ash. The author observed that this limestone soil has the properties of an Oxisol and concluded from the fact that the soil contained magnetite crystals and that the limestone has a much lower titania content, that the influence of volcanic material probably accounted for the weathering process. Definite proof of this supposition, although it is most likely true, could have been given by mineralogical analysis.

Another interesting example is the occurrence of bauxite on limestone in Jamaica. In his study on the origin of this bauxite Zans (1953) quotes Goldich and Bergquist who found 'that the ultimate source of the lateritic constituents (of the deposits associated with limestone – Ref.) were volcanic ash or pyroclastic material of intermediate (andesitic) composition'. Zans further suggests: 'Carried into the limestone area and trapped in the karst depressions, it would have undergone further alteration and desilification in the alkaline environment of the limestone thus leading to the formation of bauxite'.

Attention is drawn by Prescott and Hosking (1936) to a quite different aspect of the possible role played by rock-forming minerals. They found that the clay content of red basaltic soils appeared to be related to the feldspar content of the original basalt; illustrated in fig. 1.27, and drawn on the basis of the data given.

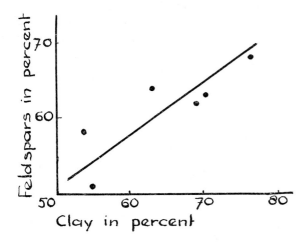

FIG. I.27. *Illustration of a possible relationship between the clay content of the soil and the feldspar content of the parent basalt (after Prescott and Hosking, 1936)*

TABLE I.55. *Mineralogical composition of the sand fractions > 50μ of a Podzol from Sumatera* (after Kiel and Rachmad, 1948)

Horizon	Depth in cm	Minerals in mutual percentages														
		Ore	Zircon	Green Hornblende	Hypersthene	Orthite	Oligoclase	Sanidine	Quartz (translucent)	Quartz (turbid)	Volcanic glass	Biotite	Biotite[1] (amorphous)	Weathering products[2]	Weathering products[3]	Humous concretions
A₁	0–30	All fractions consist mainly of humous concretions														
A₂	30–35	–	–	–	–	–	10	15	65	tr	10	–	–	–	–	–
B₂ₕ	35–40	–	–	–	–	–	17	13	44	tr	6	–	–	–	–	20
B₂ᵢᵣ	40–45	–	–	1	–	–	17	11	30	–	16	–	–	–	25	–
C	45–75	–	–	–	–	–	26	7	19	–	22	–	13	–	13	–
R	>75	–	–	2	tr	–	28	10	24	–	2	14	–	20	–	–

[1] Biotite bleached and weathered to an amorphic residue, crystal habit maintained
[2] Soft, yellowish-white isotropic colloidal material, sometimes with inclusions of fresh minerals; $n = + 1.544$
[3] Red-brown, iron-infiltrated, weathered pumice fragments

Bonnet (1939) also thought of minerals as the basic material for clay formation in the process of disintegration of andesitic tuff in Puerto Rico. He was looking for a relationship between high clay content in the horizons B₂ and C₁ of an Oxisol profile, and the absence of augite. This mineral seems to be present in large quantities in A₁, A₂, and B₁ layers which have a coarser texture. Quoted from Bonnet (1939): 'The high content of coarse clay in the horizons (B₂ and C₁) should be the result of the hydrolysis of augite. The presence of this mineral in A₁, A₂, and B₁ on the other hand, may be due to the formation of secondary augite or to the less favourable conditions of augite hydrolysis'. Of these two assumptions the first has to be rejected, as well as the supposition also given in this paper, that magnetite present in the upper three horizons and absent in the lower, would have resulted from the dehydration of sesquioxides. In order to explain the differences mentioned, in this volcanic area mixture with more recently supplied minerals would be the cause of the observed differences in augite content. We are also inclined to doubt the presence of calcite 'throughout the profile' in an Oxisol of pH 5.3–4.3 under rainfall conditions of more than 2000 mm per annum.

Although criticism can be made of the conclusions drawn in the investigations referred to, this line of approach has drawn considerable attention.

Extensive mineralogical research has been carried out in India, notably by Raychaudhuri and Mukerjee (1942) and by Raychaudhuri and Mian (1944). In the paper by Raychaudhuri and Mukerjee the quantitative mineralogical composition by weight from several localities of India is given. They also presented a tentative grouping of red soils (see table 1.56).

In comparison with the grouping of soils on the basis of mineral associations, the interpretation by Raychaudhuri and Mukerjee of the results of the mineralogical analysis based on a single mineral seems to allow for less definite conclusions. In the paper of Raychaudhuri and Mian (1944) the mineralogical data is also not very conveniently arranged, so the present authors undertook to recalculate the data of Raychaudhuri and collaborators on a numerical basis, computing the mutual percentages of the minerals present (see table 1.57).

TABLE 1.56. *Grouping of red soils of India* (after Raychaudhuri and Mukerjee, 1942)

Locality	Parent material	Preponderant mineral
Hathawara Farm, Purulia, Bihar	Granite and syenite	Zircon
Jhinkartangi, Khurda Town, Orissa	Gneiss	do
Upper Chandmari, Tura, Garo Hills, Assam	Pab-sandstone	do
Baralota, Daltonganj, Bihar	Limestone, shales, slates	Hornblende
Putida, Singhbhum, Bihar	Dalma traps and Mergui volcanics	Rutile
Tangi, Cuttac, Orissa	Older alluvium and laterite	do
Dhanmandal do	Laterite mixed with granite and sandstone	do
Tangi, Cuttac, Orissa	Older alluvium and laterite	Epidote
Dhanmandal do	Laterite mixed with granite and sandstone	do
Mawphlang, Khassi Hills, Assam	Shillong series	do
Midnapore, Bengal	Old alluvium and laterite	Tourmaline

Raychaudhuri and Mukerjee use a 'single mineralogical value' for the grouping of these Indian soils, which is indicated in the last column of table 1.56. This does not give sufficient data on the other minerals. For instance, in the first group of soils in which zircon is prevalent, epidote, and in the Hathawara-material hornblende, are just as important for determining the mineralogical picture of the soil. Zircon, although occurring in large quantities, is less characteristic of any particular soil than are epidote and hornblende, zircon being a very common mineral constituent of very different acid rocks. Therefore, the absence of zircon is much more interesting than its presence. It is also a well-known fact that this mineral often occurs as minute crystals. It is less useful as a guide-mineral for the origin of a soil, though in small crystals, it may be an indication of the texture.

In the Hathawara-sample the epidote-hornblende association is more characteristic than the 60–70% zircon. Epidote is also considered to be the more important mineral in the Jhinkartangi and Upperchandmari soils. The high percentage (23) of chlorite in the lowest layer of this sample cannot be explained.

It is striking that the three upper layers of the Baratola profile are characterized by hornblende, and even more interesting to note the occurrence of garnet with zircon at a depth of 120–150 cm. It is questionable whether limestone, shales, and slate are the source of hornblende and the rutile, which is typical of the soils which are supposed to be derived from the Dalma traps and Mergui volcanics. Kyanite is present in unusually large proportions (45%) and this points to the influence of a metamorphic material.

For a similar reason as given above for the zircon, the predominance of tourmaline in the Lalgarh material is not of great interest, but it is interesting that staurolite and epidote occur together and in quantities from 15–23%. Tourmaline is a fairly common mineral in metamorphic rocks such as gneiss and mica schists. It is also known to occur in such differing rocks as granite, granular limestone, and dolomite. It is concentrated in the coarser material, therefore, the characteristic association of staurolite-epidote (+ tourmaline).

The mineralogical data of Bengal and South Indian soils, as reported by Raychaudhuri and Mian (1944) is given in table 1.57. The material from Bogra is not typified by any specific mineral, but shows a strong inclination to metamorphic parent material. This is definitely the case in the soils of Tellicherry, where kyanite is predominant and is combined with rutile and tourmaline. It occurs again in the sample of Bankura this time with staurolite as the main component. One would be inclined to assume that biotite-gneiss is the parent rock of this last profile, as this would explain the predominance of biotite in the layers below 60 cm. (Although biotite has a specific gravity ranging from 2.7–3.1 and would therefore be classified as a heavy mineral, its flaky habit normally keeps it floating on the bromoform. It is consequently discarded in standard heavy mineral research.)

In order to evaluate the age of a soil and its mineral reserve, it is necessary to study the light fraction which contains the feldspars althoug the amount of opaque minerals (mainly magnetite and ilmenite) is a useful indication, as the accumulation of these very resistent iron oxides point to a thoroughly weathered soil. An illustrative example is presented by Van Baren and Kiel (1956) who analized four soil fertility classes in the Solomon's Islands and clearly showed the close relationship between these classes and their mineralogy. Table 1.58 gives the total composition of the sand fraction of the investigated soils.

TABLE I.57 *Mineralogical composition of various Indian soils as related to parent material*

Location	Depth of sample in cm	Opaque	Non-opaque minerals in mutual percentages													Parent material	Remarks
			Zircon	Tourmaline	Garnet	Rutile	Anatase	Staurolite	Kyanite	Epidote	Augite	Hornblende	Biotite	Muscovite	Chlorite		
Hathwara, Bihar	0– 45	27	61		2					12	4	19			2		
	45– 68	27	74		1					9		15			1	Granite and syenite	
	68–105	33	70	2	2					11	2	12			1		
	105–150	36	64	5	3					13	5	9			1		Zircon preponderant
	below 150	29	58	2						20	5	13			2		
	below 900	7	92							2			6				
Jhinkartangi, Orissa	0– 30	73	73							27							
	30– 60	66	86		1					13							
	60–255	67	80			7				13						Gneiss	
	255–300	74	85			5				7					3		
	900–1500	84	57							43							
Upper Chandmari, Assam	0– 8	88	71							29							
	8– 50	84	57							43						Pab-sandstone	
	50– 80	89	98							2							
	80–120	97	77												23		
Baralota, Bihar	0– 60	16		1	1	1					1	94			2		Hornblende preponderant
	60– 82	30			1	1				tr		96			2	Limestone, shales and slates	
	82–120	27			2	2					2	90			4		
	120–150	26	57		19				2			22					
Putida, Bihar	0– 30					26			45	27		2				Dalma traps and Mergui volcanics	
	30– 82		tr			100				tr							Rutile preponderant
	82–120	1				100				tr							
Tangi, Orissa	0– 30	13				57				43						Older alluvium and laterite	
	30– 60	22				53				47							
	60–120	3				93				7							
Dhanmandal, Orissa	0– 12	24				74				26						Laterite + granite and sandstone	
	12–120	52				68				32							
Mawphlang, Assam	0– 15	77	22	11		5				62							Epidote preponderant
	15– 38	73	27	6		16				40							
	38– 63	67	16	10		7				41						Shillong series	
	63–120	68	16	26		5				30							
Lalgarh, Bengal	0– 10	73	15	41					19	25							Tourmaline preponderant
	10–100	82	13	40		6			22	10		9				Older alluvium and laterite	
	100–120	69	24	31		4			23	18							
	210–240	74	19	38					15	25					3		After Raychaudhuri and Mukerjee (1942)
Bogra	0– 30	37	65	7	1	2	tr	15	2	3		1	1	1	2		
	30– 60	44	64	2	2	7		7	13	1		3		1		?	
	below 60	49	58	22	3			5	6	3		2			1		
	180–450	44	50	3	1	10	2	5	1	19		tr	9	1	1		Recalculated after Raychaudhuri and Mian (1944); leucoxene is included in opaque; the carbonates are discarded
	750–900	40	78	1		4	tr	5	5	3		1	1	1	1		
Tellicherry, S. India	0–120	88	14	12		13		55				2	2		2	?	
	120–163	87	53	10		10		27									
	below 163	94	24	32		7		37									
Bankura, Bengal	0– 13	89	33	2	4			36	4			4			17		
	13– 35	79	67	1		3		18				1	8		2	?	
	35– 50	85	47	7		3		36					7				
	50–120	40	10	2	1			2					85		tr		
	120–180	38	15					4	3				78				

TABLE I.58. *Results of the mineralogical analysis of soils of the Solomon Islands*

Minerals	A₂	C₁	J₂	L₁	F₁	K₂	30	31
Plagioclase	13	20	6	1	17	16	1	1
Quartz	–	–	1	–	6	2	4	2
Hornblende	1	–	2	1	7	4	3	–
Oxy-hornblende	5	5	1	2	2	2	–	–
Augite	40	37	41	67	5	8	2	–
Hypersthene	1	–	–	–	–	–	–	–
Ore	23	16	30	15	53	52	90	97
Montmorin	8	6	8	4	3	6	–	–
Iron-concretions	2	3	2	7	1	2	–	–
Rock fragments	6	7	1	1	–	2	–	–
Various	1	6	8	2	6	6		

When calculating the percentages of the dominant minerals the results in graph-form show the distribution of the data in four fields of related points (fig. 1.28). The drawing shows clearly that these fields are narrowly related to the fertility classes. It is evident that the samples numbered 22 to 36 are so deeply weathered that only iron as

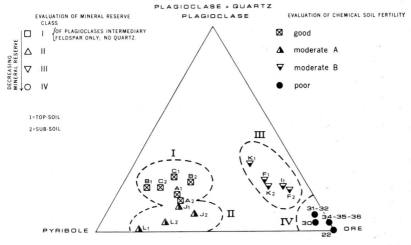

FIG. I.28. *Triangle diagram of plagioclase (+ quartz): pyribole (pyroxene + amphibole): ore ratios of soils of the Solomon Islands*

magnetite and/or ilmenite is left. The history of the sites shows that these soils are the oldest of the island, and did not profit from any rejuvenation.

In the foregoing pages the minerals and mineral associations have been used mainly for their diagnostic significance, either for a broad classification or for agricultural purposes. With respect to their value for estimating the weathering stage, Jackson et al. (1948) stated that there is a 'weathering sequence' of minerals of soils and sediments, assuming that the source of each colloidal silicate clay mineral is a specific parent mineral from which the colloidal material is a 'primary weathering product'. The weathering sequence, according to the mentioned authors comprises thirteen stages and these are represented by the following minerals:

Stage 1: Gypsum (also halite, etc.)
Stage 2: Calcite (also dolomite, arragonite, etc.)
Stage 3: Olivine, hornblende (also diopside, etc.)
Stage 4: Biotite (also glauconite, chlorite, antigorite, nontronite, etc.)
Stage 5: Albite (also anorthite, microcline, stilbite, etc.)
Stage 6: Quartz (also crystoballite, etc.)
Stage 7: Illite (also muscovite, sericite, etc.)
Stage 8: Hydrous mica-intermediates
Stage 9: Montmorillonite (also beidellite, etc.)
Stage 10: Kaolinite (also halloysite, etc.)
Stage 11: Gibbsite (also boehmite, etc.)
Stage 12: Hematite (also goethite, limonite, etc.)
Stage 13: Anatase (also rutile, ilmenite, corundum, etc.)

According to Jackson et al. (1948) the colloidal fractions of the soils usually consists of three to five minerals of the weathering sequence, one or two minerals being dominant, and with smaller amounts of adjacent minerals in the sequence. It appeared too, that the percentages of minerals of the early stages of the weathering sequence decrease with increasing intensity of weathering, whereas those of succeeding members increase.

Although the ideas of Jackson et al. seem to be sound, some criticism should be made here. Judging from the foregoing list, the authors are of the opinion that no emphasis need be placed on whether the minerals are of secondary or primary origin. This would be definitely incorrect. In the case of the example of calcite, it is considered to be of real importance whether this mineral still occurs as an original rock-building component, or whether it results from secondary crystallization of $CaCO_3$. In the latter case the calcium has been previously leached out of soil-forming minerals, for example calcic plagioclase, and afterwards redeposited by raising and evaporating soil solution, under suitable climatological circumstances.

The same objection holds for quartz versus crystoballite, and muscovite versus illite. It is common knowledge that in granitic soils quartz and muscovite occur simultaneously in large percentages (e.g. see table 1.51, the soils derived from granite, Masamba, Sulawesi). The presence of considerable amounts of crystoballite with illite as an example in the grey, bleached hydropodzolic soils of Bantam, Java, points to a stage of weathering which is undoubtedly more advanced.

Also, it seems doubtful that the same value may be attached to hornblende as to olivine and to anorthite as to albite, which are maintained to be characteristic for stages 3 and 4 respectively in the estimation of a stage of weathering. Olivine and anorthite, which are typical minerals for basic basaltic or peridotitic rocks, will disappear at a much earlier stage than the hornblende and albite or oligoclase, which are characteristic minerals for the more acid members of the andesites dominant in Java.

This criticism might be amplified by pointing to the fact that the resistance of weathering depends on circumstances of the milieu (Neeb, 1936). Not only the resistance to weathering will be influenced, but also the kind of products that are formed. Several examples will be discussed in Chapters 1 and 2 of Part II and in Chapter 1 of Part III.

LITERATURE CITED

BAAK, J. A. 1948 De mineralogische samenstelling van enkele recente vulkanische assen op Java. *Landbouw (Buitenzorg)*, 20: 269–274.

— 1949 A comparative study on recent ashes of the Java volcanoes Smeru, Kelut, and Merapi. *Meded. Alg. Proefst. Landb. Bogor*, Nr 83: pp. 37.

BALLOU, H. A. 1934 The Dutch Leeward Islands. *Trop. Agric. (Trin.)*, 11: 317–320.

BERG, R. R. 1952 Feldspatized sandstone. *J. Sed. Petrol.*, 22 : 221–224.

BEUMEE-NIEUWLAND, N. 1922 Onderzoekingen van djati-bosch gronden op Java. *Meded. Proefsta. Boschw. Buitenzorg*, 8: 1–91.

BONNET, J. A. 1939 The nature of laterization as revealed by chemical, physical, and mineralogical studies of a lateritic soil profile from Puerto Rico. *Soil Sci.*, 48: 25–40.

CLARKE, F. W. and WASHINGTON, H. S. 1924 The composition of the earth's crust. *U.S. Geol. Survey, Prof. Paper Nr 127.*

DE PERALTA, F. and DECENA, S. A. 1940 The effect of volcanic ash ejected from the Mayon volcano upon the growth of tobacco. *Philipp. J. Agric.*, 11 : 355.

DRUIF, J. H. 1934 De bodem van Deli II. Mineralogische onderzoekingen van de bodem van Deli. *Bull. Deli Proefsta. Medan*, Br 32: pp. 188.

— 1936 Some remarks about soil-mapping in Deli by aid of microscopic-mineralogical investigation. *Handel. 7de Ned. Ind. Natuurw. Cong. Batavia*, 1935: 666–680.

ESCHER, B. G. 1948 Grondslagen der Algemene Geologie. Amsterdam: pp. 442.

ERHART, H. 1956 La génèse des sols en tant que phénomène géologique. Mason, Paris, pp. 90.

GRANGE, L. L. 1949 Soils of some South Pacific Islands. *Comm. Bur. Soil Sci. Tech. Commun.* 46: 45–48.

HARDY, F., ROBINSON, C. K. and RODRIGUEZ, G. 1934 Studies in West Indian soils. VIII. The agricultural soils of St. Vincent. Trinidad, Dec. 1934: pp. 34.

HARRISON, J. B. 1934 The katamorphism of igneous rocks under humid tropical conditions. *Imp. Bur. Soil Sci (Harpenden)* : pp. 79.

IDENBURG, A. G. A. 1937 Systematische grondkaartering van Zuid-Sumatra. *Thesis Wageningen*: pp. 168.

JACKSON, M. L., TYLER, S. A., WILLIS, A. L. et al. 1948 Weathering sequence of clay-size minerals. *J. Phys. Coll. Chem.*, 52: 1237–1260.

KEMMERLING, G. L. L. 1921 De uitbarsting van den G. Kelut in den nacht van den 19den op den 20sten Mei 1917. *Vulk. Meded. Dienst Mijnw.*, Nr 2, pp. 120.

KIEL, H. and RACHMAD, H. 1948 Voorlopige mededelingen over het mineralogisch onderzoek van bodemprofielen. *Landbouw* (Buitenzorg), 20: 283–290.

KOCH, D. E. V. 1946 The manganese content of some Ceylon soils. *Trop. Agricst.* (Ceylon), 102: 219–233.

MARR, TH. 1912 Resultaten van het chemisch onderzoek der rietgronden op Java. *Arch. Suikerind. Ned. Ind.*, 20, II: 1251–1312.

MOHR, E. C. J. 1944 Soils of equatorial regions. Ann Arbor: pp. 765.

NEEB, G. A. 1935 Mineralogisch onderzoek ten behoeve van de grondkaartering. *Versl. 14de Verg. Ver. v. Proefsta. Pers.*, 1934: 67–81.

— 1936 Identification of soils by mineralogical analysis. *Verh. 7de Ned. Ind. Natuurw. Cong. Batavia*, 1935: 695–703.

NIGGLI, P. 1923 Gesteins- und Mineralprovinzen. Vol. I. Berlin: pp. 602.

PRESCOTT, J. A. and HOSKING, J. S. 1936 Some red basaltic soils from Eastern Australia. *Trans. Roy. S. Austr.*, 160: 35–45.

RAYCHAUDHURI, S. P. and MIAN, A. H. 1944 Studies on Indian red soils. VIII. Studies on the physico-chemical and mineralogical properties of some Indian red and lateritic soils. *Indian J. Agric. Sci.*, 14: 117–124.

— and MUKERJEE, K. C. 1942 Studies on Indian red soils VI. Determination of mineralogical composition. *Indian J. Agric. Sci.*, 12: 323–335.

REYNDERS, J. J. 1964 A pedo-ecological study of soil genesis in the tropics from sea level to eternal snow. *Thesis Utrecht*: pp. 159.

VAN BAREN, F. A. 1941 De mineralogische achtergrond van de bodemvruchtbaarheid in Nederlandsch-Indië. *Landbouw* (Buitenzorg) 17: 520–541.

— and KIEL, H. 1956 Relationship between the mineralogical composition and fertility of tropical soils. Trans. 5th Int. Cong. Soil Sci. D, Paris.

VAN BEMMELEN, W. 1911 Die Windverhältnisse in den oberen Luftschichten nach Ballon-visierungen in Batavia. *Verh. Kon. Magn. Meteor. Obs. Batavia*, Nr. 1: pp. 77.

YZERMAN, A. G. A. 1931 Outline of the geology and petrology of Surinam (Dutch Guiana). *Thesis Utrecht*: pp. 511.

ZANS, V. A. 1953 Bauxite resources of Jamaica and their development. *Col. Geol. and Min. Resources*, III, 4: 307–333.

CHAPTER 3

ROCK WEATHERING

At present there is overwhelming evidence that the classic Russian concept of zonal climatic soil formation is to be used with great discrimination. It should, however, be stated that 1) Dokuchaiev and his pupils were well aware of this 2) the image that the climatic zonal concept was a kind of rigid, unconditionally applicable system resulted from lack of comprehension by early soil geographers. At present it is well understood that the Russian concept only holds to its full measure when soil forming factors other than the climate over a whole geographical zone or region are – within limits – to be considered constant, thus permitting this one exogenic factor to have a directing influence on soil formation (see a.o. Rode, 1962, p. 517).

One of the factors which will modify the effect of climate is the parent material. For the study of this it is necessary to give a rigorous definition of the parent material (Muckenhirn et al., 1949); it should include references to the mineralogical and chemical composition and to the structure and texture of the rock.

The parent rock seems to influence soil formation in such a way that similar soils are formed under quite different climatic conditions. An example is the occurrence of the serpentine soils of New Caledonia (Grange, 1949). They extend from near sea level on the arid western coast (250 mm rain annually) up and over the central ranges (ca. 1700 mm and intermittent rainfall totalling 4375 mm) and down to the east coast where there is a rainfall of about 2500 mm, without the soil showing any significant change in profile characteristics.

Differences in rock composition also lead to the formation of different soils if climate is similar over the whole area (see a.o. Hardy and Croucher, 1933; Vine, 1949; Joachim, 1935). For this it is not necessary that the rocks differ in mineralogical or chemical composition; differences in structure may already be sufficient to effect soil formation. There are excellent examples (e.g. on Java, Indonesia) of the well-known fact that a stratified rock will react in very different ways to climatic differences, depending on whether the impact of rain is perpendicular or parallel to the direction of stratification, or even more effective, at an angle. Although fig. 1.29 is imaginary, it serves as a fairly lucid illustration of this fact. Rain coming in contact with the northern slope of this tectonically uplifted schistose rock will be much less effective than rain falling at the same time on the northern slope.

In the first case the result is a black and in the second a red soil.

The example conforms to the findings of Basu and Sirur (1938) who wrote that in spite of the apparent uniformity of conditions in the central region of the Deccan

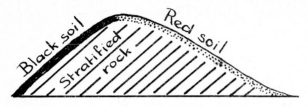

FIG. I.29. *Soil formation on a stratified rock*

Plateau, many soil types exist side by side. This phenomenon is accounted for not so much by differences in the nature of the parent material or the climate, as in the varied topography and the drainage conditions which have so greatly modified the soil climate.

The effect of volcanic ash on soil formation is another well-known example. Whereas on andesitic volcanic ash Inceptisols may be formed, Oxisols are formed on its intrusive equivalent under the same climatic conditions (see Part II, Chapter 1).

Topography and vegetation are also of influence if the other soil forming factors do not interfere. With regard to topography this has been adequately formulated by Blackie (1949) when surveying the soils of Fiji. Describing the two well-defined climatic zones, i.e. the northern dry and the southern wet zones, he also draws attention to the extreme ruggedness of the main islands. He recognized as obvious the fact that a series of local climates is operative and must therefore play a profound part in modifying the overall soil picture. A subsequent survey revealed that there was a relationship between solid geology and soil types in the dry zone of Viti Levu (Report Geological Survey, Fiji, 1952).

More examples of the effect of rocks, climate, and vegetation will be discussed in chapters of Part II.

Reference is sometimes made to what is termed 'rain-effectiveness'. Consideration will have to be given to such factors as infiltration, run-off and evaporation, since it is obvious from even the most superficial observation that what is of supreme importance is not the total amount of rainfall when speaking of R.E. but the rain which actually penetrates the soil and is directly active as a destructive factor in rock decomposition, as well as being an indispensable aid to plant growth. Some soil scientists are even of the opinion that soil formation is affected by climate principally through its influence on living things (Nikiforoff, 1935), or at least that it is mostly vegetative forces which are dominant in the development of the material from which the biological forces construct the soil (Marbut, 1934).

Further reference to rain-effectiveness is to be found in Milne's outstanding critical observations of East African soils (Milne, 1947). He stated, first of all, in his discussion of the origin of the Mamboya red loam of Tanganyika that 'in any soil well above a permanent water table, drainage ceases when the moisture has been reduced to that, held at the 'field capacity'. Data is available for this level of moisture content for various horizons down to 2 m, for a typical Mamboya red earth, sampled in 1934. The field capacity is 20%. The moisture content at the end of the dry season averaged 10% over the top two metres. The moisture deficit is therefore 10%, and this has to be made up by rain. If the bulk-density of the soil is taken to be 1.25, then 250 mm of rain would be required before any leaching could take place. For the years 1931–1935, the total precipitation of the Mamboya station (Meraga mission station) was: 764; 724; 691 and 612 mm, with the main falls occurring between the months of December and May and a few showers in June and November. In order to consider the rainfall figures in relation to the present context, it is not necessary to count the showers, occurring in what would otherwise be dry periods, since they evaporate quickly and contribute nothing to the reserves of soil moisture. Nor is it possible to accord to torrential downpours their full capacity, because part of them is lost in run-off. The most important point to be noted is that the most effective rains fall during the period when maximum demands are made on soil moisture by deciduous vegetation, which at this time develops its young, transpiring leaves. On this point, Milne quoted Staples, who found at Mpwapwa only two weeks after some 200 mm of rain had fallen, that the moisture content to 1 m depth of a red sandy loam under deciduous scrub had been reduced to less than 10%. Staples further concluded that moisture which had penetrated the soil was being used up 'astonishingly quickly' by the vegetation.

Milne himself stated that: 'A scrutiny of the rainfall figures for Meraga shows no time of the year when as much as one third of the annual gross total is likely to have been added to the soil reserves after transpiration requirements have been met with and evaporation and run-off allowed for.'

All this confirms what has been emphasized in Chapter 1 of this Part, that although total rainfall is important in weathering and soil formation the monthly distribution has a decisive effect (see a.o. Van Schuylenborgh, 1958; Tan and Van Schuylenborgh, 1959). In summary it is the soil climate which should be given most attention in the study of weathering and soil genesis. A decision should be made as to what might reasonably be expected from the complex of factors i.e. overhead climate, rock, topography, and present day vegetation, with regard to the development of the soil. It has already been pointed out that there is world-wide occurrence of soils with characteristics which are not consistent with the present day climate – soils which, in all probability, are the results of soil climate of a previous geological period (see Chapter 1, p. 77).

It should be realized at the same time, that if the overhead climate is presumed to have remained unchanged since soil formation began on a particular site with a certain rock, then the question arises as to whether the course of development during, say the first 10,000 years, is likely to be the same in a more recent period. The action of water which penetrated the first few centimetres of weathered rock must have certainly been very different from that (of water) which at the present time penetrates through a medium, modified by previous processes of chemical weathering. This can be formulated briefly by saying that there is a weathering sequence, an evolution which is parallel to every change in soil environmental conditions. Furthermore, the depth that water penetrates is unknown. It was discovered, for instance, by certain lysimeter studies on Pretoria Red Loam, that the water penetrated to a depth of no more than 130 cm, and then only occasionally, during continued wet spells. Even then, the total amount reaching that depth in any season did not exceed 5% of the 750 mm annual rainfall (Theron and Van Niekerk, 1934). The question whether soils of 5 to 10 metres thickness and more which are known to occur, are indeed solely the result of rain water as a factor in residual weathering, is one which is open for further discussion. Laterally flowing subsurface water, vegetation, and accumulation of fresh sediments on a pre-existing soil surface are other factors which may exert a distinct influence, especially in volcanic areas.

All these factors should be borne in mind when studying the soil as a living organism, the result of various dynamic forces. Genesis will only be understood, if ever, when due attention is paid to these and similar phenomena and, consequently, when the homogeneity of a profile is established by adequate mineralogical methods. Clearly, then, generalization and extrapolation must be treated with the utmost care, although neither of them can be neglected when it comes to classification. There is no doubt that increasing knowledge of the genesis of tropical soils will be accompanied by a considerable modification of the soil groups and subgroups. The present authors realize, in spite of their critical approach to soil forming factors in the foregoing pages, that the impressive amount of detailed research which has been carried out by numerous competent soil science workers justifies the statement that the evolution of the tropical soils, as seen by present day features of the soil profiles, has been following certain specific lines of development. Each of the soil forming factors, such as climate, rock, topography, and plant growth has played a part in this evolution, the predominant force changing at various stages. The only scientific course which seems to be satisfactory for studying the features of tropical soils as they may be observed today, is analysis of the characteristics of the soil profile in the field and of the properties of the individual horizons in the laboratory, with all the scientific means now available. There should be no mental restriction in this study, brought about by bias in favour of the climatic, petrographic, or any other feature, and the soil, preferably as an entity, should be examined critically. Furthermore, it must be realized that neither the climate, petrography nor morphology should strictly be considered a soil characteristic. The following sections will be devoted, therefore, to the processes of rock-weathering, in so far as they may be studied by physical, chemical and mineralogical means.

3.1. CHEMICAL AND MINERALOGICAL CHANGES DURING WEATHERING

Of the various references on this subject, the paper dealing with the investigations made by Harrison on the weathering processes of igneous rocks in British West Guiana (published posthumously in 1934) is undoubtedly an outstanding example. Harrison based his concept of weathering on extremely detailed chemical analyses of rock fragments and adjacent rims of decomposed material, complemented, wherever possible, with microscopic research. Some of Harrison's ideas can be formulated as follows, only considering the transformation of the parent rock into the parent naterial:

   a. Under tropical conditions, the weathering of *basic* and *intermediate* rock under ideal drainage conditions (oxidizing conditions) consists of the removal of large quantities of silica, and of calcium, magnesium, potassium and sodium oxide, leaving an earthy residuum of clay minerals (mainly kandites), iron- and aluminium hydroxides, a few unaltered fragments of feldspar, in some cases secondary quartz, and the various resistant minerals originally present in the rock. This residuum was called by Harrison *'primary laterite'*. As it was decided to abandon the term laterite (see Part II, Chapter 1), this residuum will be called the weathered or rotten rock zone, however thin and different from the original rock it may be.

b. Under tropical conditions, *acidic* rocks such as aplites, pegmatites or granite and granitic gneisses gradually change, through the weathering process, into pipe or pot clays, or into quartziferous and impure kaolines. The weathering zone is here generally thick.

These statements were confirmed by several examples examined by Harrison (1934). Three of them will be discussed here, viz.: weathering from dolerite, from granite, and from hornblende-schist. As it is necessary to study the chemical as well as the mineralogical changes and as a mineralogical analysis of the sometimes very thin weathering rims is hardly possible, a method was needed to translate the chemical analyses into mineralogical terms. Several methods have been developed to do this (Cross, Iddings, Pirsson, and Washington, 1922; Holmes, 1930; Imbrie and Poldervaart, 1959; Nicholls, 1962). All these methods are founded on the use of normative chemical formulae on a weight percentage basis. Recalculation from one normative mineral assemblage to another is therefore time-consuming. This practical objection against cumbersome calculation procedures was removed with the introduction of a calculation scheme based on *equivalent* normative chemical formulae by Niggli (1936). The use of normative chemical formulae of minerals based on an equivalent number of cations and thus on equivalent 'formula' weights instead of molecular weights, enabled the formulation of simple reaction equations and rapid calculation of variants. Moreover, the equivalent 'formula' weights of the various minerals vary only slightly, so that the calculated equivalent percentages practically coincide with the weight percentages. Only in some cases, i.e. high content of iron oxides, lime, and phosphates, recalculation of the equivalent percentages to weight percentages is desirable. For comparative purposes, however, the equivalent percentages are sufficient.

Three calculation schemes have been developed: 1. The standard katanorm calculation, applicable to the calculation of the mineral assemblages found in igneous and highly metamorphic rocks; 2. The standard epinorm calculation for low- to medium-grade metamorphic rocks, such as micaschists, phyllites, chlorite schists, etc.; 3. The goethite norm calculation for soils and clays. The latter method was developed by Van der Plas and Van Schuylenborgh (1970); it is, in essence, a variant of the epinorm calculation, but introduces new minerals such as goethite, smectite, and others. For the kata- and epinorm calculations, the reader is referred to Burri (1964).

The analyses of the weathering rims of dolerite, Tumatumari, Guiana, are given in table 1.59. The chemical analysis shows clearly the decomposition of feldspars as silica is partly leached and the alkaline earths and alkali metals practically completely. Iron oxides, derived from the pyroxenes, accumulate residually. Newformation of silicate minerals, however, cannot be detected from the chemical analysis although the constancy of the SiO_2 content in the outer rims could point to such process. The calculation of the normative mineralogical composition (katanorm for the rock and goethite norm for the weathered material) reveals that the primary minerals are mainly transformed into goethite, gibbsite, and kaolinite.

TABLE I.59. *Chemical and normative mineralogical composition of dolerite and its weathering products, Tumatumaru, Guiana* (chemical composition after Harrison, 1934; weight percentages)

	SiO_2[2]	Al_2O_3	Fe_2O_3	FeO	MgO	CaO	K_2O	Na_2O	TiO_2	P_2O_5	H_2O+
1[1]	16.1	26.8	34.0	2.7	0.1	tr	tr	tr	1.1	tr	18.9
2	15.5	32.8	27.8	3.2	0.1	tr	0.1	0.1	1.4	tr	19.7
3	16.1	29.1	28.6	3.3	0.1	tr	0.1	0.05	2.0	tr	20.2
4	21.2	26.9	27.9	3.1	0.7	0.5	0.3	0.8	1.8	tr	17.3
5	51.3	15.2	3.08	11.2	5.6	9.6	0.6	2.1	1.0	tr	0.3

normative mineralogical composition (equivalent percentages)[3]

	Q	Or	Plg	Pyr	Mt	Tit	Kaol	Ms	Chl	Sm	Gibb	Go	Ru	Misc
1	–	–	–	–	8.7	–	41.8	–	0.6	–	20.1	27.7	1.1	–
2	–	–	1.2	–	10.0	–	36.6	1.0	0.4	–	29.8	19.7	1.3	–
3	–	–	0.8	–	10.8	–	40.0	1.1	0.4	–	24.0	20.9	2.0	–
4	–	–	9.7	–	9.5	–	27.3	3.1	1.8	6.5	18.8	19.1	1.6	2.7
5	3.0	3.7	50.7	37.2	3.4	2.1	–	–	–	–	–	–	–	–

[1] 1 = fourth layer of the weathering zone (hard crust: 2 mm); 2 = third layer (50 mm); 3 = second layer (18 mm); 4 = first layer (3 mm); 5 = parent rock, dolerite.
[2] Harrison's (1934) data on free silica and combined silica; as the method to distinguish between both forms of silica is inadequate in many instances (Part II, Chapter 1), they were taken together as total silica.
[3] Q = free silica; Or = K-feldspar; Plg = plagioclases; Pyr = pyroxenes; Mt = magnetite; Tit = titanite; Kaol = kaolinite; Ms = muscovite; Chl = chlorite; Sm = smectite; Gibb = gibbsite; Go = goethite; Ru = rutile (anatase); Misc = miscellaneous.

In the first rim some smectite, chlorite and illites occur, but they gradually disappear being transformed into kaolinite and gibbsite.

TABLE I.60. *Chemical composition of basalt, its weathered spheroidal shells and adjacent red earth from Vietnam* (weight percentages)

Type of material	SiO_2	Al_2O_3	Fe_2O_3	CaO	MgO	K_2O	Na_2O	loss of ignition
red material 10 cm above boulder	36.7	27.6	20.1	1.2	1.2	0.5	0.0[3]	12.5
kernel of basalt	52.2	5.4	24.6	9.4	8.0	0.9	0.0[5]	1.0
greyish zone	48.7	7.4	25.1	7.4	5.8	0.9	0.0[4]	4.1
ferruginous crust of boulder	36.1	11.2	30.8	7.9	6.2	2.9	0.1	7.0
red material 10 cm below boulder	35.0	30.6	19.3	1.5	1.1	0.5	0.0[4]	12.8

The loss of silica from basic rocks upon weathering is not always as great as in the preceding example, as was found by Castagnol (1952) and Satyanarayana and Thomas (1962), when studying the weathering of basalt. Castagnol (1952) analyzed the various shells formed during the concentric weathering of basalt. Some of his results are summarized in table 1.60. The table shows clearly the loss in silica but that this is not as intense as in the case of the dolerite-weathering. As the FeO-content was not determined it is not possible to calculate the normative mineralogical composition of the different shells. The high K_2O-content in the ferruginous crust of the boulder suggests the intermediary formation of a K-bearing mineral, probably illite. This was also observed by Satyanarayana and Thomas (1962) when studying the weathering of a hornblende granulite (see Chapter 1, Part II).

The data given in table 1.61 shows the weathering of an acid igneous rock, i.e. granite. The profile consists of 22 clearly distinguishable layers to depths of 6 m, although in many cases one layer merges imperceptibly into the next. Harrison writes: 'The section did not represent a continuous katamorphism, extending regularly from the disintegrating surface of the granite to the uppermost layer. The change had taken place by more active weathering along joint planes, leaving isolated masses of granite, which masses later succombed to the same action'. Four of the layers were chosen as examples of the successive stages of weathering.

TABLE I.61. *Chemical and normative mineralogical composition of granite and its weathering products, Mazaruni quarry, Guiana* (chemical composition after Harrison, 1934; weight percentages)

	SiO_2	Al_2O_3	Fe_2O_3	FeO	MgO	CaO	MnO	K_2O	Na_2O	TiO_2	H_2O+
1[1]	66.1	22.1	1.7	0.3	0.2	tr	–	2.0	0.2	0.7	6.8
2	66.6	21.0	1.5	0.3	0.5	0.1	–	2.7	0.3	0.6	6.2
3	70.2	18.8	1.8	0.2	0.2	tr	–	2.7	0.2	0.7	5.2
4	72.1	14.7	2.2	0.3	0.7	1.1	0.2	4.7	2.7	0.7	0.5

normative mineralogical composition (equivalent percentages)[2]

	Q	Or	Plg	Cord	Sil	Kaol	Ms	Chl	Go	Ru	Misc
1	40.5	–	1.8	–	–	36.0	18.2	1.5	1.3	0.6	0.1
2	42.1	–	3.0	–	–	25.4	24.8	2.4	1.2	0.4	0.7
3	48.3	–	1.8	–	–	22.4	24.2	1.4	1.3	0.5	0.1
4	30.5	28.5	30.1	7.5	1.3	–	–	–	1.6	0.5	–

[1] 1 = argillaceous granite-sand, loose and incoherent, orange-red in colour, depth 1.70 m; 2 = granite-sand, still showing structure of granite, depth 2.00 m; 3 = granite, thin, grey coloured layers, resembling soft shale and crumbling to granite-sand, depth 3.65 m; 4 = granite mass in quarry just beneath lowest stained layer, depth 5 m.
[2] Mineral abbreviations as in table 1.59. Cord = Fe-cordierite + cordierite; Sil = sillimannite.

The table shows clearly that desilication is much less pronounced than in the weathering of dolerite. There is a residual accumulation of alumina but not of iron oxides. Also K_2O content does not decrease so strongly, indicating the formation of illitic clay minerals. This is confirmed when studying the results of the calculation of the normative mineralogical composition. During the first stage of weathering kaolinite and illites are formed at the expense of K-feldspars, plagioclases and cordierites. At later stages the illites appear to be unstable, and are transformed into kaolinite and silica, the latter being leached. The weathering of a hornblende-schist at Yarikita provides another example. As in the case of diorite weathering, the zone of alteration is thin, approximately 5 cm; also here gibbsite is formed immediately upon weathering and disappears gradually upon further weathering. Kaolinite is formed instead, partly at the expense of chlorite and partly by resilication of gibbsite to kaolinite. However, the appearance of free silica in the outer weathering shelf is probably caused by decomposition of kaolinite, the increase in kaolinite being caused by dissolution of the gibbsite and the alumina set free upon decomposition of kaolinite. This mechanism is possible and depends solely on the pH as will be shown in Chapter I of Part II.

TABLE I.62. *Chemical and normative mineralogical composition of a hornblende-schist and its weathering products, Yarikita Hill, Guiana* (chemical composition after Harrison, 1934; weight percentages)

	SiO_2	Al_2O_3	Fe_2O_3	FeO	MgO	CaO	MnO	K_2O	Na_2O	TiO_2	P_2O_5	H_2O+
1[1]	31.3	22.5	26.4	0.8	0.5	tr	–	0.1	0.1	3.1	tr	14.3
2	23.4	29.2	23.7	1.3	0.0	tr	–	0.1	0.1	4.1	tr	18.3
3	15.4	32.5	25.1	1.6	0.1	tr	0.1	0.2	–	4.4	tr	20.5
4	12.3	34.8	22.0	2.9	1.6	0.1	tr	0.2	0.3	4.9	0.1	20.8
5	49.7	12.2	tr	9.9	9.5	11.8	0.5	0.1	1.2	4.6	0.1	0.3

normative mineralogical composition (equivalent percentages)[2]

	Q	Plg	Ho	Bi	Chl	Tit	Kaol	Ms	Gibb	Go	Ru	Misc
1	6.1	–	–	–	4.2	–	61.4	1.0	–	24.3	2.9	0.1
2	–	–	–	–	3.5	–	50.8	1.0	16.0	24.8	3.8	0.1
3	–	–	–	–	4.7	–	36.0	2.1	28.6	24.3	4.3	–
4	–	3.8[3]	–	–	15.1	–	18.8	2.1	34.6	20.8	4.6	0.2
5	3.9	14.0[4]	64.5	1.1	6.7	9.6	–	–	–	–	–	0.3

[1] I = hard outer crust of the weathering zone, 3 mm; 2 = third layer, 20 mm; 3 = second layer, 20 mm; 4 = first layer, 5 mm; 5 = rock, hornblende-schist.
[2] Mineral abbreviations as in preceding tables; Ho = hornblende; Bi = biotite.
[3] Albite.
[4] 20% An.

The examples seem to indicate that Harrison's statement, mentioned on pages 154 and 155 are correct except in the last case, where the originally formed gibbsite eventually disappears. Other examples are known, some of which conform with Harrison's ideas, and some not. The examples of Idenburg (1937) and Mohr (1944) can illustrate this (see table 1.63). The weathering product of basalt does not contain any gibbsite, that of andesite contains a considerable amount of gibbsite.

Table 1.64 shows a summary of the results of several studies in the tropics. In this table attention is focused on the kaolinite and gibbsite contents by calculating the percentage of kaolinite on the basis of kaolinite + gibbsite = 100. The table also includes climatic data, where available, with particular reference to the ratio wet/dry months, 'wet' being taken to mean a monthly rainfall of > 100 mm and 'dry' < 60 mm (see Chapter 1 of this Part). Data is included on the molar SiO_2/Al_2O_3 ratios of the fresh rocks. It was hoped that the introduction of these factors would throw some

TABLE 1.63. *Chemical and normative mineralogical composition of the weathering products of basalt, Sumatera, and andesite, Java* (Chemical composition after Idenburg, 1937, and Mohr, 1944, in weight percentages; normative mineralogical composition in equivalent percentages)

Composition	basalt		andesite	
	rock	weathering product	rock	weathering product
SiO_2	50.8	35.1	52.9	16.1
Al_2O_3	16.2	28.3	18.9	40.4
Fe_2O_3	2.5	15.0	4.1	15.5
FeO	6.9	–	4.8	2.0
MgO	8.4	0.3	3.7	0.4
CaO	8.3	0.3	8.6	0.2
MnO	0.1	0.2	0.4	–
K_2O	1.2	0.2	0.9	0.1
Na_2O	3.5	tr	4.0	0.8
TiO_2	1.5	2.0	1.0	1.9
H_2O+	0.6	13.4	0.6	22.7
free silica	–	2.7	1.9	–
K-feldspars	7.0	–	5.3	–
Plagioclases	56.3[1]	–	67.5[2]	9.7[3]
Augites	15.0	–	19.2	–
Olivines	15.8	–	–	–
Magnetite	2.6	–	4.3	–
Titanite	3.3	–	1.8	–
Kaolinite	–	76.6		23.7
Illites	–	2.1		1.1
Chlorites	–	1.8		7.0
Gibbsite	–	–		41.3
Goethite	–	13.7		14.6
Rutile (anatase)	–	1.8		1.8
Miscellaneous	–	1.3		0.9

[1] 45% An;   [2] 46% An;   [3] Ab.

TABLE 1.64. *Synopsis of kaolinite content, based on kaolinite + gibbsite = 100, in weathered rock mate*

No.	Location	Type of rock	Rainfall in mm	Ratio wet/dry months
1	Eagle Mountains, Guiana	Dolerite	3850	12/0
2	Timatumari, do	do	2800	12/0
3	Mazaruni, do	Granite	2500	12/0
4	Yarakita Hills, do	Hornblende-schist	2525	12/0
5	Issorora Hills, do	Epidiorite	2925	11/1
6	Province of Oriente, Cuba	Serpentine		
7	Mayagüez, Puerto Rico	do	2125	
8	Mameyes-Yunque Road, Puerto Rico	Andesite-tuff (?)	1975	
9	Near Luquillo, Puerto Rico	do	2125	
10	Isle of Kassa, Guinea	Nepheline Syenite		
11	Bougourou Mountains, Guinea	Diabase		
12	Amboassang, Madagascar	Gneiss	1750	6/6
13	? , do	Amphibolite	1750	6/6
14	Nosizato, do	Quartz-Monzonite		
15	Ivohibe, do	Granite		
16	Ankoba, do	Microcline		
17	Tsilaizina, do	Pegmatite		
18	Amboassang, do	do		
19	Amlakfotsikely, do	do		
20	Mangalore, Malabar Coast, India	Gneiss		
21	Angidapuram, do , do	Hornblende Granulite	3500	7/5
22	Kasaragod, South Kanara, India	Basalt	3500	7/5
23	Tjisaät, Java, Indonesia	Andesite	2500	12/0
24	Sukadana, Sumatera, Indonesia	Basalt	2085	12/0
25	Kukusan Mountains, Kalimantan, Indonesia	Serpentinite	2500	12/0
26	Oro Bay, Australian New Guinea	Granite		
27	Newell-Pelliga, Australia	Shale		
28	Fernhill, Inverell, Australia	Basalt		
29	S.E. Kalimantan, Indonesia	Eocene marine clay		12/0
30	Salisbury, Rhodesia	Olivine-Dolerite	850	5/7
31	Djutitsa, Cameroon, Africa	Basalt	1800	8/4
32	Isle of Yap, Caroline Islands	Amphibolite	3200	12/0
33	Isle of Oahu, Hawaii Islands	Andesite	865	
34	do do	do	865	
35	do do	do	865	
36	do do	do	865	
37	Hamaku, do	Basaltic volcanic ash	4400	12/0

[1] Oxic taken in the sense of the 7th Approximation (1960, 1967)
[2] Muscovite (illite) in weathering rock
[3] Smectite in weathering rock
[4] Allophane instead of kaolinite

soils in different tropical regions

lar O2 — 2O3 rock	Nature of weathering product	Thickness of profile or of weathering rim (cm)	Comparative content of kaolinite of weathered rim (italics), rotten rock and soil		
			I	II	III
,I	Different outcrops		2	3	10
,8	Oxic clay[1]	600	0	15	40
,4	do	600			100
,0	do	600	0	8	80
,4	do	1350	*1*	11	60
,0	Nipe clay	480		13	20
,7?	do	390		22	70
	Catalina clay	600		90	90
	do	310		100	100
,3	Weathered rock	0.2	*1*		
,I	do	0.2	20		
	Oxic clay				54
	do				27
,4	do				73
	do				4
	do				14
	do				53
	do				53
	do				4
	do				100
,4	do	670	*2*		100
,4	do	610		94	100
,7	Weathered rock	0.2	*46*		
,4	Oxic clay	140			100
,8	do	750	*3*		30
	Dispersed weathered rock				100
	Oxic clay loam	210			100
,0	Oxic clay	700		68	40
,6	do	700		100	90
,3	do	600		100	100
	do				60
,7	do				92
,7	Weathered rock	0.2	*51*		
,0	do	0.2	*62*		
,5	do	0.2	*77*		
,5	do	0.2	*78*		
	Oxic clay	100			40[4]

light on the problem of why the kaolinite/gibbsite ratio differs so widely in the various oxic weathering products. It should be borne in mind that the columns I and II are the composition of the weathered rims (except in No. 1), which are sometimes very thin and column III for the soil derived. When comparing the results, the fact emerges that the same type of rock may yield a weathering product of a different composition. In this way the granites of Mazaruni and Oro Bay (Nos. 3 and 26) and the gneiss of Mangalore (No. 20) yield 100% kaolinite, whereas the granite of Yarakita Hills and the pegmatite of Amlakfotsikely (Nos. 4 and 19) yield a bauxitic soil (only 4% kaolinite); the gneiss of Amboassang and the pegmatites of Tsilaizina and Amboassang (Nos. 12, 17, and 18) have a kaolinite content of 50%. Similar discrepancies can be found in the materials derived from basic and intermediate rocks.

Sometimes clay minerals quite different from those in the derived soil (Nos. 21 and 25) are found in the weathering zone. Such successions of different minerals upon weathering are also found in temperate climates; Lovering (1941) found hydrous mica and sericite to be the essential clay minerals in the zones of alteration of a biotite quartz monzonite in Colorado, although beidellite is found to be prominent in the transition subzone and dickite in the inner sub-zone where intense alteration occurs.

Hervieu (1968) found in a tropical soil from basic rock of Madagascar well-crystallized kaolinite with amorphous material and some iron oxide and gibbsite in the surface layer, whereas in the rotten rock montmorillonite and interstratified chlorite are predominant. More examples of this kind will be given in the Chapters 1 and 2 of Part II.

Very probably these different reactions are related to differences in drainage pattern in turn induced by differences in climate. The amphibolite of Madagascar (No. 13) yields 30% kaolinite in a climate with six dry months, whereas that of the Isle of Yap (No. 32) yields practically 100% kaolinite in a continually wet climate.

These problems will be elaborated further in the Chapters 1 and 2 of Part II and particularly in Chapter 1 of Part III.

3.2. MORPHOLOGICAL FEATURES OF WEATHERING

Many soil scientists have drawn attention to the fact that basic rocks change rapidly into soils. An example is the nepheline-syenite of the Isle of Kassa (fig. 1.30); another, less clear example is a basalt of the Congo (fig. 1.31).

A total transformation of the minerals which takes place within a layer of only a few millimeters, or even tenths of millimeters above the fresh rocks is evident in both cases.

However, it has to be emphasized that the transformation of a basalt rock into a soil is not always as clear as represented in the figs. 1.30 and 31. The basalt of Kasaragod in India (table 1.64, No. 22) has a weathering zone of 120 cm. The reported rapid transition might therefore be caused by erosion of the original soil and depositing of material from elsewhere.

Whatever it is, the zone of alteration of quartz-rich rocks seems to be very thick, sometimes several meters as in the case of the Mazaruni granite. Lacroix (1923) and Besaire (1937) also point this out in their study of mineralogy and soils of Madagascar.

FIG. 1.30. *Abrupt transition between rock and soil of the nepheline-syenite on the Isle of Kassa, Guiana (photo B. Gèze)*

The main reason for the difference in the weathering zone of basic and acidic rocks is probably the fact that minerals of the basic rocks weather more easily and readily than those of the acidic rock. The quartz is especially resistant, so that acidic rocks never succumb so completely as the basic rocks.

Another phenomenon, directly related to rock weathering is the well-known fact that certain types of rocks are moulded into larger or smaller boulders during the weathering process. The figs. 1.32, 33, and 34 demonstrate this process clearly. Schmid, de la Souchère and Godard (1951), who described this phenomenon as occurred in the region of the basaltic soils of the Darlac Plateau (South Annam), observed the same features characterizing the transformation repeating themselves several times, always in an identical manner, and proceeding in concentric layers towards the core although the length of the intervening period varied. They related this phenomenon to the periodicity in the water content of the surroundings, in other words, to the type of climate in which a dry season alternates regularly with a wet season. The variations in time-lapse between formation of the concentric layers did not seem to follow a definite law. It was also found that the inner layers, enclosing the core of the rock, consisted of thin, tough flakes, whereas the outer layers were composed of thicker, friable flakes. The nature of these two types of flakes was not given, although the investigators did mention that the material of which the inner layers were composed was greyish-white in colour, and could be rubbed between the fingers until it became a rather gritty powder. This might well be gibbsite. That disintegration proceeds along lines which converge towards the centre is assumed to be governed by the original structure of the rock, which showed the well-defined, symmetric structures similar to the familiar organ-pipes met with in basalt. In fact, the transformation often brings this 'pre-existent' structure to light, and the disintegrated shells reveal polygonal contours, closely resembling the prisms forming the base of the organ-pipes (see fig. 1.36).

Decomposition in concentric shells is not a fixed rule, but seems to depend on the humidity of the surrounding earth. It is possible therefore, that one may find, especially on slopes, voluminous spheroids without any layer of flaky fragments but only

FIG. I.31. *Abrupt transition between rock and soil of basalt in Congo Kinshasa (photo G. Tondeur)*

FIG. I.32. *Concentric weathering of andesite in South Sulawesi (Indonesia). The three spheroidic boulders in the foreground, uncovered by erosion, form one unit (photo Mohr)*

FIG. I.33. *Concentric weathering in the Congo (photo G. Tondeur by courtesy of the Service des Publications, Ministère des Colonies, Bruxelles)*

142

FIG. 1.34. *Concentric weathering of a basalt in Vietnam. The horizon below the surface reveals a prismatic structure. A bed of shaly decomposed boulders follows immediately below, one isolated specimen of which is shown at the bottom half of the photograph (photo Vo-An-Ninh, by courtesy of M. Schmid, 1951)*

FIG. 1.35. *Close-up of isolated boulder, shown in fig. 1.34 (photo Vo-An-Ninh, by courtesy of M. Schmid, 1951)*

FIG. 1.36. *Polygonal organ-pipes of basalt, along road Addis Abeba – Debra Marcos to Blue Nile, Ethiopia (photo Van Gogh)*

FIG. 1.37. *Dacite boulder at the limit of the zone of spheroidal decomposition (photo Vo-An-Ninh, by courtesy of E. M. Castagnol, 1952)*

FIG. I.38. *Typical flaky spheroidal decomposition of dacite (photo Vo-An-Ninh, by courtesy of E.M. Castagnol, 1952)*

FIG. I.39. *An advanced stage of decomposition of dacite. Earthy layers are formed between the flakes which tend to dissociate themselves (photo Vo-An-Ninh, by courtesy of E. M. Castagnol, 1952)*

covered by a very thin film of yellowish-white material which can easily be rubbed into very fine sand (gibbsite?). If the yellowish-white material is really gibbsite, its formation can easily be understood by assuming excessive leaching through penetration of rains running along the surface (see Part III, Chapter 1).

The same phenomenon of concentric weathering was observed by Castagnol (1952) when studying the dacite and basalt-derived red earths of Southern Indo-China. The photographs (figs. 1.37, 38 and 39) clearly illustrate the various stages of the spheroidal decomposition of a dacite in a red earth profile, near the experimental station on Darlac Plateau. Although both the basalt and the dacite clearly show the characteristics of spheroidal disintegration, Castagnol reports that the flakes of the decomposed dacite are generally thicker than those of the basalt and are apparently less easily transformed into red earth.

3.3. THE MINERALOGY OF TROPICAL CLAYS

Although already in the preceding section mention has been made of different clay minerals in the various products of tropical weathering, it is worth-wile to go into more detail of the pedo-ecological and regional aspects of the mineralogy of these compounds.

Of interest is the understanding of the conditions which favour the crystallization of either minerals of the kandite type, or those of the smectite group. Edelman (1946) published a concept of the formation of montmorillonite bearing black clays. The concept was mainly based on the earlier investigations of Hardon and Favejee (1939), who had established that kaolinite is formed under conditions leading to the genesis of Oxisols, whereas montmorillonite was found to be the typical component of the colloids of neutral or slightly alkaline soils. These are encountered, inter alia, in Central and Eastern Java, around the foot of recently active volcanoes in a region where the climate is marked by a pronounced dry season. Using a schematic profile through a volcano body, the formation of montmorillonite is explained by Edelman as being the result of the influence of groundwater rich in silica and bases.

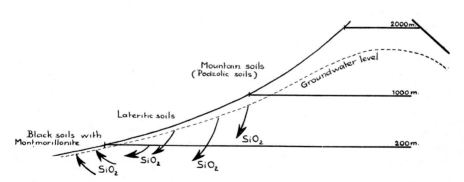

FIG. 1.40. *Schematic profile through a volcano, indicating the water movement and soil types (after Edelman, 1946)*

This is confirmed by a treatise on the clay formation in tropical soils by Schaufelberger (1955) who reviewed the characteristic clay minerals in Colombia, Ecuador, Moroc, Puerto Rico, and Indonesia and arrived at the conclusion that kaolinite is the main component of the clay fraction of the free draining areas, whereas montmorillonite is the dominant compound in badly drained depressions. The theoretical treatise on mineral transformations can be found in Part II, Chapter 3, section 4.1 (fig. 11.44), Chapter 4, section 4.1 (fig. 11.52), and in Part III, Chapter 1 (figs. 111.7 and 8).

The presence of halloysite in weathering products has been recorded by several investigators, but it seems to be a rare component. Apparently, specific conditions are necessary for its formation (see Grim, 1968, p. 519). Halloysite has not been mentioned frequently in recent literature on the clays of tropical soils. A few examples are Chang and Lee (1958) who found kaolinite and halloysite in the < 2μ fraction of the red soils of the tropical zone of Southern China, and Chang (1963) who reported the presence of halloysite in red soils derived from acid rocks, in tropical red earth from basalt as well as in young tropical soils of basaltic origin, all of Hainan Island. Hervieu (1968) finally mentions dehydrated halloysite as a component of the clay fraction of a 'humous ferrallitic ando type of soil' of Madagascar. He adds however 'or poorly crystallized kaolinite or a mixture of both'. This points to the difficulty of distinguishing between these two members of the kandite group. Reviewing the literature on kaolinite and halloysite minerals it was stated by Grim (1968, p. 130 et seq.) that next to X-ray analysis auxiliary procedures are available for identifying halloysite. He alludes to the fact that halloysite absorbs certain organic molecules. Electron microscopy showed that halloysite occurs sometimes as elongate tubular particles (Bates et al., 1950), ordered kaolinite showing in most cases the well-known pseudo-hexagonal platy form. Also the ratio of height to width of the (001) peak in the X-ray spectogram is distinctly lower than that of kaolinite, viz. 5.2 to 17.9 average. The reader specifically interested in this subject may also refer to the study of Wada (1963) who developed a new method for the quantitative determination of kaolinite and halloysite by NH_4Cl retention measurement.

D.T.A. curves have also been thought to show the distinction, the endothermic peak at 550° C of halloysite being asymmetric, the one of kaolinite symmetric. This was confirmed by the curve of hydrated halloysite of Indiana (Grim, 1968, p. 287), but Spiel et al. (see Grim, 1968, p. 293) clearly proved that small-sized kaolinite of the diameter < 0.5 micron also shows asymmetric D.T.A. curves. This is more so in the fractions 0.2–0.1μ and 0.1–0.05 μ. Spiel et al. also observed that the heating rate had effect on the endothermic reaction, the 5° C/min. and 8° C/min. thermograms being asymmetric, the 12° C/min. symmetric. A more recent example seems to add to the uncertainty as Aoki et al. (1969), studying the clay fraction of a red soil derived from basaltic andesite, used the slope ratio of the 575° C endothermic peak as an indication of the predominance of halloysite (see also: Talibudeen, 1952). X-ray analysis supported the thermogram identification. All this leads to the conclusion that at least fine-grained halloysite is not to be distinguished from equally small or badly crystallized kaolinite with a diameter below 0.1 μ.

It was stated on p. 145 that groundwater rich in silica and divalent cations was the principal factor in the formation of black clays. This is not always true; slow drainage can also have this effect and some examples to show this will be discussed in Chapter I of Part II, section 1. 2. 2.

Amorphous components also occur besides crystalline clays. The best known example is amorphous alumino-silicate (allophane) with a SiO_2/Al_2O_3 ratio between 0.5 and 1.9 (Birrell and Fieldes, 1952; Hendricks et al., 1967), or 2 according to the formula $Al_2O_3 . 2SiO_2 . 3H_2O$ of Wada (1967). This amorphous weathering product is a common and dominating constituent of Andosols derived from volcanic ash rich in glass. It is an established fact that volcanic glass is the main source of allophane, but Kanno (1962) states that also plagioclases may be weathered to form allophane. He prepared the following scheme for the transformation of volcanic glasses and plagioclases into clay minerals:

Volcanic glass $Si(OH)_4$ Allophane   Gibbsite
Plagioclases $Al(OH)_3$ Smectites   Kandites

This is confirmed by Harmse (1967) who detected allophane as a pseudomorph after feldspars in the sand fractions of soils of the Highveld Region of Transvaal, South Africa. He suggested the name 'tekto-allophane' as distinguished from the allophane resulting from the weathering of amorphous volcanic glass. Fig. 1.41 shows the tekto-allophane pseudomorphs. Fig. 1.42 gives the D.T.A. curves of the tekto-allophane, of allophane from Japan, and of the andesitic saprolite studies of Hendricks et al. (1967).

FIG. 1.41. *'Tekto-allophane' in the sand-fractions of an entrophic reddish-brown soil on dolerite from the Highveld Region (after Harmse, 1967)*

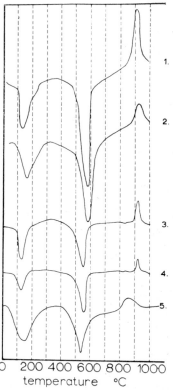

FIG. 1.42. *Thermograms of basalt andesitic clay (1, 2), andesite saprolite (3, 4) and tekto-allophane (5)*

It would seem that Harmse's 'tekto-allophane' is close to Jackson's 'halloysitic allo-phane' (Jackson, 1965).

A point of debate still seems to be whether these amorphous products, apart from the cases just quoted, are common or uncommon. Beutelspacher and Van der Marel (1961) concluded that allophane is widespread in many soils and is an important factor in accounting for the physical properties of the soils. Grim (1968), on the other hand, is of the opinion, that allophane is uncommon in soils and clays and that it is rarely an important factor in the physical behaviour of such clays. Nevertheless amorphous material does occur in many soils; it is even a diagnostic feature in the spodic horizon, as defined by the American Soil Survey Staff (7th Approximation, 1960; Supplement, 1967).

Siefermann (1959) recorded that the various red soils in the southern part of Cameroun are characterized by kaolinite, lepidocrocite, and goethite. Gibbsite is negligible or absent. The rainfall is up to 2000 mm and well divided over the year. In the equatorial part there is between 2000 and 1200 mm of rain with two peaks and 2 to 6 intervening dry months. The northern region is distinctly dry with a pluviometry of 1200 to 500 mm in 4 to 6 months. In this area the ferruginous tropical soils are found, with kaolinite and nontronite as components of the clay fraction. The young soils derived from sub-recent and recent basaltic lava and ashes have clays with allophane and some kaolinite and gibbsite. It is unlikely that in these young soils the gibbsite resulted from the breakdown of the kaolinite. More in line is the assumption that the allophane partly crystallized into kaolinite, any excess of aluminium being segregated as gibbsite.

A comparable result was obtained by Delvigne (1959) in the Congo. He pointed out that the mineralogy of the horizons of Oxisols and Ultisols is rather monotonous; the clays contained predominantly quartz, kaolinite, and hydroxides, whereas only minor amounts of illite occurred even when granite is the parent rock. If derived from basic rocks, old or sub-recent, montmorillonite is only formed when drainage is deficient. Allophane dominates the clay of young weathering products (andosols) of basaltic volcanic ash such as those encountered around Lake Kivu. An interesting weathering sequence of amphibolites is reported. In the first stage of alteration only the feldspars are decomposed, the hornblende stays intact and the clay consists exclusively of kaolinite without any iron hydroxide. In the second stage the hornblende is also severely weathered and next to kaolinite great quantities of hydroxides of iron occur as components of the clay. In the third stage a great part of the iron has been transported and kaolinite again dominates the clay fraction. The soil itself is characterized by kaolinite, hematite, and some gibbsite. Delvigne mentions the total disappearance of mica in the old Oxisols even when they were derived from micaschists. Biotite is transformed into vermiculite only at high altitude but this is very unstable and disap-pears towards the middle of the profile.

Hervieu (1968) presents as an essential part of the study of the soils of Madagascar, a detailed account of their clay composition. The choice of the soils was based on the classification by Aubert (1967). In this system the ferrallitic soils are subdivided by colour, parent material, and intensity of weathering; the ferruginous tropical soils are separated according to origin. Black rendzinas, brown calcareous soils and vertisols

are also recognized. The ferrallitic soils, according to D'Hoore (1964) comprise 34%
of the soils of Madagascar, while the ferruginous soils comprise 27%. The ferrallitic
soils belong mainly to the Ultisols, only few to the Oxisols; the ferruginous soils are
classified as Ultustalfs. There is also a great monotony in the clay composition of these
soils as can be concluded from the following examples:
Red soil on granite, containing kaolinite, gibbsite, and goethite;
Red soil on basalt, containing kaolinite, gibbsite, and goethite;
Red soil on gneiss, containing kaolinite, gibbsite, and hematite;
Red soil on sandstone, containing kaolinite and some illite.

The data on the above-mentioned examples is slightly oversimplified. The clay
minerals of the red soil on granite are, according to Hervieu, badly crystallized. As
these soils developed in an area with 1215 mm of rain falling between November and
April this is unexpected. However, the morphology of the region with a slope of 25° to
30° might stimulate such strong drainage that the possibility of crystallization of the
weathering products would be practically eliminated. The clay compounds derived
from the basalt are well-crystallized, while gibbsite and goethite occur in large amounts,
the difference being quantitative and not qualitative. In the soil on gneiss gibbsite
disappears at a depth of 1.5 meter, while the hematite is limited to the reddish horizons
up to approximately 4 meters and disappears in the yellow-coloured horizon between
4.5 and 5 meters where goethite occurs instead. The sandstone soil contains some illite
in the surface layer next to the dominating kaolinite.

The ferruginous tropical soils (Ultustalfs) sometimes contain kaolinite and montmorillonite as co-dominant components; these results can be summarized as follows:

Ferruginous tropical soil on metamorphic rock	In the surface layer kaolinite and some badly crystallized hydroxides. In the decomposed sandy material of the sub-horizon kaolinite, some illite and traces of montmorillonite occur, while the little decomposed rock has illite, some kaolinite, and montmorillonite as the clay components.
Ferruginous tropical soil and sandstone	Kaolinite and montmorillonite in equal amounts with some illite and goethite. At greater depth 90% montmorillonite.
Ferruginous tropical soil on sandy deposits	In the surface layer 60% kaolinite and 40% montmorillonite. At greater depths montmorillonite dominates.

It is evident that montmorillonite seems to dominate at greater depths, i.e. at closer
proximity to the parent material. One would assume that montmorillonite has been
converted into kaolinite specifically in the surface layers where weathering is most
advanced. Detailed examples will be discussed in Chapter 1 of Part II.

The fact emerges that even parent rocks such as sandstone and sandy deposits can be
conducive to the formation of montmorillonite. The source of the elements which
ultimately combine to form this 2 : 1 mineral is probably in the case of the sandstone the 'ciment argileux' or clayey cement of the quartz grains; small rounded
shingle-like fragments of gravel, which are part of the quartz-sandstone, may also have
contributed. The parent material in the second example is a rather soft stratified clayey
sandstone, so in both instances the composition of the rock clearly exerted a decisive
influence on the nature of the clay.

Returning to the Oxisols Boulvert (1968) shows that kaolinite, hematite, some gibbsite, and traces of goethite characterize the clay fraction of a soil which occupies the central part of toposequence in Bombon in the Centrafican Republic.

Discussing the East African black or grey clays, which are commonly known as 'black cotton soils', Milne (1936) states that two types are encountered, viz. (a) on transported material occupying low-lying ground, and (b) as sedentary soils on ground which ought to be well drained judging by its position, but which is in fact seasonally water-logged. The occurrence of type (b) seems to be inseparably linked with the texture of the parent material. This includes Jurassic clay, lava rich in calcium and shale. It should be noted that the Jurassic clay, as well as the shale is essentially fine-grained sedimentary rock. Milne also adds that in undulating country where it would be more usual to find red earth except in the depressions, continuous coverings of dark-coloured plastic clay may be found.

In 1947, in a report published posthumously on Tanganyika soils based on a reconnaissance trip carried out in 1935, Milne described a soil catena of the Usumbara foothills where grey soils are interspersed in relatively high-lying situations where red soil might have been expected. They are anomalous soils characterized by impeded drainage, and they either represent the remains of a former mature land surface with a sluggish drainage, or else a parent-rock factor is involved. This parent rock is a gneiss, only slightly different from that which is common to the whole region.

Milne suggests, by way of explaining the occurrence of these 'anomalous' soils, that a petrographic examination of the parent material might reveal a mineral composition that would direct the course of weathering towards the production of water-retentive 'fat' clay, with a higher silica and lower free iron oxide content than is the case with the sesquioxidic clay of the red earth which is readily permeable. He concludes, in connection with the possibility of water infiltration, that the 'dip of the gneiss also requires study'.

The discussion of the soil catena of Unyanuembe (Tanganyika) in which the location of authentic red earths is restricted to relatively narrow zones of free drainage, would be of equal importance.

A number of Indian soil scientists who studied the problem of the genesis of red and black soils, have reported similar experiences. Mukerji and Agarwal (1943) discussed the genetic soil types of the Bundelkhand tract which is a bare, undulating plain with irregular, rocky hills, converging on a level expanse of black soil to the north which extends as far as the River Jumna. The general slope of the country is from north to south, and passing through the level plains on the south of the Jumna to the rocky hills, the fertile black soil merges into coarse-grained red soil, interspersed with patches that are brownish to black in colour. Although geologically, the whole tract is occupied by gneiss, the climate combined with the peculiar topography has caused the formation of divergent soils under free, partial, or restricted drainage. Red soils developed with free drainage, and black soils with impeded drainage.

The black soils, in the instances cited, occupy areas which, although appearing to be flat, are in fact slightly concave or convex. Concavity leads either to a lake or a swamp, or at least to a waterlogged soil. A convex terrain constitutes a hill or ridge with steep slopes. In neither case black soils are formed.

The question now arises as to whether the topography of the site where the soils occur, does actually promote accumulation of impeded groundwater presumably rich in silica and bases, and whether the groundwater impeded in this way is responsible for the genesis of the black soils or, more specifically, of the montmorillonitic clay mineral which is so typical of them.

The other possibility is that the physical properties of the original parent materials impede the free percolation of the soil solution, derived from the access of atmospheric water, irrespective of the level of the groundwater, and therefore entirely uninfluenced by the convex or concave shape of the surrounding area. If this is so, the process which takes place by the action of soil water on fresh minerals results in a sort of equilibrium whereby a temporary storage of the ions liberated from the soil minerals occurs. Silica and cations will not be leached, the pH will remain fairly high and the result will be that a clay mineral, i.e. montmorillonite, tends to be formed. The weathering process, primarily determined by the texture and similar physical properties of the original material, has a paramount influence on the course of further soil development. Impediment to drainage will be increased, and excess of water will increasingly dominate the process of soil genesis. In this respect it is interesting to note that Hardy, Mac Donald and Rodriguez (1932) state that in Grenada (B.W.I.) basalt lava with 3000 mm of rainfall produces a red soil, whereas volcanic ash under the same amount of precipitation, develops into a black soil.

The complexity of the process of weathering is illustrated in a study of Tanganyika Red Loams by Muir et al. (1957). These authors publish, and this is rather an exception, data on the light and heavy minerals of the sand fraction of two red loams of Nachangwea as well as the mineralogy of the fraction $< 1\mu$. The results are shown in table 1.65. From this data one might conclude that soil P48 was distinctly less weathered than soil P17, the first having 53.1 % of hornblende in its heavy fraction, the other

TABLE 1.65. *Mineralogy of Tanganyika Red Loams* (after Muir et al., 1957)

Nachingwea Red Loams		Light fraction < s.g. 2.9		Heavy fraction > s.g. 2.9	
site	depth in cm	Feldspar %	Quartz %	Hornblende %	Ore %
P48	0– 20	0	94.8	53.1	29.9
	100–150	9.5	83.9	88.0	4.1
P17	0–110	0	94.6	16.0	71.0
	100–160	0	97.4	1.1	89.5

only 16.0 %. Examination of the subsoil data shows that the situation is more complex. P48 has 9.5 % feldspar and 88 % hornblende, whereas P17 contains only 1.1 % hornblende. This apparent difference in stage of weathering does not show in the clay $< 1\mu$. In both soils fine-grained kaolinite is the dominant mineral, associated with some hematite (up to 10 %) and minor amounts of goethite and illite. In other cases

there exists a definite relationship between clay and light fraction composition as was shown by Sinha and Nandal (1963). In four localities of the uplands of Chotonagpur (India) they found that whenever seritisized feldspar or muscovite were present, illite dominated the clay together with a fair amount of kaolinite; kaolinite was dominant with degraded illite of secondary importance when altered feldspar was the sole component of the light fraction.

Soils of Vietnam have been studied by Herbillon et al. (1968), particularly dealing with the influence of the pedogenetic development within a group on the composition of the clay fraction. There is evidence that in the red and yellow podzolic soils kaolinite is transformed in the A_3– and B–horizon into gibbsite particularly in the red podzolic soils. The yellow members contain some gibbsite and goethite next to the dominating kaolinite. Both soils investigated are derived from metamorphic rocks with a rainfall of 1700 mm. Red and yellow podzolic soils also occur in which kaolinite dominates the whole profile; the origin in these cases are old alluvial deposits and sandy dune material. The latter parent material leads to a soil with kaolinite dominant in the clay fraction and appreciable amounts of goethite. The red soils of Vietnam belong to the most strongly weathered soils ('sol rouge terreux') and contain only traces of kaolinite, goethite, and gibbsite in the clay fraction, which is rather exceptional. It is assumed that abundant amorphous alumino-silica gels (allophane?) occur. Herbillon et al. based this assumption on the extremely high c.e.c. of the colloidal fraction with values of 60 m.e. per 100 gram in the B-horizons. Hervieu (1968) found in Madagascar allophane as a prevalent component in the surface layer of a red soil rich in organic matter without any volcanic glass as a mineral component.

Some interesting information is found in the mineralogy of some acid sulphate soils of the Mekong delta. The clay fractions contain kaolinite, quartz, and mica, sometimes in traces but have c.e.c. values which range from 38 to 51 m.e. per 100 grams (table 1.66).

TABLE 1.66. *Clay composition of acid sulphate soils of Vietnam* (after Herbillon et al., 1968)

Sample Nr	c.e.c. m.e./100 g	mica	kaolinite	quartz
47	50.8	tr	+	+
48	46.5	tr	+	+
52	37.9	+	+	+
53	47.9	+	+	+

Chang and Lee (1958) report that red soils in both tropical and subtropical zones of Southern China at altitudes of 600 to 700 meters change into yellow soils as a result of the hydration of hematite. Once a small part of the hematite has been hydrated into goethite or limonite due to local variations in moisture, the soil attains a distinct yellowish colour although the main constituents of the clay fraction remain unchanged. (For a theoretical treatise on the hydration and dehydration reaction reference is made to Chapter 2 of Part III.)

Chang and Lee also present data on the exchange capacity of the fraction $< 1\mu$ as related to the nature of the clay components.

Soils		Clay minerals	c.e.c. m.e./100 g
I.	Oxisols	Kaolinite-gibbsite-hematite	5– 5.5
II.	Red soils of the tropical zone	Kaolinite-halloysite	10–15
III.	Red soils of the subtropical zone	Kaolinite-quartz-montmorillonite	20–25
IV.	Yellow soils of the mountainous region	Kaolinite-montmorillonite Illite-quartz Montmorillonite-quartz	24–34

Chang (1961) published a report on the mineralogical composition of the clay fraction $< 1\mu$ separated from fourty samples representing six important soil types of Hainan Island. The results are summarized as follows:

Soil and parent material	Clay minerals
Oxisols derived from acid rocks	Kaolinite (including halloysite)
Tropical red earths derived from acid rocks	Kaolinite and illite
Tropical red earths from basalt	Kaolinite (including halloysite)
Yellow earths derived from granite and tuff	ibid
'Savanah' soils derived from sediments	Kaolinite and illite
Young tropical soils derived from recent effusive volcanic rocks (basalt)	Montmorillonite and kaolinite (including halloysite)

Although the predominant clay minerals appear to be similar in the different soil types, there are differences which are to be attributed to the influence of parent rock, climate (hydrology), time, and vegetation. The sequence of transformation of layer silicate minerals in acid rocks under tropical conditions is presumably as follows: mica → illite → mixed layer minerals → montmorillonite → kaolinite. Chang finally remarks that kaolinite can be derived from potash feldspar as found in a soil weathered under tropical conditions from porphyritic granite. This confirms the observations of Harrison (1934) in Guiana and of Humbert (1947) in West Irian (Indonesia).

The weathering sequence mica-montmorillonite-kaolinite may also be reversed as was shown by Chang (1961) when studying the clay composition of some paddy soils of China. (A theoretical treatise on the transformations of montmorillonite into illite and kaolinite and the reverse can be found in the section 4.1.4.1 of Chapter 4 of Part II.)

The transformation of illite into montmorillonite has also been described by Hamdi (1959) who studied the alteration in the clay fraction of Egyptian soils. He found that alluvial Nile soils of the same source and origin, but differing in age between recent and 12,000 years, clearly exposed the conversion of illite into montmorillonite as a result of 'depotassication' due to submergence in groundwater during many thousands of years.

An important publication in which the role of the parent rock is given adequate attention, is by Turton et al. (1962) on the chemistry and mineralogy of Oxisols in South-West Australia. These authors studied the clay composition of the B-horizon of what are distinguished (see fig. 1.43) as gravelly, truncated non-laterites and of the pallid zone of a deep laterite (for the definition of laterite see Chapter 1 of Part III). They found that the grey sands of the sandy laterites and the exposed ferruginous zones contain gibbsite, which in some profiles is co-dominant with kaolinite. At greater depths in these profiles kaolinite is the main component. Here gibbsite is absent and some illite and montmorillonite occur. In the non-laterites gibbsite is seldom present

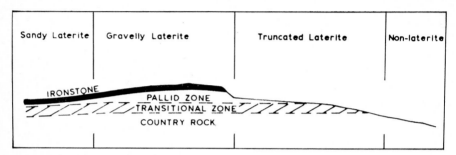

FIG. 1.43. *Geomorphological relationship of the 'lateritic' soils in S.W. Australia (after Turton et al., 1962)*

whereas illite and montmorillonite may lie much shallower. The data on parent material indicates that the rocks of the Pre-Cambrian shield including granite, gneiss, mica schist, and dolerite did not particularly influence the mineralogical composition of the weathering products; these are predominantly kaolinite and/or gibbsite. Apparently age has obliterated any differences which might have been the results of differing parent material. However, in the B, BC or C-horizons of the non-laterites the clay minerals reflected the lithology of the parent rock. It appeared that illite and kaolinite were co-dominant where parent material was acid and montmorillonite with kaolinite when the soil was derived from dolerite.

The weathering sequence established by Hseung and Hsu (1964) when studying the distribution of clay minerals in the soils of China as they occur in the regions ranging from arid to humid tropical climates, is as follows: illite → illite, vermiculite → illite, vermiculite, kaolinite → kaolinite, vermiculite → kaolinite, gibbsite. It seems justified that in this sequence the term vermiculite is used as a synonym or alternative to montmorillonite, particularly as vermiculite has the same or somewhat higher cation exchange capacity as smectite and dioctahedral forms are recorded to be found in the clays. As no mention is made of specific parent rocks the authors assume that as in the case of S.W. Australia any possible differences have been obliterated.

The detailed clay mineralogical study of red and black soils of Coimbatore and Medah (India) by Kenchanna Gowda et al. (1966) is of special value to the subject under discussion. These authors, referring to earlier research, express the opinion that extensive investigations will be required to draw an overall picture of the clay mineral distribution in these complex soils and to arrive at any definite conclusion regarding

TABLE 1.67. *C.E.C. and mineral composition of soil clays of profile 1* (Patancheru)

Depth in cm	Fraction	C.E.C. in m.e./100 kg	Kaolinite	Mineral content		
				Montmo-rillonite	Illite	Quartz and goethite
0–15	< 2μ	31.4	50	25	15	10
	Coarse		50	20	15	15
	Medium		45	30	15	10
	Fine		45	40	10	5
15–20	< 2μ	31.8	45	25	15	15
	Coarse		45	20	20	15
	Medium		45	25	20	10
	Fine		40	40	15	5
20–75	< 2μ	28.1	45	25	15	15
	Coarse		50	20	15	15
	Medium		45	30	15	10
	Fine		40	45	10	5
75 and below	< 2μ	27.0	45	25	15	15
	Coarse		50	20	15	15
	Medium		45	30	15	10
	Fine		40	45	10	5

their formation. They first analyzed two red soil profiles, one from Patancheru in the Medah district of Andhra Pradesh (table 1.67), rainfall 800 mm and temperature 8–38° C, and one from Saravanapathi in the Coimbatore district of Madras (table 1. 68), rainfall 850 mm and temperature 18–37° C. Parent material is gneiss, the slope is 3 % against nearly level, and the permeability is rapid to moderately rapid. The clay fractions of each of the four horizons of the two profiles have been separated and each of them sub-divided in coarse clay (2–0.8μ), medium clay (0.8–0.2μ) and fine clay (< 0.2μ). The authors arrived at the conclusion that it seems possible for either kaolinite or montmorillonite to be formed from the same parent material, and further that the weathering sequence is: primary minerals → illite montmorillonite → kaolinite or primary minerals → illite → kaolinite. This confirms the findings of other investigators. One problem, however, may be obvious to the attentive reader. The better aerated and drained Patancheru soil has goethite as an accessory clay component, whereas the less well drained and presumably wetter Saravanapathi clay contains hematite. This is contrary to expectation and does not fail to show that all processes of tropical soil formation are by no means as yet fully understood. This may also apparently be extended to non-tropical soils judging by a communication of Demumbrum (1962) who studied the mineralogy of the Lauderdale soil formed from Eocene sandstone in the Southern United States. He found montmorillonite, but no kaolinite, at pH values of 4 or lower and under conditions of high porosity and high temperature and rainfall.

This section may be concluded with another comparative study of Indian soils. Das and Das (1966) report on the mineralogy of clays from some black, brown, and red

TABLE 1.68. *C.E.C. and mineral composition of soil clays of profile II* (Saravanapathi)

Depth in cm	Fraction	C.E.C. in m.e./100 g	Mineral content			
			Kaolinite	Montmo-rillonite	Illite	Quartz and haematite
0–15	< 2μ	65.5	10	70	10	10
	Coarse		10	70	10	10
	Medium		10	70	10	10
	Fine		10	80	10	. .
15–25	< 2μ	32.8	10	50	25	15
	Coarse		10	50	25	15
	Medium		10	60	20	10
	Fine		10	75	10	5
25–43	< 2μ	34.8	10	50	25	15
	Coarse		10	50	25	15
	Medium		10	60	20	10
	Fine		10	75	10	5
43 and below	< 2μ	35.3	10	50	25	15
	Coarse		10	50	25	15
	Medium		10	60	20	10
	Fine		10	75	10	5

soils of Mysore. The rainfall ranges from 635–889 mm, the temperature from 12.8° C in winter to 35° C in summer, the parent material consists of blue granite, chlorite-, hornblende-, and mica-schists and other stratified metamorphic rocks. From their account may be concluded that there is no pedogenetic preference exerted by any of the rocks mentioned. The black soils of the three regions Honnali, Dadagurhonnali, and Kunchiganahali were all dominated by the clay mineral montmorillonite with subordinate a 14 Å chloritic mineral, illite and kaolinite. The brown soils of the same areas with soils from Robertsonpet in the Kolar districts added to the list show the same pattern of composition with the exception of the Kolar soil with fairly abundant kaolinite next to montmorillonite. The red soil from Honnali finally is characterized by dominant illite with a moderate amount of kaolinite, some montmorillonite and a little of the chlorite species. It is interesting to note that in the examples presented by Das and Das no mention is made of any of the hydrated sesquioxides as gibbsite or goethite.

3.4. THE TEXTURE OF THE WEATHERING PRODUCTS

As an overall effect of rock weathering, soils are formed with different distributions of sand, silt, and clay particles. This distribution is called texture and is determined by granulometric analysis.

This simple well-known fact were not be mentioned at all if the study of hundreds of thousands of samples from the Indonesian Archipelago, subjected to texture determination, had not shown that accurate information on degree and type of weathering can be derived from an evaluation of the data collected. It has been found that the main soil types are characterized by a specific particle size distribution. A brief discussion of the procedure which may contribute to a better understanding and evaluation of the method and its results, will follow:

The soil sample as collected in the field is, if necessary, crushed with a wooden pestle, and subsequently sieved through a sieve with 2 mm bores. The greater part, and in most cases all the soil, passes through and is called 'fine earth'. Any coarser components are collected as gravel, and the proportion of gravel to fine earth is determined by weighing.

Following the method as studied by the senior author in the Bureau of Soils at Washington in 1905 (and later adapted for Indonesia), ten grams of 'fine earth' are shaken head over head for six hours with 100 ml of distilled water in which were 10 drops of 10% NH_4OH in order to remove the granulation by organic matter, and to disperse loosely bound crumbs. The ammonia added is only a very weak dispersing agent as maximum dispersion is not necessary as it is desirable to leave the natural textural features as little disturbed as possible. The material of 50μ diameter and less is then subdivided in ten fractions by centrifuging and sedimentation in Atterberg cylinders. The coarser fractions are separated by sieving. The size classes of soil particles acquired in this way are:

Gravel	> 2 mm
Fraction 1 Very coarse sand	2 – 1 mm
2 Coarse sand	1 – 0.5 mm
3 Medium sand	0.5– 0.2 mm
4 Fine sand	0.2– 0.1 mm
5 Very fine sand	0.1 mm–50μ
6 Coarse silt	$50 - 20\mu$
7 Fine silt	$20 - 5\mu$
8 Coarse Clay	$5 - 2\mu$
9 Clay	$2 - 0.5\mu$
10 Colloidal clay	$< 0.5\mu$

The fractions acquired by this method are collected separately and put into glass tubes of 10 mm internal diameter, a thin slice of cork being used to keep each fraction separated from the other. It is thus possible not only to see the grain size distribution, but also to study its colour pattern (see figs. 1.44 and 45 between pages 158 and 159). It may be added that in practical soil research in Indonesia the sand fractions $> 50\mu$ – and in special cases $> 20\mu$ – were investigated with regard to their mineral content with the aid of a polarization microscope; more recently, colloidal clay $< 0.5\mu$ has been studied by X-ray diffraction methods.

The results of the granulometric analysis are represented as histograms, indicating the percentage by weight of each size class. Very interesting and characteristic graphs for specific soils are obtained in this way.

3.4.1. AEOLIAN SEDIMENTS AS PARENT MATERIAL

Volcanic ash soils can be distinguished by selection of grain size as related to distance from the point of eruption, and expressed in a histograph. The Merapi ash soils of the same pedologic age were deposited by the same eruption. These exhibit clearly not only the increasing fineness of the ash with increasing distance, but also show that the finest ashes are more susceptible to weathering, resulting in a larger clay fraction.

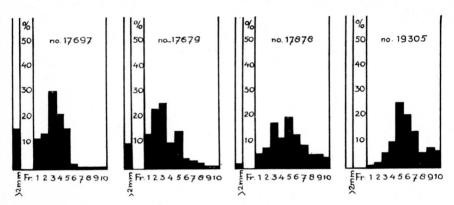

No. 17697: Ash gravelly soil
No. 17679: Ash sandy soil
No. 17878: Ash silty soil
No. 19305: Ash loamy soil
FIG. I.46. *Texture of different volcanic ash soils of Gunung Merapi, Java*

The distribution of the particles of andesitic dune sands in two stages of weathering gives a very interesting picture. There is a most perfect selection of two grain sizes, i.e. 0.5–0.2 mm and 0.2–0.1 mm, in the unweathered dune sands as found on the south coast of the Residency Jogjakarta.

The second sample is an older 'generation' of these sands. Whether the presence of very coarse, and coarse sand fractions is due to granulation, or is an original feature of this specific sediment, is not known. However, the increase in silt and clay content is conspicuous, and is due to more pronounced decomposition. This is confirmed by a decrease in content of citric-acid soluble phosphate and potash, hydrochloric acid

FIG. I.44. *Tubes with fractions resulting from the granulometric analysis of Oxisols*
1. Very old, pinkish-red Oxisol derived from tertiary quarz silt bearing clay loam; Haurgelis, W. Java
2. Very old, red Oxisol derived from andesitic breccia; Maswati, W. Java
3. Very old, red oxic palaeo-soil derived from andesitic tuff; Gunung Lawu, Central Java
4. Very old, brown Oxisol derived from tertiary andesitic tuff; Leuwiliang, W. Java
5. Rather young, yellowish-brown mountain soil derived from quaternary andesitic ash; Preanger, W. Java
6. Greyish-brown loamy clay; parent material from surrounding volcanoes, now weathering to black vertic soil; Ponorogo, Central Java

FIG. I.44.

FIG. I.45.

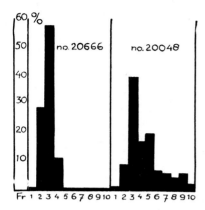

No. 20666: Grey andesitic dune sand
No. 20048: Yellowish-grey andesitic dune sand
FIG. I.47. *Texture of volcanic dune sands; south coast of Jogjakarta, Java*

soluble calcium, and the lower pH. If a volcanic ash deposit is subjected to weathering in a climate which has a seasonal dry period and to slow decomposition, a change in

FIG. I.48. *Dunes built up by volcanic sand; south coast of Jogjakarta, Java (photo Te Riele, 1932)*

colour from the original grey to a brownish colour is the first indication that disintegration of the mineral components has begun. A further sign is the lowering of the maximum of the 6th fraction ($50–20\mu$), and a shift of the maximum to the fractions 7 and 8 successively.

In this specific case, the coarser fractions consist of particles which are feebly cemented by silicic acid liberated from decomposing volcanic glass. The successive phases of weathering lead to a substantial increase of the finest fractions at the cost of the material $> 50\mu$.

FIG. I. 45. *Tubes with fractions resulting from the granulometric analysis of vertic and various other soils.*

1. Fluvial sedimentary deposit of vertic hill soil with some admixture of oxic material of volcanic origin; near Indramaju, northern plan of W. Java
2. Typical greyish-black Vertisol; Wonogiri, Central Java
3. Rather old, reddish-brown Ultisol, derived from liparitic tuff; Ranau, Sumatera
4. Young, brownish, humic soil derived from liparitic tuff; Ranau, Sumatera
5. Very young, greyish, coarse sandy, liparitic ash soil; Siantar, Sumatera
6. Greyish-white, quartz-sandy, hydro-podzolic loam ('Bleached Earth'); Bantam, W. Java

160

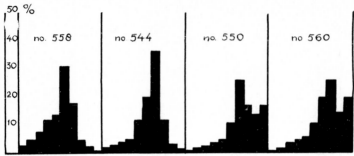

No. 558: Andesitic ash of the volcano Raun, East Java; non-weathered
No. 544: Ibid. 1rst phase of weathering
No. 550: Ibid. 2nd phase of weathering
No. 560: Ibid. 3rd phase of weathering
FIG. I.49. *Weathering sequence of volcanic ash demonstrated by texture (after Mohr, 1911)*

3.4.2. OXISOLS

If soil weathering takes place under conditions of continuous rainfall and good drainage, quite different textures result than reported in the preceding section. The coarser material is fully broken down, and in the 4th and 5th stages of weathering[1], a very conspicuous maximum of the 10th fraction dominates the picture. This maximum is found to be characteristic for all residual Oxisols of homogeneous composition. The graphs below are selected from data of a soil survey report of the residency of Jogja-karta, Java, by Te Riele (1932), and from a paper of the senior author on the results of granulometric analysis of tropical soils (Mohr, 1911). They represent successive stages of weathering.

Strictly speaking, a dacitic soil is not quite comparable to an andesitic one, owing to the content of quartz in the former material. This mineral functions as the non-weatherable skeleton, and is the cause of the consistent sand fractions $> 50\mu$. The fact that weathering stage 2, transitional to 3, is reached, can be seen from the mineralogical composition. The weatherable minerals – such as plagioclase, hornblende, augite and hypersthene – only occur in negligible quantities.

Two instances are now given of very old Oxisols which do not have the 10th fraction-maximum as might be expected. The first example is that of a yellow, strongly weather-ed pumice ash of the volcano Gunung Salak near Bogor, Java. The unweathered ash

[1] The weathering stages are classified as follows:
1. embryonic stage – fresh ash soils
2. juvenile stage – so-called 'tarapan'
3. virile stage – brown earth
4. senile stage – red earth
5. final stage – oxisol

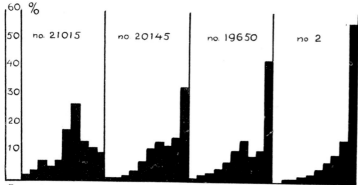

No. 21015: Brown soil from dacite tuff; Jogjakarta, Java; weathering stage 2–3
No. 20145: Brown soil from andesite tuff; Ibid. stage 4
No. 19650: Red soil from andesitic tuff; Ibid. stage 4–5
No. 2: Red andesitic soil; Priangan, West Java; stage 5
FIG. I.50. *Successive stages of weathering of Indonesian Oxisols as demonstrated by texture*

contains quantities of basic plagioclase which, in this thoroughly weathered soil, have been transformed into kaolinite in the silt fractions 50–20μ, 20–5μ, and 5–2μ. Mohr who, in 1911, detected and described this phenomenon in the paper quoted earlier, could not identify this mineral with certainty at that time. Subsequent mineralogical investigations clearly showed that the silt is dominated by kaolinite.

The second example is that of an old red soil on serpentine from Cyclope Mountains, West Irian. The size distribution curve of this soil does not show the colloidal clay maximum, as, for example, does the oxic soil of Priangan, West Java (see histogram of soil No. 2, fig. 1.50). In this sample it lies in the region of the silt fractions between 50 and 5μ. Wentholt (in Van Baren, 1953), who established this fact, reports that in this very old and senile soil, the iron of the colloidal clay fractions had recrystallized into coarser crystals of hematite or goethite. These are the principal components of the sand and silt fractions. The same phenomenon has been described from Amberbaken, West Irian. The occurrence of such a quantity of iron oxide minerals has not been reported up to now from any other part of Indonesia, though Hamilton (1948) reports

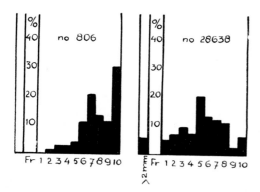

No. 806: Yellow weathered pumice ash; Gunung Salak, West Java
No. 28638: Red, old soil on serpentine rock; Cyclope Mountains, West Irian
FIG. I. 51. *Divergent texture of Oxisols of Indonesia*

162

that the presence of hematite could be established by X-ray analysis in old soils on peridotite of Central Sulawesi and on granite in South-East Kalimantan.

A similar phenomenon was described in the case of Oxisols from Mauritius by Craig and Halais (1934). They found that the amount of colloidal clay decreased from 73 to 45 % when passing from the dry to the wet districts. They explained this observation by the fact that the amount of sand, simultaneously increasing, is not composed of un-weathered fragments, but of concretions which represent a more advanced stage in the decomposition of the original material than does the mere formation of the clay fraction.

3.4.3. VERTISOLS

This soil type shows that the 10th fraction (< 0.5µ) is always less pronounced than the 9th (2–0.5µ), this being a characteristic feature of the grain size distribution. It is distinctly different from the curve of Oxisols, even in the final stage of weathering. The histograms of such soils have a typical convex development.

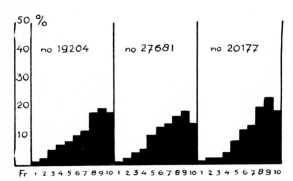

No. 19204: Black vertisol on calcareous marl; Gunung Kidul, Jogjakarta, Java
No. 27681: Yellow to brown vertisol on loamy marl; Nanggulan, Java
No. 20177: Brownish-black vertisol on marl; Wonosari, Jogjakarta, Java

FIG. 1.52. *Characteristic textures of vertisols of Indonesia*

Three graphs taken from the report of Te Riele (1932), which demonstrate this feature most clearly (fig. 1.52) are reproduced.

As with the Oxisols, the examples given here are of autochthonous residuary soils. As soon as contamination takes place – for example, with volcanic ash or oxic material

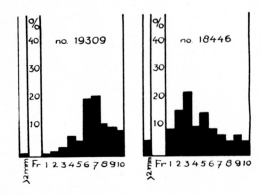

No. 19309: Black vertisol mixed with volcanic silt; Kalimenur, Jogjakarta, Java
No. 18446: Black vertisol, mixed with volcanic sand; Ibid.

FIG. 1.53. *Texture of vertisols contaminated with volcanic silt and sand, respectively*

– the soil is disturbed, and the shape of the histogram reflects the addition of foreign material. Two examples of black vertisols mixed with volcanic silt and volcanic sand elucidate this point (fig. 1.53).

3.4.4. SEDIMENTARY SOILS

The change in the histogram of residual soils which are subsequently transported will not be discussed here as it will be obvious that any amount of complications arise which do not permit a reliable interpretation of the curve without a profound knowledge of the history of the sediment based on extensive field experience. One example will be given of a river clay on the isle of Bangka. It may be expected that on this island, which is mainly built up on the well-known tin-bearing granitic basement rock, any alluvial deposit will be rich in quartz. This is the case with the alluvial clay, as given in the first histogram. A weathered river clay of Billiton Isle, derived from the same

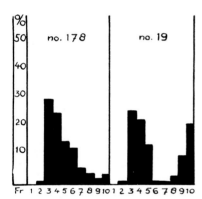

No. 178: River deposit; Banka
No. 19: Weathered river deposit; Billiton

FIG. 1.54. *Textural development by weathering of quartz-bearing parent material*

granitic parent material, was also analysed. The diagrams of the two, quoted from Mohr (1911), clearly show that clay formation took place at the expense of the silt fraction, as seen in the second diagram of fig. 1.54. But the sand fraction only decreased slightly, being mainly composed of quartz. The international scale which only distinguishes the following fractions:

Coarse sand – 2.0–0.2 mm
Fine sand   – 0.2–0.02 mm
Silt   – 0.02–0.002 mm
Clay   – < 0.002 mm

does not sufficiently bring to light those details which are invaluable in diagnosing soil and soil forming processes. This may be demonstrated by a few examples of soils which have the same content of the fraction $< 2\mu$, but appear to be quite different. This is proved if this fraction is subdivided into a 9th fraction $(2-\frac{1}{2}\mu)$, and 10th fraction $(< \frac{1}{2}\mu)$.

TABLE I.69. *Examples of soils having the same percentage of* $< 2\mu$ *fraction, but showing different percentages of subfractions* (after Mohr, 1911)

Soil No.	Type and locality	$< 2\mu$ in %	$2\text{--}0.5\mu$ in %	$< 0.5\mu$ in %
4	Oxisol, Priangan, Java	55	14	41
586	Vertisol, Madiun, Java	53	30	23
451	Oxisol, Rembang, Java	49	12	37
415	Vertisol, Semarang, Java	50	30	20
249	Oxisol, Bontaëng, Sulawesi	37	11	26
429	Vertisol, Semarang, Java	37	22	15

LITERATURE CITED

Aoki, M. Komai, V. and Yamaguchi, M. 1969 Studies on a red-coloured soil derived from Basaltic Andesite of Shibayama. *Soil Sci. and Plant Nutr.*, 15: 21–27.

Aubert, G. et al. 1967 Classification des Sols. *Travaux Comm. Péd. Cart. Sols E.N.S.A. de Grignon.*

Basu, J. K. and Sirur, S. S. 1938 Soils of the Deccan Canals. I. Genetic soil survey and soil classification: Nira Right Bank and Pravara Canals. *Ind. J. agric. Sci.*, 8 : 637–697.

Bates, T. F. 1962 Halloysite and gibbsite formation in Hawaii. *Clays and clay minerals.* *Pergamon Press, N.Y.*, pp. 315–328.

—, Hildebrand, F. A. and Swineforc, A. 1950 Morphology and Structure of Endellite and Halloysite. *Am. Mineralogist*, 35: 463–484.

Besaire, H. 1937 Les sols de Madagascar. *Soil Res.*, 5: 200–221.

Beutelspacher, H. and Van der Marel, H. W. 1968 Atlas of electron microscopy of clay minerals and their admixtures, pp. 333.

Birrell, K. S. and Fieldes, M. 1952 Allophane in volcanic ash soils. *J. Soil Sci.*, 3: 156–166.

Blackie, W. J. 1949 Soils of Fiji. *Comm. Bur. Soil. Sci. Techn. Commun.*, 46: 54–58.

Boulvert, Y. 1968 Quelques aspects de l'influence de la topographie et du matériel originel sur la répartition des sols ferrallitiques, sols ferrugineux tropicaux et vertisols dans la région de Bossangoa ou Nord-Ouest de la République Centrafricaine. *Cahiers Orstom, série Pédologie*, vol. 6, 3–4: 259–275.

Burri, C. 1964 Petrochemical calculations based on equivalents (Methods of Paul Niggli). *Israel Program for Scientific Translations, Jerusalem.*

Castagnol, E. M. 1952 Contribution à l'étude des terres rouges basaltiques et dacitiques des Hauts-Plateaux du Sud de l'Indochine. *Arch. Rech. Agron. Cambodge, Laos, Vietnam.* No. 12: pp. 123.

Chang, S. N. 1961 Clay minerals of some representative paddy soils of China. *Acta Ped. Sin.*, 9: 152.

— 1963 Clay minerals of tropical soils of Mainan Island. *Acta Ped. Sin.*, 11 : 52.

— and Lee, C. K. 1958 Composition of clay minerals in the main soil types of Southern China. *Acta Ped. Sin.*, 6 : 191–192.

Craig, N. and Halais, P. 1934 The influence of maturity and rainfall on the properties of lateritic soils in Mauritius. *Emp. J. Expt. Agric.*, 2: 349–356.

Cross, C. H. W., Iddings, J. P., Pirsson, L. V., and Washington, H. S. 1902 A quantitative chemico-mineralogical classification and nomenclature of igneous rocks. *J. Geol.*, 10: 555–690.

DAS, D. K. and DAS, S. C. 1966 Mineralogy of Clays from some Black, Brown and Red Soils of Mysore. *J. Ind. Soc. Soil Sci.*, 14, no. 1 : 43–50.

DELVIGNE, J. 1959 La minéralogie des sols congolais en relation avec le soubassement géologique. *3me Conf. Interafr. des Sols, Publ. no. 50 C.C.T.A.*, 1 : 131–138.

DEMUMBRUM, L. E. 1962 Mineralogy of a soil formed from Eocene Sandstone. *Soil Science*, 95: 423–5.

D'HOORE, J. L. 1964 Soil Map of Africa. Explanatory Monograph. *Comm. Techn. Coop. Afr.* No. 93, pp. 205.

EDELMAN, C. H. 1946 Les principaux sols de Java. *Rec. Bot. Appl.*, 26: 505–511.

GRANGE, L. L. 1949 Soils of some South Pacific Islands. *Comm. Bur. Soil Sci. Techn. Comm.*, 46: 45–48.

GRIM, R. E. 1968 Clay Mineralogy. 2nd ed. *McGraw-Hill N.Y.* pp. 598.

HAMDI, H. 1959 Alterations in the clay fraction of Egyptian soils. *Zeitschr. Pflanz. Düng. Bod.*, 84: 204–211.

HAMILTON, R. 1948 Standaard dehydratatie curven en enkele toepassingen. *Landbouw (Buitenzorg)*, 20: 275–282.

HARDON, H. J. and FAVEJEE, J. CH. L. 1939 Qualitative analysis of the clay fraction of the principle soil types of Java. *Meded. Landbouwhogesch. Wageningen*, 43 : 55–59.

HARDY, F. and CROUCHER, H. H. 1933 Studies in West Indian soils. VI. Some soil types of Jamaica. *Imp. Coll. Trop. Agric. (Trin.)*, pp. 44.

—, MC DONALD, J. A. and RODRIGUEZ, G. 1932 Studies in West Indian soils. IV. The cacao soils of Grenada. *Suppl. Trop. Agric. (Trin.)*, pp. 28.

HARMSE, H. J. VON M. 1967 Soil Genesis in the Highveld Region, South Africa. *Thesis Utrecht*, pp. 201.

HARRISON, J. B. 1934 The Katamorphism of igneous rocks under humid tropical conditions. *Imp. Bur. Soil Sci. (Harpenden)*, pp. 79.

HENDRICKS, D. M., WHITTING, L. D. and JACKSON, M. K. 1967 Clay mineralogy of andesite saprolite. Clays and clay minerals. *Proc. 15th Conf. Pittsburgh, Penn. Pergamon Press, 1967.* 395–407.

HERBILLON, A. J., PÉCROT, A. et VIELVOYE, L. 1966 Aperçu sur la minéralogie des fractions fines de quelques grands groupes de sol du Vietnam. *Pédologie*, 14: 5–16.

HERVIEU, J. 1968 Contribution à l'étude de l'alluvionnement en milieu tropical. *Mém. Orstom (Paris)*, No. 24: pp. 463.

HOLMES, A. 1930 Petrographic methods and calculations. 2nd Ed. *London*.

HSEUNG, Y. and HSU, C. C. 1964 Frequency distribution of clay minerals in the soils of China. *Acta Ped. Sin.*, 12: 266–274.

HUMBERT, R. P. 1948 The genesis of laterite. *Soil Sci.*, 65: 281–290.

IDENBURG, A. G. A. 1937 Systematische grondkaarteering van Zuid-Sumatra. *Thesis Wageningen*, pp. 168.

IMBRIE, J. and POLDERVAART, A. 1959 Mineral compositions calculated from chemical analyses of sedimentary rocks. *J. Sed. Petrol.*, 29: 588–595.

JACKSON, M. L. 1965 Free oxides and amorphous alumino-silicate. *Methods of analysis. Part I. Agron. Mono.*, 9: 578–603.

JOACHIM, A. W. R. 1935 Studies on Ceylon soils. II. General characteristics of Ceylon Soils, some typical soil groups of the island, and a tentative scheme of classification. *Trop. Agricst.*, 84: 254–274.

KANNO, I. 1962 Genesis and classification of Humic, Allophane Soil in Japan. *Trans. Joint*

166

Mtg. Comm. IV and V. Int. Soc. Soil Sci., New Zealand, 422–427.

KENCHANNA GOWDA, S. K., KRISHNA MURTI, G. S. R. and DEB, A. R. 1966 Clay mineralogy of red and black complex soils of Coimbatore and Medak. *Indian J. agric. Sci.*, 36 : 29–34.

LACROIX, A. 1923 Minéralogie de Madagascar. Vol. III: 91–144. *Paris*.

LOVERING, J. S. 1941 The origin of the tungsten ores of Boulder County, Colo. *Econ. Geol.*, 36: 227–279.

MARBUT, C. F. 1934 The work of Commission V of the International Society of Soil Science. Soil Res., 4: 139–147.

MILNE, G. 1947 A soil reconnaissance journey through parts of Tanganyika Territory, Dec. 1935–Febr. 1936. *J. Ecol.*, 35: 192–265.

MOHR, E. C. J. 1911 Ergebnisse mechanischer Analysen tropischer Böden. *Bull. Départ. Agric. Indes Néer.*, No. 47: pp. 73.

— 1944 Soils of equatorial regions. *Ann. Arbor*.

MUCKENHIRN, R. J., WHITESIDE, P. et al. 1949 Soil classification and the genetic factors of soil formation. *Soil Sci.*, 67: 93–105.

MUIR, A., ANDERSON, B. and STEPHEN, I. 1957 Characteristics of some Tanganyika soils. *J. Soil Sci.*, vol. 8, no. 1, 1–18.

MUKERJI, B. K. and AGARWAL, R. R. 1943 Studies on Bundelkand soils. I. The genetic types. *Indian J. agric. Sci.* 13 : 587–597.

NICHOLLS, G. D. 1962 A scheme for recalculating the chemical analyses of argillaceous rocks for comparative purposes. *Am. Min.*, 47: 34–46.

NIGGLI, P. 1936. Über Molekularnormen zur Gesteinberechnung. *Schweiz. Min. Petr. Mitt.*, 16: 295–317.

NIKIFOROFF, C. C. 1935 Weathering and soil formation. *Trans. 3rd Int. Congr. Soil Sci., I:* 324–326.

REPORT GEOLOGICAL SURVEY FIJI 1952 In: *Colonial Geology and Mineral Resources*, 3, No. 3, 1953, p. 265.

RODE, A. A. 1962 Soil Science. *Translated from Russian. Israel Progr. Sci. Transl. Jerusalem:* pp. 517.

SATYANARAYANA, K. V. S. and THOMAS, P. K. 1962 Studies on laterites and associated soils. II. Chemical composition of laterite profiles. *J. Ind. Soc. Soil Sci.*, 10: 211–222.

SCHAUFELBERGER, P. 1955 Tonbildung in tropischen Böden. *Schweiz. Min. u. Petr. Mitt.*, 35: 168–184.

SCHMID, M., DE LA SOUCHÈRE, P. and GODARD, D. 1951 Les sols et la végétation au Darlac et sur la plateau des Trois-Frontières. *Arch. Rech. Agron. Cambodge, Laos, Vietnam*, No. 18: pp. 107.

SIEFERMANN, G. 1959. Premières déterminations des minéraux argileux des sols du Cameroun. *3me Conf. Interafr. des Sols, Public. no. 50, C.C.T.A.*, 1: 139–150.

SINHA, M. K. and MANDAL, S. C. 1963 A mineralogical study of some acid red loam soils of Chotanagpur. *J. Indian Soc. Soil Sci.*, 11: 329–33.

SUDO, T., TAKAHASHI, H. 1956 Shapes of halloysite particles in Japanese clay. *Clays and clay minerals, Nat. Acad. Sci., Natl. Res. Council Publi.*, 456: 67–79.

TALIBUDEEN, O. 1952 The technique of differential thermal analysis (D.T.A.), *J. Soil Sci.*, 3: 251–260.

TAMURA, T. and JACKSON, M. L. 1953 Structure and energy relationships in formation of iron and aluminium oxides, hydroxides and silicates. *Science*, 117: 381–383.

TAN, K. H. and VAN SCHUYLENBORGH, J. 1959 On the classification and genesis of soils, derived from andesitic volcanic material under a monsoon climate. *Neth. J. agric. Sci.*, 7: 1–21.

TE RIELE, H. 1932 Tekst behorende bij de grondkaart van het Gouvernement Jogjakarta. *Non-published report Arch. Inst. Soil Res. Buitenzorg.*

THERON, J. J. and VAN NIEKERK, P. le R. 1934 The nature and origin of black turf soils. *S. Afr. J. Sci.*, 31 : 320–246.

TURNER, F. J. and VERHOOGEN, J. 1960 Igneous and metamorphic petrology. *2nd. ed. McGraw-Hill, New York*, pp. 694.

TURTON, A. G., MARSH, N. L., MC KENZIE, R. M. et al. 1962 The chemistry and mineralogy of lateritic soils in the south-west of Western Australia. *CSIRO Soil Publ. 20*, pp. 40

VAN BAREN, F. A. 1941 De mineralogische achtergrond van de bodemvruchtbaarheid in Nederlandsch-Indië. *Landbouw* (Buitenzorg), 17: 520–541.

VAN BAREN, F. A. 1953 The soils of New Guinea. In: Nieuw Guinea ed. W. C. Klein et al. Vol. II: 67–105. *The Hague.*

VAN DER PLAS, L. and VAN SCHUYLENBORGH, J. 1970 Petrochemical calculations applied to soils (with special reference to soil formation). *Geoderma*, 4: 357–385.

VAN SCHUYLENBORGH, J. 1958 On the genesis and classification of soils, derived from andesitic tuffs under humid tropical conditions. *Neth. J. Agric. Sci.*, 6: 99–123.

VINE, H. 1949 Nigerian soils in relation to parent materials. *Comm. Bur. Soil Sci. Techn Commun.*, 46: 22–29.

WADA, K. 1963 Quantitative determination of kaolinite and halloysite by NH_4Cl retention measurement. *Am. Mineral*, 48: 1287–1300.

— 1967 A structural scheme of soil allophane. *Am. Min.*, 52 : 690–708.

CHAPTER 4

FACTORS GOVERNING
THE FORMATION AND DECOMPOSITION
OF ORGANIC MATTER

4.1. GENERAL CONSIDERATIONS

It is not the intention to give a complete outline of the formation and decomposition processes of soil organic matter. For this reference is made to the textbooks of Waksman (1938), Russell and Russell (1950), and more specifically to those of Scheffer and Ulrich (1960) and of Kononova (1966). Only the processes of production of organic material and the rate and extent of the alteration processes of fresh organic material under tropical conditions will be briefly discussed.

As the ultimate development of a mature soil is in many cases completed in geological or at least pre-historic times, the conception of weathering can be based on the assumption that the earth was almost entirely covered with vegetation until man arrived to disturb the biological equilibrium, leaving a trail of devastation and ruin in his wake.

Vegetation provides a very important protective cover for the earth and as such it exerts a favourable influence on the water conditions as its penetrating root system stimulates rock decomposition at greater depth. It is also the source of organic matter, the dominant factor in soil formation.

Rain water striking the bare rock surface, contains only a small percentage of oxygen and carbonic acid. But as soon as organic life begins to function the weathering potency of the soil water increases because then decomposition of the organic matter produced also begins. Owing to destruction, various organic materials are supplied to the weathering liquid, carbonic acid being the most important, although several others seem to play a definite part (see p. 175). A simple example may show how the composition of the soil liquid is changed as compared with rain water, especially with regard to carbonic acid. For comparison take a soil liquid of spring and seepage water which does not naturally contain CO_2, but to which CO_2 is added by the organic life cycle which includes birth as well as decay.

	Rain water	Spring water	Seepage water
HCO_3^- (mg/l)	0.9	9	76

To these figures, quoted from Harrison (1934), may be added the data of 20 analyses of spring water given by Mohr (1938, 1944):

	Free CO_2	HCO_3^-	Total CO_2
Minium	9	15	40 mg/l
Maximum	80	128	126 ,,
Average of 20 samples	28	78	84 ,,

All these figures point to a tremendous increase in CO_2 content which is largely to be attributed to an organic source. The organic matter oxidizable by $KMnO_4$, is present in these spring waters at about 1 mg/l, the limits being 0.25 and 1.3 mg/l. This demonstrates that organic matter itself seems only of very subordinate importance. However, as will be shown in Part III, Chapter 2, such low contents may be of the greatest importance in creating low partial oxygen pressures in closed systems.

It will be appreciated that the role played by the organic matter in weathering and soil formation – especially as far as the function of supplying carbonic acid is concerned – is determined to a very large extent by the speed with which its decay and mineralization take place as opposed to accumulation.

Organic matter may be classified in two groups: a dead and a living substance. The former includes all parts of the vegetation which fall upon the soil after terminating their bio-cyclus and which, after decay, are absorbed by the soil in one way or another. Leaves, fruits, branches, dead trunks and roots fall into the category. These include: a. substances soluble in water, such as sugars, salts, etc., which are directly consumed by living soil flora and fauna; b. substances such as tannins and other similar compounds; c. celluloses and pentosans of the cell wall; d. more resistant substances, such as lignine and cutine; e. the nitrogen-containing proteins. Altogether they form the raw material subject to decomposition, and are a source of energy to the living organisms of the soil.

Living substances, micro-flora and fauna, consist of numerous sorts of organisms which may be classified in a small number of main groups: a. bacteria, the name used in a general sense; b. actinomycetes; c. fungi; d. algae; e. protozoa. Also included are other organisms belonging to the invertebrate fauna (see Russell and Russell, 1950). They all live on the waste products of the macro-flora and/or upon each other. This biological dynamism invariably leads to the production, provided oxygen is available, of carbonic acid – an essential constituent of spring and soil water.

When the production of plant waste ceases, soil organisms consume the dead organic matter stored within the soil before finally consuming each other. Organic matter is then fully mineralized. This final stage is seldom reached in temperate regions. In tropical areas, on the other hand, conditions may lead to a very close approach to complete mineralization.

Alternatively, if the supply of plant waste on and in the soil is such that soil organisms cannot convert it into mineralized compounds, then organic matter will accumulate. A prolonged building up of humus may eventually result in the formation of peat.

This phenomenon is not only attributable to too great a supply of plant waste but also to conditions which disturb the soil organisms in their activities. This may have different causes.

It should be borne in mind that with regard to temperature, moisture and oxygen supply, all living organisms are confined within certain limits which vary from group to group. One can imagine that what might be an impediment or poison to the soil-flora, might not exert a similar effect on the macro-flora. Such a condition would lead to the indefinite accumulation of plant remains. On the other hand, if mineralization proceeds at the same rate as humification, no accumulation will take place. This does not mean that no organic matter is present in the upper layers of the soil. Of course, there are always the soil-flora as the consumer, and the plant residue in different stages of decomposition as the source of food for the soil organisms. If the activity of the latter is very intensive, compared with the accumulation of plant material, the soil layer containing humus will only be very thin. If the reverse is the case, then a thick humus layer will form.

This concentration of decomposable and consumable humus will result in an increase in the number of consumer organisms. When supply and decomposition are at equilibrium, the soil water will contain predominantly carbonic acid. In the extreme case of peat formation, the water flowing off will also contain large amounts of organic substances, giving the water a dark colour. In Brazil and other South American countries, for example, rivers with dark coloured water are called 'Rio Negro', in Indonesia such water is called 'aer hitam'.

The subject of the formation of organic matter, and that of humification and mineralization, warrants further consideration.

4.2. THE FORMATION OF ORGANIC MATERIAL

The amount of plant remains from over-head vegetation depends, naturally, upon the intensity of the vegetation depositing its residues on the ground. The density and luxuriance of the foliage is closely bound up with direct and indirect radiation from the sun, for there can be no assimilation of carbon dioxide from the air without light. Over the whole year, irradiation is the least at the poles and the greatest at the equator, but the relation between irradiation and latitude is not such that it decreases proportionally to the increase in latitude. This will be evident from the following considerations.

The quantity of energy radiated by the sun to the earth, expressed in calories per square cm and per minute, is called the solar constant. This amounts to about 2 cal cm^{-2} $min.^{-1}$ when striking the surface perpendicularly (Knoch, 1929; Schubert, 1930). Not all this energy reaches the surface of the earth, as part of it is absorbed directly by the atmosphere. In the higher layers of the air (at an altitude of about 50 km), the ozone eliminates (a greater part of) the ultra-violet rays with a wavelength $< 0.3\mu$ (Vrij, 1932). This represents only a very small part of the total radiant energy. The absorption of the rays of the remaining spectrum is much greater further down in the atmosphere. Boerema (1919) records that with the sun at 60° elevation, the total radiation reaching the earth in Java amounts to:

On the Gunung Smeru   3670 m elevation 1.7 cal cm^{-2} min.$^{-1}$
On the Gunung Pangeranggo 3020 m ,, 1.65   ,,
At Tjisurupan   1200 m ,, 1.45   ,,
At Djakarta   10 m   ,, 1.25   ,,

The Djakarta figure falls to 1.13 cal cm^{-2}min.$^{-1}$ in August and December, rising to about 1.30 cal cm^{-2} min.$^{-1}$ from December to May. This shows already that the condition of the atmosphere exerts a distinct influence: in the dry, east monsoon for example, small particles of dust, forming a dry haze, have a scattering effect; rain subsequently purifies the air so that a large number of rain showers during the west monsoon promotes strong radiation in the hours of sunshine between. On mountain tops high radiant energy is apparent because of the presence of only a very small quantity of dust in the air. On the other hand, the water vapour too has an absorbing effect. Consequently in the wet monsoon the radiant energy is less powerful than that measured in the dry monsoon.

In addition to the absorption effect, the dispersion of rays in the atmosphere must be considered. This scattering causes the direct rays to be lost. Since diffusion takes place in all directions, the part directed to the earth will exert its influence as diffused light radiated from the sky.

Absorption and scattering are not equally strong for all the various rays; consequently, when passing the atmosphere the quality of the radiation will be modified. Absorption is relatively greater in the case of rays having a greater wavelength (red and infra-red) than it is with those with shorter wavelength (violet and ultra-violet). It is just the reverse with the scattering as red rays are dispersed less than their violet counterparts. The rising and setting sun assumes its red colour because of the greater distance which the rays have to travel through the lowest layers of the atmosphere. Scattered, diffused radiation (sky light) is blue to violet.

The higher one goes in the atmosphere, the less scattering and sky radiation there is. Thus, in Indonesia it has been found that sky radiation was greatest in Djakarta (10 meters above sea level), less in Tjibodas (1450 meters), and still less at the top of the Pangeranggo (3020 meters). At each of these places, sky radiation was lowest when the sun was at its highest. When the sun was lower, sky radiation was as great as the direct radiation from the sun (Vrij, 1932).

Following absorption, the atmosphere retains, in the form of heat, part of the energy radiated from the sun. In turn, this heat is reradiated in the form of dark heat rays so that each air particle becomes in point of fact a separate centre of radiation. This results in part of the dark heat radiation being lost in space, while part of it reaches the earth. This is known as counter-radiation which increases as the latitude increases, and is of great importance to the temperature of the earth.

The foregoing considerations make it clear that a whole complex of radiation phenomena is active and all components of that complex are important as far as vegetation is concerned.

Although very little is known about the influence of radiation on plant production in the tropics this is related though not necessarily proportional to the intensity of the radiation and its duration. This intensity varies each moment with the angular change in the sun's direct rays, and with the conditions of the atmosphere, e.g. whether it is cloudy or not, etc. The total production of vegetative matter per day, per year, or per vegetation period, is the result of the sum of these moments and their influence during the period in question.

Leaving cloudiness aside for the moment, and expressing the various forms of radiation in terms of heat, the following table will provide a picture of the total energy radiated to the earth by the sun, calculated in daily averages (Knoch, 1929).

TABLE I.70. *Radiant energies in calories recieved at different latitudes* (after Knoch, 1929)

	90°	80°	70°	60°	50°	40°	30°	20°	10°	0°
Annual average per day	366	378	417	500	601	694	773	830	867	880
Summer maximum per day	1103	1086	1038	1002	1015	1015	998	958	901	809
Winter maximum per day	0	0	0	51	181	326	477	627	745	863

It appears from this table that at all latitudes days occur with a higher daily radiation than at the equator. Due to absorption scattering, reverse radiation and cloudiness it is not known precisely which part of the total radiation actually does reach the earth's surface. It would be very useful indeed if the influence of all these factors on radiation of different wave lengths could be calculated and determined in figures. Such figures are not available, or at least only in part, as they are extremely difficult to determine and one has to be content with rough estimates. Knoch made the following approximations: Absorption in the atmosphere may be considered to be 20% of the radiation, about 36% is scattered, 18% being directed upwards and lost, while 18% remains useful as diffuse radiation. These percentages apply to a clear sky. If the cloud cover averages 50% half of the remaining 44% is lost again in the outer spaces as a result of radiation from the upper surface of the clouds. The earth receives only 22 + 18 = 40% of the energy radiated by the sun. In this case, we must assume that in spite of the cloudiness all of the 18% diffuse radiation will be available. This is not entirely correct. If this fact is omitted from our calculations, the earth would then receive the following amounts of energy by direct and indirect radiation (this still excludes dark counter radiation):

TABLE I.71. *Sun radiation received by the earth*

With unclouded sky	62% of the sun energy is directed to the earth	
,, 80% sunshine	53%	do do
,, 60% ,,	44.5%	do do
,, 50% ,,	40%	do do
,, 40% ,,	35.5%	do do
,, 30% ,,	31%	do do
,, 20% ,,	27%	do do

The data of Sv. Arrhenius quoted by Lundegard (1930), in table 1.72, leads to the conclusion that areas around the tropics of Cancer and Capricorn receive considerably more radiant energy than those near the equator.

In Indonesia many observations have been made with regard to the percentage of sunshine. They show that with wide variations, the average is somewhere about 50%. In some localities, like Pasuruan and Asembagus in Java, and Kupang in Timor, this figure approaches 80%, whereas in other places like Ngadiwono, Java, it falls to less than 30%. Djakarta receives 53% of the possible maximum of 4,400 hours of sunshine (Braak, 1928).

TABLE 1.72. *Direct and indirect radiation received at different northern latitudes* (after Lundegardh, 1930)

	$60°$	$40°$	$20°$	$0°$
Average percentages of sunshine	39%	51%	60%	42%
Share received by earth (see table 1.71)	35%	40.5%	44.5%	36.5%
Resulting calories cm^{-2} day^{-1} received (see table 1.70)	175	281	370	321

It is an interesting fact that from the two localities in Indonesia, which are very close to Pasuruan with 80% sunshine receives 53%, and Ngadiwono only 30 km away, with 30% sunshine receives 31% (see table 1.71). It will be obvious that when all other conditions are equal, this is bound to affect assimilation and vegetative production. In general, little has been observed of this effect on the development of plant growth, due to the fact that differences in influence are obscured by other factors. The principal factor counteracting assimilation and vegetative production is undoubtedly that a high amount of radiant energy is accompanied by drought, resulting in a shortage of water which offsets the advantages of increased radiation, arrests growth, and even leads to the shedding of leaves as e.g. in teak forests. Of course, assimilation then ceases completely. In cases where water is supplied by artificial means (i.e. irrigation), greater assimilation results in a greater vegetative production.

Next to radiation, the influence of temperature on assimilation must be taken into consideration. As yet, no conclusive experiments have been carried out on this. It is very difficult to ascertain the minimum, maximum, and optimum temperatures, not only for assimilation, but also for respiration, metabolic processes (which counteract one another in a certain sense), and for growth. Still, two general rules seem applicable. The optimum temperature for assimilation, compared with that for respiration, is rather low. It seldom reaches $30°$ C and only then in cases where the CO_2 content in the air is high. It usually lies between 20 and $25°$ C. For respiration which results in the break-down of carbohydrates into CO_2 and H_2O, the optimum temperature may be as high as $50°$ C.

Under tropical conditions this means that from the optimum temperature for assimilation upwards, the materials formed are consumed by respiration at an ever-increasing rate, theoretically to a point where all carbohydrate reserves are exhausted.

When this stage is reached, the plant will be unable to grow any further and will finally be ruined by auto-consumption, even when the soil and water conditions are optimum. The plant possesses numerous possibilities for adaptation which make it possible for the amount of organic material produced by assimilation to exceed the quantity consumed in respiration, at least by a narrow margin. On the other hand, vegetative production at higher latitudes, e.g. between 30 and 50° N and S, with average temperatures varying between 17 and 23° C, may be as prolific as it is at the equator. Similar conditions also exist in the tropics at elevations of 1,000 metres. It is not at all surprising that at similar elevations in the mountains of tropical regions, tropical rain forests occur which are just as dense as those met with at sea level.

The actual difference between vegetative production in the tropics and that occurring in more temperate climates, is not due to the difference in the maximum radiation intensity, but to the actual duration of that radiation. This period lasts 12 months in the tropics as compared, for instance, with only 4 months in the Netherlands. An immediate consequence of this fact is that leaf shedding occurs in tropical rainforest continually over the whole year, whereas in temperate climates shedding occurs only once a year.

Experimental determinations or approximate calculations with regard to the total production of organic material per hectare in the tropics have seldom been made. For this reason Vageler (1930) very cautiously estimates the yearly production of 'fresh organic matter' in the primeval forest as ranging from 100 to 200 tons/hectare. In the case of monsoon forests and savannahs the estimates are 50 and 30 tons respectively. Assuming a moisture content of 70% as an average for the different vegetation, and assuming a leaf renewal once a year, this means that a tropical rainforest produces, according to Vageler, 30–60 tons of dry matter per hectare per year, a monsoon forest 17 tons and savannah vegetation 10 tons hectare^{-1} year^{-1}. These figures seem high, as Coster (1937) estimates the organic matter production of a mountainous rainforest to be 21 tons ha^{-1} year^{-1}, corresponding with a dry matter production of 6.3 tons ha^{-1} year^{-1}, in contrast to 1–4 tons ha^{-1} year^{-1} for a beechforest in Europe. Jenny et al. (1949) estimate the dry matter production of broad-leaved rainforests in Columbia to be 9–12 tons ha^{-1} year^{-1} against 0.9–3.3 tons ha^{-1} year^{-1} of virgin Sierran forests of California. D'Hoore (1953) reports that dense equatorial forest in the Congo produced 12 tons of dry litter per hectare per annum. Nye (1961) gives a value of 22 tons ha^{-1} year^{-1} for a tropical rainforest. It seems that the figures suggested by Vageler are too high; an average production of 6–15 tons ha^{-1} year^{-1} of dry litter seems a fairly reliable value for the production of a tropical rainforest. This conclusion is supported by Klinge (1968), who determined the annual production of an Amazonian terra firme forest to be 7.4 tons ha^{-1}.

4.3. THE MINERALIZATION AND HUMIFICATION OF ORGANIC MATTER

The decay of plant residue has to be studied from at least two angles. This is especially valuable as it can be expected that the rate of decomposition of organic matter in the tropics is such that only a very low content of humus results, even in primeval forests.

This decomposition does not take place if there is an excess of water, shortage of oxygen, etc., leading to the accumulation of humus when instead, decomposition might normally have occurred.

The first aspect is the type of organisms that play a part in breaking down or 'mineralizing' humus. The second point is the kind of compounds formed and whether they have any practical bearing on soil-forming processes. Organic acids have been found which are influential here. Of the simpler ones, lactic acid (Freise, 1934; Sapper, 1935) seems to be an aggressive decomposition product of lignin. Duff and Webley (1959) found 2-ketogluconic acid as a product of baterial activity. Heath and King (1964) found gallic and protocatechuic acid to be formed during the decomposition of deciduous forest litter. Whitehead (1964) and Hennequin and Juste (1967) found p-hydroxy-benzoic acid, vanillic acid, p-coumaric acid and ferulic acid in the soil, whilst Wang et al. (1967) found, apart from these acids, also syringic acid. Simple free amino-acids have been found occasionally (Aseyeva and Valikzhanina, 1966) such as valine, glutamic acid, leucine, and others. More frequently they are combined into more complex substances and the hydrolysates of temperate and subtropical soils reveal a considerable number of amino-acids, such as α-alanine, glycine, threonine, serine, glutamic acid, aspartic acid, leucine, phenylalanine, tyrosine, cystine, lysine, arginine, ornithine, histidine, and others (Sowden, 1966; Wang et al., 1967). All these acids may have a specific effect on weathering and soil formation, as indicated by Van Schuylenborgh and Bruggenwert (1965) and Van Schuylenborgh (1966). Some of the possible activities of these acids will be discussed in the Chapters 2 of Part II and III. For a detailed discussion of the decomposition process the reader should refer to the textbooks mentioned at the beginning of this chapter. A very brief outline of the process follows.

Plant constituents supplied to the soil by the offal of natural vegetation are a source of food for soil organisms as well as for the soil organic matter. Next to the salts of the cations NH_4, K, Na, Ca and Mg, and the anions SO_4, Cl, NO_3 and $(COO)_2$, proteins, sugars, starch, cellulose and lignins are the most important organic compounds. The chemistry of these substances need not be discussed, but it will be clear that the liability to decompose and the solubility of the various products will differ considerably. In the carbohydrate group a distinction must be made between the materials easily soluble in water or dilute acid, and those soluble in dilute alkali. The first includes the sugars, amino-acids, the salts of the various elements mentioned above, while the second comprises the hemi-celluloses. The tannin substances are soluble; their break-down seems difficult, although the presence of gallic acid in the soils (Heath and King, 1964) shows that they are decomposed. Lignin, resins, and waxes, etc. are still more resistant, the first being the least resistant as it is the source of phenolic acids present in the soil (Whitehead, 1964; Hennequin and Juste, 1967; Wang et al., 1967). Research on the decomposition of cereal straws has shown that in the initial stages the hemi-cellulose encrusting the cellulose fibers is subject to severe attacks, mainly by fungi. Considerable heat and CO_2 are produced and a very great loss of cellulose occurs, which accounts for the greater part of the loss of organic matter (Russell and Russell, 1950).

Discussing the different groups of micro-organisms which compose the soil population, Robinson (1951) states that the following are the most important:

Micro-fauna:
I. Protozoa
II. Nematodes
III. Worms, insects, etc.

Micro-flora:
I. Algae and Diatoms
II. Fungi, including Actinomycetes
III. Bacteria.
    A. Autotrophic, deriving their energy from the oxidation of simple inorganic compounds and their carbon from CO_2.
       They include:
       i. Nitrifying bacteria
       ii. Sulphofying bacteria
       iii. Iron bacteria
    B. Heterotrophic, deriving their carbon from complex organic compounds.
       They include:
       i. Nitrogen fixing bacteria
         a. Symbiotic, e.g., Bacterium radicicola
         b. Non-symbiotic:
           1. Aerobic, e.g., Azotobacter
           2. Anaerobic, e.g., Clostridium
       ii. Bacteria concerned with the process of ammonification
       iii. Cellulose bacteria and other bacteria decomposing fibrous materials

In this connection it is worth-while to note that these organisms are the first to invade the newly-formed substratum which is still to be weathered, as for instance volcanic ash. Galvez et al. (1939) gave very interesting figures relating to this phenomenon. They determined the content of bacteria and moulds in a 2-weeks old ash from the Mayon Volcano in the Philippines.

TABLE I.73. *Number of organisms in certain 2-weeks old volcanic ashes, ejected by Mayon volcano* (after Galvez et al., 1939)

Sample number	number in 1 g oven-dry material	
	bacteria	moulds
2	600,000	65,000
3	250,000	185,000
4	200,000	55,000
5	800,000	10,000

Special research on the occurrence of Azotobacter failed to produce any results.

These figures are, of course, very low compared with the number of organisms present in normal arable soil, but it should be borne in mind that the material was blown out from the interior of the earth only a fortnight before the investigations took place. For the sake of comparison, it may be mentioned that in ordinary soils between

2 and 200 million bacteria have been recorded per gram of soil, the highest figures being obtained in highly cultivated and highly manured soils.

Which of the two groups mentioned (and algae and protozoa may be added) dominates the soil population, depends on such factors as moisture, access of air, temperature, acidity, and the supply of food materials. These factors have a different but quite marked influence on the number of micro-organisms, as well as on their activity. Both high moisture content and high temperature increase the activity of all organisms. An optimal limit applies to both factors. Aerobic organisms will not thrive if an excess of water results in a decrease of the oxygen supply, whereas too high a temperature proves injurious to them all. Mohr (1938, 1944) mentions that bacteria proper will only grow under such moisture conditions as prevail when the relative humidity of the surrounding air is at least 98%. Moulds can thrive under less moist conditions, i.e. with a relative humidity as low as 85%. In cases where the relative humidity varies between 85 and 98%, moulds are practically the only micro-organisms flourishing. The air supply is important as it governs the supply of oxygen both as a gas and as an element dissolved in water. An abundant supply of oxygen stimulates the growth of moulds, deficiency curbs their development. The same applies to bacteria, inasmuch that the anaerobic species become dominant as the supply of oxygen decreases. Some species are able to adapt themselves to change of circumstances.

Which micro-organisms are dominant depends on the temperature and there are three groups distinguished, though these cannot be sharply delineated. The psychrophilic micro-organisms occur at an optimum temperature of about $10°$ C, the mesophilic at an optimum of about 15 to $25°$ C, and the thermophilic at an optimum of about 50 to $65°$ C. The majority of these forms belong, at least in the temperate zones, to the mesophilic group. In the tropics, one might expect the thermophilic form to be more prevalent. Generally speaking, this applies to bacteria as well as to the actinomycetes which occupy an position between bacteria and fungi. The latter have a temperature optimum which resembles that of the higher plants, i.e. around 18 to $25°$ C. This leads to the conclusion that at temperatures below 25 or $20°$ C, conditions tend to become more favourable for moulds compared to bacteria. On the other hand, if the temperature rises above $30°$ C, and especially above $35°$ C, conditions are less favourable for moulds, while certain bacteria flourish luxuriantly.

The acidity of the medium exerts an influence on the vigour of life of the soil microflora which should not be under-estimated. A pH of 5.5 to 7.5 seems optimal for the bacteria, whereas the actinomycetes apparently prefer a pH above 7. Their numbers decrease at greater acidity. Fungi are less susceptible to pH influences and will dominate between 5.5 and 3.5.

For the sake of simplicity, these reactions of the soil population to acidity are stated as definite facts. In reality, however, this problem is much more intricate; for instance the optimum pH for the fixation of nitrogen from the atmosphere by Azotobacter is on the alkaline side (Allan and Singh, quoted by Russell and Russell, 1950). The latter authors also state that the type of bacteria depends on the soil reaction and common species of Azotobacter are usually absent in soil with a pH below 5.7, but it is best to assume for the time being that the total bacterial population is not very dependent on soil reaction. With regard to fungi Russell and Russell (1950) quote Jensen, who

178

found them tolerant to a wide pH range, although they flourished best under extremely acid conditions.

The general statement seems justified that in soils just around neutral, bacterial activity dominates, whereas in acid soils fungi develop more vigorously. It will be shown later that this is of importance to the process of decomposition or, conversely, to the accumulation of organic matter in tropical regions.

With regard to the nutrition of the micro-flora, a distinction must be made between organisms themselves, i.e. between the true organic constituents and the inorganic nutrients. As briefly mentioned before, the autotrophic organisms are able to utilize carbon derived from carbondioxide as their sole source of nutrition although most o them are also capable of utilizing more complex forms. The heterotrophic forms derive their carbon from complex components, although many of them also need carbondioxide.

The inorganic constituents not only include calcium, potassium, magnesium, phosphate, sulfate, and chloride, but also ammonium, nitrate and nitrite, and carbon dioxide. According to Jensen (quoted by Mohr, 1938, 1944), the latter group is more important to the moulds and the former to the bacteria.

In addition, bacteria and moulds may also be differentiated in their quantitative relationships. Fungi, such as for instance Aspergillus niger, use about 1/3rd of the transformed organic materials for the building up of their body substance whereas bacteria use only about 1 %. In the process of mineralization, therefore, bacteria are much more effective; they also work faster, whereas fungi fix organic substances stronger and more permanently (Rippel, 1931). This means that bacteria must be regarded as the organisms which actually break down the organic remains of leaffall, whereas the fungi convert the materials, at least in part, into new organic matter which remains in the soil.

If we now take into consideration the fact that the average soil temperature in the tropics is higher than it is in temperate regions, it will be obvious that bacterial activity will be greater than that of the fungi. The higher the temperature rises above 30° C, the more bacterial break-down will be promoted. In tropical lowlands a bare soil which is adequately moistened by rain, will exhibit a flora which is predominantly bacterial. In a mountainous area, with a dense forestal vegetation, at an elevation where the soil temperature is about 20° C, the soil will exhibit a microflora dominated by moulds. This reasoning is based on experiments and research into microbial activity in temperate regions. It is a well-known fact, however, that the composition of the soil population shows remarkably little variation in different parts of the world. The characteristic groups of algae, bacteria, fungi and protozoa are the same in the Arctic as they are in temperate and tropical climates.

In cases where bacteria predominate, i.e. where there is a high temperature, satisfactory moisture owing to permeability and limited air supply, the optimal conditions exist for the mineralization of plant residues. This combination of favourable conditions is well-developed in most of the low, hilly regions of the tropics. Consequently little organic matter will remain in either its original or humified state. On the other hand, at an elevation of about 1,000 metres and higher, organic matter will accumulate as the fungi which predominate in this ecological environment are, for their own

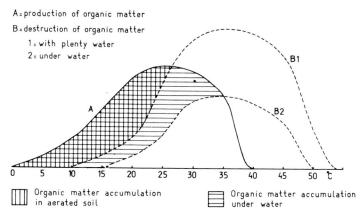

A = production of organic matter
B = destruction of organic matter
1 = with plenty water
2 = under water

Organic matter accumulation in aerated soil

Organic matter accumulation under water

FIG. I.55. *Range of destruction and accumulation of organic matter as related to temperature*

preservation, both less active and more conserving. The higher the elevation the more humus remains. The process of organic matter destruction and humus accumulation is represented in fig. 1.55. If a terrain is submerged, resulting in a lack of oxygen, conditions will become unfavourable for moulds. In the case of bacteria, only those which are anaerobic or those which can become anaerobic when the need arise will flourish. They will continue to grow as long as the soil and/or the water (as well as the vegetable remains) offer an adequate supply of inorganic food. In the low coastal stretches of the tropics, swamps and marshes are found with such conditions. Mineralization, although taking place, is less than under dry land conditions and results in a moderate accumulation of humus. This accumulation becomes less at higher pH. In limestone tracts, large-scale formation of humus is rare. Although an interesting occurrence of peat, formed under alkaline conditions, is described by Polak (1951) in Central Java it may be said that mostly alkaline water does not favour the accumulation of organic matter. Freshly deposited volcanic ash, normally rich in calcium and magnesium, gives rise to an appreciable content of these elements in soil water and will have a stimulating influence on bacterial activity. There will be only a limited amount of humus. If the ash is sufficiently weathered, and the bases are leached out, the possibility of humus accumulation increases. The degree to which this happens depends, of course, on the parent material. Acid rocks, rich in silica and low in bases, will result in the pH of the substratum reaching a sufficiently low level. Confirming this theory, in the Indonesian Archipelago peat is much rarer in Java than it is in Sumatera, Banka, Billiton, Kalimantan, and West Irian. The rocks in Java belong mostly to the andesitic types, on the other islands rhyolites (Sumatera), granites (Banka, Billiton, and Kalimantan) and sandstones (West Irian) occur.

Jenny et al. (1949), Jenny (1950), and Laudelout et al. (1960) made interesting studies on the decomposition rates of organic matter in and on tropical upland soils of Colombia and Costa Rica (temperatures ranging from 15 to 26° C) as compared with those of Californian soils (temperatures ranging from 0 to 15° C). They also found that the annual decomposition rate of the forest floor in tropical areas is much faster than in temperate areas. The forest floor decomposes at a rate of roughly 40 to 65% in Colombia and 1 to 12% in California. However, if the decomposition rates of organic matter over the entire profiles were estimated, assuming a leaf/root ratio of 1, the values were roughly 2.2% for Colombia and 1.3–1.9% for California. Jenny (1950) concluded that in the tropics of Colombia soil-humus is not readily oxidized. In the soil some unknown factor counterbalances the accelerating effect of high temperature and rainfall on the decomposition rates. This retarding factor is not operative in the decay of the forest floor which rests on top of the mineral soil. Jenny explains the high organic-matter content of tropical upland soils by the high biological nitrogen fixation (50% of the forest trees appear to be legumes), which causes the luxuriant growth of vegetation. Large amounts of litter fall on the ground; the leaves decompose rapidly and, because of the high rainfall, a large proportion of soluble and dispersible decomposition products migrate into the mineral soil. In the Sierra Nevada of California, soil organic-matter accumulation appears to be handicapped by low nitrogen increase as there are less leguminous plants. The present authors, however, think that the high organic-matter content in tropical upland soils is chiefly caused by the intensive root development. As there is a relation between root growth and top growth, root growth must be high. Organic-matter content in the soil is high as soon as temperature decreases as a result of elevation. This conclusion agrees well with that of Laudelout et al. (1960) who stated that the temperature optimum of humus synthesis is lower than the temperature prevailing in tropical lowland soils.

There may be several other reasons for the differences between the decomposition rates of organic matter on and in the soil, in tropics as well as in temperate areas. In the investigations of Jenny, the soils examined in California belong to the 'podzolized yellow-red soils' (Red-Yellow Podzolic Soils?) formed on granite (Jenny, 1948). The material derived from this highly siliceous rock will be poor in nutrients and, due to the low temperature accompanied by a pronounced dry season, conditions are unfavourable for a good vegetation growth and rapid decomposition of litter. In Colombia many upland soils are formed from volcanic ash rich in basic minerals. Luxuriant growth and rapid bacterial decomposition are to be expected. Volcanic glass in the ash yields an amorphous clay mineral, allophane, and free aluminium hydroxide upon weathering. The allophane seems to hinder the decomposition of organic matter in the soil, either by the formation of stable humus-clay complexes (Kobo and Fujisawa, 1963) or by controlling the decomposition of organic matter by micro-organisms (Aomine and Kodama, 1956; Harada, 1959). The latter investigators found that the decomposition of albumin and cellulose is more strongly retarded in allophanic soils than in other soils. Complete mineralization stops then, and polymerization and condensation reactions can begin, giving rise to the high molecular fulvic and humic acids. Such reactions can also be active in other soils when the mineralization is slowed down for other reasons, such as low temperature and low rainfall. Aluminium seems to have a stabilizing effect on humic acids probably by blocking the active groups, so that humic acids can accumulate (Kosaka et al., 1962). Bentonite is also capable of hindering the break-down of organic materials; illite and kaolinite are inactive in this process (Lynch and Cotnoir, 1956).

We can now understand the break-down of the waste material in a tropical forest in the following terms. Leaves, twigs, flowers, and fruit, and now and then heavy branches fall. Once on the ground they are immediately attacked by all sorts of gnawing insects, especially termites and ants. Expressed concisely, they are chiefly broken up mechanically, more or less comparable to the physical weathering of rocks. Spores attach themselves to the fallen matter especially as it becomes smaller (and in some cases they were attached prior to the fall of the debris), causing increasing disintegration of the solid matter. Although the greater part of the debris is mineralized on the mineral soil, a part is transported deeper by ants, termites, worms and other animals. Various changes of a chemical nature have occurred in the meantime, especially when roots die and decay. Constituents which were easily soluble, have been dissolved by atmospheric water and have either been transported downward or carried away with run-off water, where they are lost entirely. In the former case they can attack the mineral soil and horizons will begin to form.

The contents of the cells after death and decay are subjected to countless chemical reactions and the real break-down of the complex of organic substances supplied to the soil commences at this stage. All the groups of soil organisms start competing for the easily decomposable components, like the sugars, starches, proteins and aminoacids. Subsequently each of them plays its own specific part in the decomposition of the more complex, less soluble, complexes. Quoting Waksman (1938), it may be stated that the transformation of the compounds in question has been completed when the materials are decomposed to CO_2, NH_3 (in the case of nitrogenous substances), and H_2O under aerobic conditions. Of the quantitatively important substances, such as cellulose, hemi-cellulose, and lignin, cellulose is attacked by specific aerobic and anaerobic bacteria and by a number of fungi, both of the filamentous and mushroom type. Decomposition of the hemi-celluloses proceeds differently. As a group, they begin to be decomposed more rapidly than is the case with the celluloses, but the latter may have disappeared completely after a certain period, and hemi-cellulose may still be detected in the humus residue. Lignins are more resistent and a relative increase in the lignin content may be observed. It must also be mentioned that proteins may increase absolutely when the residues are poor in nitrogen, a new protein being synthesized through the activity of micro-organisms.

With respect to soil formation and rock weathering, fast mineralization of organic debris leads to the liberation of large amounts of carbondioxyde in the soil. The increased concentration of carbonic acid and the dissociation of water, which is greater at higher temperatures, are considered as the most important soil forming factors in the humid tropics under aerobic conditions i.e. conditions of rapid permeability. However, as soon as this bacterial mineralization is slowed down, either by the impoverishment of nutritional ions or by impeded permeability or by lowered temperature at higher altitudes, other organic decomposition products come into play, some of which are reported on page 175. These have quite different effects from the carbonic acid on the decomposition of minerals. Complexation and chelation reactions, reduction processes and precipitation reactions come into play leading to a quite different type of soil formation. In the former case Oxisols without plinthite will be predominantly formed, in the latter case Podzolic Soils and Oxisols with plinthite. A sharp delineation between these soils does not exist however, as many of the Latosols become podzolized in the later stages of soil formation. The parent rock is also important in this respect. In the tropics we frequently see Podzolic Soils on acid rocks because of the low content of nutritional ions and Oxisols on the intermediate and basic rocks. For details reference is made tot the Chapters 1 and 2 of Part II.

4.4. CARBON-NITROGEN RATIO

The rôle of nitrogen in soil formation is largely indirect, as one of the most important parts played by this essential component is the stimulation of micro-faunal activity. The biological cycle of this element is rather complicated because, besides its occurrence as NH_4-salts and nitrites or nitrates, the nature of the N-containing substances depends on the stage and character of the decomposition, the latter being strongly influenced in turn by the original composition of the organic remains and by the specific demands of the living vegetation.

The decomposition of organic matter involves the following changes: nitrogenous organic matter→ amino-acids and amides→ ammonium salts→ nitrites→ nitrates. In determining the N-potentiality of the soils, the carbon/nitrogen ratio of the organic matter is of importance. A low C/N ratio indicates that the organic matter is rich in nitrogen. This may have been the case initially or may be the result of an alteration which has progressed under conditions unfavourable for CO_2-evolution. A high C/N ratio of the soil humus drops if the temperature increases, as this causes increased

TABLE 1.74. *Some data on the C/N ratio of soils*

Country	Soil type	C/N ratio	Author(s)
South Africa	Pretoria Black Turf	14.1	Theron and Van Niekerk (1934)
do	Pretoria Red Loam	14.3	do
Malawi	Black Soil	15.3	Raychaudhuri (1941)
do	Red Soil	13.4	do
India	Black Cotton Soil	14.7	do et al. (1943)
do	Red Soil	10.2	do
Costa Rica	Sandy loam at 90 m elevation	11.0	Jenny et al. (1949)
	Loamy fine sand at 550 m elevation	11.6	do
	Organic sandy loam at 1250 m elevation	15.2	do
Indonesia	Sugarcane soils	14.5[1]	Van Harreveld-Lako (1926)
Philippines	Sugarcane and rice soils	11.9[2]	Villanueva and Lumang (1940)

[1] mean of 500 samples, after Hardon (1936)
[2] mean of 40 samples

microbial activity. Applied to tropical regions the C/N ratio will be higher at higher altitudes than it is at or near sea-level.

Table 1.74 shows some data on the C/N-ratio of soils. The black soils and the sugarcane soils of Indonesia seem to have similar C/N-ratios. The red soils occur at lower altitudes. The data of the Costa Rica soils show the dependence on altitude. It seems that a certain tendency may be observed towards an equilibrium in the C/N ratio.

Hardon (1936) tried to ascertain the influence of the most important factors governing humus and nitrogen content, such as rainfall, soil type, vegetation, temperature, pH, and soil texture. He found that rainfall and soil type exerted no influence. Vegetation has some influence, the highest figure being 13.0 for grass-ladang, 12.3 for primeval forest and 11.1 for land under crops. A positive relationship was found between the C/N ratio and temperature determined by altitude (fig. 1.56; see also table 1. 74); pH was found to be negatively correlated (fig. 1.57), whereas the C/N ratio varied somewhat arbitrarily with the texture.

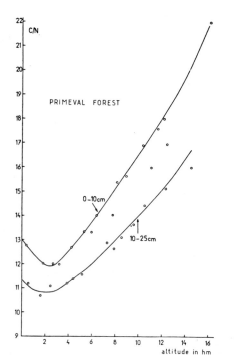

FIG. I.56. *Variation of carbon-nitrogen ratio with altitude in Indonesia (after Hardon, 1936; supplemented with data of v. Schuylenborgh, 1958, and Tan et al., 1961)*

FIG. I.57. *Relation between carbon-nitrogen ratio and pH of the soil in Indonesia (after Hardon, 1936; supplemented with data of v. Schuylenborgh, 1958, and Tan et al., 1961)*

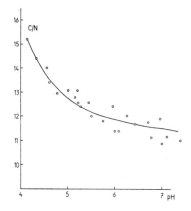

Craig and Halais (1934), who studied the influence of age (maturity) and rainfall on the properties of Oxisols in Mauritius, found that in wetter areas the content of organic matter was highest, with a slightly higher C/N ratio (table 1.75).

The influence of rainfall is noticeable to a certain extent, unless temperature differences also have to be taken into account. The relative data, however, is not given in this article.

In his paper Hardon states correctly that the factors studied are interdependent, vegetation being related to temperature, pH, texture, and rainfall. The same is also true for microbial activity, the soil micro-flora being subject to variations in soil-composition. Certain groups may increase enormously under certain ecological conditions,

TABLE I.75. *Organic matter and carbon-nitrogen ratio in soils of different rainfall zones in Mauritius* (after Craig and Halais, 1934)

Mean annual rainfall in mm	organic matter		C/N ratio	
	mature	immature	mature	immature
625–1250	4.0	6.1	9.1	9.7
1250–1875	4.9	5.6	10.4	9.6
1875–2500	5.3	7.7	11.1	10.8
2500–3125	5.7	9.4	11.2	11.3
3125–3750	6.1	10.2	12.7	11.8

but they disappear suddenly and almost entirely if the conditions of their environment change.

The factors which largely tend to suppress the activity of the micro-flora may be summarized as follows:

1. A drop in temperature makes micro-flora less active in mineralizing organic matter. At higher altitudes in the tropics with conditions similar in other respects, the breakdown will proceed at a slower rate and more 'humus' will accumulate in the soil.

2. The more acid the medium for instance with a pH of about 4.5, the less bacterial activity there will be. This degree of acidity is indicative of a low level of mineral plant food material such as Ca, Mg, and K. As a result, microbial life in the soil will be restricted, organic matter will accumulate, and peat formation will eventually take place.

3. Certain clay minerals restrict the activity of micro-organisms and organic matter accumulates in the soil if the supply of fresh organic material is abundant. Amongst these allophane seems to be most influential, followed by bentonite. Illite and kaolinite seem to be inert.

4. Only anaerobic organisms will thrive with restricted oxygen supply viz. under conditions of excess of water or continued water-logging. These organisms can only live on the organic matter available by first obtaining the energy needed for respiration (oxidation) from reduction of the substances on which they live (Einkohlung, a partial carbonization), and provided adequate nutrients are available, as for example in fine volcanic ash. This process may possibly explain the formation of certain black soils. If the soil reaction is acid and there are no inorganic nutrients then the organic matter will remain as it is, resulting in the accumulation of peat. Where no carbonization takes place, peat deposits in the tropics, especially very recent ones, are more apt to be brown or at the most dark brown, rather than black.

LITERATURE CITED

AOMINE, S. and KODAMA, I. 1956 Clay minerals of some arable soils in Miyazaki Prefecture. *J. Fac. Agric. Kyushu Univ.*, 10: 325–344.

ASEYEVA, I. V. and VALIKZHANINE, G. A. 1966 Biosynthesis of free amino acids by micro-organisms in the soil. *Sovj. Soil Sci* : 63–68

BOEREMA, J. 1919 Intensiteit der zonnestraling. *Hand. 1e Ned. Ind. Natuurw. Cong.:* 99–101.

BRAAK, C. 1928 The climate of the Netherlands Indies. *Proc. Roy. Magn. Meteorol. Observ. Batavia*, 8: pp. 272.

COSTER, CH. 1937 De verdamping van verschillende vegetatievormen op Java. *Tectona*, 30: 1–102.

CRAIG, N. and HALAIS, P. 1934 The influence of maturity and rainfall on the properties of lateritic soils in Mauritius. *Emp. J. Expt. Agric.*, 2: 349–356.

D'HOORE, J. 1953 De accumulatie van vrije sesquioxyden in tropische gronden, *Thesis Gent*, pp. 150.

DUFF, R.B. and WEBLEY, D.M. 1959 2-Ketogluconic acid as a natural chelator produced by soil bacteria. *Chem. & Ind.*; 1376–1377.

FREISE, F.W. 1934 Beobachtungen über den Verbleib von Niederschlägen im Urwald und den Einflusz von Waldbestand auf den Wasserhaushalt der Umgebung. *Forstwissensch. Zentr. Bltt*, 56: 231–245.

GALVEZ, N.L., AQUINO, D.I. and MAMISO, J.P. 1939 Agricultural value of the fine ejecta of Mayon Vocano. *Philipp. Agricst*, 27: 844–854.

HARADA, T. 1959 The mineralization of native organic nitrogen in paddy soils and the mechanism of its mineralization. *Bull. nat. Inst. agric. Sci. Tokyo*, B9: 123–199.

HARDON, H.J. 1936 Factoren, die het organische stof- en het stikstofgehalte van tropische gronden beheersen. *Korte Meded. Alg. Proefsta. Landb.*, pp. 24.

HARREVELD-LAKO, C.H. VAN 1926 Resultaten van het chemisch onderzoek der rietgronden van Java. *Med. Proefsta. Java-Suiker Ind.*, 34, No. 20: 689–851.

HARRISON, J.B. 1934 The katamorphism of igneous rocks under humid tropical conditions. *Imp. Bur. Soil Sci. (Harpenden)*, pp. 79.

HEATH, G.W. and KING, H.G.C. 1964 Litter breakdown in deciduous forest soils. *Trans. 8th Int. Cong. Soil Sci.*, III: 979–987.

HENNEQUIN, J.R. and JUSTE, C. 1967 Présence d'acides phénols libres dans le sol. Étude de leur influence sur la germination et la croissance des végétaux. *Ann. Agron.*, 18: 545–569.

JENNY, H. 1948 Great soil groups in the equatorial regions of Colombia, South America. *Soil Sci.*, 66: 5–28.

— 1950 Causes of the high nitrogen and organic matter content of certain tropical forest soils. *Soil Sci.*, 69 : 63–69.

—, GESSEL, S. P. and BINGHAM, F. T. 1949 Comparative study of decomposition rates of organic matter in temperate and tropical regions. *Soil Sci.*, 68 : 419 –433.

KLINGE, H. 1968 Litter production in an area of Amazonian terra firme forest. Part I. Litter-fall, organic carbon and total nitrogen contents of litter. *Amazoniana*, 1 : 287–302.

KNOCH, K. 1929 Die Klimafaktoren und Übersicht der Klimazonen der Erde. *In Blanck: Handb. d. Bodenl.*, II: 1–53.

KOBO, K. and FUJISAWA, T. 1963 Studies on the clay-humus complex (part 3). Adsorption of humic acid by clay. *J. Sci. Soil and Manure, Japan*, 34: 13–17.

KONONOVA, M.M. 1966 Soil organic matter. 2nd English ed. Oxford, pp. 544.

KOSAKA, J., HONDA, CH. and IZEKI, A. 1962 Transformation of humus in upland soils, Japan. *Soil Sci. & Plant Nutr.*, 8: 191–197.

LAUDELOUT, H., MEYER, J. and PEETERS, A. 1960 Les relations quantitatives entre la teneur en matière organique du sol et le climat. *Agricultura*, 8: 103–140.

LUNDEGARDH, H. 1930 Klima und Boden. Jena. pp. 480.

LYNCH, D.L. and COTNOIR, L.J. 1956 The influence of clay minerals on the breakdown of certain organic substrates. *Soil Sci. Soc. Am. Proc.*, 20: 367–371.

MOHR, E.C.J. 1938,1944 De bodem der tropen in het algemeen en die van Nederlandsch-Indie in het bijzonder. *Med. Kon. Inst. v.d. Tropen, Amsterdam*, XXXI, 2 vols, pp. 1151. Translated by R.L. Pendleton: Soils of Equatorial Regions. Ann. Arbor, 1944, pp. 765.

NYE, P.H. 1961 Organic matter and nutrient cycles under moist tropical forest. *Plant and Soil*, 13: 333–347.

POLAK, B. 1951 Construction and origin of floating islands in the Rawah Pening (Central Java). *Contr. Gen. Agric. Expt. Stat.*, 121: pp. 11.

RAYCHAUDHURI, S.P. 1941 Studies on the physico-chemical properties of associated black and red soils of Nyasaland Protectorate, British Central Africa. *Ind. J. agric. Sci.*, 11: 100–109.

— and CHAKRAVARTY, J. N. 1943 Studies of Indian red soils. VII. *Ind. J. agric. Sci.*, 13 : 252.

RIPPEL, A. 1931 Bakteriologisch-chemische Methoden zur Bestimmung des Fruchtbarkeits-zustandes des Bodens und der Kreislauf der Stoffe. In Blanck: Handb. d. Bodenl., VIII: 599–571. Berlin.

ROBINSON, G.W. 1951 Soils. Their origin, constitution and classification. 3rd ed. London, pp. 573.

RUSSELL, E.J. and RUSSELL, E.W. 1950 Soil conditions and plant growth. 8th ed. London, pp. 635.

SAPPER, K. 1935 Geomorphologie der feuchten Tropen. *Geogr. Schriften, Heft 7*, pp. 153.

SCHEFFER, F. and ULRICH, B. 1960 Lehrbuch der Agrikulturchemie und Bodenkunde. III. Humus und Humusdüngung. 2nd. ed. Stuttgart, pp. 266.

SCHUBERT, J. 1930 Das Verhalten des Bodens gegen Wärme. In Blanck: Handb. d. Bodenl., VI: 342–375. Berlin.

SOWDEN, F.J. 1966a Nature of amino acid compounds of soil: I. Isolation and fractionation. *Soil Sci.*, 102: 202–207.

— 1966b Nature of amino acid compunds of soil: II. Amino acids and peptides produced by partial hydrolysis. *Soil Sci.*, 102 : 264–271.

TAN, K. H. and VAN SCHUYLENBORGH, J. 1961 On the classification and genesis of soils developed over acid volcanic material under humid tropical conditions II. *Neth. J. agric. Sci.*, 9: 41–54.

THERON, J.J. and VAN NIEKERK, P. le R. 1934 The nature and origin of black turf soils. *S. Afric. J. Sci.*, 31: 320–346.

VAGELER, P. 1930 Grundriss der tropischen und subtropischen Bodenkunde. Berlin. pp. 210.

VAN SCHUYLENBORGH, J. 1958 On the genesis and classification of soils, derived from an-desitic tuffs under humid tropical contions. *Neth. J. agric. Sci.*, 6 : 99–123.

— 1966 Die Verlagerung von Sesquioxiden in Parabraunerden, Podsolen und sauren Brauner-den. *Z. Pflern. Düng. Bodenk.*, 114 : 9–12.

— and BRUGGENWERT, M. G. M. 1965 On soil genesis in temperate climates. V. The forma-tion of 'albic' and 'spodic' horizons. *Neth. J. agric. Sci.*, 13 : 267–279.

VILLANUEVA, L.J. and LUMANG, H.E. 1935 Carbon-nitrogen ratios of some Philippine soils. *Philipp. Agricst*, 24: 854–862.

VRIJ, M.P. 1932 Vergelijkende metingen van ultraviolette zonnestraling in de tropen en in Europa. Amsterdam. pp. 64.

WAKSMAN, S.A. 1938 Humus. Origin, chemical composition and importance in nature. 2nd ed. Baltimore, pp. 523.

WANG, TH.S.C., YANG, T. and CHENG, S. 1967 Amino acids in subtropical soil hydrolysates. *Soil Sci.*, 103: 67–74.

—, YANG, T. and CHUANG, S. 1967 Soil phenolic acids as plant growth inhibitors. *Soil Sci.*, 103:239–246.

WHITEHEAD, D.C. 1964 Identification of p-hydroxy-benzoic, vanillic, p-coumaric and ferulic acids in soils. *Nature*, 202: 417–418.

PART II

SOILS

Many soils in the tropics are red, brown, or yellow, others are dark grey, black or pale, and even white.

The red, brown, and yellow soils have received, and are still receiving names such as Laterite-, Lateritic-, Ferrallitic-, Fersiallitic-, Ferral-, Ferri-Soils, Latosols, Red and Yellow Podzolic-Red Mediterranean Soils, etc. There exists in no field of tropical soil science so much confusion in terminology as in the field of the red soils, although after World War II many valuable contributions were made to attempt to remove this confusion. It is not intended to give a review of the controversy in this field, but it should be stated that much of the confusion is caused by the fact that many of the red soils are old or even relic and find their origin in Tertiary times. Much can have happened at the time of and after their formation, such as erosion occurring for example after land uplift or change in climatic conditions; or accumulation of foreign material possibly after a landfall, or new soil formation in the eroded land or accumulated material, etc. All these factors complicate the mode of formation and the composition of the profile. Another reason for the confusion has to be attributed to geologists, who, being interested in raw materials for metallurgy classified all formations rich in iron and aluminium as laterite. Therefore, several authors (a.o. Pendleton, 1947; Aubert, 1954) have preferred to abandon the use of the terms laterite, lateritic, and laterization. The United States Soil Survey Staff has also abandoned the terms ferrallitic, fersiallitic, latosols, etc. and proposed the name Oxisol for many of the red soils (7th Approximation, 1960; supplement, 1967). This suggestion for the terminology of red soils will be followed as far as possible in this textbook.

Chapter 1 of this part will cover the study of the characteristics and formation of some members of the Oxisols.

In Chapter 2 examples of the Lateritic-, Red and Yellow Podzolic, and Mediterranean Soils (which are classified in the 7th Approximation as Ultisols and Alfisols) will be discussed. The pale and white-coloured soils are predominantly Podzols, at the present time called Spodosols (7th Approximation). The discussion of these soils will also be included in Chapter 2.

The dark grey and black soils of the tropics have received many names in the past, such as Black Cotton Soils, Regurs, Dark Clay soils, Tirs, Grumusols, etc. The 7th Approximation uses the name Vertisols for these soils. The discussion of these soils will be found in Chapter 3.

Rice is mostly grown in humid tropical regions. The methods of cultivating rice create profound changes in the soil profile. In Chapter 4 the characteristics and formation of these changes are discussed. These occur in a great variety of soils, including Oxisols, Entisols (e.g. Alluvial Soils), Inceptisols, Ultisols, etc. As cultivation and growing produce similar changes in all these soils, they will therefore be called Paddy Soils.

A special type of soils can be formed in marine sediments rich in sulfides. If these sediments are artificially drained or when they are uplifted, the sulfides oxidize; then the so-called acid sulphate soils or cat-clays are formed. As they may have formed as a result of human intervention (land-reclamation and drainage), they will be included in Chapter 4.

Volcanic soils in tropical areas will be treated in Chapter 5.

CHAPTER 1

OXISOLS

Oxisols are defined as soils having an oxic horizon or plinthite, forming a continuous phase within 30 cm of the surface.

The definition of the oxic horizon (U.S. Soil Survey Staff, 1960, 1967; Smith, 1965) is a subsurface horizon, exclusive of the argillic or natric horizon, that: a) is at least 30 cm thick; b) has a fine-earth fraction that retains 10 m.e. or less of NH_4-ions per 100 grams of clay from a 1 N NH_4Cl-solution or has less than 10 m.e. of cations extractable wit NH_4OAc and Al extractable with 1 N KCl per 100 grams of clay; c) has an apparent c.e.c. of fine earth fraction of 16 m.e. or less per 100 of clay by NH_4OAc; d) has only traces of primary aluminosilicates such as feldspars, micas, glass, and ferromagnesion minerals; e) has only traces of water-dispersible clay in some subhorizons; f) has texture of sandy loam of finer in the fine-earth fraction and more than 15% clay; g) has mostly gradual or diffuse boundaries between its subhorizons; h) has less than 5% volume that shows rock structure.

Frequently stonelines are found in and under the oxic horizon of soils formed from quartz-rich parent rocks. This indicates that oxic horizons are found mainly in ancient transported sediments. However, the stonelines can also be formed in situ, as was shown by d'Hoore (1954) and Alexander and Cady (1962).

Plinthite (from Gr. plinthos: brick) is a highly weathered mixture of sesquioxides, clay, quartz, and various other materials and is poor in humus (U.S. Soil Survey Staff, 1960, 1967). It occurs as red mottles, usually in platy, polygonal, or reticulate patterns. It hardens upon exposure to the air after repeated wetting and drying. Plinthite may occur in several horizons, such as epipedons, cambic, argillic, oxic, and C-horizons. If plinthite is present in an oxic horizon and forms a continuous phase it is equivalent to the material described by the old term laterite, although this name was primarily used for the hardened material. In this text the term plinthite will be used for the non-hardened, and laterite for the hardened material.

From a genetical viewpoint Oxisols can be roughly divided into Oxisols with plinthite and Oxisols without plinthite. The most important representative of the Oxisols with plinthite is found in the Aquox suborder, and more specifically in the Plinthaquox group. This group was closely related to what was formerly known as the Groundwater Laterite Soils or, if the groundwater level is deep but strongly fluctuating, to the Laterite Soils. As the formation of these soils is difficult to understand and much has still to be learned, the characteristics and formation will be discussed in the first section of this Chapter.

Although some members of the non-plinthitic Oxisols may contain plinthite at great depths, the typical ones do not. The U.S. Soil Survey Staff (1967) recognizes four suborders, viz. Torrox, Ustox, Humox, and Orthox. In the second section of this Chapter some examples of these soils will be discussed.

1.1. OXISOLS WITH PLINTHITE

As plinthite is the essential constituent of these soils, it is of interest to get an insight in the characteristics and composition of this material.

1.1.1. PHYSICAL CHARACTERISTICS

As far as is known the earliest description of plinthite was given by Buchanan (1807). He wrote, using the term laterite (from L. later = brick):

'Laterite. What I have called indurated clay is one of the most valuable materials for building. It is diffused in immense masses, without any appearance of stratification, and is placed over the granite that forms the basis of Malayala. It is full of cavities and pores, and contains a very large quantity of iron in the form of red and yellow ochres. In the mass, while excluded from the air, it is so soft that any iron instrument readily cuts it, and it is dug up in square masses with a pick-axe and immediately cut into the shape wanted with a trowel, or large knife. It very soon after becomes as hard as brick, and resists the air and water much better than any bricks that I have seen in India. I have never observed any animal or vegetable excivia con-tained in it, but I have heard that such have been found immersed in its structure. As it is usually cut into the form of bricks for building, in several native dialects, it is called the brick-stone. Where, however, by washing away of the soil, part of it has been exposed to the air, and has hardened into a rock, its colour becomes black, and its pores and inequalities give it a kind of resemblance to the skin of a person affected with cutaneous disorders; hence it is called itch-stone. The most proper English name would be laterite, from lateritic, the appellation that may be given to it in science'.

The word laterite obviously relates to its use as building material (see figs. II. 1 and 2) and not to the red colour, as several authors have thought. Buchanan emphasizes the ability of the material to harden irreversibly upon desiccation and he seems to stress the richness in iron and its occurrence over granite.

Plinthite is found, however, in soils over quite different parent rocks and consequent-ly Newbold (1844) laid much less emphasis on the composition when describing the soils of the Bidar district of Hyderabad (India). The extreme heterogeneity of the material (cited by Prescott and Pendleton, 1952) was described as follows:

'The laterite of Beder, generally speaking, is a purplish or brick-red, porous rock, passing into liver brown perforated by numerous sinuous and tortuous tabular cavities either empty, filled, or partially filled with a greyish-white clay passing into an ochrous, reddish and yellowish brown durst; or with a lilac-tinted lithomargic earth. The sides of the cavities are usually ferruginous and often of a deep brown or chocolate colour; though generally not more than a line or two in thickness, their laminar structure may frequently be distinguished by the naked eye. Before the blow-pipe it melts into a black clay attracted by the magnet, but it is rarely so ferruginous as to entitle it to the character of an ore of iron; though some of the nodules are picked out, and smelted by the natives. The interior of the cavities has usually a smooth polished superficies but sometimes mammillary, and stalactiform on a minute scale. The hardest varieties of the rock are the darkest coloured, and most ferruginous. The surface masses of the softer kinds present a variegated appearance. The clay and lithomarge exhibit lively coloured patches of yellow, lilac, and white, intersected by a network of red, purple, or brown. The softness of this rock is such that it may be cut with a spade; hardening by exposure to the sun and air, like the laterite of Malabar. The surface of the harder or more ferruginous varieties is usually barren, flat like a pavement and often presents a glazed or semi-vitrified appearance.'

This last statement is illustrated by fig. II. 3.

I.I.2. MICROMORPHOLOGICAL CHARACTERISTICS

The most detailed studies on the structure and composition of plinthite are those of Alexander et al. (1956), Alexander and Cady (1962), and Schmidt-Lorenz (1964). They described the structure of plinthite by studying polished specimens and thin sections of plinthite samples derived from coarse and fine-grained basic rocks (dunite, norite, dolerite, basalt), granite, gneiss, sericite schist, and some colluvial and sedimentary materials. Studies were also made on samples which were at different stages of hardening. Although a wide range of transitions occurs in the formation of plinthite, the above-mentioned authors distinguish between two structural extremes of laterite: the pisolitic and saprolitic (commonly vermicular) laterite.

The pisolitic laterite, shown in fig. II. 4, is composed of pisolitic bodies more or less closely packed in a matrix. The pisolites of several plinthites enclose muscovite, schist fragments and gibbsite-filled relics of feldspar crystals (fig. II. 5). This might indicate an early formation of the pisolites in those places in the rock which are most susceptible to weathering. They seem to be stable after their formation and only subject to dehydration. The occurrence of dehydration is indicated by the presence of shrinkage cracks (fig. II. 6). Frequently multi-layered coatings (produced by 'rhythmic precipitation') are observed in the pisolites and in cracks in the matrix (fig. II. 7). These observations point also to a hydrous condition during the formation of pisolites and matrix. The pisolitic plinthite has generally a high content of iron oxides and hydroxides, predominantly hematite and goethite (fig. II. 9), but may also contain an important percentage of the aluminium hydroxides, gibbsite and boehmite. If gibbsite is present, it may have the appearance of an early product (see above), but generally it seems to be a late formation, for it fills the spaces left by shrinkage or occurs at the surface of many pisolites (fig. II. 10). The pisolitic plinthite is formed from various rocks but its formation seems to be strongly favoured by the fine-grained basic rocks.

Early formation of pisolites, as described above, seems to be not the only mode of formation, as Rosanov and Rosanova (1961) found in the plinthite soils of Burma which always contain a pisolitic plinthite horizon on top of a cellular plinthite horizon.

The saprolitic laterite (fig. II. 11) resembles the saprolite resulting from the weathering of coarse-grained acid rocks, particularly granite. Elements of rock structure have frequently been preserved, amongst which the occurrence of gibbsite, goethite and kaolinite pseudomorphs after feldspars, ferro-magnesian minerals and micas is most illustrative. A common feature of this type of plinthite is a lattice-like network of oriented films of kaolinite mixed or overlain by goethite or hematite (figs. II. 12 and 13) and the presence of kaolinite-worms (fig. II. 14). Frequently goethite can be found as small, closely packed, spherical aggregates a few microns in size and sometimes in the form of droplets (fig. II. 15). Pores and channels occur often and they are coated or filled up with oriented films (sometimes multi-layered due to rhythmic precipitation) of iron-stained kaolinite (fig. II. 16). The porosity may vary considerably over a distance of a few centimeters and so does consequently, relative hardness. Due to this fabric this type of plinthite gives rise upon hardening and removal of the soft part, to vesicular, vermicular or cellular laterite. The mineralogical difference between the two types of plinthite is that the pisolitic plinthite contains hematite and gibbsite, whereas the saprolitic laterite contains goethite, kaolinite and quartz, the latter inherited from the parent rock.

Finally Alexander and Cady (1962) state:

'Pisolites, concretions, or definite separate bodies are present in most laterites. In addition to the true round pisolites with concentric structure, there are bodies of various sorts in which a particular kind of mineral or mineral mixture has been segregated. These bodies have definite structural boundaries, skins, or external layers that demarcate them from the rest of the structure or they have a more densely impregnated, or differently impregnated, zone that is continuous with the external matrix. Some of these are pure goethite, some are pure gibbsite, some are amorphous, and some consist of unidentifiable mixtures of clay-size iron minerals. They show evidence of several modes of origin in addition to that of a condensation of a gel, such as in the true pisolitic laterite. Some are pseudomorphs after rock minerals – gibbsite after plagioclase, goethite after olivine, kaolinite after mica. Others are pore fills into weak or open spaces. Others have no explanation to be obtained by study of micromorphology. In some laterites formed from material reworked by erosion or by colluvial action, some of the bodies identified as concretions have an external origin, i.e., they are fragments of an older crust.'

From these rather extensive quotations, it is evident that nowadays more types of plinthite than only the Buchanan one are recognized. A wide range of transitions between the two extreme types occur, giving rise to hardpans, conglomeratic, vesicular, scoriaceous, cellular and spongy laterite upon hardening.

As already mentioned in the descriptions, the colour of plinthite is strongly variable, but usually bright, in shades of pink, ochre, red and brown. Often they are strongly mottled with green and violet because of the presence of manganese compounds. Iron-rich plinthite is red or ochrous in the soft state but darkens to almost black upon hardening. Gibbsite, if present, is usually mixed with some iron causing the rose tints characteristic of some hardpans. Kaolinite has a special preference for iron fixing (Fripiat and Gastuche, 1952; Kellerman and Tsyurupa, 1962; Follett, 1965) and becomes a deep red colour. Whereas iron-rich plinthite darkens upon hardening, aluminous plinthites become lighter coloured.

I.I.3. CHEMICAL AND MINERALOGICAL COMPOSITION

The chemical composition of plinthite is as variable as its structure. A feature of plinthite is the high content of aluminium and iron oxides and hydroxides compared with other components. The Fe_2O_3 content may compose 85 % of the ferruginous laterites and the Al_2O_3 content can be as much as 60% of the bauxitic plinthite. The total silica content can vary considerably from only a few percent to as much as 60%, (Rosanov and Rosanova, 1961) all depending on the parent rock and drainage conditions. Combined silica varies from traces to 20% (Maignien, 1958). The silica/sesquioxide ratio is always lower than that of the parent rock, the extent of lowering being a function of the parent rock, drainage conditions, and intensity of weathering.

Combined silica is nearly always present as kaolinite, or halloysite, although frequently illites are found either inherited from the parent rock or as alteration products (Maignien, 1958; Gastuche et al., 1962).

Free silica is practically always an important component of plinthite. It is mainly residual especially in plinthite formations derived from acidic igneous rocks. It can also be present in amorphous forms, such as chalcedony, opal or phytolites (d'Hoore, 1954).

Although free aluminium can sometimes be the main constituent of plinthite, the oxides of iron are most common and frequent. Especially in the Buchanan type of plinthite the free Al_2O_3 content is very low (d'Hoore, 1954). The aluminium may be present as gibbsite or boehmite, while the iron minerals are goethite, hematite, magnetite, and ilmenite. Bonifas (1959) found maghemite in plinthite derived from dunite in Guinea.

Alkaline and alkaline-earth metals are nearly always absent, whereas combined water is usually present in appreciable quantities. The latter varies from about 30% in aluminous to about 10% in ferruginous plinthite.

It will be clear that a chemical analysis of plinthite material has to be interpreted with care. Due to the considerable spacial variability of plinthite, a chemical analysis of a small sample is of little value. However, this could be overcome by making analyses of a suitable number of samples of the plinthite under investigation.

Although aware of the limitations in the results of chemical analyses of laterites, table II. I has been composed for comparative purposes, giving the analyses of a number of plinthite samples and their parent rocks. The alkaline metals are not included in this table as their content in plinthite is negligible.

The table also shows the extreme variability of the composition of plinthite. It shows that in most of the plinthite samples the molar combined SiO_2/Al_2O_3 ratio tends to be 2, indicating the formation of kaolinite. In some cases (1 and 6) the ratio is much lower, indicating the presence of a considerable proportion of free alumina. In most examples a considerable loss in total SiO_2 can be observed upon weathering, in others (5, 6, and 8) the loss is small. In example 5 the loss in quartz nearly equals the gain in combined SiO_2, while the combined SiO_2/Al_2O_3 ratio is 2, indicating that quartz is dissolved during weathering and combined to Al_2O_3 to form kaolinite. Sometimes (2, 6, and 8) there is an increase in quartz and a decrease in combined silica, showing that primary minerals are decomposed whilst the liberated silica crystallized, at least partly, as free silica. In four cases (3, 4, 5, and 7) the molar Al_2O_3/Fe_2O_3 ratio decreased strongly upon weathering; this means that iron is more strongly accumulated than aluminium. In other instances (1, 2, 6, and 8) the ratio remains constant or increases slightly. In all examples (with the exception of 6) the total silica/alumina and iron-oxide ratios decrease considerably upon weathering, indicating that silica is released and removed during the formation of plinthite. The most mobile elements seem to be the alkaline and alkaline-earth metals and silicium, then aluminium which is slightly mobile; iron is the least mobile element.

It is understandable that all these variations in the formation of plinthite will depend on the type of parent rock and on other conditions, of which drainage conditions are most important.

1.1.4. DEFINITIONS

Before beginning to discuss the occurrences and genesis of the Oxisols with plinthite, it is necessary to define the soil forming processes. The suggestion of the U.S. Soil Survey Staff to abandon all old terms such as laterization and ferrallitization was accepted. It is understandable then that some difficulties arose in creating new terms for the processes responsible for the genesis of these soils.

The processes involved are those leading to formation of the oxic horizon and those responsible for the genesis of plinthite. The former were called laterization or ferrallitization. The process is a weathering process in which silica is released from the primary silicates and from part of the quartz (if present); also the alkali and alkaline earth metals are released. The latter are practically completely leached, whereas the released silica combines with alumina to form clay minerals, of which kaolinite is the final product. The remainder of the released silica is leached. This process will be called desilication (a term already used by Harrison, 1934) and as described above, it is an absolute empoverishment in silica and a residual enrichment with the stable weathering products, amongst which the iron-oxides and hydroxides are important and sometimes also quartz. However, the decrease in silica content may also be achieved by deposition of sesquioxides, transported laterally with groundwaters coming from higher situated surroundings. The decrease in silica in this sense is relative because of the actual enrichment with sesquioxides. Both processes, actual as well as relative, will be called desilication. Most frequently a combination of these two types of desilication will be responsible for the formation of oxic material.

The forming process of plinthite, the characteristic of which is the ability to harden upon exposure to the air, will be called plinthization. From the description of the structure of plinthite it is clear that this process is strongly dependent on the possibility of redistribution of the products of desilication, of which iron plays a very important rôle. It is evident that the redistribution of iron within the pre-plinthite horizon will be strongly favoured by alternative reduction and oxidation. In its turn this is only possible if a fluctuating groundwater level or apparent groundwater level is present. Besides this mechanism also certain recrystallization processes will be involved to give the plinthite its firmness.

It will be seen later that the above given description of processes involved is not

FIG. II.1. *Plinthite excavation and house of laterite bricks (Madagascar)*

FIG. II.3. *Lateritic hardpans exposed by erosion; Mt. Kukusan, South-East Kalimantan (photo 't Hoen)*

FIG. II.2. *Drying and hardening of laterite material*

1 = hematite; 2 = goethite; 3 = gibbsite; 4 = kaolinite; 5 = quartz; ■ = pore

FIG. II.5. *Gibbsite-filled relics of primary minerals (126 ×; polarized light)*

FIG. II.4. *Piece of pisolitic laterite*

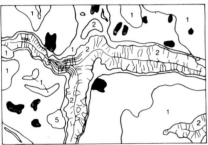

1 = hematite; 2 = goethite; 5 = quartz; ■ = pore

FIG. II.6. *Shrinkage crack, filled with multilayered goethite (126 × ; polarized light)*

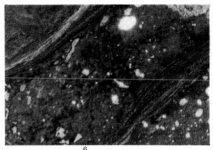

1 = hematite; 2 = goethite; 3 = gibbsite; 6 = oriented clay; 7 = amorphous iron hydrates; ■ = pore

FIG. II.7. *Multilayered clay-goethite boundaries of two opposite pisolites (51 × ; polarized light)*

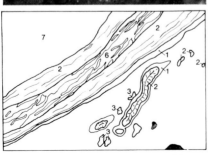

1 = hematite; 2 = goethite; 3 = gibbsite; 6 = oriented clay; 7 = amorphous iron hydrates; ■ = pore

FIG. II.8. *Enlargement of part of fig. 11.7, showing the multilayered coating of a pisolite (126 × ; polarized light)*

1 = hematite; 2 = goethite; 3 = gibbsite; 4 = kaolinite; 5 = quartz; ■ = pore

FIG. II.9. *Pisolitic plinthite (51 × ; polarized light)*

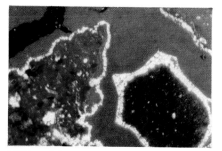

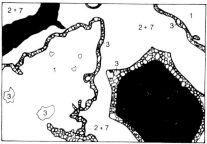

1 = hematite; 2 = goethite; 3 = gibbsite; 7 = amorphous iron hydrates; ■ = pore

FIG. II.10. *Late formation of gibbsite (126 × ; polarized light)*

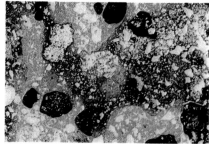

1 = hematite; 2 = goethite; 3 = gibbsite; 4 = kaolinite; 5 = quartz; ■ = pore

FIG. II.11. *Saprolitic plinthite (Groundwater laterite; 3 × ; polarized light)*

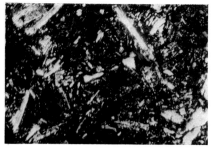

4 = kaolinite; 5 = quartz; ■ = pore

FIG. II.12. *Criss-cross positioned iron-stained kaolinite (126 × ; polarized light)*

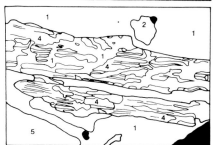

1 = hematite; 2 = goethite; 4 = kaolinite; 5 = quartz; ■ = pore

FIG. II.13. *Detail of iron-stained kaolinite-booklet of fig. 11.12 (312 × ; polarized light)*

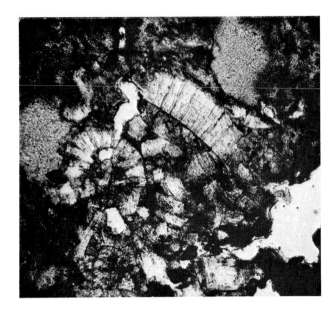

FIG. II.14. *Kaolinite worms from weathered granite, Oro Bay, W. Irian (courtesy P. Humbert; 75 ×)*

FIG. II.15. *Fine goethite droplets (126 ×; polarized light)*

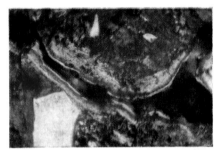

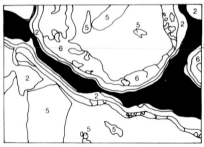

2 = goethite; 5 = quartz; 6 = oriented clay; ■ = pore

FIG. II.16. *Channel, coated with iron-stained kaolinite and goethite (312 ×; polarized light)*

FIG. II.26. *Thin section of a part of the B-horizon of a Latosol (120 ×; polarized light)* *(see p. 231)*

TABLE 11.1. *Chemical composition of rocks and their derived plinthite*

	SiO_2 (%)			Al_2O_3 %	Fe_2O_3 %	TiO_2 %	MnO %	CaO %	MgO %	H_2O %	molar ratios				
	free	comb.	tot.								a	b	c	d	e
1.	4.3	45.5	49.8	12.2	9.9	4.6	0.5	11.8	9.5	0.4	6.3	6.9	12.7	13.9	1.9
P.	5.5	7.4	12.9	34.8	24.9	4.9	0.0	0.1	1.6	20.8	0.4	0.6	0.8	1.4	2.2
2.	0.1	51.1	51.2	15.7	10.3	1.7	0.4	9.1	7.7	0.4	5.5	5.5	13.3	13.3	1.6
P.	9.4	27.7	37.1	24.6	19.0	1.0	n.r.[1]	3.9	3.8	10.3	1.9	2.6	3.9	5.2	2.0
3.	33.4	16.6	50.0	25.1	8.6	1.0	n.r.	10.0	3.0	1.1	1.1	3.4	5.1	15.4	4.6
P.	3.2	20.3	23.5	19.6	41.2	2.8	n.r.	0.2	0.4	12.0	1.8	2.0	1.3	1.5	0.7
4.	n.r.	n.r.	54.0	15.0	1.8	1.2	0.2	9.3	5.7	0.2	—	6.1	—	82	13.4
P.	n.r.	n.r.	16.4	23.5	45.0	1.8	0.1	tr.[2]	tr.	13.3	—	1.2	—	1.0	0.8
5.	49.7	5.7	55.4	21.3	4.6	0.6	n.r.	6.9	1.4	0.2	0.5	4.4	3.3	32	7.2
P.	23.9	27.5	51.4	23.7	13.4	1.5	n.r.	0.1	0.2	7.6	2.0	3.7	5.4	10.2	2.8
6.	40.2	19.3	59.5	16.4	7.8	1.3	tr.	6.4	3.6	0.6	2.0	6.2	6.6	20	3.3
P.	47.2	11.7	58.9	18.8	8.3	0.8	n.r.	2.8	n.r.	9.7	1.0	5.3	3.7	18.9	3.5
7.	n.r.	n.r.	64.8	18.9	3.8	0.6	tr.	5.2	0.9	0.3	—	5.3	—	45	7.7
P.	n.r.	n.r.	14.1	36.9	29.8	2.3	tr.	0.7	0.3	16.4	—	0.7	—	1.0	2.0
8.	31.7	41.1	72.8	14.5	1.9	n.r.	n.r.	1.0	0.8	0.7	4.8	8.5	57	101	11.8
P.	37.4	29.7	67.1	21.1	2.0	n.r.	n.r.	0.1	0.2	6.4	2.4	5.4	41	93	17.2

a = combined silica/Al_2O_3; b = total silica/Al_2O_3; c = combined silica/Fe_2O_3; d = total silica/Fe_2O_3; e = Al_2O_3/Fe_2O_3.

1. Hornblende schist, 2. quartz diorite, and 8. granite (after Hardy and Follett-Smith, 1931, and Harrison, 1934); 3. gabbro basalt and 5. hornblende granulite (after Satyanarayana and Thomas, 1962); 4. diabase (after Alexander and Cady, 1962); 7. quartz-epidote-gneiss (after Harrassowitz, 1926).

[1] n.r. = not reported; [2] tr. = trace. P = plinthite.

sufficient to explain the genesis of oxisols with plinthite, but it should be adequate for the time being.

I.I.5. OCCURRENCES OF OXISOLS WITH PLINTHITE

Marbut and Manifold (1926), Marbut (1930), Du Preez (1949), Hallsworth and Costin (1953), Tamhane (1956), Panton (1956), Stephens (1960), Maignien (1958), Satyanarayana and Thomas (1961, 1962), Alexander and Cady (1962), Aubert (1963), Raychaudhuri et al. (1963), d'Hoore (1963), Moss (1965), and many others have contributed to the knowledge of the occurrences and formation of Oxisols with plinthite.

One of the most spectacular occurrences is the high-level laterite. It is always an old formation from late Tertiary and invariably hardened. It occurs as a cap on old peneplain remnants. The thickness is generally related to the richness of their parent material in sesquioxides. The basic rocks seem to form thicker crusts than acidic ones, though thick crusts may also occur on the acidic rocks. In that case the iron must have been accumulated by solutions flowing down from higher situated parts, to result in a topographic concentration. The high-level laterites are dense and hard if the area is large; they can be of a vesicular or pisolitic structure. If the area is small the laterite is softened somewhat.

A second occurrence is the low-level plinthitic soil. These laterites are formed in valleys or in lower parts of undulating areas, where the water table is high during a part of the year. Sesquioxides may have been accumulated by the fluctuations of the ground-water table. In areas where the base level of erosion has been maintained for a considerable length of time, the vertical fluctuations of the water table during the wet and dry season will take place in the same soil horizons. This seems to lead to plinthitic soils with an extremely high sesquioxide concentration and with a very dense structure and hard consistency.

A third occurrence is the colluvial or alluvial laterite at the bottom of slopes or in the floodplain of a valley. It commonly contains fragments of old laterites from higher levels. The fragments are cemented by iron oxides, which may originate from the colluvium by decomposition of weatherable minerals present or from the solutions coming downward from higher parts. In these soils a layering parallel to the surface is characteristic, resulting from the rearrangement of the materials by the action of current water.

Sometimes plinthite may be found in argillic horizons or in cambic horizons where weathering has produced a clay and sesquioxide material. These horizons are only slightly pervious and are saturated with water in the wet season. Another example of the formation of an impervious layer was found by Mohr (1933) in the case of the weathering of volcanic ashes. Under certain circumstances the silica released at the top can precipitate at some depth and cement the loose ash. This enables the iron and manganese to be redistributed giving rise to a structure characteristic of plinthite. This process may be regarded as more or less the tropical equivalent of the pseudogley formation in the temperate climate. The material thus obtained hardens upon exposure to the air. For details about the conditions under which plinthite is formed, see p. 228.

A rough idea about the geographical distribution of laterite soils in some parts of the world can be obtained from figs. II. 17, 18, 19, 20, and 21.

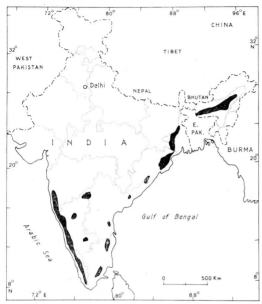

FIG. II.17. *Laterite areas in India (after Raychaudhuri, 1963)*

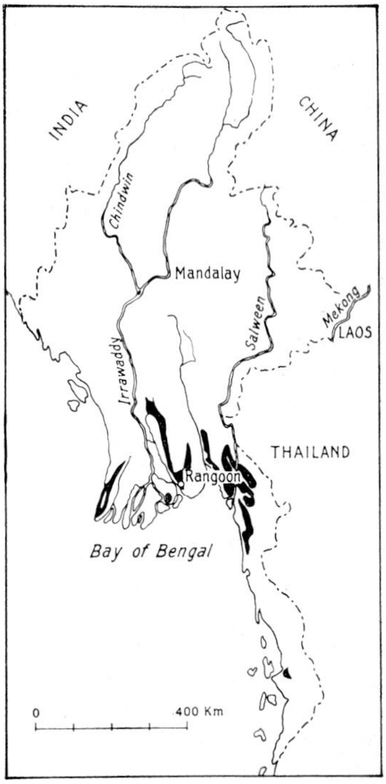

FIG. II.18. *Plinthitic Oxisol areas in Birma (after Rozanov, 1966)*

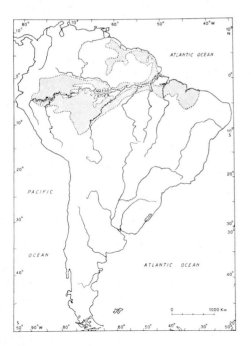

FIG. II.19. *Plinthaquox areas in S. America (after Ganssen, 1966)*

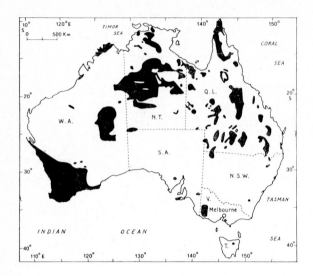

FIG. II.20. *Laterites in Australia (after Prescott and Pendleton, 1952)*

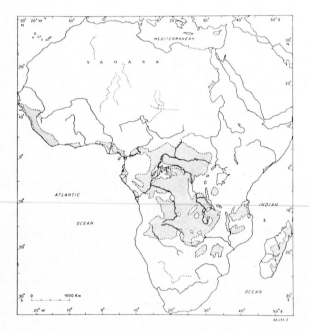

FIG. II.21. *Laterite soils in Africa (according to d'Hoore, 1963)*

I.I.6. THE PROFILE OF OXISOLS WITH PLINTHITE

It is difficult to describe a representative profile of an Oxisol with plinthite because of the extremely wide variations, but it will be attempted to give an idealized picture of a profile, developed on hard rock. Having studied the literature on laterite soils it is thought to be justified in stating that a modal profile consists of five zones: 1) the top soil; 2) the plinthite zone; 3) the mottled clay; 4) the pallid zone; 5) the rotten rock with 6) the rock.

1) The upper zone, in the following indicated as zone I, is a soil with texture varying from clay to loam with greyish brown, reddish brown, yellowish red, yellowish brown or brownish yellow colour. Sometimes an A$_2$-horizon is present and a cambic or argillic horizon. The consistency, when moist, is generally friable and the structure subangular blocky or granular. Small iron concretions may be present. There is generally a clear transition to

2) the plinthite zone (indicated with II). This horizon may be partly hardened. The colour is red, mottled with yellow or even violet. The texture can be clayey or sandy, depending on the nature of the parent rock. The structure is pisolitic or vermicular, vesicular, cellular, if hardened. In the soft state it is granular or subangular blocky. The pores are frequently filled with whitish, yellowish, or greyish material. If moist, it can be dug out and hardens upon exposure to the air. The non-hardened part is extremely firm, the firmness decreasing with depth. The horizon merges diffusely into

3) the mottled clay zone (indicated with III). It is a very pale yellow to white clay matrix with many coarse to very coarse red, yellow, brown, blue or violet mottles. These mottles do not harden and have the same consistency as the white clay material. The zone merges diffusely into

4) the pallid zone (indicated with IV). It is a very pale yellow to white homogeneous clay. The lower part of it shows features, such as layering and folding, due to the original rock structure and these become gradually more visible when merging into

5) the rotten rock (indicated with V), where the green, yellow and brown-coloured, half weathered minerals become visible. Its appearance varies of course with the type of parent rock.

No indication of the thickness of the horizons is given, because this is variable. In some cases the pallid zone is extremely thick (Walther, 1915; Hallsworth and Costin, 1953), 8 meters or more; in other cases the plinthite horizon is very thick as compared with the mottled clay and pallid horizons. In other cases the pallid zone is absent; the mottled clay zone rests then immediately on the rotten rock and shows in the lower parts features of the original rock structure. The reason for this absence could be the fact that weathering has not yet reached such a depth as to form a water table due to the fact that the increasing weathering depth worsens the drainage conditions (see the chapter on formation of the laterite soil profile). Another reason could be a surface sheet erosion that keeps pace with the weathering rate.

Very frequently zone I, the top soil, is not present, or only a thin layer of softened hard laterite. The U.S. Soil Survey Staff does not classify such soils as Oxisols but as Entisols, as the hardened plinthite (laterite) is considered as the parent material for new soil formation.

In order to show the variability in the profiles of Oxisols with plinthite the best investigated profiles will be discussed in the next section. Profile descriptions can also be found in publications of Aubert (1954, 1963), Hallsworth and Costin (1953), d'Hoore (1954), Alexander and Cady (1962), Maignien (1958), and others.

I.I.7. ANALYTICAL DETAILS OF PROFILES OF OXISOLS WITH PLINTHITE;
SOME REMARKS ON THE SOIL FORMING PROCESSES

Profile I (Satyanarayana and Thomas, 1961). Location: 600 m. from Angidipuram railway station (Malabar, India) towards Shoranur. Climate: rainfall 3000–3750 mm annually, falling predominantly from May to November; temperature, mean annual: 27° C (varying between 15.5° and 35.5° C). Vegetation: grasses, shrubs, and trees. Topography: sloping to the east (about 15 % slope).

Zone	Depth in meters	
I	0–0.30	Yellowish brown (5YR4/6) clay loam soil, with pebbles about 2 cm size; few grass roots. pH of fine earth material (< 2 mm) is 4.0; that of the whole sample 5.8.
II.1	0.30–1.83	Hard laterite layer; top portion is crumbly and breaks into irregularly shaped pieces; cellular and porous below. Irregularly mottled with red (10R4/8), reddish brown (2.5YR4/4) and yellow (10YR7/6). Quartz in grains and irregular small bits seen embedded in the iron matrix. No roots. pH of fine earth material 4.6; of the whole sample 5.8.
II.2	1.83–4.57	Reddish yellow (7.5YR7/8); vermicular structure; iron structural cavity filled with yellow (10YR7/8) and white (2.5Y8/2) clay matter; quartz grains occur throughout the depth either in the ferruginous material or in the clay matrix.
III	4.57–5.50	Soft laterite material unsuitable for quarrying (mottled clay?). pH of fine earth material 4.6; of whole sample 6.3.
V	5.50–6.70	Weathered boulders; hornblende pyroxene granulite which retains rock structure and colour, but lighter in weight; embedded in clayey material. Clay is light yellowish grey and soft.
VI	+6.70	Hard bed rock; hornblende granulite.

In the same area, about 90 meters down the slope where the terrain is nearly flat, the laterite horizon is covered with colluvial material of about 1.70 m thickness. The description is:

Zone	Depth (in m)	
I.1	0–0.69	Yellowish red (5YR5/8 to 5YR4/8) clayey soil with pebbles up to 2 cm size. Granular. Grass roots up to 15 cm.
I.2	0.69–1.68	Dark red (2.5YR3/6) clayey soil. Weakly laminar structure. About 10 to 20 percent pebbles, pebble size increasing with depth.
II.1	below 1.68	Hard laterite layer with irregular junction but distinct demarcation; vesicular laterite enclosing yellowish clay inside vesicules shattering into gravels followed by the sequence of horizons of the first profile.

It is evident that the profile is eroded, the eroded material being collected down-slope. New soil formation has started in the original plinthite zone which has hardened to laterite because of its exposure to the air. Consequently, the soil should be classified as an Entisol according to the 7th Approximation. Nevertheless the profile will be used as an example of an Oxisol as it was once an Oxisol and as it is one of the few examples which were analysed as accurately as it should be.

As indicated in the profile description there is a striking difference between the pH of the fine earth fraction and of the whole sample. This difference is possibly due to a 'concentration' effect leading to a stronger 'suspension effect' in the fine earth fraction-water suspension as compared with that in the whole sample-water suspension.

The cation exchange characteristics are presented in table II. 2. It shows that the exchange complex is strongly unsaturated, following the requirements for being oxic. It shows that the soil is in its ultimate stage of weathering.

TABLE II.2. *Cation exchange characteristics of profile I* (after Satyanarayana and Thomas, 1962)

Zone	c.e.c. (m.e. per 100 g of soil)	exchangeable cations (as percentage of c.e.c.)			
		Ca	Mg	K	H + Al
I	4.5	2.1	2.1	1.4	94.4
II.1	5.6	5.4	3.1	2.5	89.0
II.2/III	5.8	4.1	4.1	1.8	90.0

The elemental analysis (table II.3) was slightly modified from the data given by Satyanarayana and Thomas (1962), as they only reported the total iron-oxide content and did not distinguish between ferric and ferrous iron. This distinction however, is necessary for a good understanding of the processes involved in the formation of the profile. It is therefore assumed that ferrous and ferric iron are present in equal portions in the parent rock (VI). As Satyanarayana and Thomas (1961) report that the weathered rock (V) still contains pyroxenes and hornblende, indicating that the ferrous iron of the rock is not yet completely oxidized, it is assumed that half of the ferrous iron had been oxidized. The iron in the solum is thought to be present entirely as ferric iron. These authors do not mention the presence of sodium and phosphorus containing minerals, although these are certainly present. Assuming that the P_2O_5-content of the rock does not deviate much from that reported for the weathered rock and calculating the Na_2O-content as the remainder to 100%, table 3 was composed.

TABLE II.3. *Chemical composition of profile I*

Hor.	SiO_2 free %	SiO_2 comb. %	Al_2O_3 %	Fe_2O_3 %	FeO %	MgO %	CaO %	K_2O %	Na_2O %	TiO_2 %	P_2O_5 %	H_2O+ %
I	36.7	15.5	17.6	19.4	–	0.4	0.4	1.3	–	1.8	0.3	6.8
II.1	23.9	27.5	23.7	13.4	–	0.2	0.1	0.3	–	1.5	0.3	9.1
II.2/III	28.5	25.7	20.6	11.4	–	0.5	0.2	0.7	–	1.5	0.3	10.8
V	42.6	6.5	17.5	12.9	1.1	1.7	7.2	6.8	0.2	1.0	0.5	2.0
VI	49.7	5.7	21.3	2.3	2.3	1.4	6.9	7.3	1.7	0.6	0.5	0.2

From this table important conclusions can be drawn about the soil formation process. The trends in the silica/sesquioxide ratios (table II.3a) indicate that the desilication process is weakly exhibited, which is in accordance with the findings of Harrison (1934) when examining the weathering of similar rocks. One may conclude that in the formation of this laterite soil little has been removed.

On the other hand, the combined SiO_2/Al_2O_3 and combined SiO_2/H_2O ratio suggest that kaolinite has been formed, especially in the laterite horizon (zone II). This could be verified when calculating the mineralogical composition of this profile.

TABLE II.3a. *Derived molar ratios of profile I*

Hor.	$\dfrac{SiO_2}{R_2O_3}$	$\dfrac{SiO_2}{Al_2O_3}$	$\dfrac{SiO_2}{Fe_2O_3}$	$\dfrac{Al_2O_3}{Fe_2O_3}$	$\dfrac{\text{comb. } SiO_2}{Al_2O_3}$	$\dfrac{\text{comb. } SiO_2}{H_2O}$
I	3.0	5.0	7.2	1.4	1.5	0.7
II.1	2.7	3.7	10.2	2.8	2.0	0.9
II.2/III	3.3	4.5	12.7	2.8	2.1	0.7
V	3.1	4.8	9.3	2.0	0.6	1.0
VI	3.9	4.4	31.8	7.2	0.4	8.6

The high free silica content of the rock suggests an acid parent rock. However the rock is a hornblende granulite, i.e. a metamorphic rock, chemically equivalent to rocks of the gabbro and basalt family. The reason for the high free silica content is the inadequate analysis technique. Satyanarayana and Thomas (1962) used Harrison's technique (1934) and this method is inadequate for the analysis of fresh rocks and partly weathered rocks, although it can render fairly reliable data on free and combined silica when applied to highly weathered material. As a matter of fact, the calculation of the katanormative mineralogical composition of the rock (see table II.4) shows that hardly any quartz is present.

The chemical analysis suggests that the change from VI to V is not very intensive. There is some dissolution of total silica and aluminium, with a residual accumulation of iron. There is some hydration, but the contents of calcium, magnesium and potassium remain more or less the same. Sodium has been dissolved. The mineralogical compositions of both materials, however, show a thorough change, as will be reported later.

The greatest chemical change has occurred in the zones II.1, 2, and III. Calcium, magnesium, potassium and sodium have been nearly completely dissolved and removed, indicating that the potassium feldspars and plagioclases were fully decomposed. The hydration is considerable indicating the formation of hydrated minerals. The aluminium content remains fairly constant, indicating the formation of a stable clay mineral (see the molar ratios combined silica/Al_2O_3 and combined silica/H_2O). The chemical analysis shows nothing specific about the process that could be responsible for the formation of the very particular plinthite material. The fairly constant iron content (with the exception of I, see below) in the solum leads to the very important conclusion that a redistribution of the iron over short distances must have occurred (due to alternating oxidative and reductive conditions).

Finally, the thin soil layer (zone I), which is very probably formed from the laterite crust, shows a considerable decrease in combined SiO_2 and Al_2O_3, whereas it shows an increase in Fe_2O_3 and free SiO_2. This could possibly be caused by the decomposition of kaolinite (see also p. 222) with the subsequent formation of free silica and aluminium hydroxide. This however, contradicts the fact that the Al_2O_3-content in zone I has decreased, and it therefore seems more likely that a lateral removal of kaolinite with the rainwater has occurred, with the subsequent residual accumulation of quartz and iron minerals, which form the most stable part of the plinthite and laterite skeleton. This fact has frequently been observed when plinthite material is exposed to the atmosphere and hardens (see a.o.: Rosanov and Rosanova, 1964); it could have been confirmed by Satyanarayana and Thomas (1961), if they had analysed the soil material of the lower profile (see profile description).

In order to get information about the mineralogical composition of the solum and bedrock, the normative mineralogical compositions have been calculated from the chemical data according to the system developed by Niggli. For particulars the reader should refer to Burri (1964) and Van der Plas and Van Schuylenborgh (1970). The results are shown in table II.4.

TABLE II.4. *Normative mineralogical composition of profile 1* (weight percentages)

Zone	Q	Or	Plg	Bi	Ho	Mt	Ms	Kaol	Go	Hm	Misc
I	28.9	–	–	–	–	–	10.2	28.3	16.0	11.7	5.0
II.1	23.6	–	–	–	–	–	2.4	56.4	10.3	3.8	3.6
II.2/III	30.8	–	–	–	–	–	6.1	45.8	12.7	–	4.4
V	15.9	12.5	1.5	–	0.5	–	46.0	–	0.6	11.9	11.0
VI[1]	2.8	41.7	41.2	3.2	7.1	2.4	–	–	–	–	1.5

Q = quartz; Or = K-feldspar; Plg = plagioclases; Bi = biotite; Ho = hornblende; Mt = magnetite; Ms = muscovite (illite); Kaol = kaolinite; Go = goethite; Hm = hematite; Misc = miscellaneous.
[1] hornblende-biotite variant of the katanorm.

The table shows that the conclusion drawn earlier can be confirmed: kaolinite has been removed from the top soil resulting in the residual accumulation of iron minerals, quartz and illite (compare I and II.1).

A thorough change has taken place upon weathering (VI→ V). The plagioclases are nearly completely transformed but only part of the potassium feldspars. Instead, illite has been formed. The iron-bearing minerals have been decomposed and transformed to goethite and hematite. Upon further weathering (V → II and III) the illites disappear and kaolinite is formed. The question whether or not the formation of kaolinite has proceeded in this profile via the formation of illite is difficult to answer. As will be shown later (Part III, Chapter 1) the transformation of illite into kaolinite depends predominantly on the $[K^+] / [H^+]$ -ratio in the soil solution. This ratio can be lowered by leaching and as the solum is older than the weathering rock, it is understandable that illite is unstable in the solum. However, it is also possible that kaolinite has been formed directly from the feldspars; if the internal drainage of the upper part of the solum was more rapid than that of zone V at the present time this direct formation of kaolinite would have been possible.

Although it is possible that hematite instead of goethite is present in zone V (see p. 434), it is thought that this is the consequence of an erroneous determination of the crystal water.

In conclusion, it can be stated that the desilication process was only weak and that the formation of the oxic material can be characterized as the transformation of the feldspars and ferro-magnesian minerals into quartz, kaolinite and iron hydroxides. Redistribution of iron has taken place over short distances within the various zones.

Profile 2 (Satyanarayana and Thomas, 1961). Location: 33.4 km from Mangalore on the Mangalore-Kasaragod road (South Kanara, India). Climate: is similar to that of profile 1. Vegetation: grasses and scrub jungle bordering cultivated fields. Topography: rolling.

Zone	Depth (in m)	
I	0–0.25	Yellowish red clayey soil (5YR4/6), loose, with about 50% pebbles of different sizes up to 2.5 cm. pH of fine earth material, 4.5; of the whole sample, 4.8.
II.1	0.25–3.50	Hard laterite layer with intricate pattern of red (7.5R5/8), reddish yellow (5YR6/8) and white (2.5Y8/2). Top boundary irregular but well marked and crumbly, and followed by quarryable vermicular plinthite. Quartz grains are few. pH of fine earth material, 5.0; of the whole sample, 4.9.
II.2 (+III)	3.50–4.90	Plinthite with clay increasing to the bottom. At the bottom portion the typical plinthite appearance is lost and resembles reddish yellow clay (7.5YR6/6) with yellow and red portions scattered.
V	4.90–6.10	Weathered rock boulders with clay of the above description in between. Rock boulders weathering concentrically with red and yellow colours at the outer face, and rock structure and colour in the centre. pH of the fine earth material, 4.6; of the whole sample, 4.7.
VI	+6.10	Hard bed rock; basalt or meta-gabbro with vertical cleavages.

The same remark can be made in respect to the classification as in profile 1. This profile would probably also be classified as an Entisol, as the plinthite has already hardened and new soil formation is superimposed.

The analyses of profile 2 (Satyanarayana and Thomas, 1962) are represented in tables II.5, 6 and 6a. Table II.5 shows that the pH level and base saturation are still lower than in profile 1. The process of desilication is much more pronounced than in profile 1 (tables II.6 and 6a). Both observations point to stronger weathering either because of greater age and/or an easier weatherability of the rock of profile 2.

TABLE II.5. *Cation exchange characteristics of profile 2*

Zone	c.e.c. (m.e./100 g of soil)	exchangeable cations (as percentage of c.e.c.)			
		Ca	Mg	K	H + Al
I	7.0	1.6	0.5	0.8	97.2
II.1	4.2	3.4	2.6	0.3	93.7
II.2/III	4.5	5.2	7.8	0.2	86.8
V	4.6	2.3	3.5	0.1	94.1

In this profile it is remarkable that the K_2O content is practically constant (table II.6); potassium is therefore preserved, the K-feldspars of the rock being completely transformed into illites (table II.7). This is possible as will be shown in Part III, and this transformation depends not only on the $[K^+]$ / $[H^+]$ -ratio, but also on the H_4SiO_4-activity of the soil solution. The mentioned ratio must be larger than in profile I and this could be caused by a slower internal drainage.

Table II.7 shows some interesting facts. In the first place the lateral removal of kaolinite from the topsoil as could be demonstrated in profile I, is absent in this profile. On the other hand some of the iron in the topzone is dissolved and accumulated

TABLE II.6. *Chemical composition of profile 2*[1]

Zone	SiO₂ (%)		Al₂O₃ %	Fe₂O₃ %	FeO %	MgO %	CaO %	K₂O %	Na₂O %	TiO₂ %	P₂O₅ %	H₂O+ %
	free	comb.										
I	10.5	21.0	23.2	31.5	–	0.5	0.2	0.5	–	2.3	0.2	10.1
II.1	3.2	20.3	19.6	41.2	–	0.4	0.2	0.6	–	2.8	0.2	11.7
II.2/III	9.2	11.9	31.1	30.0	–	0.3	0.1	0.3	–	3.2	0.2	13.7
V	6.6	23.3	27.4	23.7	–	0.8	0.7	0.5	0.2	2.6	0.2	14.0
VI	33.4	16.6	25.1	4.2	4.4	3.0	10.0	0.5	0.7	1.0	–	1.1

[1] The data were slightly adapted to those of Satyanarayana and Thomas (1962); about half of the iron in the bedrock was considered to be present as Fe(II), while the Na_2O-content was assumed to be the difference between 100 and the sum of the other oxides. In zone V the Na_2O-content was arbitrarily chosen to be 0.2 %. Furthermore it was assumed that the iron in this zone and in the solum was fully in the ferric state.

in zone II.1. The bottom of the solum appears to contain gibbsite; probably this had been leached from the top and accumulated at the bottom. Aluminium is therefore more mobile in this profile than iron, a fact which is frequently encountered in tropical soil formation. The leaching of sesquioxides from the surface layers and deposition at lower depths is a process common in podzolization.

TABLE II.6a. *Derived molar ratios of profile 2*

Hor.	$\dfrac{SiO_2}{R_2O_3}$	$\dfrac{SiO_2}{Al_2O_3}$	$\dfrac{SiO_2}{Fe_2O_3}$	$\dfrac{Al_2O_3}{Fe_2O_3}$	$\dfrac{comb.\ SiO_2}{Al_2O_3}$	$\dfrac{comb.\ SiO_2}{H_2O}$
I	1.2	2.3	2.7	1.2	1.5	0.6
II.1	0.9	2.0	1.5	0.7	1.8	0.5
II.2/III	0.7	1.2	1.9	1.6	0.6	0.4
V	1.2	1.9	3.4	1.8	1.4	0.5
VI	2.8	3.4	15.4	4.6	1.1	4.6

As a matter of fact the top zone of Oxisols is slightly podzolized in many cases. The weak podzolization of the topzone has to be added to the processes, leading to the genesis of Oxisols.

The high content of ironoxides in the II.1 layer cannot only be explained by enrichment from the top zone. Probably also upward movement of reduced iron with rising groundwater during the rainy seasons and oxidation and deposition in the zone of the fluctuating groundwater are responsible for this accumulation.

TABLE II.7. *Normative mineralogical composition of profile 2* (weight percentages)

Hor.	Plg	Or	Q	Cord	Aug	Ms	Kaol	Gi	Go	Hm	Misc
I	–	–	4.6	–	–	4.0	52.4	–	23.4	10.1	5.6
II.1	–	–	0.6	–	–	5.0	43.1	–	45.5	–	5.9
II.2/III	–	–	–	–	–	2.4	40.8	19.3	32.3	–	5.1
V	1.7	–	–	–	–	4.0	55.2	3.4	26.3	–	9.4
VI	63.0	2.7	9.2	11.1	6.9	–	–	–	–	–	7.2

The symbols have the same meaning as in table II.4. Cord = cordierite; Gi = gibbsite.

Finally we see, that, in the toplayer, some of the goethite is dehydrated to hematite (see p. 434).

It can be stated in conclusion that profile 2 was formed by strong desilication, redistribution of plagioclases into kaolinite and gibbsite, and some leaching of iron- and aluminium-hydroxide.

A very peculiar profile (profile 3) was described by Hallsworth and Costin (1953). It is the Newell-Pelliga profile formed in the Pelliga forest and on Jurassic shales. The description reads as follows:

Zone	Depth (m)	
I	0–0.15	Reddish brown stony sandy loam; single grain to weak crumb; containing pisolites 10–20 cm in diameter and occasionally up to 30 cm. Quartz pebbles and pieces of ferruginous sandstone are present, which increase with depth.

II.1	0.15–0.38	Reddish brown very stony sandy loam. Consists entirely of ferruginous sandstone pieces which appeared to have fractured from horizon below.
II.2	0.38–0.51	Dark brown indurated sand, slightly vesicular in parts. Clearly defined from horizon below although strongly adherent to it.
II.3	0.51–0.61	Purple brown indurated horizon. Vertical structure markedly laminated into laminae 0.3 to 0.6 cm thick. When split into a horizontal plane the surface shows mottling due to concentric rings of red and yellow oxide.
II.4	0.61–0.71	Purple and brown laminated indurated horizon. The laminae are much thinner, about 1.5 mm thick and the whole layer is more easily broken than the one above. Changes fairly quickly to
III	0.71–0.91	Mottled red and white clay, extending in broad tongues to the layer below, the red patches diminishing in size and frequency and finally passing into
IV	0.91–1.83	Creamy white clay. Quite hard and still showing a shale-like structure but generally soft.
V	1.83–2.13	Decomposing shale.

As can be seen, all the horizons characteristic for an Aquox or Plinthaquox, except the upper part of the solum (71 cm) which has hardened, are present within 2 meters.

The total elemental analysis (private information of Dr. E. G. Hallsworth, CSIRO, Adelaide, Australia) is presented in table II.8.

TABLE II.8. *Chemical composition of profile 3*[1]

Zone	SiO_2 %	Fe_2O_3 %	Al_2O_3 %	TiO_2 %	MnO %	Na_2O %	K_2O %	H_2O+[4] %
I.1	89.2	5.3	1.4	0.2	tr	tr	tr	4.8
I.2	89.3	6.1	1.7	0.3	tr	tr	tr	2.5
II.1	69.4	25.2	4.1	0.2	tr	tr	tr	1.1
II.2	50.0	42.2	4.3	0.4	tr	tr	tr	3.1
II.3	16.2	78.7	4.1	0.8	–	tr	0.1	0.1
II.4	34.3	52.8	10.9	0.8	tr	tr	0.1	1.3
III.	68.1	6.9	22.8	2.0	–	tr	0.3	–
IV. h[2]	73.6	1.2	19.6	1.8	–	tr	0.5	3.3
IV. s[3]	73.8	1.2	19.6	1.7	–	tr	0.3	3.4

[1] Zone I was divided in two subsections (0–7.5 cm: I.1 and 7.5–15 cm: I.2). [2] IV. h – hard part of the pallid zone; [3] IV. s – soft part of the pallid zone. [4] The data for crystal water were obtained by subtracting the sum of the oxides from 100; they will therefore be too high for the toplayers because of the organic-matter content.

It is very striking that from the bottom to the top the silica content decreases and after II.3 increases, whereas the reverse happens for the Fe_2O_3 content. Apparently two processes were involved in the genesis of this profile: in the lower part of the solum a desilication process and in the upper part a leaching of iron oxide leading to the extreme accumulation of iron oxide in layer II.3. The podzolic character of the genesis of this profile is therefore much more pronounced than in the preceding profile. Very probably this is caused by the parent rock, which is a shale. Shale is a very slowly permeable rock and in the wet season water-logged conditions will have prevailed, thus favouring the conditions for the accumulation of organic matter (see Chapter 4, Part I). Thus, reduction of iron and chelation were favoured and these have diffused downwards leading to the accumulation of iron at lower depth. However, there has also been an upward movement of the groundwater and ferrous-iron solution occurring in the bottom has been transported to higher parts in the profile thus depriving the pallid zone from its ironoxides. In this way ironoxide has been additionally accumulated in the middle part of the profile. The fact that the ironoxide content of zone IV is

TABLE II.8a. *Derived molar ratios of profile 3*

Zone	$\dfrac{SiO_2}{R_2O_3}$	$\dfrac{SiO_2}{Al_2O_3}$	$\dfrac{SiO_2}{Fe_2O_3}$	$\dfrac{Al_2O_3}{Fe_2O_3}$
I.1	32	106	45	0.4
I.2	27	88	39	0.5
II.1	5.8	29	7.3	0.3
II.2	2.7	20	3.2	0.2
II.3	0.5	6.7	0.6	0.1
II.4	1.3	5.4	1.7	0.3
III	4.3	5.1	26	5.2
IV.h	6.1	6.4	154	24
IV.s	6.1	6.4	154	24

negligible points to the probability that the accumulation of ironoxides in the middle part of the solum has not originated from other sources by lateral movement of groundwater from elsewhere; otherwise the ironoxide content of the pallid zone would probably also have been higher.

The Al_2O_3 shows a quite different distribution pattern; it increases practically continually with depth. Whether this is caused by the decomposition of clay minerals with the subsequent dissolving and leaching of the formed Al-hydroxide or by the clay minerals without decomposition cannot be answered with certainty. A lateral removal of clay minerals is possible, as has been shown, but the first mechanism seems to be more probable as it is supported by the behaviour of titanium. The titanium content increases also with depth, which is opposite to the behaviour in the profiles discussed earlier. Normally a residual accumulation of TiO_2 can be observed in the upper part of the solum, which is understandable as rutile or anatase are very stable minerals. Whether or not the mobilization of titania can be explained in the same way as that of aluminium, is questionable. Possibly titanium has formed during the weathering process titanic acid, which exhibits the same solubility characteristics as Al-hydroxide (see also Chapter 5 in Part III).

Table II.9 shows the normative mineral composition of the profile. It shows the desilication process very well (IV.h→ II.3) and the leaching of ironoxides (I.1 → II. 3). The illites are unstable under these particular soil forming conditions and decrease from 4% in the bottom to negligible amounts in the top. This could indicate very acid conditions.

The kaolinite content increases continually; a downward movement of kaolinite is not very probable as there is no definite accumulation horizon. Lateral removal is possible, although it is not believed to have occurred in the genesis of this profile. Most

TABLE II.9. *Normative mineralogical composition of profile 3* (weight percentages)

Zone	Q	Kaol	Ms	Go + Hm	Ru
I.1	90.1	3.4	0.4	6.1	0.3
I.2	88.3	4.2	0.4	6.8	0.4
II.1	64.5	10.2	–	25.1	0.2
II.2	45.0	10.8	–	43.8	0.3
II.3	11.3	10.0	0.3	77.7	0.7
II.4	20.8	25.9	1.1	51.4	0.8
III	38.2	51.3	2.2	6.4	1.9
IV	48.9	44.3	3.8	1.2	1.8

Q = free silica; Kaol = kaolinite; Ms = muscovite (illite); Go = goethite; Hm = hematite; Ru = rutile (anatase).

probably decomposition of kaolinite is involved with the subsequent formation of gibbsite and silica; because of the acid conditions gibbsite dissolves and leaches. These acid conditions would also explain the leaching of titanium from the upper part of the profile.

It can be concluded that the genesis of the profile involves a distinct desilication and a prominent redistribution of iron (plinthization). Probably decomposition of kaolinite has occurred.

Profile 4 (Carroll and Woof, 1951; Hallsworth and Costin, 1953). Location: Fernhill, Inverell, New South Wales, Australia. Topography: hilly; the profile is located near the top of a hill of basalt.

Zone	Depth (m)	
I.1	0–0.30	Bright red loam with irregularly shaped concretions, mostly hard, but some of which crush readily. Fine crumb structure. Friable. Gradual transition to
I.2	0.30–1.22	Bright red loam with more frequent concretions.
II.1	1.22–2.74	Red indurated zone of large nodular concretions of irregular shape, largely composed of goethite and hematite, in a reddish clay matrix. Clear transition to
II.2	2.74–3.20	Orange-coloured clay with hard nodules of bauxite and with patches of hard yellow clay. Gradual transition to

II.3	3.20–3.50	Red clay with some hard bauxite nodules and small clayey concretions with yellow interiors. Gradual transition to
II.4	3.50–3.89	Hard concretions of bauxite of spherical to irregular shape. The nodules are grey to white with occasional concentrations of iron oxide at the center. A small quantity of earth is associated with the nodules. Sharply defined from
III	3.89–4.95	Red and white mottled clay with white mottling increasing downwards. The white portion is hard, compact clay, difficult to break; the red more friable and less dense.
V.1	4.95–7.00	Light brown to olive green kaolinitic clay, with small white mottlings associated with vermicular holes. Compacted at the junction with horizon III.
V.2	+7.00	Clay that can be easily broken into angular fragments with the fingers, but is tough and tenacious and not friable.

According to the 7th Approximation (supplement 1967), this profile is probably a Gibbsiaquox (see table II.11).

The chemical analysis of profile 4 (Carroll and Woof, 1951) is shown in table II.10. The air-dried samples were sieved to remove the largest nodules, and the remainder of the soil was slightly crushed to pass a 2 mm sieve. The figures given in the table are expressed as percentages of the fine earth fraction and calculated from those of Carroll and Woof (1951), who gave the contents of the different elements as percentages of the ignited samples. The data show that the solum has been strongly impoverished of silica, whereas iron oxides and especially alumina accumulated. Hydration of the bed rock (basalt) is very evident. Consequently, the desilication process is very pronounced. Also the redistribution process responsible for the formation of plinthite, is very

TABLE II.10. *Chemical composition of profile 4[1] and molar ratios*

Zone	SiO_2 %	Al_2O_3 %	Fe_2O_3 %	FeO[2] %	TiO_2 %	H_2O+[3] %	free Fe_2O_3 %	molar ratios			
								$\dfrac{SiO_2}{R_2O_3}$	$\dfrac{SiO_2}{Al_2O_3}$	$\dfrac{SiO_2}{Fe_2O_3}$	$\dfrac{Al_2O_3}{Fe_2O_3}$
I.1/2	7.4	31.8	31.2	5.5	11.0	13.1	22.8	0.2	0.4	0.5	1.3
II.1	10.3	40.9	16.3	5.7	7.9	18.9	9.8	0.3	0.4	1.2	2.8
II.2	11.5	36.8	18.3	3.7	7.0	22.7	14.5	0.4	0.5	1.4	2.6
II.3	12.0	31.7	12.7	2.8	14.3	26.4	11.5	0.5	0.6	2.0	3.2
II.4	3.3	63.1	0.2	–	5.4	28.0	–	0.1	0.1	55	619
III	32.7	39.2	2.3	–	10.1	15.8	2.4	1.4	1.4	39	27
V.1/2	23.7	38.9	16.2	2.0	6.1	13.0	13.3	0.8	1.0	3.4	3.3
VI[4]	48.3	16.3	2.4	9.0	1.1	2.4	–	3.4	5.0	10.3	2.1

[1] All data are corrected to the sum of 100.

[2] FeO figures of I.1/2, II.1 and II.2 are somewhat too high because of the presence of organic matter. Consequently, Fe_2O_3 figures are too low because these were calculated from total iron (as Fe_2O_3) and FeO (calculated as Fe_2O_3).

[3] H_2O figures are corrected for the organic matter content.

[4] Further rock composition: MgO, 7.3%; CaO, 9.4%; Na_2O, 2.9%; K_2O, 0.9%.

evident. Iron is at a minimum in the mottled zone and the lower part of the plinthite horizon. It seems as if these zones have lost their iron to the upper part of the solum, whereas aluminium accumulated residually.

It seems that layer II.4 was at the time of its formation the pallid zone, the zone of permanent reduction. The ferric and ferrous iron released by the parent rock was reduced or remained reduced. The soluble ferrous iron was translocated to upper horizons during periods of wetness causing a rise of the groundwater table, of course under different physiographic conditions from to-day. The reduced iron was predominantly oxidized during the periods of standstill and lowering of the groundwater table and deposited as some ferric hydroxide. The proposed mechanism can be observed in table II.11, giving the normative mineralogical composition of the profile.

The explanation of the presence of ferric iron in the zones beneath layer II.4 is difficult but one assumption is that a gradual land uplift after the formation of the pallid zone occurred. This has led to better drainage and oxidation conditions. Ferrous iron of the parent rock was oxidized and deposited as ferric oxide or hydroxide. Groundwater will now fluctuate in the layers formed by proceeding weathering, giving rise to a new mottled clay zone. Apparently, the uplift was so strong that a new pallid zone was unable to form. As a matter of fact, the assumed uplift has actually occurred in this area (Carroll and Woof, 1951).

The normative mineralogical composition of the rock, calculated according to Burri (1964), shows that it is an ultra-basic rock, in which quartz is absent. It is therefore quite understandable that this rock has been weathered to a soil without free silica and with a high content of Al-hydroxides. The normative mineralogical composition of the profile (table II.11) shows that in layer II.4, which was the pallid zone before the assumed land uplift, practically all aluminium is present as free Al-hydroxide. Only a

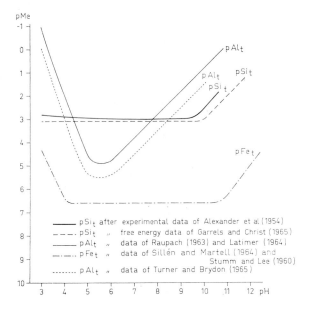

FIG. II.22. *Solubilities of a-morphous silica, Al- and Fe hydroxides at 25°C and 1 atm. total pressure (subscript* t *means sum of all dissolved species)*

214

small part was combined with silica to form kaolinite. The upper part of the solum shows with depth increasing kaolinite and decreasing bauxite percentages; layer I.1/2 shows a lower gibbsite content, which may be explained by the mechanism of lateral removal of the soft part of the laterite material as mentioned before. The trend in the kaolinite and gibbsite contents of the upper part of the profile can be explained by assuming that during the formation of the plinthite zone some kaolinite was decomposed, the aluminium accumulating as hydroxides and the silica moving away as dissolved silicic acid. This mechanism is only possible if the pH of the medium is between 4.3 and 7.8 as is shown in fig. II.22, representing the relation between experimentally determined soluble silica (in equilibrium with amorphous silica: Alexander, Heston, and Iler, 1954; Krauskopf, 1956), the calculated concentrations of dissolved Fe (III)- and Al-species (in equilibrium with their respective amorphous hydroxides; Sillén and Martell, 1964; Raupach, 1962 a and b; Latimer, 1964; Garrels and Christ, 1965; and Stumm and Lee, 1960) and pH.

Decomposition of kaolinite was actually observed by d'Hoore (1954) and Fripiat (1954) with the aid of the electron microscope especially in soils with a herbaceous vegetation. The grasses appeared to be able to attack kaolinite and to assimilate silica. The latter is returned to the soil with the dying leaves and leached away or deposited as phytoliths, which were observed in many soils with laterite by Riquier (1960). More details are reported in section 1.1.8.2.

TABLE II.11. *Normative mineralogical composition of profile 4* (weight percentages)

Zone	Kaol	Bau	Go + Hm	Leu	Ru	Ilm
I.1/2	15.9	36.4	31.2	–	4.8	11.7
II.1	22.0	48.0	16.3	–	1.6	12.2
II.2	25.2	42.4	20.8	3.6	–	8.0
II.3	27.9	35.6	15.3	14.7	–	6.4
II.4	7.2	87.3	0.1	–	5.4	–
III	70.2	17.5	2.2	–	10.1	–
V.1/2	51.1	24.6	16.2	–	3.9	4.2
	Or	Plg	Ol	P	Mt	
VI	5.8	55.2	15.4	20.0	3.6	

Kaol = kaolinite; Bau = bauxite; Go = goethite; Hm = hematite; Leu = leucoxene; Ru = anatase; Ilm = ilmenite; Or = K-feldspars; Plg = plagioclases; Ol = olivine; P = pyroxenes; Mt = magnetite.

Another possibility for the explanation of the trend in kaolinite and gibbsite content reported in table II.11 may be the resilication of gibbsite into kaolinite. This was already suggested by Harrison (1934) and Jackson et al. (1948). The silica should then have moved upwards with the groundwater during the wet season and combined with aluminium dissolved from gibbsite. It can be expected that resilication would have been strongest near the source of silica (apparently II.4 being once the pallid zone) and weaker at some distance. This is actually found in the profile (table II.11).' Which of the two processes is most likely is difficult to decide.

Fig. II.22 also shows that if iron and aluminium hydroxides are the weathering products, aluminium will be more mobile than iron because of the different solubilities of the hydroxides. This is true if complexing agents such as silicic, phosphoric, and organic acids are absent or present only in minor amounts. In the profile under investigation the molar ratio Al_2O_3/Fe_2O_3 which increases with depth (table II.10) points to this situation. As a matter of fact this is found in many tropical soils.

It is evident that after the uplift of the area, drainage conditions have ameliorated, resulting in a more oxidative weathering of the rock. The result is the formation of ferric oxides and hydroxides in the newly formed weathering zone (V.1/2 in table II. 10 and 11).

It can be concluded that the following processes have led to the genesis of this profile: a) desilication; b) redistribution of iron and aluminium (plinthization); c) probably decomposition of kaolinite; d) land uplift.

Finally, a last profile (profile 5) will be discussed briefly, as it shows some characteristics which can occur in Oxisols and which were not present in the preceding profiles. It is a profile developed in eocene marine clay (Schellmann, 1966) and situated in the south east of the isle of Kalimantan (Indonesia: see fig. II.23). A profile description is not available as the author took an auger sample every half meter. However, the samples were thoroughly analyzed. The horizon notations as indicated in the tables result from the study of the analytical details and thin sections, reported by Schellmann (1966).

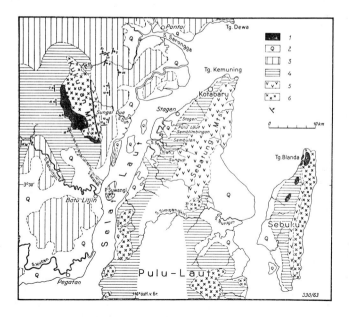

FIG. II.23. *Part of S.–E. Kalimantan (after Schellmann, 1966); 1. location of the profile; 2. Quaternary; 3. Late Tertiary; 4. Early Tertiary; 5. magmatic rock; 6. peridotite and serpentine*

The analytical details are given in tables II.12 and 13. Table II.12 shows that the pH (KCl) values of the upper horizons of the profile are higher than the pH (H₂O) values. This indicates, that the content of amphoteric components is large. Furthermore, soil pH has to be so low that the dissociation of protons by the colloidal silicate and humus complex is negligible, so that a net positive charge is established. A net positive charge in the upper horizons implies that the isoelectric pH-value of the

TABLE II.12. *Cation-exchange characteristics, pH, and clay content of the plinthite soil (profile 5) on eocene clay* (after Schellmann, 1966)

Zone	Depth in m	pH		exchangeable cations in percentages of sum of cations					c.e.c. in me 100 g.	$< 2\mu$ %
		H₂O	KCl	H + Al	Ca	Mg	K	Na		
I.	0–0.5	4.9	5.1	70	28	–	–	2	6.5	33
II.1	0.5–1.0	5.0	5.8	67	32	–	–	1	3.5	27
II.2	1.0–1.5	5.0	5.6	77	22	–	–	1	3.9	31
II.3	1.5–2.0	4.9	5.6	78	21	–	–	1	5.0	32
III	2.0–2.5	4.6	4.1	68	26	–	2	3	8.6	33
V	2.5–3.0	4.5	4.0	75	21	–	2	2	12.0	39
VI	7.0	5.1	4.8	36	19	24	19	2	18.6	n.r.[1]

[1] n.r. = not reported.

amphoteric iron hydroxides (aluminium hydroxide is present in only minor amounts: see table II.14) should be higher than 5, which indicates a poor crystallization of this hydroxide since the isoelectric pH-value of well-crystallized goethite is 3.2 (Van Schuylenborgh and Sänger, 1949; Van Schuylenborgh and Arens, 1950). This confirms the statements of Schellmann (1966) who found in the upper horizons three types of goethite, two of which are poorly crystallized as indicated by the broadening of the characteristic X-ray reflection lines (see below).

The cations exchange capacity values of the horizons reflect the trend in clay content and clay composition: the lower the c.e.c., the lower the clay content. In the V and VI zones and in the II.3 and III zones, the clay content is nearly equal, but the kaolinite/illite ratio changes in favour of illite, causing a higher c.e.c. value for the VI and for the V horizon.

The chemical composition of the profile is represented in table II.23. The table shows again an iron content decreasing with depth and an increasing silica content, pointing to a pronounced desilication process. The plinthization process (oxidation-reduction) is illustrated by the accumulation of iron and manganese in the plinthite horizons. Schellmann (1966) distinguishes between three types of goethite, viz.: goethite I, relatively accumulated goethite with numerous quartz inclusions; goethite II, absolutely accumulated goethite without quartz relics; goethite III in pores, present within goethite II, and mostly in needles. Gibbsite was found in some laterite horizons as late formations in pores, present within goethite II and III.

TABLE II.13. *Chemical composition of the plinthite soil on eocene clay* (after Schellmann, 1966)

Zone	SiO₂ %	Al₂O₃ %	Fe₂O₃ %	FeO %	K₂O %	Na₂O %	TiO₂ %	MnO %	Cr₂O₃ %	NiO %	H₂O+ %
I	14.8	11.1	57.6	0.3	0.1	0.1	0.4	0.2	2.3	0.3	12.5
II.1	8.4	10.4	64.9	0.1	0.1	tr.	0.3	0.2	2.1	0.3	13.1
II.2	15.1	12.7	54.9	0.1	0.2	tr.	0.4	0.7	1.7	0.5	12.6
II.3	21.5	14.8	44.7	0.1	0.3	0.1	0.6	0.8	1.9	0.5	12.3
III	50.3	14.9	20.4	0.1	0.9	0.1	1.0	0.1	0.4	0.1	8.2
V	63.2	17.8	7.2	0.1	1.2	0.1	1.1	tr.	0.1	tr.	7.0
VI	67.6	18.7	5.3	0.2	1.7	0.1	0.8	tr.	tr.	n.d.	8.0

TABLE II.14. *The normative mineralogical composition of the plinthite soil in eocene clay* (weight percentages)

Hor.	minerals					
	Q	Kaol	Ms	Go	Gi	Misc[1]
I	2.0	27.4	0.8	66.1	–	6.8
II.1	–	17.8	0.8	74.0	4.9	2.6
II.2	–	32.2	1.8	63.0	0.1	2.4
II.3	3.8	36.0	3.4	53.6	–	3.2
III	32.6	33.5	8.1	23.7	–	2.1
V	43.4	35.4	10.7	8.3	–	2.2
VI	45.2	31.1	15.1	5.9	–	2.6

[1] misc = albite + chromite + rutile.

The silica, aluminium, and potassium contents which increase with depth point to the decomposition of quartz, kaolinite, and illite upon weathering and soil formation. This is confirmed by table II.14, representing the normative mineralogical composition (calculated from table II.13 and agreeing fairly well with the experimentally estimated mineralogical composition: Schellmann, 1966) and by the fact that Schellmann actually observed the decomposition of quartz; the quartz grains became increasingly corroded upon weathering.

It will be clear that it is impossible to give a definite scheme for the formation and occurrence of plinthite soils, as the factors involved are manifold. The processes involved are: 1) desilication: the partial removal of silica and nearly complete removal of the alkali and alkaline earth metals, showing the destruction of the primary minerals; 2) plinthization: redistribution of iron hydroxides because of alternating reduction and oxidation conditions in the soil as a result of the seasonal distribution of rains; 3) weak to moderate podzolization of the top zone.

The intensity of these processes will vary, depending on local conditions such as physiographic position, parent material, and others.

1.1.8. THE SOIL FORMING PROCESS

1.1.8.1. *General outline of the process*

It is a reasonable suggestion that the three processes, mentioned above, are not acting simultaneously and with the same intensity, and that their duration will play an important role. The profile descriptions and the analytical details seem to indicate that the whole process can be divided into three stages. The first stage is connected with free or nearly free drainage. The rock is disintegrated by the atmospheric effects of heating and cooling, wetting and drying, by hydration and hydrolysis, carbonation, oxidation and dissolution effects, all influenced by soil fauna and vegetation. Secondary minerals such as kaolinite, gibbsite, goethite, etc., are formed; bases, silica and part of the aluminium are removed; in short the desilication has a profound impact on the parent material. As long as the weathered layer is not too thick and the weathering zone high above the base level of erosion, drainage will be free. Upon continuous weathering, the contents of both clay minerals and amorphous sesquioxide colloids are raised and the base level of erosion approached, leading at a certain moment to the stage that the permeation of the soil with rainwaters is slow enough to prevent the dispersion of all the water in the wet season. Consequently a temporary groundwater table is established. In the dry season, however, the water can still disperse sufficiently and disappears. In this second stage (appearance and disappearance of groundwater), reduction processes will start, especially if the roots are penetrating deeply enough. The second stage is therefore characterized by the occurrence of weathering and soil formation reactions under alternating reductive and oxidative conditions. The transformations during this stage are more or less comparable with those involved in pseudo-gley formation (more details on p. 229) and they will be different from that of stage 1. The material formed will show mottling, whereas the upper part of the profile will have a uniform colour. It is evident that in stage 2 the plinthization process begins.

Upon further weathering and approach of the base level of erosion, drainage and evapotranspiration are not able any more to remove all the water even in the dry season and a permanent groundwater table will be established. Normal gley formation will be superimposed upon that of pseudo-gley. A zone of constant reduction comes into existence and rock-weathering will proceed from this moment on, under reducing conditions. There is still a fluctuating groundwater table, although the highest water level is lowered gradually upon weathering and the mottled horizon grows thicker. Part of the originally formed mottled clay is now only moistened by capillary rise above the water table and the upper part will not be moistened at all. This part can dry to some extent and this is assumed to lead to the special characteristics of the plinthite material. The drying causes a certain dehydration and crystallization of amorphous iron and iron oxyhydrates into cryptocrystalline and crystalline hydroxides and oxides, thus cementing the material. The schematic representation in fig. II.24 may be helpful in visualizing this description of the three stages of development.

During the three stages of development the upper layer, which was once formed by oxidative weathering of the bedrock, has changed increasingly under the influence of the vegetation. The result is, sometimes accentuated by the type of the bedrock present, a surface soil with podzolic features. Frequently the surface layer is somewhat

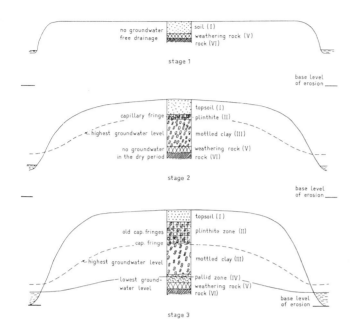

FIG. II.24. *Schematic representation of the three stages in the genesis of an Oxisol with plinthite*

homogenized by biological activity, this too depending on the type of the parent material. Roots penetrate into the subsoil in the dry season and part of them will die in the wet season because of excess of water and consequent lack of oxygen; animals burrow into the subsoil in the dry season and come to the surface in the wet season. Termites are especially active, as they make passageways down to the level of the water table (Yakushev, 1968). In this way drainage paths for the rain water are formed, leading to the inhomogeneous wetting of the subsoil which contributes to the special characteristics of the plinthite material such as clay coatings along tracks and fissures (fig. II.16).

From all this information it will be evident that the composition of zone V (the weathered rock) of a mature plinthite soil profile will strongly deviate from that of the weathered material formed at the beginning of the forming process. The latter was the result of oxidative weathering and the former a reductive process. It is therefore not correct to consider zone V of a mature plinthite soil as the parent material of the top soil, and this applies to all zones of a plinthite soil: These are more or less individual horizons formed under their own particular conditions. Naturally there is some, and frequently even strong, influence from underlying and upper horizons; but the inter-relationships between the top zone and the parent material are not so strong compared to temperate climates where weathering is not deep.

These ideas have led to the designation of the different zones in the Oxisols with plinthite with Roman numerals. Subhorizons in the topzone can then be indicated by letters of the alphabet. In this way the horizons of a profile can be referred to in the following manner: IA_1, IB_1, IB_{2t}, II, V, VI; or IA_1, IA_2, IB_2, IC, II, III, etc. If new soil formation has started in zone II after erosion of I, the horizon designation could be, e.g., IIA$_1$, IIC$_1$, IIC$_2$, III, etc. This suggestion was not followed in the profile descriptions in section 1.1.7.

Another consequence of the genesis of plinthite soils is that the only reference material can be the original bedrock if it is desired to study the changes in the profile quantitatively. A chemical analysis of an Oxisol with plinthite without including the bedrock lacks any scientific significance from the viewpoint of soil genesis.

It happens frequently that not all horizons of plinthite soils are present. E.g. the pallid zone and even the mottled horizon may be absent; in other cases the pallid zone is extremely thick as compared with the mottled and laterite horizon. Sometimes the laterite horizon is extremely thick and there can be a repetition of laterite horizons. All these deviations can be accounted for by differences of parent material and by physiographic changes during the formation process and will be discussed under the paragraphs in question.

So far the forming process is considered as residual. This is quite opposite to the ideas of Campbell (1917), who has suggested that the development of laterite is due to the addition of materials carried by the ground waters from other parts of the drainage basin; consequently he has suggested too that the rock in which the laterite is developed is unimportant. Of course, lateral enrichment of the soil with sesquioxides does occur. Especially at the foot of hills and in cases of laterized sandstones we have to assume absolute concentration as the main process of laterization, as the sandstones themselves are generally poor in iron. But many of the profiles presented before point so obviously to a residual soil formation that we shall confine ourselves to the discussion of this type in the following paragraphs.

1.1.8.2. *Soil forming factors*

a) Parent material. The parent rock does not appear to be an all-important factor, as laterite soils are formed on all types of rocks. They are found on granites, dolerites, basalts, volcanic ashes, sedimentary rocks, and even on calcareous rocks (Stephens, 1946) and limestones (Zans, 1953; Panton, 1956; Butterlin, 1961). Nevertheless, the bedrock does influence to some extent the type of the laterite soil. Acid bedrocks generally give rise to plinthite soils rich in iron hydroxides and basic rocks to bauxitic ones; the plagioclases of the basic rocks yield gibbsite most readily. However, many transitions and exceptions can be encountered and recent data have shown that drainage conditions and the ionic content of the percolating water are factors of extreme significance in the formation of the different plinthite soils. This will be discussed later (1.1.8.3.).

b) Climate. One of the most important factors in the formation of plinthite soils is the fluctuating ground water table. Therefore all circumstances favouring such a fluctuation promote plinthite formations. These circumstances are: 1) a high temperature; 2) an uneven distribution of the precipitation over the year.

High temperatures greatly increase evapotranspiration (see Chapter 1, Part I), thus causing a fluctuation of the groundwater during the rainy season and a considerable lowering after the rains. High temperatures also increase weathering depths thus promoting the genesis of deep Oxisols.

Exact data about the most favourable temperatures are lacking, but it is believed that mean annual temperatures of 25° C are high enough. Exceptions are known however; Oxisols with plinthite can occur at lower temperatures and can be absent at even higher temperatures.

An uneven distribution of precipitation is a characteristic of monsoonal climates. Monsoonal climates are the subequatorial climates with two wet seasons and two dry seasons per year; the tropical climate has one wet and one dry season. Continuously wet conditions, as occur in several areas of the equatorial belt, are less apt to produce soils with plinthite. In the wet season a water table will be established or will be raised if the topographical situation is suitable and if drainage is slow enough. In the dry season the water table disappears or is lowered because of drainage and evapotranspiration. Of course the absolute quantity of rain is also important, as it must be higher than the storage capacity of the soil layer present. According to Maignien (1964) the rainfall minimum should be 1200 mm/year, whilst there seems to be no upper limit, as Mohr (1933) found plinthite soils in Indonesia at a precipitation of about 4000 mm and Maignien (1964) reported the presence of well defined plinthite soils in Lower Guinea at an annual rainfall of 6000 mm.

Hallsworth and Costin (1953) draw attention to the possibility that a fluctuating water table could also be caused by alternate warmer and cooler seasons with a more or less constant rainfall. Decreased evapotranspiration during the cooler season would allow the water table to rise, particularly in favourable physiographic positions, and increased water loss during the warmer season lowers it again. It should therefore be possible for plinthite formation to take place in subtropical and even warm temperate climates. An example could be the plinthite soils of Madagascar on the high plateaus where the mean annual temperature is 10° C (Maignien, 1964).

c) Vegetation. Both Glinka (1927) and Erhart (1935) were of the opinion that plinthite soils were especially developed under a forest vegetation. Hallsworth and Costin (9153) concluded from climatic conditions which are considered to have been responsible for plinthization and from the plant fossils found in associated deep leads, that a rain forest existed during the period of the genesis of soils with plinthite in New South Wales (Australia). The same authors are also of the opinion that in localities with more impeded drainage conditions swamp communities could have prevailed. Rosanov and Rosanova (1961) and Rosanov (1964) stated that the vegetation of laterite soils in Burma was a moist tropical forest. Induration of the original plinthite soils would have occurred after the disappearance of the forest cover, as is also maintained by several other authors (Aubert, 1950, 1959; Alexander and Cady, 1962). Reforestation leads to the disappearance of indurated horizons. Rosevaer (1942) reported a measurable reversal of hardening under a teak planting in about 16 years.

The rôle of the vegetation in soil formation is manifold. It protects the top soil from excessive drying out by filtering the sun's rays (1), it protects the soil from erosion by breaking the impact of rain drops and slowing down surface runoff (2), it decreases the effective precipitation (actual precipitation – surface runoff – evapotranspiration) (3), it produces organic material, the decomposition products of which can react with the mineral particles and promote changes in the parent material to form the soil (4), and it promotes the biological activity in the soil (5).

Especially the aspects (1), (2) and (4) are of interest in the hardening of plinthite soils. (Later it will be shown that aspect (5) is also of extreme significance in the formation of plinthite soils.) Removal of vegetation and consequent increased erosion cause higher temperatures in the top layer of the soil and larger temperature fluctuations in the subsoil, as is shown by table 11.15. Desiccation can therefore proceed to greater depth under a savannah vegetation. High temperature and desiccation accelerate ageing and crystallization of amorphous iron and aluminium hydrates (as was shown a.o. by van Schuylenborgh and Arens, 1950), thus cementing other materials imbedded in these hydrates. In this respect it is of interest to point to the preference of

TABLE II.15. *Soil temperatures at different depths and times, dependent on vegetation* (after d'Hoore, 1954)

	depth (cm)	T °C at 8	T °C at 11	T °C at 14
No vegetation	1	26.8	44.0	53.5
	10	27.5	31.7	36.8
Savannah vegetation under grass	1	24.7	41.5	50.4
	10	27.8	32.9	40.1
	20	27.5	33.4	41.1
Under shrubs	1	21.6	22.7	26.9
	10	23.0	22.9	24.8
	20	23.8	23.8	25.4
Air temperature (°C)		22.2	28.3	36.0

iron hydroxides to be absorbed by kaolinite (Fripiat and Gastuche, 1952; Kellerman and Tsyurupa, 1962; Follett, 1965), mentioned earlier.

A peculiar effect of vegetation was observed by d'Hoore (1954), Fripiat (1954) and Maignien (1958, 1961). The vegetation in question was a savannah. Firstly it appeared to attack the kaolinite and to assimilate the silica more strongly than a forest vegetation (see table 11.16). In this way the gibbsite content of the upper layer was increased, whilst the mobilized silica was returned to the soil, at least partly in the form of phytoliths, as was observed by Riquier (1960). Secondly the savannah debris had a considerable effect on the mobilization of iron. Probably it complexes iron, moves down into the soil to some depth and deposits the iron upon oxidation of the organic part of the complex. In this way even crusts could be formed, whereas under forest no such crust was observed. Similar soils were reported to be present in Madagascar by Segalen (1956), viz. leached ferruginous tropical soils and cuirassic ferruginous tropical soils.

It should be emphasized here, that the mechanism of crust formation is not essentially inherent to, though it can contribute to the plinthization process.

It would be of interest to see whether or not plinthite soils have occurred under the Sudanese savannah, which is to be considered to be formed as a result of climatic conditions and not to be a man-induced degradation phase of the original forest.

Maignien (1958, 1961) pointed this out and classified the soils as leached tropical ferruginous soils. The soils are shallower than 2.50 m and the indurated ferruginous horizon, either pisolithic, concretionary or crusty, is commonly situated at a depth of 15–150 cm and the thickness varies between 15 cm and 70 cm. These are dimensions uncommon to plinthite soils, except in cases of very poor drainage; the drainage of the soils is actually poor and they have therefore undergone strong influences by water excess and the subsequent high organic matter content. The case is more or less comparable to profile 3. Although certainly desilicated and enriched in sesquioxides, the soils are also strongly podzolized and form in this way a very special type (azonal) of plinthite (laterite) soils that should be distinguished from the normal (zonal) type of plinthite soils.

TABLE II.16. *SiO₂-content of Gramineae and forest species in Congo, expressed as weight percentages of material dried at 105°C* (after d'Hoore, 1954)

Gramineae	SiO_2 %	Forest species	SiO_2 (%) a	b
Brachyaria brizantha	4.5	Gilbertiodendron dewevrei	0.5	2.5
Brachyaria eminii	2.7	Scorodophleus zenkeri	0.1	1.8
Chloris gayana	4.1	Anonidium mannii	0.2	1 4
Cynodon dactylon	3.7	Musanga cecropioides	0.2	1.5
Cynodon major	2.6	Cynometra hankei	0.1	2.6
Digitaria umfolozi	4.1	Combretodendrum africanum	0.4	0.9
Echinochloa pyramidalis	4.7	Pterigopodium oxyphyllum	0.1	1.7
Panicum maximum	6.8	Pterocarpus soyauxii	0.1	0.5
Panicum maximum var. major	4.3	Panda oleosa	0.4	0.9
Paspalum dilatatum	2.8	Albizzia gumnifera	0.1	0.3
Pennisetum purpureum	3.6	Symphonia globulifera	0.1	0.2
Setaria sphacelata	3.1	Palisota spec.	1.7	3.7

a = stems; b = leaves

In conclusion, it may be stated, that a tropical rain forest is the original vegetation of the plinthite soils, and if the present soil has a savannah cover, this is the result of forest degradation. In some cases this savannah vegetation is able to contribute to the formation of extremely hard iron crusts, caused by a podzolization of the surface soil.

d) Physiography. Since a fluctuating groundwater table contributes greatly to the formation of plinthite soils in hot climates, it can be assumed that all topographic situations that favour such a fluctuation will also promote plinthite formation.

Many authors (a.o. Hallsworth and Costin, 1953; Stewart, 1954; Panton, 1956) have stated that a peneplain physiography is very suitable for plinthite formation. However, in such cases only climates with a marked alternation of wet and dry seasons, such as the subequatorial and tropical climates, can induce a fluctuation of the water table level. Broad valleys, e.g. the Amazon valley, with a flat topography are also favourable sites for plinthite formation, as was reported by Marbut (1930), Panton (1956), Sombroek (1966) and others.

Hallsworth and Costin (1953) point out the fact that plinthite soils may also occur in areas with undulating physiography and that in these cases the formation was less dependent on climate. They concluded that considerable fluctuations in the level of the water table may have occurred in the lower areas, since variations in water loss by variations in evapotranspiration due to seasonal fluctuations in temperature are magnified by topographic concentration.

As plinthite soils also occur on moderate slopes, although then limited to the lower areas lateral movement of groundwater downslope appears to have been of importance in the transportation of sesquioxides from higher slopes and their accumulation in lower areas. This mechanism was indicated by Hallsworth and Costin (1953), d'Hoore (1954), Riquier (1954), Maignien (1956, 1958) and Aubert (1963). Soils in such situations may contain a much higher content of sesquioxides than would be found in the case of rock weathering *in situ*. Campbell (1917), Greene (1947) and others suggest that this lateral transport is particularly responsible for sesquioxide accumulation in rocks which are poor in iron and aluminium bearing minerals, such as sandstones.

The profile descriptions given earlier, show that the corresponding horizons may vary considerably in thickness. These variations can be attributed, at least partly, to the physiography or changes in physiography (Hallsworth and Costin, 1953). In areas where the base level of erosion has been attained, watercourse entrenchment cannot proceed farther. The consequence is that the vertical fluctuations of the water table, due to seasonal variations of precipitation or temperature, occur in the same soil layer over a long period of time. Sesquioxide accumulation is then limited to a rather narrow band (the thickness depending on the capillarity of the material) above the highest water table level. Hence, the laterite horizon will be rather thin. However, sesquioxide accumulation will be extremely high due to the length of time in which the same water table fluctuations were being repeated. Consequently, such a horizon will become extremely hard upon exposure to the air.

On the other hand, in areas where the base level of stream entrenchment has not been attained the watercourses are still cutting downwards, thus lowering the ground water table continuously. Sesquioxide accumulation will then occur at progressively greater depths and new mottled and pallid horizons and weathering zones will be formed. If this lowering of the water table is sufficiently slow and even, there would be virtually no discontinuity in the zone of sesquioxide precipitation which would extend downwards into what hitherto had been mottled and pallid horizons. The latter zones change continuously in position but not in thickness. In this way plinthite zones are formed much thicker than would correspond with the zone of capillary fringe. The same result would occur when there is a gradual land-uplift during the desilication and plinthization processes and especially if this land-uplift keeps pace with the downward cutting of the watercourses and the weathering rate of the rock.

If there is, however, a gradual rise of the water table in an already present plinthite soil profile, as would be caused by slow land sinking or faulting or by increased precipitation on a land surface at base level of erosion, the mottled clay layer is reduced and transformed into a pallid zone. At the same time the lower part of the plinthite layer becomes the new mottled zone and the mobilized sesquioxides are moved upwards and are deposited in the upper part of the profile. In this way the pallid zone grows gradually thicker and the plinthite zone gradually thinner. Profiles are formed with a very thick pallid zone in proportion to the plinthite horizon.

Hallsworth and Costin (1953) observed the occurrence of soils with multiple laterite horizons. They explain the formation of these profiles as due to a relatively sudden entrenchment. If this happens, the area of sesquioxide accumulation would change suddenly from a higher to a lower level, resulting either in a discontinuity in the sesquioxide horizon or, where the changes in the level of the water table were greater, in the isolation of all of the original plinthite soil profile and the formation of a completely new profile below.

The same authors also state that profile replication may occur either on a regional or a local scale. The former would occur in areas where the land surface has undergone a relatively sudden uplift, resulting in correspondingly quicker stream entrenchment. Where, on the other hand, the profile replication occurs on a small scale in the same locality, stream entrenchment was probably retarded by the local occurrence of hard and soft bands in the bedrock. This retardation would have led to a constant water table level over a long period with the subsequent formation of a soil profile with

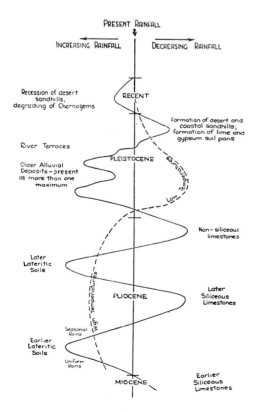

FIG. II.25. *Genesis of Oxisols with plinthite as related to change in climatic conditions in Queensland (after Whitehouse, 1940)*

plinthite. After the intersection of the hard band a period of rapid entrenchment would follow until the next hard layer is encountered and a new profile would start to form. Such local multiple plinthite zones would be expected to be shallower than those due to regional land movements. This was actually found by Hallsworth and Costin in New South Wales (Australia).

e) Age. The present-day climatic and topographic positions of the plinthite soils prove that many of them are old. This is particularly evident in arid areas; the present climatic conditions here do not allow the genesis of Oxisols with plinthite. An excellent example is the occurrence of laterite soils in Australia. Whitehouse (1940) indicates that the laterite soils of Queensland are the result of two humid periods in the Pliocene. Hanlon (1945) and Collwell (1950: Cited by Carroll and Woof, 1951) date the laterite soils of New South Wales of Miocene or Pliocene age (see fig. II.25).
Michel (1960) reports that the laterites of Senegal and Upper Gambia are of Lower Cretaceous, Eocene and Neogene age. Schnell (1949) considers the laterites of Guinea to be of Pre-Kamasian age. Schellmann (1966) found plinthite soils on marine deposits of Eocene age in S. E. Kalimantan (Indonesia).

Apart from these old formations more recent formations also occur, as indicated by many authors (Campbell, 1917; Marbut, 1932; Harrison, 1933; Sombroek, 1966; and many others). Leneuf (1959) and Leneuf and Aubert (1960) have tried to calculate the formation rate of Oxisols with plinthite, and more particularly of the desilication process, in a granitic bedrock under the forest vegetation of the Ivory Coast. They based their calculations on: 1) the quantity of water yearly drained from the soil, using Hénin's formulation,[1]) and being 1000 l/sq.m. at T = 26° C and P = 1800 to 2500 mm; 2) the chemical composition of the bedrock; 3) the content elements (Si, Ca, Mg, K, Na) in natural spring water and in the seepage water at the base of the laterite profile; and 4) the assumption of complete decomposition of the rock over a thickness of one meter; this stage was supposed to be reached if all the silica of the silicates has

TABLE II.17. *Composition of rock and drainage water and number of years needed for complete ferrallitization* (after Leneuf and Aubert, 1960)

	Bedrock contents in kg/m^3	Drainage water contents in p.p.m.	Number of years needed for complete ferrallitization (drainage: 1000 mm; see text)
Si total	883.5	15.0	76,254
Si silicates	547.0		47,417
Ca	24.8	5.5	12,833
Mg	0.4	3.1	938
K	102.8	2.1	64,025
Na	81.6	23.9	10,400

[1] $D = \dfrac{\gamma P^3}{1 + \gamma P^2}$, where $\gamma = \dfrac{1}{0.15\,T - 0.13}$, D = annual drainage in mm, P = annual precipitation in mm, and T = temperature in °C.

been eliminated. This last assumption is, of course, purely hypothetical, as part of the silica combines with aluminium to form kaolinite.

The composition of the rock, the mean composition of the water samples and the mean number of years needed for complete ferrallitization (elimination of the silicates) are reported in table II.17. From this table Leneuf and Aubert (1960) concluded that, as a mean, a period of 50,000 years is needed to complete the desilication of a granite over a thickness of one meter. The authors emphasized that this number has only a theoretical value, as the complete removal of silicates and constant climatic conditions were postulated. They also state that only $\frac{1}{2}$ to $\frac{2}{3}$ of the silicium is drained off in the case of the granite under investigation, so that a shorter time could be assumed for the ferrallitization. On the other hand, the thickness of an Oxisol profile with plinthite is generally greater than 1 meter; if instead a depth of 4 meters is taken, about 120,000 years would be needed for the formation of such a profile.

However it may be, the above mentioned considerations make it clear that plinthite Oxisols are almost certainly formed under changing climatic conditions. The Quaternary era in the tropics is known to have had a number of pluvial and interpluvial periods. Fig. II.25 and table II.18 give the time-scale for the subdivision of the Quaternary in Queensland (Australia) and East Africa. The table shows that an Oxisol with plinthite or a laterite soil can be formed under the effect of three pluvials whilst the present-day conditions seem to be an interpluvial. It will be difficult, if at all possible, to trace the influence of the climatic variations on the development of the plinthitic Oxisol profile. It may be suggested that an interpluvial (drier) period predominantly affects the top part of the profile, whereas the lower part is preserved because it is not moistened. At the next pluvial period the development of the lower part can proceed where it had stopped, in this way resulting in a profile in which the lower part does not show the effect of the dry period. Its development has only been retarded. The top part, however, can be strongly influenced in that the decomposition of the organic material is essentially different. Under normal humid tropical conditions the decomposition of the organic material is rapid and complete, so that the organic substances yield only carbon dioxide, water, nitrate, sulphate and phosphate. Carbonation of the material is then a predominating process. Under drier conditions, however, bacterial life is strongly inhibited so that the decomposition products are different from those formed under humid conditions. Organic acids possibly come into play and lead to a type of podzolization process, thus contributing to the removal of sesquioxides from the top soil, a process which was already mentioned when discussing the effect of a savannah vegetation on soil formation. It could lead to increased deposition of iron in an already formed plinthite horizon. If this effect is not minimized during a subsequent pluvial period, a profile with an extremely dense, and eventually extremely firm, top part of the plinthite zone would be the result. In this way one could defend the idea that the variation of the climate has not essentially changed the composition of the profile. On the other hand, local conditions of topography, parent material, etc. can have been such, that the climatic variations have resulted in the formation of very complicated profiles.

TABLE II.18. *Time scale of the pluvial and interpluvial periods in East-Africa of the Quaternary era, compared with the European equivalents* (Wollstedt, 1965; Holmes, 1966)

GLACIAL and INTERGLACIAL Phases	High Sea Levels (p. 708)	Black Sea Levels	Lake Levels Caspian Sea	Lake Levels East Africa	PLUVIAL and *Interpluvial* Phases in East Africa	Years B.P.
	Present day	High		Low after fluctuations from	Climate becoming less humid	
(W IIc)	*Flandrian* rise of sea-level from		slightly higher.....		NAKURAN	10,000–13,000
				Minor recession	Short dry interval	
W IIb		Low		High	┌Later MAKALIAN (dated to 11,000 B.P.)	13,000–20,000
W IIa/b		?		Recession		28,000
W IIa		Low		High	└Earlier MAKALIAN	30,000–60,000
W I/IIa	*Epi-monastirian*	High		Low	*Interpluvial*	60,000–95,000
W I		Low		High	GAMBLIAN	95,000–125,000
R/W (Eemian; Ipswichian)	*Monastirian*	High		Low	*Interpluvial*	125,000–235,000
R II		Low		High	┌KANJERAN (in part)	235,000
R I/II		High		Low	│?	
R I		Origin of	—	High	└KANJERAN (in part)	360,000
M/R (Holsteinian; Hoxnian)	*Tyrrhenian*	Black Sea	Tectonic movements			360,000–670,000
M				High	KAMASIAN	670,000–780,000
G/M (Cromerian)	*Milazzian*				*Interpluvial*	780,000–900,000
G				High	KAGUERAN	900,000–1,150,000
D/G (Villafranchian)	*Sicilian*			?	?	1,150,000–1,370,000

W = Würm; R = Risz; M = Mindel; G = Günz; D = Donau.

1.1.8.3. *The process*

As already mentioned in section 1.1.8.2, three phases in the genesis of Oxisols with plinthite have been distinguished (see fig. II.24), although it is realized that these stages are not sharply separated. As a matter of fact, the given scheme is considered to be illustrative of the ideas of Simonson (1959), who stated that all soil forming processes occur in all soils; only the balance among the processes is not the same and is determined by the geographical position. To this may be added that even within one profile or soil body or pedon the balance can be strongly different, depending on the position in the profile.

In the following short discussion the process will be considered, for the sake of simplicity, to be separated into the three stages mentioned.

Stage 1. It can be expected that processes of hydration, carbonation, hydrolysis, oxidation and dissolution act during this first stage. It has been proved that formation of new minerals occurs, of which kaolinite and hydrated oxides of iron and aluminium are the most important. Sometimes illite and montmorillonite may crystallize, but this is only temporary. Bases and part of the silica and aluminium are removed because the drainage is free. As soon as vegetation starts to grow, with subsequent addition of organic matter to the soil, iron may be mobilized; this mobilization will, however, be of minor importance in the beginning, as the decomposition of the organic debris is too rapid to allow the organic acids a significant rôle. The material will be rapidly decomposed into CO_2 and H_2O, and this carbonic acid, although it may intensify the weathering reactions tremendously, will not have a marked effect on the mobilization of iron.

How the processes are proceeding and why in one case practically only kaolinite and in a second case predominantly gibbsite is formed, is still a matter for investigation. The experimental and physico-chemical approach to these problems will be discussed in Part III, Chapter 1.

The process called in the preceding pages the desilication process continues in the later stages of development, although under different conditions.

Stage 2. When soil development reaches stage 2, a quite different process comes into play, viz. the dissolution of iron and manganese and their deposition into mottles, or in other words, the formation of the mottled clay zone. It is assumed that this zone will have in the beginning the characteristics of a pseudo-gley, as the rock acts in this stage as an impervious layer. Consequently, part of the profile is under poorly aerated conditions in the wet season, whereas in the dry season water evaporates and air will be plentiful. In other words processes of reduction and oxidation will become active, whereas in the first stage only oxidation processes prevailed. During the reduction state iron and manganese are reduced in places where the redox-potential is low enough; they then become mobile and diffuse to places where the redox-potential is higher, e.g. in the neighbourhood of pores which still contain some oxygen. At these places oxidation and deposition take place. The iron and manganese may be mobilized at the bottom of the profile, transported with the rising groundwater and oxidized in the higher situated layers, but may also move over short distances within individual layers.

Upon continuous weathering the layers above the highest groundwater level are moistened with groundwater only by capillarity (see fig. 11.24) and this is thought to be the moment that the mottled clay is transferred into the typical plinthite. Only weak reduction and, consequently, slight translocations of iron and manganese occur in this fringe. Ageing and crystallization of the already accumulated iron, manganese, and aluminium hydroxides come into play thus giving the plinthite its very firm consistence. To this may be added the transformation of the silicic acid in the rising saturated or even supersaturated soil water into opal, chalcedony, or trydimite. It is thought that the process of the transformation of the rock into plinthite material might be summarized from a chemical viewpoint as follows:

If a mineral aggregate is involved in the process of weathering, one of the processes is the hydration of the minerals. Water is confined to the surface and the crevices and fissures of the aggregates. At the surface and in the fissures therefore, 'micro-drainage' conditions are poor, although 'macro-drainage' may be good. Under these conditions high pH values and high salt concentrations may occur at the surface and in the fissures of the mineral aggregates. This implies that conditions are favourable for the formation of amorphous Al-hydroxide gels or pseudo-boehmite (Gastuche and Herbillon, 1962; Hsu and Bates, 1964; Hsu, 1966, 1967), amorphous Fe (III)-hydroxides (under high redox-potentials: see fig. 111.9), amorphous silica (figs. 111.7 and 8), and even clay minerals of the smectite group (such as montmorillonite, fig. .8).

In this way the mineral aggregate changes into a mixture of the amorphous and crypto-crystalline products mentioned. All these products are metastable from a thermo-dynamical point of view and will be transformed (aged) into stable minerals, according to reactions such as (1), (2), and (3):

$$Fe(OH)_3 \text{ (a, s)} \rightarrow \alpha\text{–FeOOH(s)} + 2H_2O \text{ – – – – – – – – – – – – – – – – – – (1)}$$
(amorphous ferric-   (goethite)
      hydroxide)
$$Fe(OH)_3 \text{ (a,s)} + AlOOH(s) \rightarrow \alpha\text{–FeOOH(s)} + Al(OH)_3 \text{ (s)   – – – – – – – – – (2)}$$
            (pseudo-boehmite)   (gibbsite)
$$2Fe(OH)_3 \text{ (a,s)} + AlOOH \text{ (s)} \rightarrow \alpha\text{–Fe}_2O_3 \text{ (s)} + Al(OH)_3 \text{ (s)} + 2H_2O \text{ – – – – – – (3)}$$
                    (hematite)

which all have negative standard free-energy changes of reaction, as can be calculated from the standard free-energies of formation, listed by Garrels and Christ (1965), and Krauskopf (1967). Consequently, the aggregate will be transformed into a more or less porous fabric of minerals which are more stable than the original ones (see figs. ii.5, 6, and 8, where pseudomorphic gibbsite, and goethite in an amorphous iron-hydroxide mass can be observed). 'Micro-drainage' then becomes better and montmorillonite can be transformed into kaolinite and finally into gibbsite (fig. iii.8). In the wet periods the pores and fissures are filled with the rising Fe^{2+}- and Mn^{2+}-ions and H_4SiO_4 bearing soil solution, oxidation takes place and the pores are gradually filled with iron-minerals containing some manganese and silicic acid, giving rise to a firm fabric. This is the redistribution process, or plinthization, which acts over very short as well as larger distances. As gibbsite is more soluble than the iron hydroxides it will be, at least partly, leached and the spaces left can be refilled by iron hydroxides. The silicic acid may help in the formation of a firm fabric by the formation of opal or chalcedony.

It will be clear that such a material will greatly harden upon exposure to the air and upon frequent wetting and drying because of the continued loss of moisture (dehydration) and crystallization. Such a hardening invariably occurs after deforestation, e.g. by shifting cultivation, with the subsequent erosion of the surface soil. The soft material of the laterite, being predominantly kaolinite, is washed out by the rains giving the laterite a porous, vesicular, vermicular, or cellular appearance.

During the second stage, and possibly also in the first stage, a textural B-horizon can be formed, as the soil is not yet sufficiently deprived of exchangeable bases, so that clay may be mobile (Part III, Chapter 4). That such early formation of an argillic horizon can occur is shown by the occasional occurrence of prominent clay coatings in the plinthite zone (fig. ii.16). At later stages this argillic horizon can be destroyed because the clay becomes immobile as it is changed into an H-Al-clay and the clay coatings are destroyed as the result of swelling and shrinking of the soil colloids and the activity of the biosphere (growing plant roots, burrowing soil animals) or because the clay is transformed by desilication processes as discussed in Part III, Chapter 1.
Stage 3. As already mentioned, stage 3 starts when a permanent groundwater table is present. The formation of the pallid zone, the permanently reduced zone commences

and the mottled clay is now formed as a normal gley horizon. Also the weathering (desilication) proceeds from this moment on under permanently reduced conditions.

At this stage the top zone has been strongly deprived of nutritional elements and the consequence is that the decomposition of the organic material proceeds in a manner different from that at earlier stages. The decomposition of organic material in the tropics is generally very fast and complete if drainage conditions are not too bad and the soil not absolutely deficient in nutrients. As soon as the bacterial activity slows down, the decomposition of organic material also retards and intermediate decomposition products are formed. These products may be capable of complexing certain metals, e.g. iron and manganese and mobilizing these elements. The surface soil can therefore be podzolized in the sense that some iron and/or manganese are leached down and deposited at a depth where the conditions for complexing are less favourable than in the surface soil. As this is a process commonly occurring in podzolic soils and podzols, it will be discussed in Chapter 2 of this Part, and the more theoretical aspects in Chapter 3 of Part III.

It is realized that the short description of the soil formation process is insufficient to explain all the characteristics of the Oxisols with plinthite. One of these is the simultaneous precipitation of both manganese and iron oxides on the same spot. From a chemical point of view this is difficult to explain. Another question is how to explain the reduction of iron beyond the zone of root activity; it is very difficult to explain how the low partial oxygen pressures necessary for the reduction of iron can be obtained without the interference of organic matter. The answer to these questions can only be given after a thorough study of the factors influencing the redox processes in the soil. As this is a purely theoretical problem, it will be discussed in Part III, Chapter 2.

1.2. OXISOLS WITHOUT PLINTHITE

Typical Oxisols without plinthite are deep and friable to very friable soils with an oxic horizon. Horizon differentiation is indistinct as the horizon boundaries are diffuse. There is generally no clay movement and the structure is granular or subangular blocky and very stable. The soils are porous and have a rapid permeability. The oxic horizon does not harden upon exposure to the air as do Oxisols with plinthite. If the solum is very deep (e.g. thicker than 4 meters), it is sometimes underlain by a mottled clay horizon. Otherwise the solum lies directly on the weathered rock. Concretions are absent or near-absent and are generally soft. Manganese concretions are frequently present. Due to the high porosity, depth and stable structure most Oxisols without plinthite are only slightly susceptible to erosion and certainly less susceptible than other soils under similar topographical conditions.

Fig. II. 26 (see p. 199) shows a photograph of a thin section of a part of the B-horizon of a Latosol. It is evident that there is no segregation of iron; its distribution is very homogeneous. The material is very porous and the formation of this horizon has obviously taken place under oxidating conditions. The process responsible for the even distribution of iron is sometimes called rubefaction, a term used by Kubiena for the reddening of the Red Mediterranean Soils.

232

The A, B, C nomenclature will be used in the description of the Latosol profiles as the weathering conditions do not diverge greatly even over considerable depths. The increasing reducing conditions, which leave their mark so strongly on the formation of Oxisols with plinthite, are absent here.

1.2.1. SOME OXISOL PROFILES WITHOUT PLINTHITE

In the course of time several types of Latosols have been described, some with fundamental analytical details, but only few are analyzed up to and including the bedrock. However, this is necessary to obtain a clear insight into the transformations that have taken place during the formation of the soils. As far as the authors are aware, the best investigated Latosols are those formed on serpentine rocks (Bennett and Allison[1], 1928; Roberts[1], 1942; Schellmann, 1964; our own investigations on serpentinites in West-Irian, Indonesia). As the soils in question are very similar, the investigation of Schellmann (1964) will only be discussed.

Profile 6. Kukusan mountains, S. E. Kalimantan, Indonesia. During a geological investigation in 1956 by Gaertner and Wirtz (see: Schellmann, 1964) it appeared that the Kukusan mountains were covered with a thick layer of ferruginous material. Samples were taken every half meter up to and including the rock. A profile description was not made. From the analytical details and the too brief description of the geological samples, the following succession of horizons may be concluded:

A_1	0–1	m	Brownish friable material with some concretions
B_1	1–2	m	Brown to yellowish brown friable material with very few concretions
B_2	2–5	m	Yellowish brown to yellow friable material
B_3	5–6.5 m		Yellow friable material
C_1	6.5–7	m	Yellow friable material
C_2	7–7.5 m		Strongly weathered serpentine with brownish discolourations
R	+ 7.5 m		Very weakly weathered serpentinized peridotite

The profile is situated at an altitude of approximately 500 m above sea level. The rainfall varies monthly from 300 mm in January to 120 mm in September, so it is very high. The mean annual temperature is approximately 24° C. The vegetation is a tropical rain forest. There is no dry season in the year: water movement in the profile is always downwards. Internal and external drainage are good. Classification places this soil in the Typic Haplorthox subgroup.

The analyses of Schellmann (1964) include pH, exchangeable bases, total elemental composition, X-ray and DT-analyses, and electron microscope investigations. The $pH(H_2O)$ varies from 5.0 in the A_1 to 5.3 in the B_3 horizon and increases from there on to 8.0 in the C_2 horizon. The pH(0.1MKCl) increased from 5.9 in the A_1 to 6.5 in the B_3 horizon and decreased from there on to 5.7 in the C_2 horizon. In this soil pH(KCl) is therefore higher than $pH(H_2O)$ which is indicative of strongly weathered soils with a nearly complete removal of electronegative substances such as silicic acid and an accumulation of electropositive substances such as sesquioxides may be. This

[1] Already discussed in Part I, Chapter 3.

conclusion is confirmed by the chemical and mineralogical analyses as will be shown later.

Exchangeable Ca, Na, and K are constant throughout the profile and amount to 3.5 m.e., 0.3 m.e., and 0.1 m.e./100 g of soil, respectively. Exchangeable Mg decreases from 40.4 m.e./100 g of soil in the C_2 horizon to 14.1 m.e./100 g in the C_1 horizon. From there on it cannot be traced anymore. The high value of exchangeable Mg in the C_2 and C_1 horizon points to the presence of a smectitic clay mineral, which was confirmed by mineralogical, X-ray, and DT-analyses.

The chemical analysis is given in table II.19 and the derived molar ratios in table II.19a. The tables show very clearly that the desilication process is well advanced. Furthermore it appears that under the prevailing conditions the insoluble oxides of Ti, Cr, and Fe accumulate 7 to 8 times the amount in the rock, which indicates that this profile is a residual soil. Magnesium is nearly completely removed. Al_2O_3 and Fe_2O_3 increase slightly from the A_1 to the B_2 horizon, whereas SiO_2 decreases; it seems therefore that some podzolization is active, which is particularly evident from the derived molar silica/sesquioxide ratios. It is probable that this process cannot be observed in the field. Table II.19a shows that Al has decreased with respect to Fe upon weathering, which can be explained on the basis of the solubility products of aluminium and iron hydroxide. Signs of reduction processes are not present and the conclusion can be drawn that the processes involved in the formation of this profile are the desilication process and to some extent eluviation of iron and aluminium.

TABLE II.19. *Chemical composition of profile 6* (Schellmann, 1964)

Hor.	SiO_2 %	Al_2O_3 %	Fe_2O_3 %	FeO %	MgO %	Cr_2O_3 %	NiO %	MnO %	TiO_2 %	SO_3 %	P_2O_5 %	H_2O+ %	Total %
A_1	7.6	10.9	65.1	0.1	0.3	2.2	0.4	0.3	0.3	0.3	0.1	12.7	100.3
B_1	3.7	13.8	65.4	n.d.	0.4	1.8	0.7	0.8	0.3	0.6	tr	13.4	100.9
B_2	2.5	12.1	68.7	0.1	0.9	2.4	1.0	0.8	0.2	0.5	tr	12.5	99.7
B_3	7.3	9.8	60.4	n.d.	6.4	2.7	1.0	0.9	0.1	0.3	tr	11.6	100.4
C_1	19.0	8.4	50.0	n.d.	7.6	2.1	1.2	0.7	0.1	0.2	tr	10.6	99.9
C_2	34.0	5.6	34.9	0.1	11.4	1.4	1.8	0.5	0.1	0.1	tr	9.7	99.1
R	39.4	2.5	8.4	0.3	33.2	0.3	2.1	0.1	tr	n.d.	tr	13.3	99.6

Interesting conclusions can be drawn if the mineralogical changes in the profile are studied. The normative mineralogical composition was established from the chemical analysis by combining the goethite-norm (Van der Plas and Van Schuylenborgh, 1970) and the epinorm (Burri, 1964) calculations (table II.20).

The increase of kaolinite in the top of the profile is contradictory to what can be deduced from figs. III.7 and 8. In fact one should have expected a decrease of kaolinite in the uppermost horizons, as has actually been found in the Laterite Soils, as drainage in the upper part of the profile is better than in the lower part, approaching conditions characteristic for the stability field of gibbsite. The increase of kaolinite in the top soil might be explained in various ways: 1) Actual enrichment in silica to form kaolinite from gibbsite. Although this reaction is possible, it is not likely to be the responsible factor here, as there are no signs of a fluctuating, temporary water table, which could have enriched the surface with dissolved silica. Vegetation in the form of leaf shedding could have supplied the surface soil with silica.

TABLE II.19a. *Molar SiO$_2$/sesquioxide ratios of profile 6*

Horizon	SiO$_2$/R$_2$O$_3$	SiO$_2$/Al$_2$O$_3$	SiO$_2$/Fe$_2$O$_3$	Al$_2$O$_3$/Fe$_2$O$_3$
A$_1$	0.2	1.2	0.3	0.3
B$_1$	0.1	0.5	0.1	0.3
B$_2$	0.1	0.3	0.1	0.3
B$_3$	0.3	1.3	0.3	0.2
C$_1$	0.8	3.8	1.0	0.3
C$_2$	2.1	10.3	2.6	0.2
R	8.5	26.8	12.5	0.5

TABLE II.20. *Normative mineralogical composition of profile 6* (percentages given are weight percentages)

Hor.	Ser %	Aug %	Mt %	Sp %	Chl %	Q %	Mm %	Kaol %	Gi %	Go %	Misc %
A$_1$	–	–	–	–	–	–	0.9	15.5	7.7	73.9	2.0
B$_1$	–	–	–	–	–	–	1.3	6.3	17.5	71.4	3.5
B$_2$	–	–	–	–	–	–	2.8	1.6	17.4	74.3	4.0
B$_3$	–	–	–	–	18.3	–	3.9	1.7	3.8	68.0	4.3
C$_1$	–	–	–	–	15.5	5.8	17.1	–	–	57.2	4.3
C$_2$	13.0	–	–	–	15.7	21.5	7.2	–	–	39.6	3.0
R	43.6–76.8	40.4–0	7.3–0	3.9–0	0–7.2	0–5.8	–	–	–	4.1–9.6	0.7

Ser = serpentine; Aug = augite; Mt = magnetite; Sp = spinell; Chl = chlorite; Q = silica; Mm = montmorillonite; Kaol = kaolinite; Gi = gibbsite; Go = goethite; Misc = miscellaneous (chromite + rutile).

Although data is available on the amount of organic material falling onto the soil, there is only little information on its mineral content, especially in respect to SiO$_2$, Al$_2$O$_3$, and Fe$_2$O$_3$. Some data was published by Van Schuylenborgh (1957, 1958), who analyzed litter samples of four rainforests in Java (Indonesia) on soils derived from andesitic volcanic ash and of two rainforests grown on ash soils derived from dacitic material. The results with respect to Si, Al, and Fe are given in table II.21. This data reveals that vegetation could have contributed to the increase of the silica content in the surface soil, as the silica/sesquioxide ratios are much higher than those of the solum. However, there is too little data available to allow any general conclusion. 2) A second possibility may be the assumption that in the surface soil another process is acting than in the subsoil, a suggestion already made earlier. Upon the impoverishment of the surface soil in nutrients due to prolonged leaching, the bacterial decomposition of organic matter (mineralization) slows down gradually; the consequence is that intermediate organic decomposition products come into play in soil formation. Some of these products may complex iron and aluminium and, if soluble complexes

TABLE II.21. *Mean composition of litter of rainforests on Java* (Indonesia)

Forest on soil from	SiO_2 %	Al_2O_3 %	Fe_2O_3 %	SiO_2/Al_2O_3	SiO_2/Fe_2O_3
andesite	2.51	1.15	0.20	3.8	42
dacite	8.75	0.30	0.15	49	146

are formed, cause an increased mobility of the metals. Upon decomposition of the organic part of the complexes or upon hydrolysis at some depth, the metal is set free, hydrolyzed and precipitated. Consequently kaolinite is enriched residually. More details about this process will be discussed in Chapter 3 of Part. III. 3) Finally, it is possible that the initial stages of desilication have taken place under poorer drainage conditions than the present-day ones. Schellmann (1964) stated that weathering already started before the pre-eocene upheaval of the Kukusan-mountains and it is therefore likely that the drainage conditions were poorer than at present; consequently, transformation of kaolinite into gibbsite, which is induced by prolonged and intensive leaching (see figs. III.7 and 8), was not possible. The deeper layers, especially the present B_2 horizon, have only minor amounts of silicate clay minerals: apparently drainage conditions improved gradually upon upheaval with the subsequent complete destruction of the original minerals. Silica was leached and gibbsite and goethite accumulated. Upon increase of the weathering depths leaching of the subsoil was reduced again and under these conditions the formation of chlorites and even smectites appears to be possible. The presence of montmorillonite and amorphous silica in the C_1 and C_2 horizons especially indicates slow drainage (see figs. III.7 and 8). As a conclusion it seems justified to assume that mechanism 2) offers an acceptable explanation for the peculiar distribution of minerals in the upper four horizons.

The interdependance of amorphous silica and montmorillonite is interesting. In the C_2 horizon there is an excess of silica over montmorillonite, whereas in the C_1 horizon the reverse is true and serpentine has disappeared in the C_1. Apparently montmorillonite has been formed at the expense of serpentine and silica. Chlorites seem to be formed under a wider variety of conditions as they occur in the C_2, C_1, and B_3 horizons in equal amounts.

As the Oxisols without plinthite show a similar pattern of mineral transformation, only the environmental conditions and the analyses of some further profiles will be reported, with some additional remarks if necessary.

Oxisols do not occur only at low or moderately high altitudes. They also occur at higher altitudes between 1000 and 2500 meters e.g. in Africa, Burma and Vietnam (Maufe, 1928; Ellis, 1952; Ruhe and Cady, 1954; Fridland, 1961; Rosanov and Rosanova, 1961, 1964; Young and Stephen, 1965). Some of these Oxisols have a dark horizon in the subsoil and are then called Dark Horizon Latosols (Ruhe and Cady, 1954; the soils reported by Ellis, 1952, are probably similar).

The environmental conditions can be summarized as follows: The rainfall is seasonal, in Africa from November to April (Ellis, 1952; Young and Stephen, 1965), in Burma and Vietnam from April to November (Fridland 1961; Rosanov and Rosanova, 1964);

it varies between 875 mm to 1400 mm annually. In the wet season precipitation exceeds evapotranspiration and in the dry season the reverse is true. The open-pan evaporation varies from 800 to 1250 mm annually (Young and Stephen, 1965). The temperature varies from approximately $18°$ C in the dry season to $25°$ C in the wet season. Drainage conditions are always good. The vegetation varies from tropical evergreen mountain forest to open savannah. Parent materials are various: granites to basalts and derived sediments. The soils are of Tertiary to Late Quaternary age (Ruhe and Cady, 1952; Young and Stephen, 1965).

The best investigated soils of this type are the red clays to the North of Salisbury, S. Rhodesia (Maufe, 1928; Ellis, 1952), and will therefore be discussed. A profile (profile 7) was studied at the Agricultural Experiment Station, Salisbury. The vegetation was formerly an open savannah with *Brachystegia spiciformis* and *Isoberlinia globiflora*. The altitude is 1470 m above sea level; rainfall is 850 mm annually and falls from November to March. The rains are preceded by two dry hot months and are followed by a short autumn passing to a dry, cold winter, in which, however, the day temperatures may be quite high. The rainy season is a period of intense chemical and biological activity, whereas during the dry season such activity is brought almost to a standstill. The parent rock is an olivine-dolerite. The soil is considered to be very largely residual, as the ground in the vicinity is level with only a very slight slope to the west.

The (short) profile description reads as follows:

Horizon	Depth (m)	
A_1	0–0.15	Brownish red, firm (dry) clay with excellent crumb structure. Numerous roots. pH 6.1.
B_1	0.15–0.37	Reddish-brown, firm clay. Crumb structure. Numerous roots. pH 5.8.
B_{21}	0.37–1.35	Red, friable clay. Crumbly. Numerous roots. pH 5.6.
B_{22}	1.35–1.43	A layer of compacted soil fragments and pebbles, with faces stained with iron and manganese. The thickness of this layer varies. Forms a wavy line. pH 5.3.
B_3	1.43–2.70	Brown loamy soil, stained with iron and manganese. Very friable. Concretions are present. pH 5.7.
C_1	2.70–3.60	Reddish-brown almost completely decomposed rock. pH 5.9. Strongly mottled with red.
C_2	3.60–6.00	Yellow-grey-green decomposing rock. pH 6.2–7.2.
R	+6.00	Almost unweathered olivine-dolerite.

In the whole profile and in the parent rock fine concretions occur of a shiny metallic-looking appearance. They appeared to consist of titaniferous magnetic iron oxide (composition: SiO_2, 1.8%; Al_2O_3, 1.6%; TiO_2, 12.4%; Fe_3O_4, 83.0%).

The profile dries out rapidly and readily to the B_{22} horizon. The lower layers dry out more slowly with fairly large, mainly vertical cracks. The B_{22} horizon appears to be the limit of normal drying and this could be the reason for its specific characteristics.

There is some clay translocation from the top to the B horizons; the clay contents of the A_1, $B_1 + B_{21} + B_{22}$, and B_3 horizons are: 48%, 54%, and 47%, respectively. The clay content of the C_1 horizon is 30% and of the C_2 horizon 10%.

In the profile of Ruhe and Cady (1954) the B_{22} is about 65 cm thick and consists of a friable, weak fine to medium subangular blocky structure. Reddish brown to dusky red firm subrounded aggregates occur. This horizon showed a slightly higher organic matter content than the horizons above and below. This could also be true for the profile of Ellis (see above) as the black-staining could be caused not only by manganese. However, data on the C content is not available.

A complete analysis of the top soil, subsoil, decomposing rock and fresh rock is presented by Maufe (1928; table II.22). The normative mineralogical composition is shown in table II.23.

TABLE II.22. *Chemical composition of profile 7*

	SiO$_2$ %	Al$_2$O$_3$ %	Fe$_2$O$_3$ %	FeO %	MgO %	CaO %	Na$_2$O %	K$_2$O %	TiO$_2$ %	P$_2$O$_5$ %	MnO %	H$_2$O+ %
Topsoil	42.5	25.2	16.9	–	0.9	0.2	0.1	0.2	1.9	tr	0.3	11.9
Subsoil	40.9	27.2	17.9	–	0.5	0.2	0.1	0.2	1.6	0.05	0.2	11.9
Decomposing rock	43.8	23.3	16.7	–	2.9	2.7	0.8	0.2	1.4	0.1	0.2	8.4
Rock	47.7	15.3	1.0	8.0	9.6	13.7	1.9	0.5^5	0.7	0.1	0.1	–

TABLE II.23. *Normative mineralogical composition of profile 7* (weight percentages)

	Plg	Bi	Aug	Ol	Kaol	Mm	Ms	Zo	Q	Go	Misc
Topsoil	0.8	–	–	–	62.0	3.4	1.5	0.7	10.5	19.1	1.9
Subsoil	0.8	–	–	–	66.4	1.9	1.5	0.6	7.3	19.9	1.5
Decomposing rock	6.8	–	–	–	44.9	9.5	1.6	10.4	7.4	17.8	1.6
Rock	48.3	5.0	31.8	12.7	–	–	–	–	–	–	2.3

Plg = plagioclases; Bi = biotite; Aug = augite; Ol = olivine; Kaol = kaolinite; Mm = montmorillonite; Ms = muscovite (illite); Zo = zoisite; Q = quartz; Go = goethite; Misc = miscellaneous.

Note the predominance of kaolinite and the presence of some montmorillonite pointing to the fact that this profile is far less leached than profile 6.

The profile should be classified either as a Eutrustox or a Sombrihumox.

Other members of the Oxisols without plinthite are what the Belgian soil scientists call the Ferrisols and Ferralsols (Sys, 1961; d'Hoore, 1963). The Ferrisol has a profile with a structural B horizon with clay skins on the surface of the aggregates. The shiny coatings are not always evident when the profile is dry. They may be clay or mixed alumino-silica or alumina gel coatings (see also p. 239). The weatherable mineral reserve is generally low but may exceed 10% of the 50-250μ fraction. The silt/clay ratio (silt, 20-2μ; clay, < 2μ) is generally wider than 0.2 on alluvium and sedimentary rocks, and wider than 0.15 on igneous and metamorphic rocks. The Ferralsol has no clay skins, a very low mineral reserve and a narrow silt/clay ratio. As far as known, there is no information available on a complete profile including the bedrock; however, the upper part of several profiles from Zambia and Cameroon[1]) has been investigated.

[1] Thanks are due to Mr H. J. M. Verhoeven, who collected the samples.

All these profiles show very clearly the podzolic tendencies in the soil forming process and one of them will be described (profile 8 from Cameroon, Bambuta-province, north of Oschang, Djuttitsa). It is a high-level, and consequently, humic representative of an intergrade between a Ferrisol and Ferralsol; it has been formed on material weathered from basaltic rock. The profile was taken on a slightly convex flat plateau with a slope of 5% and altitude of 1900 m above sea level. Internal and external drainage are good. The vegetation is a herbaceous grass vegetation with *Sporobolus pyramidalis*. There is some sheet erosion between grass clumps. The precipitation is 1800 mm annually, falling within 8 months. No data about temperature was available. The profile description, made in the wet season, reads as follows:

Horizon	Depth (cm)	
o	2–0	Numerous roots of the grass sod.
A_{11}	0–20	Dark reddish brown (5YR 3/3: d)– black (5YR 2/1: m) clay with a moderately developed, fine crumb structure. Very friable. Some hard nodules are present. Numerous fine roots. Clear and smooth boundary to
A_{12}	20–38	Dark reddish brown (5YR 3/4: d–2.5YR 2/4: m) clay with a well developed, fine crumb structure. Friable. Numerous fine roots. Abrupt and smooth boundary to
B_1	38–50	Dark red (2.5YR 3/6: d)– dusky red (10R 3/4: m) clay with a weakly developed, fine subangular blocky structure. Firm. Sticky. Some hard concretions. Many roots. Clear and smooth boundary to
B_2	50–130	Red (2.5YR 5/6: m) clay with a weakly developed, medium to coarse subangular blocky structure; at the lower part also angular blocky elements occur. Shiny coatings on structural peds. Sticky. Common to many fine pores. Common to many fine roots. Some hard red fragments. Gradual and smooth boundary to
B_3	130–?	Red (10R 4/6: d)– dark red (10R 3/6: m) clay with very fine blocky structure. Sticky. Many fine pores. Some firm nodules with shiny surfaces. Very few roots. The biological activity (termites) occurs predominantly in the lower part of the profile.

The profile should be classified as a Typic Acrohumox. The analyses are presented in tables II.24, 25, 26, and 27.

TABLE II.24. *Chemical composition of profile 8*

Hor.	SiO_2 %	Al_2O_3 %	Fe_2O_3 %	CaO %	MgO %	Na_2O %	K_2O %	TiO_2 %	MnO %	H_2O+ %
A_{11}	23.6	27.7	11.9	0.8	0.4	tr	tr	2.0	0.12	33.9
A_{12}	20.7	33.0	14.6	0.5	0.2	tr	tr	2.0	0.11	29.0
B_1	19.5	36.0	15.7	0.5	tr[1]	tr	tr	2.1	0.11	28.4
B_2	18.8	37.6	16.3	0.4	tr	tr	tr	2.0	0.10	25.9
B_3	18.4	39.9	16.2	0.4	tr	tr	tr	1.8	0.10	24.1

[1] tr = trace.

TABLE II.25. *Grain size distribution, pH, C, and chemical composition of the clay separates of profile 8*

Hor.	grain sizes (%)			pH		C %	clay separate				
	> 50μ	50–2μ	< 2μ	H₂O	0.01 M CaCl₂		SiO₂ %	Al₂O₃ %	Fe₂O₃ %	TiO₂ %	MnO %
A₁₁	7.0	26.7	66.3	5.8	4.6	9.6	20.2	32.6	18.0	1.4	0.09
A₁₂	4.0	16.4	79.6	5.4	4.8	4.1	16.0	35.9	17.3	1.3	0.08
B₁	2.9	11.3	85.8	5.6	5.1	1.8	15.2	34.9	18.0	1.0	0.08
B₂	3.1	10.8	86.1	5.6	6.2	0.9	14.3	38.9	18.4	1.0	0.07
B₃	2.7	10.4	86.9	5.7	6.5	0.5	13.3	36.5	16.8	1.3	0.08

Note the with depth ever increasing clay content. Whether this is the result of lateral removal of clay, of wind erosion, of translocation of clay-sized minerals or of decomposition products cannot be decided with certainty. Probably, the dissolution of gibbsite in the surface at low pH and its deposit at higher pH values in the deeper horizons is the active mechanism. This could explain the presence of shiny, amorphous coatings

TABLE II.26. *Derived molar ratios of profile 8*

Hor.	material	SiO₂/R₂O₃	SiO₂/Al₂O₃	SiO₂/Fe₂O₃	Al₂O₃/Fe₂O₃
A₁₁	soil	1.1	1.4	5.3	3.7
	clay	0.8	1.1	3.2	2.4
A₁₂	soil	0.8	1.1	3.8	3.6
	clay	0.6	0.8	2.5	3.2
B₁	soil	0.7	0 9	3.3	3.6
	clay	0.6	0.7	2.3	3.0
B₂	soil	0.7	0.8⁵	3.1	3.6
	clay	0.6	0.6	2.1	3.3
B₃	soil	0.6	0.8	3.0	3.9
	clay	0.5	0.6	2.1	3.4

TABLE II.27. *Normative mineralogical composition of profile 8* (weight percentages)

Hor.	Kaol	Go	Gi	Ru	Misc
A₁₁	58.7	18.2	13.9	2.5	6.7
A₁₂	48.9	18.8	27.0	2.3	3.0
B₁	45.6	19.6	30.5	2.3	2.0
B₂	41.7	19.4	35.4	2.1	1.4
B₃	39.3	18.7	38.5	1.9	1.6

on the structural peds. There is also some illuviation of iron hydroxide; both facts result in the residual accumulation of kaolinite in the surface horizons.

In general it can be concluded that the dominant soil forming process is a strong desilication, accompanied by processes which occur in the genesis of podzolic soils.

The Oxisols of Hawaii have been the subject of intensive study and many investigators have contributed to it. A schematic diagram of the occurrence of the Oxisols in relation to rainfall, parent material, relief, and age was given by Tamura et al. (1953) and this diagram is represented in fig. II.27. The Hydrol Humic, and Ferruginous Humic Latosols will be discussed in some detail.

The Hydrol Humic Latosols (Cline, 1955) are soils with highly humic A_1 horizons over red or yellowish-red, sometimes slightly mottled, plastic and sticky B horizons, which gradually merge into strongly weathered parent material. The soils are always

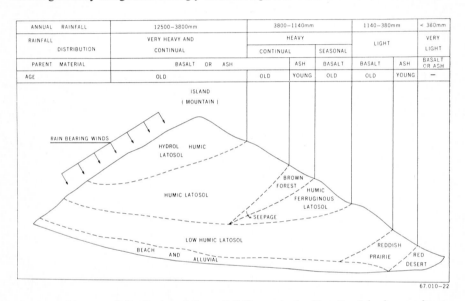

ANNUAL RAINFALL	12500–3800mm			3800–1140mm		1140–380mm		< 380mm
RAINFALL DISTRIBUTION	VERY HEAVY AND CONTINUAL			HEAVY		LIGHT		VERY LIGHT
				CONTINUAL	SEASONAL			
PARENT MATERIAL	BASALT OR ASH			ASH	BASALT	BASALT	ASH	BASALT OR ASH
AGE	OLD			OLD	YOUNG	OLD	OLD	YOUNG	—

67.010–22

FIG. II.27. *Diagram of distribution of Great Soil Groups in the Hawaiian Islands according to relief, rainfall, parent material, and age (after Tamura et al., 1953)*

moist and the vegetation is extremely luxurious (dense rain-forest). The soils cannot be rewetted once they have been dried. They shrink tremendously on drying and form sand to gravel-size aggregates which are very stable ('pseudo-sand' granulation). They do not swell again to their former volume. The changes by drying are irreversible and this is the reason why these soils strongly erode upon deforestation. Many volcanic ash soils in Indonesia, formed under continual rainfall, show the same characteristics with respect to drying. Samples of such soils should not be allowed to dry in the air before analysis.

The exchange capacity varies from 20 to 60 m.e. per 100 g of soil. From 60 to 90 per cent of their exchange capacity is accounted for by their organic matter.

Hough et al. (1941) analyzed a typical Hydrol Humic Latosol profile (profile 9) of the Hilo family (Cline, 1955). The profile was situated on the gently sloping side of a small knoll in the Pepeeko plantation, Hamakua, Island of Hawaii. The rainfall was approximately 4400 mm/year; elevation was 270 m and the parent rock a basaltic volcanic ash. The short profile description reads as follows:

Horizon	Depth (cm)	
A₁	0–15	Pale yellowish-brown heavy silty clay; friable to plastic; granular; pH 5.2.
B₁	15–45	Dark yellowish-brown clay; soft, friable to plastic, with a weak crumb structure. Very plastic when wet; pH 5.2.
B₂	45–71	Brown clay, friable or plastic, weak crumb structure. Very plastic when wet; pH 5.2. Gradual boundary to
C	71–96	Reddish yellowish-brown clay. Soft, friable to plastic. Weak crumb structure. Very plastic when wet; pH 4.9.

The analyses and derived data are shown in tables II.28, 28a, and 29. The high organic-matter content is very striking; it would suggest that, together with the high rainfall, podzolic tendencies in the soil formation process could occur. Definite trends of

TABLE II.28. *Chemical composition of profile 9 and of the colloidal fractions in percentages of carbon-free material* (after Hough et al., 1941)

Hor.	mate-rial	SiO_2	Fe_2O_3	Al_2O_3	MgO	CaO	K_2O	Na_2O	TiO_2	MnO	SO_3	P_2O_5	H_2O+	org.[1] matter
A₁	soil	16.0	35.6	20.6	1.4	1.0	0.3	0.4	8.8	0.1	0.7	0.7	14.4	20.2
	coll.	14.0	32.8	24.6	0.4	0.6	0.5	0.9	6.6	0.1	0.7	3.0	16.5	22.9
B₁	soil	11.6	30.5	30.1	1.3	0.2	0.2	0.2	5.9	0.2	1.6	0.4	17.9	10.7
	coll.	10.7	35.6	28.3	0.6	0.3	0.2	tr	6.7	0.2	0.7	2.7	14.3	13.4
B₂	soil	14.7	33.0	26.1	1.0	0.2	0.4	0.5	7.1	0.2	1.4	0.7	14.8	14.3
	coll.	12.4	36.2	24.7	0.5	0.3	0.4	0.2	6.9	0.2	0.7	2.5	15.2	18.8
C	soil	14.1	31.2	26.9	0.6	0.1	0.5	0.2	6.2	0.2	2.2	0.4	17.3	10.0
	coll.	14.2	32.4	28.2	0.6	0.2	0.4	0.2	6.0	0.2	0.9	2.8	13.9	11.2

[1] as percentages of the whole soil or colloid fraction.

podzolization, however, are absent. Apparently, either the organic material forms insoluble complexes with iron and aluminium or it is unable to form complexes at all. Only alumina seems to be slightly mobile.

The same conclusion can be drawn from the mineralogical composition of the

TABLE II.28a. *Molar ratios of profile 9*

Hor.	material	SiO_2/R_2O_3	SiO_2/Al_2O_3	SiO_2/Fe_2O_3	Al_2O_3/Fe_2O_3
A₁	soil	0.6	1.3	1.2	0.9
	colloid	0.5	1.0	1.1	1.2
B₁	soil	0.4	0.7	1.0	1.5
	colloid	0.3	0.6	0.8	1.3
B₂	soil	0.5	1.0	1.2	1.2
	colloid	0.4	0.8	0.9	1.1
C	soil	0.5	0.9	1.2	1.4
	colloid	0.5	0.9	1.1	1.4

242

profile (table II.29). It was calculated from the chemical data, using the fact that Tamura et al. (1953) found allophane to be the clay mineral; the composition of allophane was supposed to be $Al_2O_3.SiO_2.2H_2O$ (Wada, 1967). As no data is available for FeO, magnetite could not be calculated into the mineral assemblage, although it is present (Tamura et al., 1953). The profile has a fairly constant composition. As the molar silica/sesquioxide ratios are very low and certainly lower than those of a basaltic

TABLE II.29. *Normative mineralogical composition of profile 9* (weight percentages)

Hor.	material	Allo	Go	Gibb	Q	Ms	Chl	Ru	Misc
A₁	soil	25.6	36.5	10.1	6.6	2.4	4.8	9.7	4.2
	colloid	22.8	31.3	18.8	5.8	3.9	1.4	6.4	9.7
B₁	soil	19.9	31.3	29.8	5.1	1.6	4.5	6.0	1.8
	colloid	18.1	31.6	28.1	4.6	1.5	2.0	6.5	7.6
B₂	soil	24.5	32.2	19.8	6.3	3.2	3.5	7.1	3.4
	colloid	20.5	33.8	31.3	5.3	3.1	1.7	6.9	7.4
C	soil	23.6	33.1	23.0	6.0	4.2	2.1	6.3	1.7
	colloid	23.1	28.4	23.5	6.0	3.1	2.0	5.9	7.9

Allo = allophane; Go = goethite; Gibb = gibbsite; Q = free silica; Ms = muscovite (illite); Chl = chlorite; Ru = rutile (anatase); Misc = miscellaneous.

volcanic ash, from which the profile has been derived, the dominant soil forming process is the desilication.

Although these soils have certainly an oxic horizon, they are not classified as Oxisols according to the 7th Approximation. The presence of allophane as a weathering product of volcanic glass, the very high organic-matter content and the subsequent specific physical properties of these soils (irreversible dehydration) give the soils such typical properties that a special suborder, the Andepts, was created in the Order of the Inceptisols. The discussed profile is placed in the Great Group of the Hydrandepts and is representative for the Subgroup of the Typic Hydrandepts.

The Ferruginous Humic Latosols have a horizon where heavy minerals (oxides of iron and titanium) have been concentrated. Consequently, the apparent specific gravity is high: values of 2.0 are common. This layer is dense and massive when wet, but develops an unstable granular structure when it dries out. It is slowly permeable to water and resists penetration of roots. In a few places erosion has exposed this layer and it has become so hardened that it has properties comparable to those of laterite crust.

Under the layer of high specific gravity lies material that appears to be a very friable silt loam or silty clay loam; mechanical analysis, however, shows clay contents of 60 to 75%. There is practically no evidence of any alumino-silicate clay. This suggests that the clay minerals have completely decomposed during soil formation or that they never formed. Van Baren (1941) preferred the latter explanation, as he demonstrated by means of an anomalous soil of Sumatera (Indonesia) that due to the excess of rainfall, crystallization of any clay mineral may be prevented by eluviation. Dean (1947) discussed the same possibility for Hawaiian soils developed from volcanic ash, aeolian material, and weathered basalt. This gives rise to the hypothesis that, with conditions of very heavy rainfall and rapid permeation, the weathering of porous, partly crystalline materials such as volcanic ash and lava, is accompanied by such a rapid removal of the products of decomposition that there is little opportunity for the formation of kaolinic minerals. On the other hand, with only moderate rainfall there is an obvious formation of these crystallized weathering products from the same parent materials.

The C horizon is usually a compacted clay and is grossly different from the clays of the solum.

A schematic profile description reads as follows (profile 10):

Horizon	Thickness (cm)	
A₁	8–20	Greyish-purple silt loam with granular structure and with a dense population of plant roots.
A₂	15–23	Purple silt loam with massive structure when wet and very weak granular structure when dry. High apparent specific gravity.
AB	5–20	Transition zone.
B	10–90	Reddish brown friable clay of a very uniform texture but having the physical properties of a silt loam.
C		Compacted impervious plastic clay of weathered basalt or trachyte.

The soils are located in areas having an annual rainfall varying from 1100 to 3800 mm. The rainfall distribution is seasonal. The soils occur on long slopes having a series of benches or on gently rolling slopes of the intermediate elevations of the mountain peaks or ranges. They are situated between the Low Humic Latosols on the lower elevation of these slopes with less rainfall and more pronounced and longer dry periods, and the Humic Latosols on the higher elevations with heavy and continual rainfall. The soils are generally developed from basaltic rocks.

The original vegetation of these areas has been removed, but probably the vegetation was an open koa forest with a sparse growth of grass between the trees.

The soils may show typical erosion patterns: the B horizon erodes relatively easily and the A horizon less easily, and the result is shown in fig. II.28.

Several authors have made analyses of representatives of this soil group (Sherman et al., 1949; Fujimoto et al., 1949; Sherman et al., 1955). Cline (1955) divided the soils into

TABLE II.30. *Chemical composition of profile 10* (after Sherman et al., 1949)

Hor.	SiO_2 %	Al_2O_3 %	Fe_2O_3 %	TiO_2 %	MnO %	pH
A₁	13.0	13.2	43.2	17.4	0.4	4.6
A₂	14.0	13.2	48.1	18.9	0.3	4.2
AB	8.5	15.8	46.8	12.2	0.1	4.3
B₁	4.6	17.8	47.4	10.2	0.1	4.3
B₂	2.3	27.6	42.5	8.9	0.1	4.5
C	9.0	36.0	28.7	6.7	0.1	4.4

five families, of which the Haiku family has the deepest profiles and occurs in the highest rainfall areas. An analysis, although not complete, is given in tables II.30 and 30a (profile 10). The analysis shows with depth a: 1) decreasing silica content; 2) increasing alumina content; 3) rather constant iron oxides content; 4) decreasing titania content. These trends are not always present; especially the behaviour of alumina and iron oxide can be different. There are soils in this group where the alumina content decreases with depth and soils where the iron oxides increase and decrease as well with depth. The clay content increases with depth, but the clay composition varies as is shown in table II.31.

TABLE II.30a. *Derived molar ratios of profile 10.*

Hor.	SiO$_2$/R$_2$O$_3$	SiO$_2$/Al$_2$O$_3$	SiO$_2$/Fe$_2$O$_3$	Al$_2$O$_3$/Fe$_2$O$_3$
A$_1$	0.5	1.7	0.8	0.5
A$_2$	0.5	1.8	0.8	0.4
AB	0.3	0.9	0.5	0.5
B$_1$	0.2	0.4	0.3	0.6
B$_2$	0.1	0.1	0.1	1.0
C	0.3	0.4	0.8	2.0

FIG. II.28. *The effect of erosion on a Ferruginous Humic Latosol on Kauai (Hawaii). In the background the typical erosion of the B horizon with the overhanging A horizon. In the foreground is a soil remnant being held together by tree roots. The A and B horizons have been eroded from the surrounding area exposing the surface of the impervious C horizon (from Sherman et al.,1949)*

The variability in composition points to the complexity of the processes involved in the formation of these soils. The formation of the profile with crust-horizon is especially difficult to understand. Sherman (1950) has paid considerable attention to this problem. The formation of these crusts seems to be the result of the special characteristics of topography, parent material, and climate. The friable layer above the impervious C horizon behaves as a water conducting layer and the constituents of the laterally

TABLE II.31. *Composition of colloid fraction of two Ferruginous Humic Latosol profiles* (after Sherman et al., 1949).

Origin	Hor.	SiO₂ %	Al₂O₃ %	Fe₂O₃ %	TiO₂ %	MnO %	SiO₂/Al₂O₃
Maui	A₂	24.5	27.1	32.6	5.2	0.1	1.5
	B	14.2	34.7	29.3	4.8	0.1	0.7
Kauai	A₂	5.4	10.1	59.6	21.0	0.1	0.9
	B	4.4	13.0	59.5	6.9	0.1	0.6

moving soil solution accumulate at the lower, more level, positions of the slope if the climate is favourable for this, i.e. when there is a pronounced dry season; in other words a mechanism which is similar to the formation of Oxisols with plinthite at the foot of hills or in colluvial deposits. Sherman's ideas can be easily deduced from the schematic diagram of fig. II.29. The high TiO_2 and Fe_2O_3 contents of the Ferrugin-

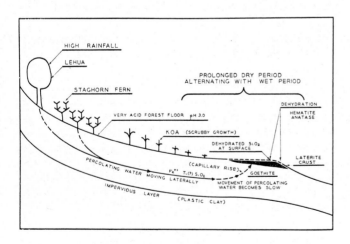

FIG. II.29. *The location of Ferruginous Humic Latosols with crusts in relation to lateral movement of water from wetter higher elevations*

ous Latosols in the lower positions support his claims. However, it remains difficult to explain why silica and especially alumina do not accumulate, as the latter is the most mobile constituent of soils of higher elevations. However that may be, the soil formation process is very complicated and an exact scheme cannot be given yet.

If it is assumed that only kaolinite, gibbsite, goethite and anatase are the main minerals occurring in these soils (see also: Tamura et al., 1955), the mineralogical composition can be calculated. The result (table II.32) shows, that gibbsite is strongly leached from the surface horizons, goethite shows a maximum in the B_1 horizon, and that kaolinite and anatase accumulate in the top layers. The podzolic tendencies are strongly developed, although there are in the present profile no indications of instability of kaolinite. This can possibly be explained by assuming that the soil is not only

TABLE II.32. *The normative mineralogical composition of profile 10* (weight percentages)

Hor.	Kaol	Go	Gi	Ru
A_1	29.4	49.6	3.1	17.9
A_2	28.8	51.2	2.0	18.0
AB	18.9	54.4	13.9	12.8
B_1	10.3	55.5	22.4	11.8
B_2	4.9	47.1	39.2	8.8
C	19.0	31.4	42.9	6.7

leached vertically with rainwater, but also laterally enriched with dissolved substances, amongst which silicic acid descending from higher elevations, which stabilizes kaolinite (see Chapter I, Part III).

Many Ferruginous Humic Latosols certainly contain an oxic horizon and belong therefore to the Oxisols. They can be classified into the Suborder of the Ustox or Humox, depending upon the humidity of the soil during the year. Other Ferruginous Humic Latosols have definite signs of the presence of an argillic horizon. In that case they should be classified as Ultisols. As the organic-matter content is rather high they belong to the Suborder of the Humults and, as seasonal temperature differences are only slight, to the Great Group of the Tropohumults. The profile discussed is probably a Haplohumox.

Summarizing, it may be stated that the Oxisols without plinthite occur under a wide range of tropical climatic conditions; the drainage conditions, however, are always good or else permeability is rapid. As soon as these conditions deteriorate, soils are formed having some characteristics of Oxisols with plinthite. The Ferruginous Latosols are such examples.

The most important process involved in the formation of Oxisols without plinthite is the desilication process. However, also podzolization processes of varying intensity occur, resulting in the varying characteristics of the surface horizons of these soils.

I.2.2. THE SOIL FORMING PROCESS

As already stated desilication and podzolic processes play a rôle in the formation of Oxisols without plinthite. The former process will be discussed in Chapter I of Part III. The latter will be studied in the Chapter on Podzolic Soils, and in Chapter 3 of Part III. Only some additional remarks are to be made now.

In the discussions of the Oxisol profiles without plinthite, strong emphasis was laid on the drainage conditions of the horizons when studying the mineral transformations. This was as a result of various observations made by the senior authors.

An interesting observation is the occurrence of successive layers of red soils, black soils, and red soils again, provided by the Mount Lawoe volcano in the Madiun region of Central Java (Indonesia). The oldest part of this volcano complex was formed in the Late-Miocene era. The andesitic effusiva of the Tertiary volcano have been worn down to a low elevation, with very old latosolic soils covering the remnants. These old soils emerge through a very thick mantle of black, weathered products of effusiva, belonging to the second cycle of volcanic activity of the complex. The tuffaceous sediments produced at that time are of a different nature from the Tertiary material. They are very pale tuffs with a very high content of almost colourless volcanic glass. The last phase of the activity consisted of extensive flows of volcanic mud, known as 'lahars', which moved mainly in a southern and south-eastern direction. These young Quaternary products weathered to reddish-brown or red Latosols.

The question now arises as to why the effusiva of the Old-Quaternary volcanic phase weathered to black soils, whereas both the Tertiary and Young-Quaternary material developed into lateritic soils.

The solution to this problem lies principally in the texture and composition of the erupted material. Sufficient leaching and eluviation of both silica and bases were prevented by the efflata of the second phase which consisted mainly of very fine ash, usually containing a noticeable amount of sodium. Furthermore, any possible transportation to lower levels in the sharp dry season was checked. The environment proved just as conducive, therefore, to slightly alkaline conditions as to the presence of sufficient silica; the more so, since the pale tuffaceous parent material is richer in SiO_2 than the normal andesitic tuffs which predominated in the first and last phases of active volcanism.

The necessity of free percolation of rain water for ferrallitization is likewise proved by the occurrence of three more or less contemporaneous flows of the Mount Tengger complex (East Java, Indonesia) of which two have weathered into a red soil and one into a black soil. These flows occur, topographically, on the same level, spread out next to each other like the fingers of one hand. Climatic conditions are the same in each case because the flows are all situated within a small area. Nevertheless there is an important difference in texture. The middle flow is fine-grained, thereby impeding the circulation of water, whereas the other two are of a texture which permits the free percolation of atmospheric water.

Recent flows from Mount Merapi (fig. 11.30) demonstrate the fact that even during one short period of activity, a volcano can produce materials of different habit.

The most conclusive evidence is to be found on the saddle between the regions of Madiun and Kediri, sloping down from the Mount Wilis volcano and up again to the Mount Pandan in the eastern part of Central Java. A number of river incisions are apparent in the broad tuffaceous flow which connects the two volcanoes. The colour of the main flat surface is pure black, though it becomes predominantly red at the sloping borders of these flats. Percolation of water and eluviation of excess silica and bases took place here without hindrance and the result was an oxic weathering product (fig. 11.31).

FIG. II.30. *Lahar flows of different texture and composition from the volcano Mount Merapi*

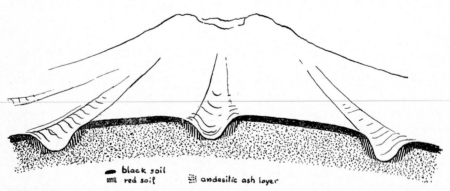

black soil
red soil
andesitic ash layer

FIG. II.31. *Cross section from east to west of the saddle between Mount Wilis and Pandan (Central Java)*

Fairly conclusive corroboration of the points made above was provided by K. C. W. Venema (personal communication), who observed in 1936 a thick andesitic mud-stream, which had been weathered by desilication, on the slopes of the volcano Mount Merapi (East Java). A layer of round, red discs of andesitic gravel was found in this mud-stream, and the individual pebbles of this deposit often over-lapped each other like tiles on a roof. The intermittent gaps were filled with fine-grained material (fig. II.

32). The andesitic material in the space between the pebbles had not weathered to a red clay, but to a grey substance which evinced all the characteristics of montmorillonite.

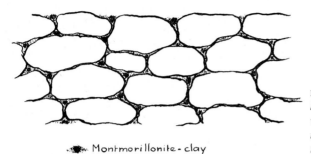

Montmorillonite - clay

FIG. II.32. *Diagrammatic illustration of a tropically weathered mud-stream, with montmorillonitic clay between the pebbles.*

This phenomenon is adequately explained by the assumption that free drainage was rendered impossible by the over-lapping position of the pebbles. This meant that water, which could, therefore, only percolate slowly, stagnated in the holes between the pebbles, with the result that the andesitic material weathered into grey, montmorillonitic clay.

LITERATURE CITED

ALEXANDER, G. B., HESTON, W. M. and ILER, H. K. 1954 The solubility of amorphous silica in water. *J. Phys. Chem.*, 58: 453–455.

ALEXANDER, L. T. and CADY, J. G. 1962 Genesis and hardening of laterite in soils. *Soil Cons. Serv. Techn Bull.* 1282, pp. 90.

ALEXANDER, L. T., CADY, J. G., WHITTIG, L. D. and DEVER, R. F. 1956 Mineralogical and chemical changes in the hardening of laterite. *Trans. 5th Int. Cong. Soil Sci.*, E: 67–73.

AUBERT, G. 1950 Observations sur la dégradation des sols et la formation de la cuirasse latéritique dans le Nord-Ouest du Dahomey (A.O.F.). *Trans. 4th Int. Cong. Soil Sci.*, 3: 127–128.

— 1954 Les sols latéritiques. *Trans. 5th Int. Cong. Soil Sci.*, I: 103–119.

— 1959 Influence des divers types de végétation sur les caractères et l'évolution des sols en régions équatoriales et subéquatoriales ainsi que leurs bordures tropicales semihumides. *Coll. Sols et Végétation des régions tropicales CCTA/FAO Abidjan*, 41–47.

— 1963 Soils with ferruginous or ferrallitic crusts of tropical regions. *Soil Sci.*, 95: 235–243.

BENNETT, H. H. and ALLISON, R. J. 1928 The soils of Cuba. *Trop. Plant Res. Foundation. Washington.*

BONIFAS, M. 1959 Contribution à l'étude géochimique de l'altération latéritique. *Mem. Serv. Carte Geol. d'Alsace et de Lorraine*, No. 17: pp. 159.

BUCHANAN, F. 1807 A journey from Madras through the countries of Mysore, Canara, and Malabar. *London.*

BURRI, C. 1964 Petrochemical calculations based on equivalents. *Translated from German. Jerusalem.*

BUTTERLIN, J. 1961 Nouvelle précisions au sujet des sols rouges ferrallitiques trouvés sur les calcaires de la République d'Haiti. *C.R. Soc. Geol. France, fasc.* 4: 109–111.

250

CAMPBELL, J.M. 1917 Laterite: Its origin, structure, and minerals. *Min. Mag.*, 17: 67–77, 120–128, 171–179, 220–229.
CARROLL, D. and WOOF, M. 1951 Laterite development on basalt at Inverell, New South Wales. *Soil Sci.*, 72: 87–99.
CLINE, M.G. 1955 Soil survey of the territory of Hawaii. *U. S. Dept. Agric. Soil Survey Series 1939*, No. 25.
COLWELL, J.D. 1950 Pedology of the red and black soils of the Inverell District and its relationship to land utilization. *Thesis, Sidney.*
DEAN, L. A. 1947 Differential thermal analysis of Hawaiian soils. *Soil Sci.*, 63: 95-105
D'HOORE, J. 1954 L'accumulation des sesquioxides libres dans les tropicaux. *Publ. INEAC, Sér. Sci.*, 62: pp. 132.
— 1963 La carte des sols d'Afrique au 1/5,000,000. *Coll. CCTA/FAO. Lovanium. Congo Léop. Afr. Soils*, 9, 1964: 55–64.
ELLIS, B.S. 1952 Genesis of a tropical red soil. *J. Soil Sci.*, 3: 52–63.
ERHART, H. 1935 Traité de Pédologie, T. 1. *Strasbourg.*
FOLLETT, E.A.C. 1965 The retention of amorphous, colloidal 'ferric hydroxide' by kaolinites. *J. Soil Sci.*, 16: 334–341.
FRIDLAND, V.M. 1961 Soils of the hilly territories of Northern Vietnam. *Sovj. Soil Sci.*, No. 12: 1323–1338.
FRIPIAT, J.J. and GASTUCHE, M.C. 1952 Etude physico-chimique des surfaces des argiles. Les combinaisons de la kaolinite avec les oxides de fer trivalents. *Publ. I.N.E.A.C., Sér. Sci*, No. 54.
—, GASTUCHE, M.C. and COUVREUR, J. 1954 Nature de la fraction argileuse des sols du Congo Belge et du Ruanda-Uruandi. *Trans. 5th Int. Cong. Soil Sci.*, II: 430–438.
FUJIMOTO, G., SHERMAN, G.D. and CHANG, A.E. 1949 The chemical composition of the separated mineral fractions of a Ferruginous Humic Latosol profile. *Soil Sci. Soc. Amer. Proc.*, 13: 166–169.
GANSSEN, R. 1966 Atlas zur Bodenkunde. In: Meyers grosser physischer Weltatlas. *Mannheim.*
GARRELS, R.M. and CHRIST, CH.L. 1965 Solutions, minerals, and their equilibria. *New-York.*
GASTUCHE, M.C., FRIPIAT, J.J. and DEKIMPE, C. 1962 La génèse des minéraux argileux de la famille du kaolin. Génèse et synthèse des argiles. *Coll. Int. No. 105*, CNRS: 57–65.
— and HERBILLON, A. 1962 Etude des gels d'alumine: crystallisation en milieu désionisé. *Bull. Soc. Chim. France:* 1404–1412.
GLINKA, K. D. 1927 The great soil groups of the world and their development. *Londen.*
GREENE, H. 1947 Soil formation and water movement in the tropics. *Soil and Fert.*, 10: 253–256.
HALLSWORTH, E.G. and COSTIN, A.B. 1953 Studies in pedogenesis in New South Wales. IV. The ironstone soils. *J. Soil Sci.*, 4: 24–45.
HANLON, F.N. 1945 Bauxites of New South Wales. *Proc. Roy. Soc. N.S. Wales*, 78: 94–112.
HARDY, F. and FOLLETT-SMITH, R.R. 1931 Studies in tropical soils. II. Some characteristics of igneous rock soil profiles in British Guiana, South America. *J. agric. Sci.*, 31: 739–761.
HARRASSOWITZ, H. 1926 Laterit. Material und Versuch erdgeschichtlicher Auswertung. *Fortschr. Geol. u. Paleontl.*, 4: 253–556.
HARRISON, J.B. 1934 The katamorphism of igneous rocks under humid tropical conditions. *Imp. Bur. Soil Sci.;* pp. 79.
HOLMES, A. 1966 Principles of Physical Geology. *Nelson, London.*
HOUGH, G.J., GILE, P.L. and FOSTER, Z.C. 1941 Rock weathering and soil profile devel-

opment in the Hawaiian Islands. *U.S. Dept. Agric., Techn. Bull.* 584: pp. 26.

HSU, P. H. 1966 Formation of gibbsite from ageing hydroxy-aluminum solutions. *Soil Sci. Soc. Am. Proc.*, 30: 173–176.

— 1967 Effect of salts on the formation of bayerite versus pseudo-boehmite. *Soil Sci.*, 103: 101–110.

— and BATES, T. F. 1964 Formation of X-ray amorphous and crystalline aluminum hydroxides *Min. Mag.*, 33: 749–768.

JACKSON, M. L., TYLER, S. A., WILLES, A. L. et al. 1948 Weathering sequence of clay-size minerals in soils and sediments. I. *J. Phys. Coll. Chem.*, 52: 1237–1260.

KELLERMAN, V. V. and TSYURUPA, I. G. 1962 Problems of the strength of the bond between iron films and minerals formed in the soil. *Sovj. Soil Sci.*, No. 13: 1367–1372.

KRAUSKOPF, K. B. 1956 Dissolution and precipitation of silica at low temperatures. *Geochim. Cosmochim. Acta*, 10: 1–26.

— 1967 Introduction to geochemistry. *New-York.*

LATIMER, W. M. 1964 Oxidation potentials, 2nd ed., 6th printing. *Englewood Cliffs.*

LENEUF, N. 1959 L'altération des granites calco-alcalins et des granodiorites en Côte d'Ivoire Forestière et les sols qui en sont dérivés. *Thesis, Paris.*

— and AUBERT, G. 1960 Essai d'évaluation de la vitesse de ferrallitisation. *Trans. 7th Int. Cong. Soil Sci.*, IV: 225–228.

MAIGNIEN, R. 1956 De l'importance du lessivage oblique dans le cuirassement des sols en O.A.F. *Trans. 6th Int. Cong. Soil Sci.*, V: 463–467.

— 1958 Le cuirassement des sols en Guinée. *Mem. Serv. Carte Géol. d'Alsace et de Lorraine*, No. 16: pp. 239.

— 1961 Le passage des sols ferrugineux tropicaux aux sols ferrallitiques dans les régions sudouest du Sénégal. *Sols Afric.*, 6: 113–172.

— 1964 Survey of research on laterites. *UNESCO NS/HT/125*: pp. 135.

MARBUT, C. F. 1930 Morphology of laterites. *Proc. 2nd Int. Cong. Soil Sci.*, V: 72–80.

— and MANIFOLD, C. B. 1926 The soils of the Amazon Basin in relation to agricultural possibilities. *Geogr. Rev.*, 16:414–442.

MAUFE, H. B. 1928 On the formation of red soil and of black vlei soil form dolerite at Salisbury, Southern Rhodesia. *S. Afr. J. Sci.*, 25: 156–167.

MICHEL, F. 1960 L'évolution géomorphologique des Bassins du Sénégal et de la Haute Gambie. *Rev. Géom. Dyn.*: 117–143.

MOHR, E. C. J. 1933 De bodem der tropen in het algemeen, en die van Nederlandsch-Indië in het bijzonder. Deel I. Tweede Stuk. *Amsterdam.*

MOSS, R. P. 1965 Slope development and soil morphology in a part of South-West Nigeria. *J. Soil Sci.*, 16: 192–209.

NEWBOLD, J. T. 1844 Notes, chiefly geological, across the Peninsula from Masulipatam to Goa, comprising remarks on the origin of the regur and laterite; occurrence of manganese veins in the latter and on certain traces of aqueous denundation on the surface of Southern India. *J. Asiatic Soc. Bengal*, 13: 984–1004.

PANTON, W. P. 1956 Types of Malayan laterite and factors affecting their distribution. *Trans. 6th Int. Cong. Soil Sci.*, V: 419–423.

PENDLETON, R. L. 1947 Analysis of some Siamese laterites. *Soil Sci.*, 62: 423–440.

PREEZ, J. W. DU 1949 Laterite. A general discussion with a description of Nigerian occurrences. *Bull. Agric. Congo Belge*, 40: 53–66.

PRESCOTT, J. A. and PENDLETON, R. L. 1952 Laterite and lateritic soils. *Comm. Bur. Soil Sci. Techn. Commun.*, 47: 1–51.

RAUPACH, M. 1962a Solubility of simple aluminium compounds expected in soils. I. Hydro-

xides and oxyhydroxides. *Austr. J. Soil Res.*, 1: 36–45.
— 1962b Solubility of simple aluminium compounds expected in soils. II. Hydrolysis and conductance of Al^{3+}. *Austr. J. Soil Res.*, 1: 36–45.
RAYCHAUDHURI, S. P. et al. 1963 Soils of India. *New Delhi.*
RIQUIER, J. 1954 Formation d'une cuirasse ferrugineuse et manganésifère en région latéritique. *Trans. 5th Int. Cong. Soil Sci.*, IV: 227–236.
— 1960 Les phytolithes de certains sols tropicaux et des podzols. *Trans. 7th Int. Cong. Soil Sci.*, V: 425–431.
ROBERTS, R. C. 1942 Soil survey of Puerto Rico. *U.S.D.A., Bur. Plant Ind.*, Ser. 1936, No. 8: pp. 495.
ROSANOV, B. G. 1964 Laterite and laterization. *Sovj. Soil Sci.*, No. 13: 1367–1372.
— 1966 Soil map and land resources of Burma. *Sovj. Soil Sci.*, No. 3: 1601–1605.
— and ROSANOVA, I. M. 1961 Soils of the humid monsoon tropical zone of Burma. *Sovj. Soil Sci.*, No. 12: 1338–1346.
— and — 1964 Soils of the mountainous subtropics and high mountains of Burma. *Sovj. Soil Sci.*, Suppl. No. 13: 1376–1382.
ROSEVAER, R. D. 1942 Soil changes in Enugu plantation. *Farm and Forest* 5(1).
RUHE, R. V. and CADY, J. G. 1954 Latosolic soils of central African interior high plateaus. *Trans. 5th Int. Cong. Soil Sci.*, IV: 401–407.
SATYANARAYANA, K. V. S. and THOMAS, P. K. 1961 Studies on laterites and associated soils. I. Field characteristics of laterites of Malabar and South Kanara. *J. Ind. Soc. Soil Sci.*, 9: 107–118.
— and — 1962 Studies on laterites and associated soils. II. Chemical composition of laterite profiles. *J. Ind. Soc. Soil Sci.*, 10: 211–222.
SCHELLMANN, W. 1964 Zur lateritischen Verwitterung von Serpentinit. *Geol. Jahrb.*, 81: 645–679.
— 1966 Die lateritische Verwitterung eines marinen Tons in Südost-Kalimantan. *Geol. Jahrb.*, 84: 163–188.
SCHMIDT-LORENZ, R. 1964 Zur Mikromorphologie der Eisen- und Aluminiumoxydanreicherung beim Tonmineralabbau in Laterite Keralas und Ceylons. *Proc. 2nd Int. Working. Meeting on Soil Micromorph.*: 279–291.
SCHNELL, R. 1949 Végétation et flore des Monts Nimba. *Thesis, Paris.*
SÉGALEN, P. 1956 Les principaux groupes de sols du Nord-Ouest de Madagascar. *Trans. 6th Int. Cong. Soil Sci.*, V: 561–565.
SHERMAN, G. D. 1950 The genesis and morphology of Hawaiian Ferruginous Laterite crusts. *Soil Sci. Soc. Amer. Proc.*, 13: 166–169.
— FOSTER, Z. C. and FUJIMOTO, CH. K. 1949 Some of the properties of the Ferruginous Humic Latosols of the Hawaiian Islands. *Soil Sci. Soc. Amer. Proc.*, 13: 471–476.
— FUJIOKA, J. and FUJIMOTO, G. 1955 Titaniferous-ferruginous laterite of Meyer Lake, Molokwai, Hawaii. *Pac. Sci.*, 9: 49–55.
SILLÉN, L. G. and MARTELL, A. E. 1964 Stability constants of metal-ion complexes. *London: The chemical Society.*
SIMONSON, R. W. 1959 Outline of a generalized theory of soil genesis. *Soil Sci. Soc. Amer. Proc.*, 23: 152–156.
SMITH, G. D. 1965 Lectures on soil classification. *Pedologie*, No. 4: pp. 134.
SOIL SURVEY STAFF 1960 Soil classification. A comprehensive system. *U.S. Dept. of Agriculture.*
— 1967 Supplement to the soil classification system. *U.S. Dept. of Agriculture.*
SOMBROEK, W. G. 1966 Amazon soils. *Thesis Wageningen.*

STEPHENS, C.G.1946 Pedogenesis following the dissection of laterite regions in southern Australia. *C.S.I.R.O. (Austr.)*, Bull. No. 206.
— 1960 The Australian soil landscape. *Proc. 7th Int. Cong. Soil Sci.*, V: 20–26.
STEWART, G.A.1954 The soils of monsoonal Australia. *Trans. 5th Int. Cong. Soil Sci.*, IV: 101–108.
STUMM, W. and LEE, G.F.1960 The chemistry of aqueous iron. *Schweiz. Z.f. Hydrologie* 22: 295–320.
SYS, C. et al.1961 La cartographie des sols au Congo. *Publ. d.INEAC, Sér. techn.*, No. 66: pp. 141.
TAMHANE, R.V.1956 Development and significance of major soil groups of India. *Trans. 6th Int. Cong. Soil Sci.*, V: 487–497.
TAMURA, T., JACKSON, M.L. and SHERMAN, G.D.1953 Mineral content of Low Humic, Humic and Hydrol Humic Latosols of Hawaii. *Soil Sci. Soc. Amer. Proc.*, 17: 343–346.
—, — and — 1955 Mineral content of a latosolic Brown Forest Soil and a Humic Ferruginous Latosol of Hawaii. *Soil Sci. Soc. Am. Proc.*, 19: 435–439.
TURNER, R. C. and BRYDON, J. E. 1965 Factors affecting the solubility of Al(OH)₃ precipitated in the presence of montmorillonite. *Soil Sci.*, 100 : 176–181.
VAN BAREN, F.A.1941 De mineralogische achtergrond van de bodemvruchtbaarheid in Nederlandsch-Indië. *Landbouw (Buitenzorg)*, 17: 520–541.
VAN DER PLAS, L. and VAN SCHUYLENBORGH, J. 1970 Petrochemical calculations applied to soils (with special reference to soil formation). *Geoderma*, 4: 357–385.
VAN SCHUYLENBORGH, J.1957 Investigations on the classification and genesis of soils derived from andesitic tuffs under humid tropical conditions. *Neth. J. agric. Sci.*, 5: 195–210.
— 1958 On the genesis and classification of soils derived from andesitic tuffs under humid tropical conditions. *Neth. J. agric. Sci.*, 6: 99–123.
— and ARENS, P.L.1950 The electrokinetic behaviour of freshly prepared *y*- and *a*-FeOOH. *Rec. trav. chim. Pays-Bas*, 69: 1557–1565.
—and SÄNGER, A.M.H.1949 The electrokinetic behaviour of iron- and aluminium-hydroxides and -oxides. *Rec. trav. chim. Pays-Bas*, 68: 999–1010.
WADA, K.1967 A structural scheme of soil allophane. *Am. Min.*, 52: 690–708.
WALTHER, J.1915 Laterit in Westaustralien. *Z, deutsch. Geol. Ges.*, 67B: 113–132.
WHITEHOUSE, F.W.1940 The lateritic soils of Western Queensland. *Queensl. Univ. Dept. Geol.*, Paper 2 No. 1.
WOLLSTEDT, P.1965 Das Eiszeitalter. III. Afrika, Asien, Australien und Amerika. *Stuttgart.*
YAKUSHEV, V.M.1968 Influence of termite activity on the development of laterite soil. *Sovj. Soil Sci.*, No. 1, 109–111.
YOUNG, A. and STEPHEN, I.1965 Rock weathering and soil formation on high-altitude plateous of Malawi. *J. Soil Sci.*, 16: 322–333.
ZANS, V.A.1953 Bauxite resources of Jamaica and their development. *Col. Geol. and Min. Resources*, III, 4: 307–333.

CHAPTER 2

LATERITIC SOILS,
PODZOLIC SOILS AND
PODZOLS
Oxisols, Ultisols, Alfisols and Spodosols

As it was decided in Chapter 1 of this Part to follow the suggestions of the American Soil Survey Staff to abandon terms as Laterite, laterization, etc. and to use new names, it would have been logical to be consistent in this Chapter. However, serious difficulties arose in doing so, because the American Soil Survey Staff classifies the soils predominantly according to their morphological characteristics, whereas this book is predominantly concerned with the genetic aspect of soils. E.g., some of the soils known as 'lateritic' soils are at present classified as Oxisols, others as Ultisols and even Alfisols, depending on the presence of oxic and argillic horizons, and on base saturation. In all these soils, however, similar processes are active, although in different degrees. Also, some of the soils known as 'podzolic' are at present classified as Ultisols, and others as Alfisols, based on the difference in base saturation; in these podzolic soils again similar processes are acting although in a varying degree.

As it was decided to arrange the soils to be discussed in this Chapter according to the decreasing intensity of the desilication process, so that other soil forming processes are emphasized and as this genetic concept is better illustrated by the terms 'lateritic', 'podzolic', and 'podzol', three sections were prepared, viz. Lateritic Soils, Podzolic Soils, and Podzols. In the discussion, however, the new terms as suggested by the American Soil Survey Staff (1960, 1967), will be used as much as possible.

The soils to be discussed occur frequently in the tropics, even the Podzols (Spodosols). In a general sense it can be stated that these soils are products of the acid parent materials, such as granites, rhyolites, sandstones, etc., although they may occur on more basic parent materials (e.g. the Lateritic Soils). In the latter case, Podzolic Soils and Podzols are restricted to higher altitudes in the tropics. If occurring at lower elevations the parent materials are extremely acid, and water saturation is frequently present. Before discussing the soils and their formation, the processes involved will be outlined.

The soils of this Chapter are considered to be the result of some process of podzolization, perhaps too simple a term, as the process is a very complex one. It can be divided into several subprocesses, as for the Oxisol forming process. For the moment the process of podzolization will be defined as that complex of processes that leads to the formation of Podzols. A Podzol profile consists of a layer of raw organic material on top of the mineral soil followed sometimes by a thin A_1 horizon and invariably by an ash-grey coloured A_2 horizon ('albic' horizon), in turn lying over a B horizon with humus, iron, and aluminium accumulation ('spodic' horizon) and, although not essentially, clay accumulation, merging into the parent material and, finally, the parent rock. It can therefore be assumed that the following processes are involved:

a) Alteration processes, converting the parent rock into the parent material. This process is not characteristic for podzolization as it occurs in the formation of all soils if formed *in situ* from rocks. This process consists of the weathering of the primary minerals with the subsequent formation of clay-sized minerals and salts and is qualitatively similar in temperate and in tropical climates, depending predominantly on the permeability and drainage conditions in the weathering zone (see also Chapters I of this Part and of Part III). Quantitatively, however, there are large differences as a consequence of the temperature difference.

b) Leaching of the soluble salts.

c) Formation of organic substances capable of complexing sesquioxides (especially iron) and leaching of the ensuing complexes if the latter are soluble.

d) Accumulation of sesquioxides at some subsurface horizon, sometimes accompanied by the accumulation of organic matter.

e) 1. Translocation of clay particles, accompanied by 2. decomposition of clay minerals. A clear distinction between clay migration and clay destruction is not always possible as, in certain soils, both processes may occur simultaneously.

f) Adsorption or precipitation of organic acids on already formed sesquioxide segregations.

Mostly these processes do not act at the same time; the order of processes given above seems reasonable, except that translocation of clay may already have occurred at an early stage, e.g. immediately after soluble salts and lime when present have been leached. A sharp separation of the processes will not occur, there will be considerable overlapping depending on parent material, climate, and drainage.

It is probably advantageous to choose names for the processes mentioned as was done in the case of Oxisol formation. The processes arranged under a) and b) are not restricted to the soils in question, but occur in the formation of all soils and will not receive specific names. Reference will be made to them as weathering or alteration and salt leaching.

The process listed under c) could be called deferritization (as opposed to desilication) as iron is particularly able to form soluble complexes. It leads to the residual enrichment of silica in the surface layers. As this process is predominantly the result of the formation of soluble organo-metal complexes, or chelates, it could also be called *cheluviation*, as proposed by Swindale and Jackson (1956). The accumulation (process d) in the subsurface horizon could then be called ferritization or *chilluviation*. As the destruction of clay minerals (process e2) is strongly promoted by the presence of chelating organic compounds, this process can be considered part of the cheluviation process.

The clay migration (process e1), although connected with the physico-chemical properties of clay minerals, is a purely mechanical process, and removal of clay from the surface horizons could be called *argeluviation* and for the accumulation of clay into the subsurface horizons, *argilluviation*. This name was chosen after Dudal's suggestion was made in one of the discussions during the Conference on Mediterranean

Soils in Madrid (1966). He proposed to classify soils with clay migration, but without clay destruction, as argilluvic soils (see also p. 282).

The last process, suggested by some authors (see Chapter 3 of Part III) as the final stage in podzol-formation, could be called *organic precipitation.*

Summarizing, the following arrangement of processes leading to the formation of Podzols can be made:

1. Weathering and salt-leaching.
2. Eluviation: a. argeluviation
             b. cheluviation or deferritization
3. Illuviation: a. argilluviation
             b. chilluviation of ferritization.
4. Organic precipitation.

If one or more of these processes, except 1, is missing Podzolic Soils are formed. If, for instance, cheluviation and organic precipitation do not occur, Grey Brown Podzolic Soils and some Red and Yellow Podzolic Soils are formed.

Sometimes, Podzols, such as Groundwater Podzols, may be formed by lateral accumulation of sesquioxides and organic matter. The enrichment of sesquioxides in the subsurface horizons is then far greater than can be accounted for by the loss from the surface horizons. As the process is essentially identical to the vertical movement of sesquioxides it will be also considered as chilluviation or ferritization.

It is understandable that rocks or sediments poor in sesquioxides and rich in coarse minerals are specially suited for the formation of Podzolic Soils and Podzols. This is notably true for the tropics. Podzolization needs the cooperation of organic acids; all conditions favourable for an incomplete mineralization of the organic substances will promote podzolization. Lack of nutrients slows down the mineralization of organic matter and so does temporary lack of oxygen (see Chapter 4 of Part I). Consequently, sandstones with moderate drainage will give Podzols, somewhat richer materials Red-Yellow Podzolic Soils, whereas still richer materials yield the Lateritic Soils.

Some soils will now be discussed, occurring under tropical or subtropical conditions, which show definite signs of podzolization or, better, some subprocess of podzolization.

2.1. LATERITIC SOILS (OXISOLS, ULTISOLS AND ALFISOLS)

2.1.1. GREY BROWN LATERITIC SOILS

One of the earliest investigations of lateritic soils is that of Hardy and Follett-Smith (1931). They examined igneous rock soil profiles in British Guiana, South America. The profiles in question are situated in undulating land in the North-West district at an elevation of 60 m. The parent rocks in this area are Archean acidic gneisses and gneissose granites, traversed by dykes of dolerite outcropping in flat-topped hills. The Kamwatta Creek profile (profile 11) is formed from gneissose granite, composed of 52% andesine, 38% quartz, 4% hornblende, 2% K-feldspar, 2% secondary muscovite, and 2% chloritisized biotite.

The profile consists of a 5 cm thick black-coloured layer of sandy texture (A₁), over a 45 cm thick dark grey horizon of sand texture (A₃), in turn lying over a 7.5 cm thick pale brown sandy clay (B₁), followed by a 12.5 cm thick brownish yellow clay (B₂), over an orange-pink clay (C) of 120 cm thickness, resting on rock.

The analysis, though incomplete, is shown in table II.33. As the CaO and MgO

TABLE II.33. *Chemical composition of profile 11* (weight percentages)

Hor.	SiO$_2$	Al$_2$O$_3$	Fe$_2$O$_3$	TiO$_2$	H$_2$O+	total
A$_1$	88.9	4.1	1.0	0.2	2.6	96.8
A$_3$	85.0	7.3	3.1	0.2	3.5	99.1
B$_1$	75.9	13.4	3.5	0.2	5.3	98.3
B$_2$	66.9	20.6	3.1	0.3	7.8	98.7
C	63.7	23.4	3.3	0.2	8.6	99.2
R[1]	72.5	16.2	2.3	0.2	0.1	95.3

[1] CaO: 3.3; MgO: 0.7.

contents in the solum were negligible it will be assumed that the K₂O and Na₂O contents are also negligible as confirmed by the percentage total.

Tables II.33 and 33a (giving the molar silica/sesquioxide ratios) show that the weathering process (R → C) is definitely a desilication process: silica has been lost partly and sesquioxides enrich residually. In the solum, however, a quite different process is acting. This process is possibly destruction of the originally formed kaolinite, the decomposition products, H₄SiO₄ and gibbsite, leach out, whereas quartz accumulates residually.

TABLE II.33a. *Derived molar ratios of profile 11*

Hor.	SiO$_2$/R$_2$O$_3$	SiO$_2$/Al$_2$O$_3$	SiO$_2$/Fe$_2$O$_3$	Al$_2$O$_3$/Fe$_2$O$_3$
A$_1$	32	37	247	6.7
A$_3$	15.6	19.7	72	3.6
B$_1$	8.3	9.7	58	6.0
B$_2$	5.0	5.5	56	10.1
C	4.2	4.6	51	11.0
R	7.0	7.6	86	11.4

Iron is removed from the thin A₁ horizon and accumulates mostly in the B₁ horizon. This is undoubtedly accomplished by the organic matter, which decomposes rather slowly in this strongly leached profile and gives the profile surface layers their dark grey colour. In other words, subprocess 2b of the podzolization seems to be active.

TABLE II.34. *Normative mineralogical composition of profile 11* (weight percentages)

Hor.	Q	Kaol	Go	Hm	Ru	(W)
A₁	88.0	10.8	1.0	–	0.2	(5.6)
A₃	77.8	18.4	3.6	–	0.2	(1.9)
B₁	61.4	34.5	4.0	–	0.1	(0.6)
B₂	43.3	32.8	3.5	–	0.4	(0.6)
C	36.5	59.8	3.1	0.5	0.1	(–)

Q = silica; Kaol = kaolinite; Go = goethite; Hm = hematite; Ru = rutile (anatase); (W) = excess crystal water.

Aiso the combined silica content, and more specifically the combined silica/Al_2O_3 ratio points to destruction of the clay. Although the determination of the quantity of combined silica is sometimes inadequate (see p. 204), the values can lead to some conclusions. The combined silica/Al_2O_3 ratios are 1.5, 1.2, 1.1^5, 1.1, and 2.1 for, respectively, the A₁ + A₃, B₁, B₂, C horizon, and the rock (R). This indicates destruction of the clay mineral in the surface layers, a conclusion supported by the data of table II.34, where the normative mineralogical composition of the profile was calculated as indicated in Chapter 3 of Part I. The upward increase of excess crystal water indicates that an increasing part of the silica is amorphous. This amorphous silica could have been formed during the destruction of kaolinite.

It is thought, however, that decomposition of kaolinite is not the sole process responsible for its gradual, but considerable decrease in the subsurface and surface horizons. Lateral removal could have occurred, as was frequently reported in Chapter 1 of this Part. Excessive drainage and leaching during the initial stages of weathering and soil formation might be another possibility (Van Baren, 1941; p. 242 and figs. III. 7 and 8 of Chapter 1 of Part III). Upon increasing weathering depth, drainage of the weathering zone becomes slower thus creating conditions where kaolinite becomes increasingly stable. Consequently, the kaolinite increases and the silica content decreases downwards.

It is hardly possible to classify this soil in terms of the 7th Approximation (1960, 1967), as insufficient morphological and chemical data are available; however, as the material is oxic, the soil belongs to the order of the Oxisols.

A soil group intensively studied by Van der Merwe (1962) in South Africa, is the Grey Ferruginous Lateritic Soil group, which could equally well be called, in analogy with the foregoing profile, a Grey Brown Lateritic Soil. Horizon colours and thicknesses are similar, although they cannot be compared conclusively as profile 11 was described too superficially.

The soils occur under an annual rainfall of 560 to 710 mm. The precipitation occurs during the summer months (October to March) mainly in the form of thunderstorms and heavy downpours. The summers are extremely hot an the winters quite mild; the mean annual temperature is approximately 18° C. The vegetation is a typical savannah: open woodland and orchard country of evergreen and deciduous tree and bush, open woodland country of typical evergreen and deciduous tree and thorn forest and thorn country. A great variety of grasses occur, dominantly belonging to the genera *Themeda*, *Hyparrhenia, Panicum, Urochloa, Digitaria*, etc.

The topography ranges from gently undulating to undulating. Surface drainage is good but internal drainage is generally poor. The ground is drained by numerous dry, shallow springs which empty themselves during the rainy season into several rivers. The elevation ranges from 500 to 1300 m above sealevel. The monotonous surface relief is infrequently broken by low hills and hillochs.

The soils are almost entirely confined to, and derived from, Red Granite of the Bush Veld Igneous Complex and the Old or Grey Granite-Pietersburg Plateau and east of the Drakensberg.

One of the most important factors in the formation of these soils is the seasonal saturation with water. Due to the poor water absorbing capacity as a consequence of the sandiness and shallowness of the soil, the soils are in the wet season saturated with water. In the dry season they dry rapidly. The conditions are similar to those of pseudo-gley formation, a process which is thought to be a transitional stage in plinthite formation. As a matter of fact, these soils can be considered as such an intermediate stage, as will be shown by the analyses.

The typical soils consist of a grey sand with a slightly coherent, friable structure, varying in thickness from 5 to 20 cm, overlying a grey, friable sandy gravel (quartz grit) with a few ferruginous concretions in its lower section, 15 to 20 cm thick. Underlying this is a light brown, mottled black and brown, gravelly clayey sand. The gravel consists of uncemented ferruginous concretions, slightly dense, 15 to 18 cm thick. The underlying horizon is a brown ferruginous concretionary layer, a well cemented hardpan, called 'ouklip'. The interstices are filled with the loose material of the subsoil. The lower section of this horizon is similar to the 'ouklip' layer but contains undecomposed fragments of the parent rock. The foundation consists of a clayey material containing an occasional iron oxide concretion. When exposed the 'ouklip' is extremely hard, dark brown, slag-like and honeycombed.

A typical example is the Klipkop profile (profile 12), which is of residual origin and in virgin land.

Location: On the farm Klipkop, 19 km north-west of Brits on the Hartebeestpoort Irrigation scheme; Physiography of surrounding area gently undulating.
Elevation: 1130 m above sea.
Rainfall: 560 mm per annum.
Parent rock: 'Coarse biotite-granite with much pink feldspar', Red Granite.
Vegetation: Bush, trees and grass (Thorn Country).
Profile:

Horizon[1]	Depth (cm)	
A₁	0–10	Grey sandy soil, friable, deficient in organic matter, containing a fair amount of quartz grit.
A₃	10–30	Light grey, friable, gravelly sand (quartz grit) with a few ferruginous concretions in the lower part of the horizon.
B₂₁	30–45	Light brown, mottled black and brown, gravelly sandy clay; the gravel consists of iron oxide concretions. Slightly dense.
B₂₂	45–75	Brown, mottled black, light brown and yellowish brown, layer of

ferruginous concretionary matter, well cemented, forming a hardpan. The interstices of this layer are filled with light grey patches of sand and clay, similar to that described under A_3.

C   75–90   Similar to B_{22}, but granite fragments together with iron oxide concretions are incorporated in the soil mass which is well cemented; compact.

W   90–150   Pink, mottled black, desintegrated granite consisting of quartz and fresh minerals mixed with some soil. Rotten rock.

R   150+   Red granite.

[1] Horizon notations adapted by the present authors to the physical and chemical analyses.

Although the granulometric analysis (table II.35) probably gives an erroneous picture of the particle-size distribution because of the high content of concretions (fraction > 2 mm), it suggests clay migration. The chemical analysis (table II.36) suggests some clay destruction, which is erroneous as we shall see later. Iron has moved considerably and possibly aluminium too. Iron is more mobile in this profile than aluminium, in the clay as well as in the soil. However, during weathering (R→ W→ C) iron accumulated much more strongly than aluminium. It is interesting to see that manganese accumulates in the same horizon as iron which is related to the alternating reductive and oxidative conditions (see Chapter I of this Part).

TABLE II.35. *Grain-size distribution and some chemical data* (profile 12)

Hor.	grain-size distribution %			C %	pH	> 2 mm %
	> 50μ	50–2μ	< 2μ			
A_1	78.9	12.4	9.4	0.9	7.4	54.4
A_3	76.4	12.7	11.8	0.6	6.8	63.5
B_{21}	51.1	16.6	32.8	0.5	6.1	61.0
B_{22}	61.1	18.5	20.5	0.3	6.3	63.5
C	58.5	23.5	18.3	0.3	6.4	60.0
W	52.4	21.3	27.0	0.1	6.7	67.5

The trends in the silica/sesquioxide ratios (tables II.36a and 37a) are normal for podzolic soils. On the other hand, desilication is involved in the formation of rotten rock (W) and the C material, as the molar ratios point to a considerable removal of silica during weathering.

The calculations of the normative mineralogical compositions of the clay fraction and of the soil from the chemical analyses lead to some interesting conclusions, which are in accord with the statements above. The clay composition was calculated according to the rules of the goethite norm (Van der Plas and Van Schuylenborgh, 1970), and the soil composition by a combination of the epinorm rules of Niggli (Burri, 1964) and the goethite norm. The results are represented in tables II.38 and 39. The parent rock consists of approximately 35% quartz, 22% K-feldspars, 25% plagioclases (albite) and

TABLE II.36. *Chemical composition of profile 12*[1] (after Van der Merwe, 1962)

Hor.	SiO$_2$	Al$_2$O$_3$	Fe$_2$O$_3$	FeO	CaO	MgO	Na$_2$O	K$_2$O	Mn$_3$O$_4$	TiO$_2$	P$_2$O$_5$	H$_2$O+[2]
A$_1$	77.8	9.1	3.7	n.d.[3]	0.3	0.5	1.5	3.2	0.1	0.8	tr	2.0
A$_3$	72.7	9.9	7.3	n.d.	0.3	0.4	1.4	3.1	0.1	1.0	0.1	2.9
B$_{21}$	60.4	14.4	13.5	n.d.	0.4	0.5	1.0	2.5	0.4	1.0	0.1	5.8
B$_{22}$	57.3	16.0	14.3	n.d.	0.2	0.7	1.2	3.0	0.7	0.8	0.1	5.7
C	61.3	15.5	10.1	n.d.	0.3	0.5	1.8	4.4	0.4	0.8	tr	5.2
W	62.9	17.0	7.1	n.d.	0.6	0.4	3.0	4.4	0.2	0.7	tr	4.3
R	72.0	14.0	0.7	3.4	0.9	0.6	3.0	4.0	tr	0.3	tr	0.6

[1] weight percentages; [2] H$_2$O+ = loss on ignition, corrected for organic-matter content; [3] n.d. = not determined.

TABLE II.36a. *Derived molar ratios of profile 12*

Hor.	SiO$_2$/R$_2$O$_3$	SiO$_2$/Al$_2$O$_3$	SiO$_2$/Fe$_2$O$_3$	Al$_2$O$_3$/Fe$_2$O$_3$
A$_1$	11.5	14.5	56	3.8
A$_3$	8.5	12.4	27	2.2
B$_{21}$	4.4	7.1	11.8	1.7
B$_{22}$	3.9	6.1	10.7	1.7
C	4.7	6.7	16.1	2.4
W	4.9	6.3	23	3.7
R	7.4	8.8	46	5.3

15% hornblende and micas. Upon weathering a considerable part of the feldspars, quartz, micas are destroyed while hornblende disappears completely. As secondary products kaolinite, montmorillonite, illite, and iron oxide are formed.

TABLE II.37. *Chemical composition of the clay fraction of profile 12*[1] (after Van der Merwe, 1962)

Hor.	SiO$_2$	Al$_2$O$_3$	Fe$_2$O$_3$	CaO	MgO	Na$_2$O	K$_2$O	Mn$_3$O$_4$	TiO$_2$	P$_2$O$_5$	H$_2$O+
A$_1$	50.1	31.0	12.4	0.9	1.2	0.2	2.2	0.2	1.3	0.2	17.3
A$_3$	49.5	31.4	12.8	0.6	1.9	0.2	1.7	0.2	1.2	0.2	17.0
B$_{21}$	47.8	32.3	14.3	0.6	1.2	0.2	1.3	0.2	0.9	0.1	16.0
B$_{22}$	44.4	30.9	19.6	0.5	1.2	0.2	1.4	0.5	0.9	0.1	15.4
C	46.8	30.8	16.8	0.6	1.2	0.1	1.4	0.3	0.9	0.1	14.1
W	50.2	33.4	11.6	0.7	1.2	0.2	1.4	0.2	0.9	0.1	13.1

[1] weight percentages.

TABLE II.37a. *Derived molar ratios of clay* (profile 12)

Hor.	SiO_2/R_2O_3	SiO_2/Al_2O_3	SiO_3/Fe_2O_3	Al_2O_3/Fe_2O_3
A_1	2.2	2.7	10.8	4.0
A_3	2.1	2.7	10.3	3.8
B_{21}	2.0	2.5	8.9	3.5
B_{22}	1.7	2.4	6.0	2.5
C	1.9	2.6	7.4	2.9
W	2.1	2.6	11.6	4.5

In the upper part of the solum quartz and feldspars are enriched again, probably residually as a result of downward movement of clay minerals (table II.39). Destruction of clay is not evident, if present at all. Illite seems even to be more stable than kaolinite (table II.38) under the prevailing conditions. Probably the temporary dryness of the top

TABLE II.38. *Normative mineralogical clay composition* (profile 12),[1] (weight percentages)

Hor.	Q	Kd	Ms	Sm	Go	Ru	Str	Hsm
A_1	4.1	44.4	17.2	20.0	12.2	1.2	0.6	0.2
A_3	0.1	44.3	13.0	28.1	12.6	1.1	0.6	0.2
B_{21}	0.4	54.3	9.8	20.0	14.3	0.7	0.3	0.2
B_{22}	0.1	55.8	6.2	16.7	19.6	0.8	0.3	0.5
C	2.9	52.4	6.0	20.6	16.8	0.7	0.3	0.2
W	1.9	59.5	6.1	19.7	11.5	0.7	0.3	0.2

[1] Q = silica; Kd = kandites; Ms = muscovite (illite); Sm = smectites; Go = goethite; Ru = rutile (anatase); Str = strengite; Hsm = hausmannite.

part of the profile with the subsequent high contents of potassium and magnesium in soil moisture are the reason for the persistence of feldspars and 2:1 clay minerals (see figs. III.7 and 8, Chapter I of Part III). It is evident that clay migration (argeluv-

TABLE II.39. *Normative mineralogical composition of profile 12*[1] (weight percentages)

Hor.	Q	Or	Ab	Kd	Ms	Sm	Go	Ru	Hsm	Misc
A_1	52.4	17.9	14.5	4.2	3.5	1.9	3.0	0.6	0.1	1.9
A_3	49.1	15.4	12.2	5.2	3.4	3.3	8.2	1.1	0.1	2.0
B_{21}	33.4	13.3	8.5	17.8	3.2	6.6	14.7	1.0	0.5	1.0
B_{22}	31.6	3.0	10.7	11.4	20.9	3.4	16.0	0.8	0.8	1.4
C	27.6	18.1	15.8	9.6	11.4	3.8	11.4	0.7	0.3	1.3
W	21.2	24.6	19.7	16.1	10.8	5.3	7.1	0.7	0.2	4.3

[1] Symbols have the same meaning as in table II.38. Or = K-feldspar; Ab = albite.

ation) is one of the most important processes involved in the formation of this profile. Iron and manganese minerals are dissolved in the top layers and deposited predominantly in the B_{22} horizon (tables 11.36, 37, 38 and 39), doubtless as a consequence of the temporary reduction conditions in the wet season probably together with cheluviation.

In terms of the 7th Approximation the profile is probably a Tropaqualf.

2.1.2. REDDISH-BROWN LATERITIC SOILS

Examples of Reddish Brown Lateritic Soils are the well investigated Davidson clay loam (Middleton, 1930; Anderson and Byers, 1931; Brown and Byers, 1932; Marbut, 1935; Hardy and Rodriguez, 1939; Nyun and McCaleb, 1955; England and Perkins, 1959) of Georgia and North Carolina and the Aiken, Cohasset, and Melbourne loams of California (Storie and Harradine, 1958; Harradine, 1966). From the viewpoint of soil formation studies it is unfortunate that the soil profiles morphologically best described (the more recent publications) lack analytical details, whereas the sketchily described profiles (the older publications) are adequately analyzed. Nevertheless, it will be tried to compile the data available in such a way, that a fairly complete idea can be obtained about the composition and formation of Reddish Brown Lateritic Soils.

In California the soils in question (Harradine, 1966) are developed most frequently on basic igneous intrusive rocks, on meta basic igneous rocks, and on sedimentary materials with a high ferro-magnesium mineral content. The climate is Mediterranean and vegetation is a mixed forest of pines, firs and hardwood. The Aiken loam series is an example of a well-drained Californian Reddish Brown Lateritic Soil developed from basic volcanic rocks. They occur on broad, gently sloping ridges and steeper side slopes at elevations ranging from 450 m to 1450 m. Vegetation is mainly coniferous forest of ponderosa pine, Douglas fir, and white fir, with associated hardwoods of black oak and madrone.

The average annual precipitation varies from 750 to more than 1500 mm during the moist season with snow in the winter months. The average temperatures vary from 2° to 4° C in January, and from 22° to 23° C in July; the mean annual temperature ranges from 7° to 13° C.

As the soils seem to be similar to the Reddish Brown Mediterranean Soils, and as the climate is far from tropical, they will not be discussed here.

The Reddish Brown Lateritic Soils of Georgia, U.S.A., are described and investigated by England and Perkins (1959). An example is the Davidson series, which occurs in the southern part of the Piedmont Plateau and is derived from basic metamorphic rocks, mainly diorite gneiss and hornblende schist. Climatic details were not given by the authors, but according to Pearson and Ensminger (1957) the climate of the South Eastern Uplands has a mean winter temperature of 7° C and an average annual rainfall of 1250 to 1500 mm. The distribution is such that 50–70% of the total annual precipitation falls during the cool season from October to March. In the growing season there is frequently a water shortage. The profile to be discussed here (profile 13), is situated in an abandoned field overgrown by pine and mixed hard woods; the topography is undulating to rolling.

The description reads as follows:

Horizon	Depth (cm)	
		Davidson clay loam, Jasper County.
A_1	0–6	Dark reddish brown (2.5YR3/4:m) clay loam with moderate medium and fine granular structure. Slightly hard, friable, and sticky. Small amount of organic matter. Few roots. Gradual and wavy boundary.
A_3	6–11	Dusky red (10R3/4:m) clay loam with moderate and fine granular and medium subangular blocky structure. Hard, friable to firm, and sticky. Small amount of organic matter and few roots. Abrupt and wavy boundary.
B_1	11–36	Dark red (10R3/6:m) clay with strong medium subangular blocky structure. Very hard, and very sticky. Very little organic matter and very few fine roots. Few iron concretions. Diffuse and irregular boundary.
B_{21}	36–91	Dark red (2.5YR3/6:m) clay with strong medium and fine angular and subangular blocky structure. Very hard, very firm, and very sticky. Few quartz fragments and iron concretions. Few clay skins on peds. Diffuse and irregular boundary.
B_{22}	91–196	Red (2.5YR4/6:m) clay with weak medium angular blocky structure. Very hard, very firm, and very sticky. More sand grains than above. Common medium and distinct yellow (10Y7/8:m) and reddish-yellow (7.5YR6/8:m) mottles. Diffuse and irregular boundary.
C	196+	Strong brown (7.5YR5/6:m) clay. Massive. Slightly hard, friable, and sticky. Common medium and distinct reddish-brown (5YR4/4:m) mottles. Some freshly desintegrated dark gneiss rock in places.

Although the description shows a weak clay migration, the analysis shows a considerable increase in clay content from the A_1 to B_1 horizon. This could be attributed to

TABLE II.40. *Physical and some chemical characteristics of profile 13*

Hor.	grain size distribution (%)			C %	pH	free Fe_2O_3 %	clay/free Fe_2O_3 ratio
	> 50μ	50–2μ	< 2μ				
A_1	29	40	31	4.1	5.6	5.4	5.7
A_3	26	29	45	1.6	5.2	5.9	7.7
B_1	10	24	66	0.4	5.5	6.0	11.0
B_{21}	14	34	52	0.2	5.7	8.6	6.0
B_{22}	14	37	49	0.1	5.6	7.3	6.7
B_3	20	33	47	0.1	5.3	6.7	7.0
C	19	40	41	0.1	5.1	9.1	4.6

lateral removal and clay destruction. The occurrence of these processes can be deduced from the fact that cheluviation is taking place (see 'free iron' content, table II.40), base saturation (table II.41) and exchange capacity are lowest in A_1 and A_3 if corrected for the organic-matter content, and that silica and gibbsite occur in the A horizon, probably formed by destruction of clay minerals (table II.42).

TABLE II.41. *Cation exchange characteristics of profile 13*

Hor.	exchangeable cations (m.e./100 g of soil)					c.e.c. m.e./ 100 g of soil	Base saturation %
	Ca	Mg	K	Na	Al + H		
A1	3.9	1.4	0.5	0.1	8.3	14.2	42.3
A3	1.7	1.2	0.3	0.1	8.1	11.4	29.0
B1	1.2	1.3	0.1	0.1	6.8	9.5	29.0
B21	0.2	1.1	0.1	0.1	10.1	11.6	13.0
B22	0.1	1.0	0.0^5	0.1	10.6	11.9	11.0
B3	0.1	0.7	0.1	0.1	11.8	12.8	8.0
C	0.2	1.4	0.1	0.2	11.0	12.8	14.0

As the iron content is high and kaolinite is the dominant clay mineral, it could be concluded that desilication is an important soil forming process. Definite proof however was not given. Superimposed on the desilication, deferritization took place as result of argeluviation and cheluviation.

TABLE II.42. *Estimation of clay-sized minerals* (weight percentages)

Hor.	Kaol	V	Q	Gi	Go	A
A3	40	10–40	10	10	–	10
B22	40	10–40	10	–	–	10–40
B3	40	10–40	–	–	–	10–40
C	40	10	–	–	10	10

Kaol = kaolinite; V = vermiculite; Q = silica; Gi = gibbsite; Go = goethite; A = amorphous.

In terms of the 7th Approximation this profile should be classified into the Order of the Ultisols, Suborder Udults, Great Group Rhodudults (probably), and Subgroup Typic Rhodudults.

The Reddish Brown Lateritic Soils of North Carolina are formed under warmer conditions. The climate seems to be subtropical (Hardy and Rodriguez, 1939) and the vegetation was a deciduous forest. The mean annual temperature is 15.5° C, the mean summer temperature 25° C, and the mean winter temperature 5.5° C. The average rainfall is approximately 1100 mm, fairly uniformly distributed throughout the year, though slightly more during the summer months.

Middleton (1930) briefly described a profile near Greensboro (profile 14):

Horizon	Depth (cm)	
A₁	0–23	Slightly reddish-brown clay loam. Clay content 25.9%.
B₁	23–91	Deep-red brittle clay, breaking into large lumps which finally crumble into smaller angular and subangular peds. Clay content 54.0%.
B₂	91–152	Light-red friable crumbly clay. Clay content 41.3%.
C	152+	Ochrous-yellow, black, and reddish-brown decomposed diorite rock.

The analysis of the soil is shown in tables II.43 and 43a. From the data on the clay content reported in the profile description, the SiO_2, and Fe_2O_3 contents and from the molar ratios, one could conclude that a considerable destruction of clay minerals has occurred in the A₁ horizon. Definite proof can only be given by the analysis of the colloidal fraction. Fortunately, the chemical composition has been determined by Anderson and Byers (1931), while Nyun and McCaleb (1955) made mineralogical analyses by X-ray and DTA. The latter authors found that predominantly kaolinite

TABLE II.43. *Chemical composition of profile 14* (weight percentages; after Middleton, 1930)[1]

Hor.	SiO_2	Al_2O_3	Fe_2O_3	CaO	MgO	K_2O	MnO	TiO_2	P_2O_5	SO_3	H_2O+
A₁	70.5	12.5	6.1	0.8	0.5	0.6	0.2	1.8	0.1	0.1	6.6
B₁	52.7	22.9	10.6	0.5	0.4	0.5	0.1	1.4	0.1	0.1	10.4
B₂	50.5	23.1	14.9	0.3	0.6	0.3	0.1	1.5	0.2	0.1	9.3
C	52.6	21.0	13.4	0.3	1.0	0.7	0.5	1.2	0.2	0.1	9.1

[1] Na_2O absent; FeO not determined.

and halloysite were present in the clay fraction and some accessory vermiculite, hydrous mica, and montmorillonite. The chemical analysis is reported in tables II.44 and 44a. The data do not suggest severe clay destruction. Therefore the conclusion is drawn that the sharp increase in clay content from the A to the B horizon is either the

TABLE II.43a. *Derived molar ratios of profile 14*

Hor.	SiO_2/R_2O_3	SiO_2/Al_2O_3	SiO_2/Fe_2O_3	Al_2O_3/Fe_2O_3
A₁	7.3	9.6	31	3.2
B₁	3.0	3.9	13.2	3.4
B₂	2.6	3.7	9.0	2.4
C	3.0	4.3	10.5	2.5

TABLE II.44. *Chemical clay analysis of profile 14* (weight percentages; after Anderson and Byers, 1955)[1]

Hor.	SiO$_2$	Al$_2$O$_3$	Fe$_2$O$_3$	CaO	MgO	K$_2$O	MnO	TiO$_2$	P$_2$O$_5$	SO$_3$	H$_2$O+
A$_1$	34.4	32.1	12.4	0.6	0.9	0.5	0.2	1.0	0.3	0.2	17.1
B$_1$	36.9	31.7	16.0	0.6	0.4	0.4	0.1	0.9	0.2	0.1	13.1
B$_2$	35.4	29.4	20.6	0.4	0.4	0.2	0.1	1.0	0.2	0.1	12.3
C	35.2	29.7	20.1	0.5	0.1	0.2	0.3	1.0	0.4	0.1	12.5

[1] Na$_2$O present only in traces; FeO not determined.

result of weathering *in situ*, and/or of lateral removal as reported to occur in the Oxisols (Chapter I of this Part). Cheluviation of iron has certainly taken place.

TABLE II.44a. *Derived clay molar ratios*

Hor.	SiO$_2$/R$_2$O$_3$	SiO$_2$/Al$_2$O$_3$	SiO$_2$/Fe$_2$O$_3$	Al$_2$O$_3$/Fe$_2$O$_3$
A$_1$	1.4	1.8	7.2	4.0
B$_1$	1.5	2.0	6.2	3.1
B$_2$	1.4	2.1	4.6	2.2
C	1.4	2.0	4.7	2.3

Desilication has also occurred as the molar silica/sesquioxide ratio of diorites is generally larger than 4. This ratio is lower in the C horizon and weathering has therefore resulted in a partially desilicated parent material.

The conclusions mentioned above, can be substantiated by calculation of the normative mineralogical compositions of the clay fraction and of the soil, if the modal composition is taken into account. The results of these calculations are represented in tables II.45 and 46.

TABLE II.45. *Normative mineralogical composition of the clay fraction of profile 14* (weight percentages)

Hor.	Kd	Ms	Sm	Gibb	Go + Hm	Ru	Str
A$_1$	71.1	4.4	3.3	6.7	13.8	0.9	0.9
B$_1$	76.2	3.5	1.5	1.4	15.9	0.8	0.6
B$_2$	74.7	1.6	1.5	–	20.6	1.0	0.6
C	75.5	1.6	0.7	0.2	20.1	1.0	0.9

Kd = kandite (kaolinite + halloysite); Ms = muscovite (illite); Sm = smectite; Gibb = gibbsite; Go = goethite; Hm = hematite; Ru = rutile (anatase); Str = strengite.

It should be mentioned that the calculation reveals the presence of predominantly kaolinite and halloysite as clay minerals, which confirms Nyun and McCaleb's (1955) findings; also the presence of small amounts of 2 : 1 minerals agrees with the results of these authors. The vermiculite, reported by Nyun and McCaleb (1955), can be accounted for by assuming that this results from the weathering of biotite, which was found to be present in the soil (table II.46) increasing with depth. The accord between

TABLE II.46. *Normative mineralogical composition of profile 14* (weight percentages)[1]

Hor.	Q	Bi	Kd	Ms	Sm	Gibb	Go + Hm	Ru	Misc
A_1	59.3	0.5	21.3	4.7	0.9	1.9	6.9	1.8	2.7
B_1	27.0	0.7	53.6	3.7	0.8	0.8	11.0	1.3	1.1
B_2	22.3	1.6	57.5	0.9	0.6	–	15.2	1.3	0.6
C	26.7	3.6	50.1	3.0	0.3	–	14.4	1.3	0.7

[1] Mineral notations as in table II.45; Bi = biotite.

the calculated mineralogical composition and the semi-quantitative estimations of Nyun and McCaleb (1955) points to the validity of the rules used in these calculations.

The appearance of gibbsite in the surface layers is difficult to explain. Usually it is a product of kaolinite decomposition, which could have occurred in this case, but then the existence of illites and smectites is difficult to explain. Gibbsite can be formed directly from illite (see figs. III.7 and 8 in Chapter I of Part III), but then the illite content should have decreased. It is more realistic to assume that the presence of illites and smectites in the mineral assemblage is due to admixtures of foreign materials. This assumption is not very improbable as the sudden decrease in clay content of the A_1 horizon points to lateral removal. It is then also possible that foreign material is admixed in the surface.

In terms of the 7th Approximation the soil is probably an Oxisol, as the content of primary minerals and 2 : 1 layer silicates is very low. Possibly it is a Humox.

In conclusion it can be stated that desilication of the parent rock and lateral removal of clay are important processes in the formation of the 'lateritic' soils. The podzolization processes, such as cheluviation, argeluviation, and destruction of clay are still not very pronounced, although certainly present.

2.2. PODZOLIC SOILS (ULTISOLS AND ALFISOLS)

Well-investigated soils are the Grey Brown Podzolics and the Red and Yellow Podzolics. The former occur predominantly in humid, temperate climates, although they may occur in the tropics at higher altitudes. The Red and Yellow type occurs in humid, warm-temperate, as well as in tropical climates.

2.2.1. RED AND YELLOW PODZOLIC SOILS (ULTISOLS: figs. II.33 and 34)

These comprise a group of soils with very thin A_1 horizons over leached, light-coloured A_2 horizons underlain by red, yellowish-red, or yellow finer textured B horizons that grade into lighter-coloured, often reticulately mottled C horizons. In the south eastern United States of America the Red and Yellow Podzolic Soils occur associated with the Reddish Brown Lateritic Soils, the former being restricted to acid parent materials, the latter to more basic materials. The vegetation consists of conifers and oaks; in sandy parts of the region pine is dominant. Rainfall varies from 760 mm to 1500 mm annually. The average summer temperatures vary from $24°$ tot $27°$ C and the average winter temperatures from $5°$ to $8°$ C. The Yellow Podzolics occur, after Marbut (1935), predominantly on unconsolidated sands and clay of Tertiary age in the coastal plain on smooth and flat areas; the Red Podzolics occur in the Piedmont Plateau and the Appalachian regions on rolling areas with good drainage produced by thorough dissection or by underlying gravels and sands and on old rocks ranging from crystalline gneisses and schists to limestones, shales, and sandstones.

In the tropics, as e.g. in Indonesia (Dames, 1955; Van Schuylenborgh, 1956; Tan and Van Schuylenborgh, 1961; Dudal, 1962), the Red-Yellow Podzolic Soils occur at temperatures of approximately $25°–28°$ C without seasonal fluctuation, precipitation of 3000–4000 mm annually, under an evergreen tropical lowland rain forest and on dacitic and rhyolitic volcanic ash and (calcareous) sandstones. The Yellow Podzolics occur on moderately well-drained sites and the Red ones on the well-drained sites.

In the south eastern United States of America, the Yellow Podzolic Soils are mainly members of the Norfolk and closely related series. They are predominantly sandy loams consisting of a thin layer of pine needles with some leaf mould from deciduous trees, underlain by a dark A_1 horizon of sand texture; the sand grains are usually grey. The A_2 horizon consists of pale-yellowish sand or loamy sand and is, as the A_1 horizon, single-grained. The A_2 horizon is underlain by a yellow or faintly yellow, friable, sandy clay B horizon, which is usually, after Marbut (1935), 'structureless'. The colour is uniform and may have a reddish shade locally. This layer is underlain by mottled, red, yellow, and grey sandy clay. The thickness of the successive horizons depends on the texture of the parent material and on relief.

The dominant soils of the Red Podzolic Soils are members of the Cecil series. The two principal types are Cecil clay loam and Cecil sandy loam. The clay loams are considered as soils (Marbut, 1935) in which the A horizon, originally sandy, has been removed by erosion, thus exposing the B horizon to the direct atmospheric influences. The normal profile, the sandy loam, consists of the usually very thin layer of leaf mould made up mainly of leaves from deciduous trees, but may contain from place to place different proportions of needles from conifers. The leaf mould is underlain by a light-textured, dark-coloured horizon over a pale-yellow or greyish-yellow single grained sand, loamy sand, or light sandy loam. The B horizon is a red clay containing some sand, the proportion of the latter depending on the parent rock. The structure is angular blocky and the colour of the peds is redder on the outsides than in the insides, thus suggesting the presence of clay skins. The thickness of the B horizon varies from 150 to 250 cm. It is underlain by reddish or yellowish loose material derived from disintegration of crystalline gneisses and schists, not yet thoroughly decomposed. The unweathered gneisses and schists lie at depths differing greatly from place to place, attaining in places a depth of 30 metres or more.

A more accurate description of a Red-Yellow Podzolic Soil can be found in the 7th Approximation (U.S. Soil Survey Staff, 1960, p. 235). The profile (prof. 15: Typic Hapludult) occurs in Houston County, Alabama. Parent material: alluvium from Coastal Plain material. Vegetation: old pecan orchard; sod of bermuda grass, broom-sedge, and weeds. Topography: less than 1 % slope, facing east; low terrace. Climate: approximately 1400 mm precipitation and 19°–20° C, annual mean. The description reads as follows:

Horizon	Depth (cm)	
Ap	0–13	Brown or dark-brown (7.5YR4/4) fine sandy loam, yellowish-brown (10YR5/4) when dry; single grained; loose; abundant roots; diffuse, wavy boundary.
A&B	13–25	Yellowish-red (5YR4/6) sand clay loam, yellowish red (5YR5/6) when dry; an interfingering of fine sandy loam A horizon and sandy clay B horizon; sandy loam is firm; sandy clay is friable; few, very fine pores; numerous dark streaks along old root channels; gradual boundary.
B_{21t}	25–50	Red (2.5YR4/6) heavy sandy clay loam or sandy clay, red (2.5YR5/6) when dry; crushed colour slightly lighter than uncrushed; moderately fine and medium, blocky structure; firm, plastic; few, fine roots; common, very fine pores; few, dark specks and dark streaks along old root channels; gradual boundary.
B_{22t}	50–64	Yellowish-red (5YR5/6) heavy sandy clay loam, red (2.5YR5/6) when dry; surfaces of peds slightly darker than interiors; moderate, fine and medium, blocky structure; friable, plastic; few roots; common, very fine pores; few, black specks and streaks along old root channels; gradual boundary.
B_{23t}	64–76	Yellowish-red (5YR5/8) light sandy clay loam, red (2.5YR5/8) when dry; surfaces of peds slightly darker than interiors; weak, fine, blocky structure; friable, slightly plastic; few roots; common, very fine pores; gradual boundary.
B_{3t}	76–94	Strong brown (7.5YR5/8) heavy fine sandy loam or loam, reddish yellow (5YR6/8) when dry; very friable, very slightly plastic; few roots; gradual boundary.
C_1	94–127	Reddish-yellow (7.5YR6/8) sandy loam, reddish yellow (7.5YR7/8) when dry; very friable.
IIC_2	127–152	Yellow (10YR8/6) coarse sand, dominantly yellow (2.5Y8/6) when dry; a moderate amount of variegation caused by darker and lighter colours.

The few analytical details of this profile are summarized in table 11.47. The only fact that can be obtained from this table is that clay migration (argeluviation) is a part of the soil formation process. The clay separate composition and base saturation suggest an ultimate stage in soil formation, indicating that desilication might be involved too.

FIG. II.33. *Red and Yellow Podzolic Soils*

a. *From Guinee with a prominently develop-ed A₂ and B₂t horizon (photo Van Es)*

b. *From Indonesia with a weakly developed A₂ and well-developed B₂t horizon (photo Buringh)*

FIG. II.34. *Profile 18: Oxic Plinthaquult*
(see p. 278)

FIG.II.36. *Profile 19: Ultic Palexeralf*
(see p. 286)

FIG. II.37. *Profile 21: Ultic Haplustalf*
(see p. 293)

FIG. II.38. *Profile 24: Typic Tropohumod (A₂ material runs as saturated paste along the wall, as the B$_{ir}$ horizon is water-stagnating; see p. 299)*

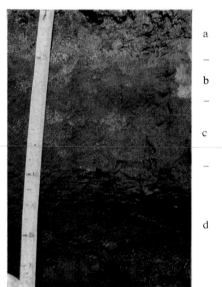

a
–
b
–
c
–
–
d

FIG. II.49. *Paddy soil on andesitic volcanic ash, 10 km W. of Bogor (Java, Indonesia)* a = *reduced topsoil of 18 cms thickness;* b = *mottled horizon with at 25-35 cm a hardened iron accumulation layer;* c = *manganese accumulation horizon (35-61 cm);* d = *stratified andesitic volcanic ash (see p. 346)*

a
–
b
–
c
–
d

FIG. II.50. *Paddy soil in Reddish Brown Latosol, S. of Bogor near Sindangsari village (Java, Indonesia)* a = *reduced topsoil of 15 cms thickness;* b = *iron accumulation horizon (15-20 cm);* c = *manganese accumulation horizon (20-28 cm);* d = *latosol with some manganese and iron concretions (see p. 346)*

TABLE II.47. *Some analytical details of profile 15*

Hor.	grain size distribution			C %	pH 1:5	c.e.c. m.e./ 100 g soil	Base sat. %	clay separate[1]		
	> 50μ	50–2μ	< 2μ					Kaol	Q	Gi
Ap	80.5	11.5	8.0	0.5	5.7	3.2	34			
A & B	62.8	15.9	21.3	0.2	4.7	3.6	31			
B$_{21t}$	47.2	14.7	38.1	0.2	4.7	5.0	28	50		5
B$_{22t}$	50.8	15.3	33.9	0.2	4.7	8.0	24			
B$_{23t}$	59.4	12.2	28.4	0.1	4.7	6.9	20	50	5	5
B$_{3t}$	67.4	9.7	22.9		4.5	5.6	16			
C$_1$	82.2	4.7	13.1		4.6	3.8	16			
IIC$_2$	97.7	0.1	2.2		5.2	0.8	37			

[1] Kaol = kaolinite; Q = quartz; Gi = gibbsite.

More information is needed to get a good insight into the formation processes of Red-Yellow Podzolic soils. Many investigators have made researches in this field, but with controversial results. Pearson and Ensminger (1949) estimated the mineralogical composition of the clay separates of the soils in question and found from the top to the bottom a decreasing quartz and an increasing kaolinite content (see also: Rich and Obenshain, 1955), whereas gibbsite either increased, decreased or remained more or less constant. The quartz content in the clay fraction was always considerable, ranging from 10 to 50% and decreasing with depth. This was also found by Krebs and Tedrow (1958), but is not in accordance with the scarce data of profile 15 and the data of McCaleb (1959). This author did not mention the presence of quartz in the clay fraction. He found in the Red Podzolic soils of *igneous* origin 70–90% kandite, the halloysite increasing from 10% in the A to 40% in the C horizon. Vermiculite and gibbsite made up minor amounts in the soils. The Red-Yellow Podzolic soils have 40 to 60% kaolinite and 30 to 40% vermiculite in their clay fractions; halloysite was restricted to the B$_2$ horizon and below with the exception of the A$_2$ horizon and did not exceed 20%. No gibbsite occurred below the B$_{31}$ horizon. The Yellow Podzolic soils ranged from 40 to 80% kaolinite and 20 to 40% vermiculite throughout the profile; gibbsite exceeded kaolinite in the C horizon. Profiles from *sedimentary* rocks differed from the above as follows: no gibbsite occurred below the B$_2$ horizon except for the B$_{31}$ horizon of the red soil. There was more kaolinite or equal quantities of kaolinite and vermiculite in all profiles. Illite was present in the red-yellow and yellow soils throughout but none was present in the red. Montmorillonite appeared in small amounts in the lower C horizons in all profiles as the shale component was encountered.

McCaleb (1959) also found when examining 18 profiles of Red-Yellow Podzolic soils developed on igneous and sedimentary rocks, that the A horizon increases in thickness from the red to the yellow members, whereas the B horizons have a relatively constant thickness within each group. The mean clay distributions are tabulated in table II.48 for the soils developed on igneous rocks. The clay contents of soils derived from sedimentary rocks are slightly different but show the same tendency.

TABLE II.48. *Clay distribution of Red-Yellow Podzolic Soils* (weight percentages; after Mc-Caleb, 1959)

Hor.	Red	Red-Yellow	Yellow
A_1	9.4	4.6	6.3
A_2	10.2	6.3	6.4
B_2	49.3	46.4	42.5
C_1	22.7	27.0	23.0
C_2	6.5	6.6	–

The table shows that all profiles have textural B_2 horizons; clay percentages in the C_1 horizons are indicative of the amount of *in situ* formation of clay. In view of the rather thin A horizon compared with the B horizon we have to assume that also new-formation of clay occurs in the B horizon together with migration (see later). This is in contradiction to what Simonson (1950) stated, viz. that the C horizons contain frequently more clay-sized minerals than the solum above, but in accordance with the analyses of Krebs and Tedrow (1958).

The cation exchange capacity of the B_2 horizons (McCaleb, 1959) is, as a mean for the B_2 of the soils from igneous rocks, 12 m.e./100 g of soil; this indicates that a part of the clay is non-kaolinitic, which is in accordance with the mineralogical data.

The free iron oxide percentages (table II.49) of the soils from igneous rocks show that iron has moved from the A into the B horizon and that iron migration is at least partly independent of clay migration. The yellow soils show a steady increase with depth, which may be associated with slow internal drainage. The soils from sedimentary rocks show the same tendencies. These results indicate that cheluviation is certainly a

TABLE II.49. *Per cent free iron oxide in R.- Y. Podzolic soils* (weight percentages; after McCaleb, 1959)

Hor.	Red		Red-Yellow		Yellow	
	a	b	a	b	a	b
A_1	1.2	7.8	0.4	11.5	0.6	10.5
A_2	1.4	7.3	0.6	10.5	0.6	10.7
B_2	5.1	9.7	3.4	13.7	3.2	13.3
C_1	3.0	7.6	1.2	22.5	4.0	5.8
C_2	1.3	5.0	0.9	7.3	5.4	–

a = free Fe_2O_3; b = clay/free Fe_2O_3.

part of the soil forming process.

On these and some additional data controversal theories on the soil forming process are developed by Simonson (1950) and by McCaleb (1959). Before discussing these theories, further information about the characteristics of the soils will be given.

Fairly complete analyses of Red-Yellow 'Podzolic' soils are published in the work of Marbut (1935). Two profiles of the Cecil series were selected, of which the clay separates had also been analyzed. One profile (profile 16) was that of a Cecil fine sandy loam from Rutherford County in the south western part of the United States of America near the eastern foot of the Blue Ridge Plateau. It is derived from crystalline rock,

TABLE II.50. *Grain size distribution of profile 16* (weight percentages; after Marbut, 1935)

Hor.	Depth (cm)	$> 50\mu$	$50-5\mu$	$< 5\mu$
A	0–13	61.5	22.9	15.6
B₂	13–91	27.4	21.4	51.2
C₁	183–244	71.6	14.2	14.2
C₂	284+	89.7	8.8	1.5

probably gneissic. The C_2 horizon consists of grey disintegrated but not leached rock which has not suffered much chemical decomposition (table II.51). The colour of the A horizon is reddish brown and shows less grey than the highly sandy, highly eluviated A horizon of many Cecil sandy loams. The A horizon contains 15% of clay (table II. 50) and is higher than the mean value reported by McCaleb (1959: see table II.48). This high percentage and the colour suggest that the A horizon is one developing in a former B horizon. This probability is further supported by the higher content of Fe_2O_3 in A than in C_2 (table II.51). An explanation for its presence, since it is clearly an accumulation, in any other way than as a B horizon now being converted into an A

TABLE II.51. *Chemical composition of profile 16* (weight percentages; after Marbut, 1935)

Hor.	SiO₂	Al₂O₃	Fe₂O₃	CaO	MgO	K₂O	Na₂O	MnO	TiO₂	P₂O₅	H₂O+
A	64.6	15.6	4.8	0.2	0.7	2.6	0.4	0.1	1.8	0.1	9.3
B₂	46.0	27.3	11.1	0.2	0.7	1.4	0.6	0.0	1.5	0.1	11.6
C₁	47.0	24.8	9.9	0.6	2.3	3.1	0.7	0.1	1.8	0.7	8.7
C₂	55.7	22.1	4.5	2.5	1.5	5.2	2.9	0.1	0.9	1.2	3.1

TABLE II.51a. *Derived molar ratios of profile 16*

Hor.	SiO₂/R₂O₃	SiO₂/Al₂O₃	SiO₂/Fe₂O₃	Al₂O₃/Fe₂O₃
A	5.9	7.0	36	5.1
B₂	2.3	2.9	11.1	3.9
C₁	2.6	3.2	12.6	3.9
C₂	3.8	4.3	33	7.8

after the former A has been removed by erosion, and that considerable progress has been made in the transformation, is difficult.

Table II.51a shows clearly that during weathering ($C_2 \rightarrow C_1$) a considerable amount of silicic acid has been removed resulting in the residual accumulation of sesquioxides. Desilication is therefore a part of the formation process. Furthermore, more alumina than iron oxide has been removed, which was already frequently reported as occurring in desilication.

The abrupt decrease in the silica/sesquioxide ratios from the A to the B_2 can be caused by: 1) clay destruction; 2) differential downward movement of clay minerals; 3) erosion (lateral migration) of clay minerals either by water or wind action leaving behind the coarser-grained skeleton rich in quartz. The answer to the question which of these processes is the most important in the formation of this profile, can only be approached by chemical and mineralogical analysis of the clay separates. The chemical analysis (tables II.52 and II.52a) shows that the clay fraction is rich in alumina and that clay destruction may have occurred as the SiO_2/Al_2O_3 decreases considerably. However, the normative mineralogical composition shows that there is no indication of clay destruction (table II.53). The decreasing SiO_2/Al_2O_3 ratio seems to be the result of the removal of alumina by leaching; also iron has migrated from the A to the

TABLE II.52. *Chemical composition of the colloid fraction of profile 16* (weight percentages; after Marbut, 1935)

Hor.	SiO$_2$	Al$_2$O$_3$	Fe$_2$O$_3$	CaO	MgO	K$_2$O	Na$_2$O	MnO	TiO$_2$	P$_2$O$_5$	SO$_3$	H$_2$O+
A	34.5	36.8	11.3	0.2	0.6	0.3	0.1	0.1	1.0	0.3	0.2	14.4
B$_2$	32.0	37.0	14.7	0.2	0.1	0.2	0.1	0.1	1.0	0.1	0.1	13.2
C$_1$	28.8	40.1	11.0	0.2	0.1	0.2	0.1	0.1	1.1	0.8	0.1	16.6

TABLE II.52a. *Derived molar ratios of the colloid*

Hor.	SiO$_2$/R$_2$O$_3$	SiO$_2$/Al$_2$O$_3$	SiO$_2$/Fe$_2$O$_3$	Al$_2$O$_3$/Fe$_2$O$_3$
A	1.3	1.6	8.2	5.2
B$_2$	1.2	1.5	5.8	3.9
C$_1$	1.0	1.2	7.0	5.7

B_2 horizon. The results are in accordance with the data reported in that the clay mineral is predominantly kaolinite with some admixtures of 2:1 minerals, whilst gibbsite increases with depth and free silica is absent. We can conclude that the above mentioned mechanism of clay destruction is not a factor in the formation of this profile. The other two mechanisms remain therefore (see above); the general presence of clay skins points to the second mechanism but does not rule out the third mechanism. As erosion of this profile has occurred, both processes seem to play a rôle.

Some further conclusions may be drawn on studying the normative mineralogical composition of the whole soil. As, according to the description of Marbut (1935), the C_2 is relatively undecomposed rock, both the epinormic (a) and the katanormic (b)

TABLE II.53. *Normative mineralogical composition of the clay separates of profile 16* (weight percentages)

Hor.	Kaol	Ms	Sm	Gibb	Go	Ru	Str
A	69.1	2.9	2.2	12.8	11.0	1.0	1.0
B_2	69.1	1.6	0.4	12.5	15.1	1.0	0.3
C_1	60.9	1.6	0.5	23.4	10.4	1.2	2.0

Kaol = kaolinite; Ms = muscovite (illite); Sm = smectite; Gibb = gibbsite; Go = goethite; Ru = rutile (anatase); Str = strengite.

composition was calculated. The real normative composition of C_2 lies then somewhere between these extremes (table II.54). The table shows that albite is slightly less readily weatherable than K-feldspar. Both minerals give rise predominantly to kaolinite and silica upon weathering. Mica seems to be inherited from the parent material. The A horizon looses a considerable amount of kaolinite, either by eluviation and/or erosion. It is interesting to note that the micas and silica are much less mobile

TABLE II.54. *Normative mineralogical composition of profile 16* (weight percentages)

Hor.	Q	Or	Ab	An	Sil	Ms	Chl	Kaol	Sm	Gibb	Go	Ru	Misc
A	47.6	–	3.5	–	–	23.0	1.8	11.8	0.3	2.2	6.6	2.0	1.2
B_2	17.2	–	4.8	–	–	11.2	2.0	42.1	0.2	8.3	12.4	1.4	0.5
C_1	20.2	–	5.8	–	–	26.3	8.0	21.9	0.1	3.6	10.8	1.9	1.5
C_2 (a)	15.6	–	24.6	–	–	44.4	–	–	–	–	4.3	1.0	10.1
C_2 (b)	8.0	31.8	25.3	5.5	9.7	–	–	–	–	–	4.4	1.0	14.3

Q = silica; Or = K-feldspar; Ab = albite; An = anorthite; Sil = sillimanite; Ms = muscovite; Chl = chlorite; Kaol = kaolinite; Sm = smectite; Gibb = gibbsite; Go = goethite; Ru = rutile; Misc = miscellaneous.

and enrich residually.

Similar conclusions can be drawn from the analyses of a Cecil clay loam profile (profile 17) from Lanett, Chambers County, Alabama. Grain size distribution and erosion show the same tendencies as that of profile 16 (table II.55). The parent rock, however, is different from that of profile 16, and is very likely a schistous material (see table II.59). The chemical analysis does not lead to conclusions about desilication being involved, as the C_1 horizon was not included (tables II.56 and 56a). The data

TABLE II.55. *Grain size distribution of profile 17* (weight percentages)

Hor.	Depth (cm)	> 50μ	50–5μ	< 5μ
A	0–18	33.6	44.1	22.3
B_{21}	20–61	24.9	22.3	52.8
B_{22}	64–150	17.2	41.5	41.3
C_2	610–760	29.3	52.3	18.4

again point to cheluviation and argeluviation having been active. The chemical (tables

TABLE II.56. *Chemical composition of profile 17* (weight percentages; after Marbut, 1935)

Hor.	SiO_2	Al_2O_3	Fe_2O_3	CaO	MgO	K_2O	Na_2O	MnO	TiO_2	P_2O_5	SO_3	H_2O+
A	67.2	11.3	9.5	tr[1]	0.7	1.0	0.4	0.1	2.1	0.2	0.1	8.7
B_{21}	53.1	21.0	11.6	tr	1.0	1.3	0.3	0.1	1.6	0.1	0.1	10.1
B_{22}	52.5	22.1	11.7	tr	1.8	2.1	0.3	0.1	1.3	0.1	0.1	8.7
C_2	57.8	18.4	9.6	tr	2.7	3.1	0.3	0.2	1.3	0.2	tr	6.5

[1] tr = trace.

TABLE II.56a. *Derived molar ratios of profile 17*

Hor.	SiO_2/R_2O_3	SiO_2/Al_2O_3	SiO_2/Fe_2O_3	Al_2O_3/Fe_2O_3
A	6.6	10.2	19.0	1.9
B_{21}	3.2	4.3	12.3	2.9
B_{22}	3.0	4.0	12.0	3.0
C_2	4.0	5.4	16.3	3.0

II.57 and 57a) and normative mineralogical analyses (table II.58) show that clay destruction is still less evident than in profile 16. Only iron has migrated. The clay mineral is predominantly kaolinite and only minor amounts of 2:1 minerals are present. There is less gibbsite than in profile 16 and it decreases slightly with depth.

TABLE II.57. *Chemical analysis of the colloid fractions of profile 17* (weight percentages; after Marbut, 1935)

Hor.	SiO_2	Al_2O_3	Fe_2O_3	CaO	MgO	K_2O	Na_2O	MnO	TiO_2	P_2O_5	SO_3	H_2O+
A	35.2	35.8	12.8	0.3	0.4	0.3	tr	0.2	1.0	0.2	0.1	13.2
B_{21}	34.3	34.5	15.2	0.1	0.2	0.3	0.1	0.1	1.1	tr	0.4	13.8
B_{22}	36.1	34.1	14.9	tr[1]	0.1	0.4	0.2	0.2	0.8	tr	0.4	12.6

[1] tr = trace.

The mica content increases slightly with depth. Whether or not these data point to a destruction of mica is not clear, as the differences are probably not consistent.

TABLE II.57a. *Derived molar ratios of the colloids*

Hor.	SiO_2/R_2O_3	SiO_2/Al_2O_3	SiO_2/Fe_2O_3	Al_2O_3/Fe_2O_3
A	1.4	1.7	7.3	4.4
B_{21}	1.3	1.7	6.0	3.6
B_{22}	1.4	1.8	6.5	3.6

Anyway, it is evident, that argeluviation is the most important process in the formation of this soil. A combination of eluviation and lateral removal or erosion, as suggested to be active in the previous profile, is also possible.

The normative mineralogical composition of the profile is reported in table II.59.

TABLE II.58. *Normative mineralogical composition of the clay fractions of profile 17* (weight percentages)

Hor.	Kaol	Ms	Sm	Gibb	Go	Ru	Str
A	72.6	2.5	2.1	8.3	12.7	1.0	0.7
B_{21}	71.9	3.1	0.9	7.5	15.5	1.2	tr
B_{22}	73.8	3.5	0.7	5.6	15.3	0.8	tr

Kaol = kaolinite; Ms = muscovite; Sm = smectite; Gibb = gibbsite; Go = goethite; Ru = rutile (anatase); Str = strengite.

In this table the chlorite variant of the C_2 epinorm was calculated, as the occurrence of the ottrelite-minerals is not very likely. For the B_{22} horizon only the chlorite variant was reported. The table reveals that muscovite and chlorite have been transformed predominantly into kaolinite upon soil formation, which is normal for well drained, leached soils (see figs. III.7 and 8, Chapter I of Part III). The high silica content in the A as compared with the B horizon seems to indicate a residual enrichment due to the removal of kaolinite. However, other components do not enrich as in the previous profile, possibly as a consequence of their simultaneous removal.

The soils of the young and old coastal plain of Surinam (Northern South America) have been intensively studied. Those of the old coastal plain belong to the Order of the Ultisols (Slager and Van Schuylenborgh, 1970). One example of an Ultisol with hydromorphic characteristics will be discussed (profile 18). Although the parent material was not collected, valuable information was obtained from the analysis of the solum. The profile is situated on a slightly elevated, flat plateau and formed in a medium-textured, pleistocene, marine, Coropina deposit (Lelydorp clay). Altitude: 7 m + NSP (mean sea level). The area is used in shifting cultivation. Drainage is imperfect. Groundwater table fluctuates strongly between the surface and 2 metres.

TABLE II.59. *Normative mineralogical composition of profile 17* (weight percentages)

Hor	Q	Ab	Ot+ Mg–Ot	Chl	Kaol	Ms	Sm	Gibb	Go	Ru	Misc
A	51.5	3.3	–	–	16.7	6.8	0.5	1.9	13.7	2.1	3.3
B$_{21}$	27.7	2.6	–	–	39.7	6.1	0.5	4.1	12.4	1.4	5.6
B$_{22}$	26.9	1.6	–	4.1	32.2	17.0	0.3	2.6	12.6	1.4	1.4
C$_2$ (a)	40.2	2.8	16.1	–	–	28.7	–	–	10.8	1.3	–
C$_2$ (b)	37.6	2.8	–	10.0	9.3	28.4	–	–	10.6	1.3	–

(a) = epinorm; (b) = chlorite variant. Q = silica; Ab = albite; Ot = ottrelite; Mg–Ot = Mg-ottrelite; Chl = chlorite; Kaol = kaolinite; Ms = muscovite; Sm = smectite; Gibb = gibbsite; Go = goethite; Ru = rutile (anatase); Misc = miscellaneous.

The actual groundwater table at sampling date was 130 cm. The climate is sub-equatorial with a total precipitation of roughly 1900 mm annually. The wet seasons are from April to August and December to February, in which roughly 1350 mm of rain is falling. The profile description reads as follows (see fig. II.34, p. 270):

Horizon	Depth (cm)	
A$_{11}$	0–24	Dark greyish brown (10YR4/2:m) silt loam with little organic matter; strong, very fine, subangular blocky structure with few, fine biopores; friable; common, fine roots. Gradual and smooth boundary.
A$_{12}$	24–41	Grey (10YR6/1:m) silty clay loam with common organic matter; strong, very fine, subangular blocky structure with few, fine biopores; slightly firm; few, fine roots. Clear and wavy boundary.
B$_{1tg}$	41–77	Grey (10YR6/1:m) silty clay with strong, very fine, angular blocky structure; many stress-cutans: very few, very fine biopores; sticky and slightly plastic; common, large, distinct, yellowish red (5YR5/8) mottles; very few roots. Gradual and smooth boundary.
B$_{2tg}$	77–104	Light grey (5Y6/1:m) clay; strong, fine, angular blocky structure with many stress-cutans; very few, fine biopores; sticky and slightly plastic; common, medium, prominent, red (10R4/8) nodules and many, medium, distinct, reddish yellow (7.5YR7/8) mottles. Clear and smooth boundary.
B$_{3tg}$	104–135	Light grey (5Y6/1:m) silty clay; strong, fine angular blocky structure with many stress-cutans; very few fine biopores; sticky and plastic; abundant, large, prominent, dark red (7.5R3/8) soft and hard nodules; common, medium, faint, reddish yellow (5YR6/8) mottles.

The profile description and table II.60 place this soil in the subgroup of the Oxic Plinthaquults. The soil is strongly base-unsaturated, suggesting beginning destruction of clay minerals. Erosion is negligible as the profile lies in a flat area and clay distribution is such that the losses of clay from the A horizon account for the gains in the B horizon. Argeluviation will therefore be an essential process. Iron shows a tremendous mobility (see also tables II.61 and 61a) which proves that reduction and cheluviation

TABLE II.60. *Analytical details of profile 18*

Hor.	grain size distribution (%)			pH 0.01M CaCl₂	C (%)	exchangeable cations and c.e.c. (m.e./100 g of soil)						base sat. (%)	free Fe₂O₃ (%)
	> 50μ	50–2μ	< 2μ			Ca	Mg	K	Na	Al+ H	c.e.c.		
A₁₁	0.8	72.4	26.8	3.6	1.9	1.1	0.3	0.1	0.2	5.2	6.9	24	0.2
A₁₂	0.6	60.5	38.9	3.6	1.1	1.1	0.4	0.1	0.2	6.2	7.9	21	0.3
B₁ₜg	0.9	50.8	48.3	3.6	0.6	1.1	0.4	0.1	0.2	7.6	9.4	20	3.2
B₂ₜg	1.1	39.9	59.0	3.6	0.5	1.1	0.3	0.1	0.2	9.0	10.7	16	5.5
B₃ₜg	7.0	49.4	43.6	3.6	0.4	1.1	0.4	0.1	0.2	8.1	9.8	18	9.7

are very active in the soil formation process. Total chemical analysis shows that aluminium is also very mobile, but this is very probably due to the migration of clay. The question whether or not transformations in the clay fraction occur can only be answered by an analysis of the clay fraction of the soil horizons. Tables II.62 and 62a show that the clay is a mixture of 1 : 1 and 2 : 1 layer minerals. Also here considerable mobility of iron can be noticed. Aluminium is also mobile and this could indicate a), in accordance with the investigations of Hallsworth (1963), that clay minerals with a low SiO_2/Al_2O_3 ratio are more mobile than those with a higher SiO_2/Al_2O_3 ratio; b) that

TABLE II.61. *Chemical composition of profile 18* (weight percentages)

Hor.	SiO₂	Al₂O₃	Fe₂O₃	FeO	CaO	MgO	MnO	K₂O	Na₂O	TiO₂	P₂O₅	H₂O+
A₁₁	82.2	8.6	1.1	0.1	0.1	tr[1]	tr	0.6	0.1	1.4	0.1	6.1
A₁₂	77.9	12.6	1.6	0.1	0.1	0.1	tr	0.9	0.2	1.4	0.1	6.1
B₁ₜg	70.2	15.5	4.5	0.2	0.1	0.1	tr	1.1	0.2	1.4	0.1	6.9
B₂ₜg	62.1	17.1	7.1	0.5	0.1	0.2	tr	1.3	0.2	1.1	0.1	7.9
B₃ₜg	64.9	15.3	10.4	0.5	0.1	0.2	tr	1.3	0.2	1.0	0.1	6.4

[1] tr = trace.

TABLE II.61a. *Derived molar ratios of profile 18*

Hor.	SiO₂/R₂O₃	SiO₂/Al₂O₃	SiO₂/Fe₂O₃	Al₂O₃/Fe₂O₃
A₁₁	15	16	208	13
A₁₂	9.8	10.5	154	15
B₁ₜg	6.5	7.7	41	5.4
B₂ₜg	4.9	6.2	23	3.7
B₃ₜg	5.0	7.2	16	2.3

clay destruction has occurred with the subsequent migration of alumina from the A and its accumulation in the B₂ horizon. However, the calculation of the mineralogical

TABLE II.62. *Chemical composition of the colloidal fraction of profile 18* (weight percentages)

Hor.	SiO$_2$	Al$_2$O$_3$	Fe$_2$O$_3$	FeO	CaO	MgO	MnO	K$_2$O	Na$_2$O	TiO$_2$	P$_2$O$_5$	H$_2$O+
A$_{11}$	51.9	30.3	2.7	0.2	–	0.6	tr[1]	2.0	0.2	1.6	0.1	11.2
A$_{12}$	50.4	31.3	3.0	0.3	–	0.6	tr	1.9	0.2	1.4	0.1	11.6
B$_{1tg}$	47.0	30.8	6.3	0.7	–	0.6	tr	1.9	0.2	1.1	0.1	11.7
B$_{2tg}$	44.2	30.1	8.9	1.3	–	0.5	tr	1.9	0.2	0.9	0.1	12.1
B$_{3tg}$	45.6	28.9	9.0	1.3	–	0.6	tr	2.0	0.2	0.9	0.1	11.6

[1] tr = trace.

composition (table II.63) shows, that free alumina does not occur and therefore only the differential migration of clay minerals can account for the trend in the SiO$_2$/Al$_2$O$_3$ ratio.

TABLE II.62a. *Derived molar ratios of the colloid fractions*

Hor.	SiO$_2$/R$_2$O$_3$	SiO$_2$/Al$_2$O$_3$	SiO$_2$/Fe$_2$O$_3$	Al$_2$O$_3$/Fe$_2$O$_3$
A$_{11}$	2.8	2.9	50	17
A$_{12}$	2.6	2.7	43	16
B$_{1tg}$	2.3	2.6	18	6.8
B$_{2tg}$	2.1	2.5	12	4.7
B$_{3tg}$	2.2	2.7	12	4.5

Table II.63 shows that montmorillonite is transformed into kaolinite and halloysite in the course of the soil forming process. This is undoubtedly the result of stronger leaching of the top soil as compared with the subsoil (see figs. III.7 and 8 of Chapter I of Part III).

Table II.63 also shows that the changing mineralogical composition of the clay fraction is substantiated by the c.e.c. values.

TABLE II.63. *Normative mineralogical composition* (weight percentages) *and the c.e.c.'s* (m.e./ 100 g) *of the clay fractions of profile 18*

Hor.	Q	Kaol	Hal	Ms	Mm	Go	Ru	Str	c.e.c.
A$_{11}$	10.7	40.9	13.8	16.3	13.7	2.9	1.6	0.2	13
A$_{12}$	7.5	44.9	12.9	15.9	14.0	3.2	1.4	0.2	13.5
B$_{1tg}$	3.3	43.5	10.6	15.9	18.5	6.9	1.2	0.2	14
B$_{2tg}$	–	39.5	11.6	16.4	21.6	9.9	0.9	0.2	16
B$_{3tg}$	2.2	35.2	11.4	17.0	23.1	10.1	0.9	0.2	18

Q = silica; Kaol = kaolinite; Hal = halloysite-4; Ms = muscovite (illite); Mm = montmorillonite; Go = goethite; Ru = rutile; Str = strengite.

Summarizing, we can state that the following processes are active in the formation of this soil: 1. differential argeluviation (kaolinite more mobile than illite and mont-morillonite); 2. cheluviation of iron; 3. transformation of montmorillonite into kaolinite.

These processes are reflected in table 11.64, which shows the mineralogical changes in the profile. The table clearly shows the migration of clay, their maximum accumulation in the B_{2tg} horizon and the dissolution of iron in the top soil. However, it does not

TABLE 11.64. *Normative mineralogical composition of profile 18* (weight percentages)

Hor.	Q	Ab	Kaol	Hal	Ms	Mm	Go	Ru	Str	Misc
A_{11}	73.4	–	11.8	3.7	4.4	3.7	1.1	1.2	0.1	3.7
A_{12}	60.8	0.8	17.5	5.0	7.0	5.4	1.7	1.5	0.1	5.0
B_{1tg}	48.3	0.8	21.0	5.1	9.3	8.9	4.9	1.4	0.1	5.1
B_{2tg}	34.3	0.6	23.3	6.8	11.6	12.7	8.4	1.0	0.1	6.8
B_{3tg}	42.2	0.8	18.3	5.0	10.6	10.1	11.5	0.9	0.1	5.0

Mineral abbreviations as in table II.63; Ab = albite; Misc = miscellaneous.

show that kaolinite is more mobile than the 2 : 1 lattice minerals as this is obscured by the transformation process of montmorillonite into kaolinite. These facts can be deduced from tables 11.62a and 63.

All the examples show that clay destruction cannot be considered as the mechanism responsible for the difference in clay content between the A and B horizons of Red-Yellow Podzolic soils, as thought by Simonson (1950). Even in the very fine clay fraction considerable changes in clay composition do not occur as can be deduced from an analysis of the 0.2–0.08 μ fraction of a Red-Yellow Podzolic soil by Rich and Obenshain (1955). Table 11.65 shows this analysis and table 11.66 gives the normative mineralogical composition. Table 11.66 shows that some of the swelling minerals in the C_1 horizon are transformed into kandites upon soil formation, although not as evident as in the previous profile 18. Free silica and free alumina, frequently signs of silicate

TABLE 11.65. *Chemical composition of the 0.2–0.08μ fraction of a Red-Yellow Podzolic soil* (after Rich and Obenshain, 1955; weight percentages)

Hor.	SiO_2	Al_2O_3	Fe_2O_3	CaO	MgO	K_2O	Na_2O	TiO_2	H_2O+
A	35.2	28.5	15.7	0.1	0.9	0.9	0.1	0.5	17.4
B_1	36.7	29.0	16.9	0.1	0.7	0.9	0.1	0.6	16.0
B_2	35.0	29.7	16.7	0.1	0.7	0.8[5]	0.1	0.5	15.9
B_3	36.5	29.9	16.2	0.1	0.7	0.9	0.1	0.7	15.4
C_1	39.3	30.0	13.7	0.1	0.7	0.9	0.1	0.6	15.4

mineral destruction, are negligible. Within the solum clay composition is remarkably constant; only the kaolinite/halloysite ratio changes, which depends on the rather dubious determination of crystal water. Clay destruction according to Simonson's theory (1950) cannot therefore be considered as the most important process in the formation of Red-Yellow Podzolic soils.

TABLE II.66. *Normative mineralogical composition of the 0.2–0.08μ fraction of table 11.65* (weight percentages)

Hor.	Q	Kaol	Hal	Ms	Sm	Go	Gibb	Ru
A	0.3	34.3	36.1	7.7	3.3	17.7	–	0.5
B1	0.3	45.0	21.7	7.7	5.8	18.9	–	0.6
B2	–	53.3	15.8	7.4	2.6	19.1	1.2	0.6
B3	0.4	55.3	14.8	7.9	2.6	18.3	–	0.7
C1	0.1	45.6	21.2	7.6	9.7	15.3	–	0.6

Q = silica; Kaol = kaolinite; Hal = halloysite-4; Ms = muscovite (illite); Sm = smectite; Go = goethite; Gibb = gibbsite; Ru = rutile.

Nevertheless, it remains difficult to explain 1) the frequently great difference in clay content between the A and B horizons; 2) the fact that the A horizon is often too thin and the B horizon too thick for a mere eluviation of clay from the A horizon. In some of the cases erosion is responsible, as indicated in the discussion of profiles 16 and 17. However, McCaleb (1959) pointed out that clay formation *in situ* in the B horizon may also be responsible; the presence of clay skins in the B horizon could then be explained by migration of clay over short distances within the B horizon.

Summarizing, it can be concluded that in the formation of Red and Yellow Podzolic Soils the following processes are responsible: 1) desilication; 2) argeluviation; 3) cheluviation; 4) clay transformations (swelling minerals → kandites); 5) lateral removal of clay. They may act simultaneously, but mostly only part of them are active.

2.2.2. RED AND BROWN MEDITERRANEAN SOILS (ALFISOLS)

Although Mediterranean Soils are not very common in tropical areas, they occur locally when specific aspects of the climate under which they are formed prevail. These seem to be sharp alternation of wet and very dry periods. The dry period causes a severe desiccation of the soil. This fact is considered to be the most important factor in the formation of Mediterranean Soils. However, as the duration of the period of drought can vary and as desiccation can be accomplished at higher as well as lower temperatures than those specific for Mediterranean pedogenesis, several intergrades to other soils are possible. Whereas the specific soils belong to the Xeralfs (according to the 7th Approximation), intergrades to Ustalfs and Udalfs are found in the cooler climates, to Ultisols in more humid areas, to Vertisols and Aridisols under drier conditions, etc.

Mancini (1966) prefers to abandon the term 'Mediterranean' because the climate under which they are formed cannot be defined (see p. 283). Dudal proposed during the Conference on Mediterranean Soils in 1966 to use the name Red and Brown Argilluvic Soils (see also: FAO-UNESCO Project: World Soil Map; Dudal, 1968).

The term Terra Rossa, formerly used to indicate Red Mediterranean Soils, is now-adays only used for a specific Red Mediterranean Soil formed on limestone in a karst landscape; it is considered as a relic soil probably formed in and since a Würm pluvial period.

The parent rocks on which Mediterranean Soils are formed are very different. They range from hard limestones to basalts, andesites, schists, shales, granites, etc. As already mentioned, the typical Terra Rossa is only formed on hard limestone in a karst landscape. In the special climate under which the soils are formed, structure and texture and especially the stratification of the rock are important (see p. 128).

Mancini (1966: see above) suggests that it is dangerous to define the Mediterranean climate in terms of averages, as the amount of rainfall as well as its distribution vary strongly. Nevertheless as a whole it is characterized by a mild, wet winter and a warm, very dry summer. In spite of the objections of Mancini (1966), some figures of temperature and rainfall will be mentioned here. The average temperature in the summer ranges from 15° to 20° C; that in the winter from 8° to 10° C. Frost is practically absent and the precipitation varies from 400 to 1000 mm annually. The higher the rainfall the higher the temperature must be to desiccate the soil in summer. It is understandable that this climate has a strong effect on the pedoclimate, specifically if the surface is barren or scantily covered by a vegetation. For classifying these soils, it is necessary to know whether there are more than 60 consecutive days in more than 7 out of 10 years, during which the soil is continuously dry in the zone between 18 and 50 cm and whether there is a difference of more than 5° C between mean summer and mean winter soil temperatures at a depth of 50 cm ('7th Approximation'). In other words, a certain variation in the climate is permitted.

As the Mediterranean area was strongly deforested in Roman times and during the early Middle Ages, the exact composition of the original vegetation is not known. However, it is pretty certain that the vegetation was a hardleaf forest with several *Quercus* species, such as *Q. ilex*, *Q. suber*, *Q. calliprinos*, *Q. infectoria*, *Q. cerris*; furthermore Palmae species did occur and *Pinus pinea*. After deforestation, the soils were cultivated with cereals and olive (*Olea europea*) as the most important crops. The consequence of clearing the forests was severe erosion, leading to decapitation of the soils and even to their complete removal. In areas where the vegetation has not been strongly affected by man, the soils tend to have umbric or even mollic epipedons (Brown Mediterranean soils) whereas in areas where deforestation has been severe, Red Mediterranean soils are encountered.

It is still not certain whether the Mediterranean soils are the result of the interaction of present days climate and rock or are to be considered as paleosols formed under a somewhat more humid climate.

The general soil characteristics can be summarized as follows (see also Buringh, 1968): The soils are rather heavily textured, have lost the lime and have argillic subsurface horizons with a rather high base saturation (> 40%) and angular blocky, sometimes prismatic, structure. The clay minerals are predominantly illite, with some admixtures of smectites and kandites. In the clay fraction goethite can be found and also other iron compounds (see p. 293), giving the soils their specific red colours. The surface horizon consists of an ochric epipedon and the organic matter content is smaller than 2%. The colour is of a high chroma especially in the B horizon and the hue is redder than 5YR for the red members and 5YR or yellower for the brown members. Most soils are stony and have rock outcrops. Complete profiles are rare; they are truncated and consist of material that has been transported. The deep soils are ABCR profiles.

The characteristic *Brown Mediterranean Soils* have an ABC profile. The A horizon is brown to reddish brown (7.5YR or 10YR) and has a clay texture; the structure is granular; lime is absent and the organic matter content is mostly not larger than 2%. The B horizon is a brown to reddish-brown (5YR or yellower) clay with angular blocky or prismatic structure. The material is heavier than that of the A horizon and clay skins occur on all ped faces in the B_{2t} horizon. Slickensides may be present in the lower part. Base saturation is greater than 35% and increases with depth. The C horizon is a reddish clay, often slightly calcareous and has sometimes a red colour due to the red parent material.

The *Red Mediterranean Soils* have an A horizon, which has a red or brownish-red (5YR or redder) colour. It is a clay with granular structure and low organic matter content (1%). It has often an A_p horizon and sometimes a weak A_2 horizon is present. The horizon does not contain $CaCO_3$. The B horizon is red (5YR or redder) and is a clay with angular blocky or prismatic structure. It is more heavily textured than the

FIG. II.35. *A sinkhole in the limestone region, G. Sewu, Jogjakarta (Java, Indonesia). In the foreground are limestone remains of the edge of the hole. In the center the lake is now dry, the bottom being covered by a red soil, which has been washed into the sinkhole after deforestation of the surrounding limestone hills*

A horizon and clay skins are present on all ped faces in the B_{2t}. Base saturation is greater than 35% and increases with depth. Organic carbon is low and sometimes some $CaCO_3$ is present. The lower part of the horizon shows often intersecting slickensides. The C horizon is a reddish, sometimes slightly calcareous clay. As these soils are generally cultivated, the A_p horizon frequently occurs in former textural B horizon.

The Terra Rossa, a palaeosol, is a strongly weathered, noncalcareous clay, only occurring in karst landscapes with hard limestone and has a low clay content. The soil occurs in cracks in the rock, in organ-pipes and in depressions and sinkholes (fig. II. 35). The material is often mixed with limestone and many rock outcrops occur, so that the soil is discontinuous. The A horizon is generally weakly developed and not thicker than 10 cm. It is a clay with a reddish-brown to brick red colour (2.5YR or redder). The B horizon consists of bright red to brick red clay, often with clay skins on peds. Slickensides occur frequently in the lower part of the B horizon. There is an abrupt transition to the hard limestone rock, mostly at a depth of less than 50 cm. All horizons are discontinuous due to the presence of limestone boulders and outcrops. In the clay often quartz grains occur, indicating a mixing of materials derived from various parent materials.

The foregoing shows clearly that it will be very difficult to formulate some idea of the soil formation processes. However one thing is certain: argeluviation certainly took place. Clay destruction is not probable, as this was not even shown to be definitely present in the Red-Yellow Podzolic Soils. Whether or not desilication and cheluviation occur is not clear. Both processes will be weaker than in the preceding soils as the climatic conditions are not very favourable. The presence of deeply red coloured iron oxides or hydroxides in the soils needs special attention. It will be tried to trace the extent of these processes by discussing some profiles.

Reifenberg's publication (1952) can be used to decide whether or not desilication occurs during the weathering process of the rock. In this work several rocks and their weathering zones were analyzed. One of the profiles was situated at the frontier of

TABLE II.67. *Weathering of basalt under a Mediterranean climate* (after Reifenberg, 1952)

		basalt (I)	weathering zone (II)
SiO_2	%	44.7	35.7
Al_2O_3	%	15.5	34.9
Fe_2O_3	%	7.5	7.9
FeO	%	3.7	0.7
CaO	%	15.3	4.9
MgO	%	7.9	3.6
K_2O	%	1.4	3.1
Na_2O	%	1.1	0.9
P_2O_5	%	1.7	2.8
H_2O+	%	0.9	5.8
SiO_2/R_2O_3		3.3	1.5

Lebanon and Syria in the neighbourhood of Banias. The climate approaches the Mediterranean climate very closely. Rainfall is 900 mm and the mean winter temperature approximately 14° C. There are five completely dry months in the summer with soil temperatures up to 40° C. The rock is a black basalt with feldspar, augite, and olivine. The chemical composition of both the basalt and its weathering zone are shown in table 11.67, together with the molar silica/sesquioxide ratio. It appears that silica and alkaline earths are lost, whereas alumina especially accumulates. Ferrous iron oxidizes to ferric iron. Desilication therefore does occur, although not as intensely as under tropical conditions. This can also be concluded from the normative mineralogical composition of both materials (table 11.68).

TABLE 11.68. *Normative mineralogical composition of the materials of table 11.67* (equivalent percentages)

	Q	Plg	Bi	Aug	Ol	Kaol	Ms	Chl	Sil	Go	Hm	Mt	Misc
II	–	8.5	–	–	–	22.0	27.3	14.7	9.6	1.0	4.9	–	12.0
I	5.4	45.0	13.7	22.5	2.1	–	–	–	–	–	–	8.0	3.3

Q = free silica; Plg = plagioclases; Bi = biotite; Aug = augites; Ol = olivine; Kaol = kaolinite; Ms = muscovite (illite); Chl = chlorite; Sil = sillimanite; Go = goethite; Hm = hematite; Mt = magnetite; Misc = miscellaneous.

Lamoureux (1967) showed that in the case of calcareous rocks, the composition of the impurities is important for the result of weathering. He found that if the molar SiO_2/R_2O_3 ratio in the rock was smaller than 4 (the SiO_2/Al_2O_3 for montmorillonite), the weathered material was always richer in silica relative to aluminium than in the rock. When the ratio was higher than 4, the weathered material was poorer in silica. This could mean that alumina and silica, not present as montmorillonite, are altered and leached easily, whereas silica and alumina combined into crystal lattices of montmorillonitic clays are not attacked, as montmorillonite is a stable mineral in the weathering environment.

It is interesting to note that in the weathering zone of the basalt (tables 11.67 and 68) the activity of water is apparently not high enough to hydrate hematite to goethite. This can be understood if the salt concentration in the weathering zone rises to a level so that water activity is reduced considerably, which could occur in the dry season (see Chapter 2 of Part III p. 434). The problem will be discussed in the examination of the next profile (p. 289).

This profile (profile 19) has been chosen from the excursion guide of the Conference on Mediterranean Soils in Madrid (Gragera and Guerra, 1966). It was situated along the road from Madrid to Ciudad Real at a distance of 143 km from Madrid. The slope is 3 % and the land cultivated. The profile lies on Silurian shale and the parent material is a mixture of weathering products of the shale and the quartzitic crests of surrounding hills. The profile description reads as follows (see fig. 11.36, p. 270):

Horizon Depth (cm)

A_p 0–15   Grey yellowish brown (10YR4/3) sandy loam, poor organic matter, with weak crumb structure. Many, slightly rolled, quartzite pebbles. Abrupt and smooth boundary.

A_1 15–30   Grey yellowish orange (10YR6/3) sandy loam with moderate, angular blocky structure. Some ferruginous concretions and slightly rolled quartzite fragments of various sizes are present. Gradual and smooth boundary.

B_1 30–50   Grey brown (7.5YR5/4) loam with a strong, coarse angular blocky structure. Some ferruginous concretions and fragments of slightly rolled quartzite. Gradual and irregular boundary.

B_{2t} 50–100   Reddish brown (2.5YR4/6) clay with strong, coarse prismatic structure. Prominent clay skins on structural units. Some concretions and quartzite fragments. Hard when dry. Gradual and irregular boundary.

B_3 100–130   Strongly decomposed shale with clay loam texture. Platy structure. Gradual and irregular boundary.

C   130–150   Altered shale with loam texture.

This description and the analytical data (table II.69) place this soil in the subgroup of the Ultic Palexeralfs.

Profile description and the grain size distribution show that clay has migrated and that sheet erosion has occurred, washing away the finer particles and leaving behind

TABLE II.69. *Horizon characteristics of profile 19*

Hor.	grain size distribution (%)			O.M. (%)	pH (KCl)	base saturation (%)	c.e.c. (m.e./ 100g)	free Fe_2O_3 (%)	clay/free Fe_2O_3 ratio
	$> 50\mu$	$50–2\mu$	$< 2\mu$						
A_p	60.0	28.0	12.0	1.7	5.5	60	7.3	4.2	2.9
A_1	62.9	26.1	11.0	1.1	5.0	47	6.0	4.3	2.6
B_1	47.1	30.0	22.9	0.6	5.0	62	6.5	4.2	5.4
B_{2t}	24.3	30.8	44.9	0.4	5.3	63	17.0	5.3	8.5
B_3	31.8	42.2	27.0	0.2	4.5	70	24.5	4.7	5.7
C	35.8	39.3	24.9	0.2	4.7	69	20.0	3.6	6.9

TABLE II.70. *Chemical composition of the clay fractions of profile 19* (after Gragera and Guerra, 1966; weight percentages)

Hor.	SiO_2	Al_2O_3	Fe_2O_3	MgO	CaO	Na_2O	K_2O	TiO_2	H_2O+
A_p	44.5	25.1	9.3	2.1	0.4	0.3	3.9	0.5	13.8
A	42.6	25.3	9.9	2.0	0.4	0.3	3.6	0.5	14.6
B_1	43.2	25.2	10.9	2.4	0.6	0.2	3.5	0.5	13.6
B_{2t}	41.0	25.3	11.9	2.1	0.8	0.2	2.6	0.4	15.5
B_3	42.6	24.2	12.1	2.4	1.0	0.2	2.3	0.3	15.8

coarser grained material. Base saturation and pH are low for a typical Mediterranean soil and the suggestion that soil formation has started in a period with a more humid climate than the present day climate, is a reasonable one.

Although the clay fraction was not completely analyzed (FeO not determined), it can be concluded from tables II.70 and 70a that a clay component with low SiO_2/Al_2O_3 ratio or free alumina has migrated. Moreover, iron has moved considerably so that the molar Al_2O_3/Fe_2O_3 ratio decreased, which is nearly invariably found in podzolic soils.

TABLE II.70a. *Molar ratios of clay fraction of profile 19*

Hor.	SiO_2/R_2O_3	SiO_2/Al_2O_3	SiO_2/Fe_2O_3	Al_2O_3/Fe_2O_3
A_p	2.7	3.0	12.8	4.2
A	2.3	2.9	11.5	4.0
B_1	2.3	2.9	10.6	3.6
B_{2t}	2.1	2.8	9.2	3.3
B_3	2.3	3.0	9.3	3.1

More information can be obtained from the normative mineralogical composition, reported in table II.71. The results agree sufficiently with those of the DT and X-ray analysis (Gragera and Guerra, 1966). These authors found a downwards increasing kaolinite content and only traces of quartz. The fact that there is a considerable excess of crystal water (table II.71) means that illites, smectites, and possibly iron oxide are strongly hydrated. This could explain the fact that Gragera and Guerra found a wide exothermic peak between 200° and 500° C in the DTA and the presence of a weak 14 Å line in the X-ray pattern; they attributed this to the presence of allophane, but this is thought to be incorrect. Furthermore Gragera and Guerra found small proportions of chlorite. Although it would have been possible to calculate a chlorite variant of the goethite norm, it was decided not to do this, as the FeO content was not determined.

TABLE II.71. *Normative mineralogical composition of the clay fractions of profile 19* (weight percentages)

Hor.	Q	Kaol	Ms	Sm	Go	Ru	H_2O+ excess
A_p	0.1	13.5	32.8	37.0	15.9	0.6	7.5
A	0.2	21.0	29.8	31.5	16.9	0.6	6.2
B_1	0.5	24.2	27.7	29.2	17.7	0.6	5.4
B_{2t}	0.5	32.2	20.2	25.3	21.4	0.5	7.0
B_3	0.4	28.0	18.5	32.9	19.7	0.5	6.7

Q = silica; Kaol = kaolinite; Ms = muscovite (illite); Sm = smectite; Go = goethite; Ru = rutile (anatase).

Table II.71 shows kaolinite to increase with depth with a maximum in the B_{2t}, a decreasing illite and smectite content (with a minimum in the B_{2t} horizon for smectite) and an increasing amount of goethite (with a maximum in the B_{2t} horizon). As it is not likely from a thermodynamical point of view (see figs. III.7 and 8), that smectites and illites are newly formed in surface horizons, this distribution of clay minerals can only be explained by assuming that kaolinite has migrated, leaving a residual enrichment of illites and smectites. Also the cheluviation of iron has contributed to this residual enrichment. We can therefore conclude that during the formation of this soil clay destruction has not taken place, but that a differential argeluviation has occurred, kaolinite being more mobile than the illites and smectites. This was also noticed in profile 18.

Gragera and Guerra (1966) reported the occurrence of hematite in the clay fraction, whereas in the calculation of the normative mineralogical composition no possibility was found to bring this mineral into the assemblage, as there is a large excess of crystal water. However, if hematite is actually present, it has to be assumed that the hydration energy of the illites and smectites is such that water activity is reduced so strongly in the dry period that goethite dehydrates to hematite (see also p. 434). This dehydration can be promoted by high salt concentrations in the weathering zone, which will occur in the dry periods. It still has to be assumed that the dehydration process is faster than the rehydration of hematite to goethite.

TABLE II.72. *Partial chemical composition of profile 19* (after Gragera and Guerra, 1966; weight percentages)

Hor.	SiO_2	Al_2O_3	Fe_2O_3	MgO	CaO	Na_2O	K_2O	TiO_2
A_p	75.7	10.5	5.6	0.8	1.0	n.r.	n.r.	0.7
A	76.3	10.0	5.8	0.8	1.3	n.r.	n.r.	0.7
B_1	60.3	13.3	6.3	1.1	1.2	n.r.	n.r.	0.7
B_{2t}	58.8	12.1	8.2	1.5	1.4	n.r.	n.r.	0.8
B_3	58.2	12.1	7.8	2.1	1.3	n.r.	n.r.	0.7
C	60.6	17.7	5.6	2.2	1.1	0.7	3.1	0.5

[1] n.r. = not reported.

TABLE II.72a. *Molar ratios of the horizons of profile 19*

Hor.	SiO_2/R_2O_3	SiO_2/Al_2O_3	SiO_2/Fe_2O_3	Al_2O_3/Fe_2O_3
A_p	9.1	12.3	36	2.9
A	9.5	13.0	35	2.7
B_1	6.7	8.7	29	3.3
B_{2t}	5.6	8.1	19	2.3
B_3	5.8	8.2	20	2.4
C	4.8	5.8	29	5.0

As Gragera and Guerra (1966) did not report the K_2O and Na_2O contents of the solum (table II.72), it is not possible to follow the mineralogical changes in the soil.

However, the analysis is sufficient to show that considerable argeluviation and cheluviation has taken place. It is fairly certain that the C material is not the parent material of the solum, so we have to indicate this horizon with IIC.

In conclusion it may be stated that the following processes have been active in the formation of this soil: 1. colluviation (formation of the parent material); 2. cheluviation of iron; 3. differential argeluviation (kaolinite more mobile than the 2:1 layer minerals); 4. erosion (lateral translocation).

A more fully analyzed profile (profile 20) of a Brown Mediterranean soil comes from Estremadura in the valley of the Rio Guadiana, Spain. The area is level and the slope 0–5%. There is very little runoff and drainage conditions are moderately good. Groundwater level lies approximately at 5 m depth. The area is cultivated. The maximum summer temperature is 40° C and the minimum winter temperature 0° C. Rainfall is seasonal and amounts 450–500 mm annually. Profile description reads as follows:

Horizon	Depth (cm)	
A$_p$	0–15	Grey yellowish orange (10YR6/4:d) to brown (7.5YR4/4:m) sandy loam; massive; slightly hard, very friable, slightly sticky and plastic; many fine roots. Gradual and smooth boundary.
A$_1$	15–37	Grey yellowish orange (10YR6/4:d) to brown (7.5YR4/4:m) loam; massive; slightly hard, very friable, slightly sticky and plastic; many fine roots. Gradual and smooth boundary.
B$_1$	37–57	Reddish brown (5YR5/6:d) to reddish brown (5YR4/4:m) loam; weak, coarse, angular blocky structure; slightly hard, very friable, slightly sticky and plastic; many fine roots. Gradual and smooth boundary.
B$_{2t}$	57–100	Strong orange brown (7.5YR6/6:d) to light brown (7.5YR5/6:m) clay loam; moderate, coarse, angular blocky structure; clay cutans on ped faces; very hard, friable, very sticky and plastic; many fine roots. Clear and smooth boundary.
C	100–160	Grey yellowish orange (10YR6/4:d) to brown (7.5YR4/4:m) silt loam; very weak, coarse, subangular blocky structure; very hard, very friable, sticky and plastic.

Profile description and the analytical data of table II.73 place this soil into the subgroup of the Typic Haploxeralfs.

TABLE II.73. *Some characteristics of profile 20*

Hor.	grain size distribution			C (%)	pH (0.01M CaCl$_2$)	free Fe$_2$O$_3$ (%)	clay/ free Fe$_2$O$_3$	c.e.c. (m.e./ 100g)	base sat. (%)
	> 50μ	50–2μ	< 2μ						
A$_p$	55.1	34.3	10.6	0.6	5.0	1.6	6.6	3.3	90
A$_1$	44.3	43.8	11.9	0.5	4.2	2.0	6.0	3.4	75
B$_1$	35.9	49.5	14.6	0.2	4.9	3.0	4.8	5.5	90
B$_{2t}$	36.8	35.3	28.9	0.2	5.3	3.7	7.7	8.7	95
C	29.7	53.5	16.8	tr	5.5	3.4	5.0	9.2	100

Table II.73 reveals that base saturation is high; it is also evident that argeluviation and iron cheluviation have taken place. The clay/free iron ratio is not constant, so iron transport is not only determined by clay migration.

TABLE II.74. *Chemical composition of profile 20* (weight percentages)

Hor.	SiO_2	Al_2O_3	Fe_2O_3	FeO	CaO	MgO	MnO	Na_2O	K_2O	TiO_2	P_2O_5	H_2O+
A_p	74.9	8.9	2.8	0.2	2.3	0.4	0.0^5	1.6	1.6	0.8	0.2	2.5
A_1	75.3	9.5	2.9	0.2	2.6	0.4	0.1	1.3	1.6	0.8	0.2	2.4
B_1	71.0	11.7	4.2	0.3	2.8	0.6	0.1	1.5	1.8	0.9	0.2	3.2
B_{2t}	68.3	13.2	5.0	0.3	3.2	0.7	0.1	1.2	1.8	0.8	0.2	3.7
C	71.1	13.4	4.8	0.2	1.9	0.8	0.1	1.5	2.2	0.9	0.2	4.1

TABLE II.74a. *Derived molar ratios*

Hor.	SiO_2/R_2O_3	SiO_2/Al_2O_3	SiO_2/Fe_2O_3	Al_2O_3/Fe_2O_3
A_p	12	14	71	5.0
A_1	11	13	69	5.1
B_1	7.8	10	45	4.4
B_{2t}	7.1	8.8	36	4.1
C	7.3	9.0	40	4.4

The total chemical analysis of the profile (tables II.74 and 74a) reveals that iron is more mobile than aluminium, which supports the previous fact. The data also suggest the occurrence of argeluviation or migration of free alumina.

TABLE II.75. *Chemical composition of the colloidal fractions of profile 20* (weight percentages)

Hor.	SiO_2	Al_2O_3	Fe_2O_3	FeO	CaO	MgO	MnO	Na_2O	K_2O	TiO_2	P_2O_5	H_2O+
A_p	45.1	25.3	11.2	0.6	0.2	1.4	0.1	0.4	3.7	1.1	0.7	10.5
A_1	45.2	25.6	11.4	0.7	0.2	1.3	0.1	0.5	3.8	1.1	0.6	10.4
B_1	43.4	26.0	12.5	1.1	0.2	1.2	0.1	0.4	3.1	0.8	0.6	9.8
B_{2t}	42.7	26.2	12.4	0.6	0.2	1.2	0.1	0.4	3.4	0.9	0.6	9.6
C	44.8	26.4	12.2	0.7	0.2	1.1	0.1	0.4	3.2	0.8	0.7	9.5

TABLE II.75a. *Derived molar ratios of colloidal fractions of table II.75*

Hor.	SiO_2/R_2O_3	SiO_2/Al_2O_3	SiO_2/Fe_2O_3	Al_2O_3/Fe_2O_3
A_p	2.36	3.0	11	3.5
A_1	2.34	3.0	11	3.5
B_1	2.17	2.8	9.2	3.3
B_{2t}	2.12	2.8	9.2	3.3
C	2.23	2.9	9.8	3.4

Whether or not clay mineral transformations occur can be deduced from the analysis of the clay fractions (tables II.75 and 75a) and from the calculation of the normative mineralogical composition (table II.76). Tables II.75 and 75a suggest that the B horizon contains more clay minerals with low SiO_2/Al_2O_3 ratio than the A and C horizon, and/or that clay destruction has occurred with leaching of free alumina. Table II.76 shows however, that no free alumina is present; differential clay migration is therefore the one possibility. This is evident from table II.76, where downward increase in kandites can be observed with the residual enrichment of illites and smectites in the clay fractions of the upper horizons. It is evident that iron has also moved in the clay-sized fraction.

TABLE II.76. *Normative mineralogical composition of the colloid of profile 20* (weight percentages)

Hor.	Q	Kand	Ms	Sm	Go	Str	Ru
A_p	4.4	22.9	31.4	26.6	11.6	2.0	1.1
A_1	5.2	23.6	32.6	23.8	12.0	1.5	1.1
B_1	3.9	29.4	27.0	23.6	13.5	1.7	0.9
B_{2t}	3.0	27.6	29.6	23.7	13.5	1.7	0.9
C	5.8	30.5	27.5	20.4	12.9	2.0	0.9

Q = silica; Kand = kandites (kaolinite + halloysite); Ms = muscovite (illite); Sm = smectites; Go = goethite; Str = strengite; Ru = rutile (anatase).

If the soil and clay analyses are combined and the normative mineralogical composition of the soils is calculated in the manner mentioned earlier (p. 131), table II.77 is obtained. It clearly shows the differential argeluviation process. It seems that the illites are the least mobile in this profile. Albite seems to be a stable mineral under the

TABLE II.77. *Normative mineralogical composition of profile 20* (weight percentages)

Hor.	Q	Ab	Kand	Ms	Sm	Go	Ru	Misc
A_p	57.0	14.1	2.4	12.6	2.8	3.0	0.9	7.1
A_1	57.1	11.5	2.8	14.2	2.8	3.2	0.8	7.5
B_1	49.9	12.2	4.3	15.1	3.4	4.7	0.8	9.6
B_{2t}	44.7	8.5	8.0	15.5	6.8	4.6	0.8	10.2
C	46.4	12.6	5.1	18.1	3.4	5.2	0.9	8.2

Mineral abbreviations as in table II.76; Ab = albite; Misc = miscellaneous (epidote + tremolite + xonolite + strengite + traces of K-feldspars).

prevailing soil forming conditions.

Finally some remarks will be made on the nature of the iron compounds present. It was Kubiena (1956, 1962) who stated that the red colour of the Mediterranean soils was due to the formation of hematite. Evidence accumulated since indicates that this is incorrect. Our analyses of several profiles never reveal the presence of hematite. Yaalon et al. (1966) reported that goethite is the main iron oxide in Mediterranean Soils. Very recently Lamoureux and Segalen (1969) stated that the red colour of the soils was due to the presence of amorphous iron hydroxides. This fact is in accordance with the analyses of profile 19 (p. 289) and with the thermodynamic considerations in Chapter 2 of Part III (p. 434). The dominant iron compound in Brown Mediterranean Soils was goethite according to Lamoureux and Segalen (1969).

As already mentioned, soils similar to the Mediterranean soils also occur in countries other than those bordering the Mediterranean sea. Examples of drier (warmer) variants can be found in the Sudan. Here red soils occur on slight elevations in Vertisol areas. An example is a profile (profile 21) from Umm Seinat, approximately 70 km south of Gedaref[1]). The slope of the area is 1 to 0.1 %. Relief is normal. The soil is well-drained. The surface is smooth and hard and covered with reddish-coated sand and some fine gravel. Termites in the area form large, cone-shaped red termite mounts. Rainfall is approximately 730 mm annually, 90 per cent falling from June through September. The months December, January, February, and March are always completely dry. Rainfall is variable with respect to time and place of precipitation and great annual fluctuations occur. The average maximum daily temperature is 36° C and the average minimum one 21° C. The rainy season is 5° to 8° C cooler than the dry season.

The vegetation is a mixed woodland with *Combretum hartmannianum, Lannea fructicosa, Anogeissus schimperi*, and *Accacia seyal*. Tall grasses and few shrubs occur, in places. The profile description reads as follows (see also fig. II.37, p. 271):

Horizon	Depth (cm)	
A_{11}	0–10	Brownish grey (7.5YR4/2:d) to black brown (7.5YR2/2:m) loamy sand; massive; slightly hard; many small and few large biopores; fine and large roots. Gradual and smooth boundary.
A_{12}	10–30	Grey reddish brown (5YR4/3:d) to dark reddish brown (5YR3/2:m) sandy loam with parches of brownish grey (7.5YR4/2:d) to black brown (7.5YR2/2:m). Otherwise as A_{11}. Gradual and smooth boundary.
B_1	30–60	Dark reddish brown (5YR3/3:d and m) sandy clay loam; massive; slightly hard to hard; many fine and few large biopores; few fine roots. Gradual and smooth boundary.
B_{21t}	60–85	Reddish brown (2.5YR4/6:d and m) sandy clay loam; weak, medium and coarse, subangular to angular blocky structure; hard; faint, shiny, dark reddish brown (2.5YR3/6:d) coatings on ped faces; biopores and roots as in B_1; some fine, gritty, gravel. Gradual and smooth boundary.
B_{22t}	85–105	Reddish brown (2.5YR4/6:d and m) sandy clay; weak, medium and coarse, subangular blocky structure; hard; faint, shiny, dark reddish brown (2.5YR3/6:d) coatings on ped faces; biopores and roots as in B_1 and B_{21t}; some fine, gritty, gravel; termite tunnels. Gradual and smooth boundary.

[1] Personal communication by W. A. Blokhuis.

B₃	105–135	Reddish brown (2.5YR4/6:m) sandy clay; massive; hard; with greyish (N4 and N5) streaks and reddish brown (5YR4/6:m) patches; common fine roots; iron-manganese nodules. Gradual and smooth boundary.
C	135–160	Reddish orange (10R4/6:m) and brown (7.5YR4/6:m) sandy clay with grey (N4 to N6 :m) spots and grey black (N4 to N6:m) spots and grey black (N3:m) iron-manganese nodules.

Classification places this soil into the Ultic Haplustalfs (see also tables II.78 and 79).

Analytical details and profile description reveal that the soil has been strongly leached and argeluviated. It seems that the A horizon is not residual. This is quite possible as there is a considerable termite activity and the heavy downpours in the rainy season may spread material of the termite mounts over the surface. The chemical analysis (tables II.80 and 80a) supports this suggestion. Cheluviation of iron is clear. The SiO_2/R_2O_3 ratio decrasing with depth suggests either dissolution of free alumina and/or migration of clay. In contrast to the previous profile, iron is less mobile than alumina. The chemical analysis (tables II.81 and 81a) of the clay fraction (leaving out the A horizon as this is not residual) shows that differential clay migration could have occurred, or dissolution of free alumina, or destruction of clay minerals.

TABLE II.78. *Analytical details of profile 21*

Hor.	grain size distribution			C (%)	pH (0.01M CaCl₂)	free Fe₂O₃ (%)	clay/free Fe₂O₃ ratio
	> 50μ	50–2μ	< 2μ				
A₁₁	82.2	13.6	4.2	0.5	6.6	1.1	3.8
A₁₂	79.4	5.5	15.1	0.6	6.0	2.1	7.2
B₁	72.4	4.9	22.7	0.3	4.8	2.8	8.1
B₂₁ₜ	58.5	8.9	32.6	0.3	4.5	3.9	8.4
B₂₂ₜ	52.2	2.7	45.1	0.2	4.5	5.0	9.0
B₃	52.2	8.4	39.4	0.1	4.4	5.2	7.6
C	52.2	9.2	38.6	tr	4.7	4.7	8.2

TABLE II.79. *Exchange characteristics of profile 21*

Hor.	exchangeable cations (m.e./100g of soil)					c.e.c. (m.e./100g of soil)	base saturation (%)
	Ca	Mg	Na	K	Al + H		
A₁₁	3.0	0.9	0.1	0.4	–	4.5	100
A₁₂	3.4	2.6	0.2	0.2	2.6	9.0	71
B₁	3.9	3.4	0.2	0.1	7.9	15.5	50
B₂₁ₜ	5.0	4.2	0.3	0.1	13.0	22.6	43
B₂₂ₜ	6.4	4.8	0.3	0.1	13.8	25.4	46
B₃	7.4	5.2	0.3	0.1	14.5	27.5	47
C	9.0	6.1	0.3	0.1	11.9	27.4	57

The calculation of the normative mineralogical composition of the clay fraction (table II.82) helps to form a decision in respect to these possibilities. Table II.82, neglecting again the A horizon, shows a with depth slightly increasing kaolinite (with a maximum in the B_3 horizon) and decreasing silica content (with a minimum in the B_3 horizon). As it is unlikely from a thermodynamical point of view, that kaolinite has decomposed, whilst the illites and smectites seem stable (see figs. III.7 and 8), we have to accept the fact that kaolinite has migrated leading to a differential accumulation of silica. In contradiction to this is the fact that smectites and illites do not accumulate residually; however, the constancy in illites and smectites can be explained by assuming that these

TABLE II.80. *Chemical composition of profile 21* (weight percentages)

Hor.	SiO_2	Al_2O_3	Fe_2O_3	FeO	CaO	MgO	MnO	TiO_2	Na_2O	K_2O	P_2O_5	H_2O+
A_{11}	94.3	2.1	1.5	tr	0.2	0.1	tr	0.3	tr	0.1	tr	0.4
A_{12}	88.3	4.4	2.6	0.1	0.2	0.2	tr	0.6	0.1	0.1	tr	2.6
B_1	83.5	6.6	3.1	tr	0.1	0.2	tr	0.6	0.1	0.2	tr	2.6
B_{21t}	77.6	9.8	4.8	0.0^5	0.1	0.3	tr	0.7	0.1	0.2	tr	4.6
B_{22t}	72.3	12.3	6.1	0.2	0.1	0.3	tr	0.8	0.1	0.3	0.1	5.7
B_3	74.7	11.9	6.3	0.2	0.2	0.3	tr	0.9	0.1	0.2	0.1	5.1
C	75.4	11.0	6.0	0.1	0.2	0.3	0.1	0.8	0.1	0.2	0.1	4.8

TABLE II.80a. *Derived molar ratios of profile 21*

Hor.	SiO_2/R_2O_3	SiO_2/Al_2O_3	SiO_2/Fe_2O_3	Al_2O_3/Fe_2O_3
A_{11}	52	76	168	2.2
A_{12}	24	34	82	2.4
B_1	16	22	58	2.7
B_{21t}	10	14	40	3.0
B_{22t}	7.6	10	30	3.0
B_3	8.0	11	31	2.9
C	8.7	12	33	2.9

TABLE II.81. *Chemical composition of the clay fractions of profile 21* (weight percentages)

Hor.	SiO_2	Al_2O_3	Fe_2O_3	FeO	CaO	MgO	MnO	TiO_2	Na_2O	K_2O	P_2O_5	H_2O+
A_{11}	49.8	22.3	13.8	0.3	–	0.4	tr	2.0	0.2	0.7	0.6	12.8
A_{12}	48.3	25.6	11.8	0.8	tr	0.5	tr	1.4	tr	0.5	0.4	11.4
B_1	49.6	24.1	11.6	0.7	0.1	0.5	tr	1.5	tr	0.5	0.3	12.1
B_{21t}	49.2	25.6	12.3	0.7	0.1	0.4^5	tr	1.4	tr	0.5	0.4	11.7
B_{22t}	48.6	26.5	12.2	0.9	0.1	0.5	tr	1.3	tr	0.5	0.4	11.8
B_3	47.7	26.8	11.6	0.8	0.2	0.5	tr	1.3	tr	0.4	0.4	11.8
C	49.7	26.0	10.7	0.8	tr	0.5	tr	1.3	tr	0.4	0.4	11.5

minerals have also migrated slightly, thus counteracting the residual accumulation. As a matter of fact we have to conclude, as in the previous profiles, that kaolinite is more mobile than the illites or smectites.

Finally, table II.83 shows the normative mineralogical composition of the soil horizons. The table clearly shows the process of argeluviation and iron-cheluviation. Hematite could not be traced in the calculations, nor did X-ray analysis reveal its presence.

TABLE II.81a. *Derived molar ratios of the clay fractions*

Hor.	SiO_2/R_2O_3	SiO_2/Al_2O_3	SiO_2/Fe_2O_3	Al_2O_3/Fe_2O_3
A_{11}	2.7	3.8	9.7	2.6
A_{12}	2.4	3.2	9.8	1.1
B_1	2.6	3.5	11	3.1
B_{21t}	2.4	3.3	9.7	3.0
B_{22t}	2.3	3.1	8.5	2.7
B_3	2.3	3.0	10	3.4
C	2.6	3.2	12	3.7

TABLE II.82. *Normative mineralogical composition of the clay fractions of profile 21* (equivalent percentages)

Hor.	Q	Kaol	Ms	Sm	Go	Str	Ru
A_{11}	21.2	46.6	7.0	11.6	10.9	1.0	1.7
A_{12}	12.1	53.5	4.6	18.6	9.5	0.7	1.1
B_1	16.0	50.0	4.6	18.1	9.4	0.6	1.3
B_{21t}	13.2	52.6	4.6	18.1	9.7	0.7	1.1
B_{22t}	11.3	54.2	4.6	18.5	9.6	0.7	1.1
B_3	9.8	56.9	3.8	18.7	9.3	0.6	1.1
C	12.5	54.7	3.8	19.0	8.5	0.6	1.0

Q = silica; Kaol = kaolinite; Ms = muscovite (illite); Sm = smectite; Go = goethite; Str = strengite; Ru = rutile.

TABLE II.83. *Normative mineralogical composition of profile 21*

Hor.	Q	Ab	Kaol	Ms	Sm	Go	Str	Ru	Misc
A_{11}	92.3	–	3.2	1.2	0.5	1.1	tr	0.2	1.5
A_{12}	82.7	1.0	8.1	1.7	2.8	2.1	0.1	0.5	0.9
B_1	77.0	0.9	13.5	1.0	4.1	2.5	0.1	0.5	0.3
B_{21t}	66.6	0.9	19.8	1.5	5.9	3.8	0.2	0.5	0.8
B_{22t}	57.0	0.9	24.4	2.3	8.3	4.8	0.3	0.9	0.8
B_3	58.8	0.9	23.4	2.4	7.4	4.9	0.2	0.7	1.3
C	61.3	0.9	21.4	2.3	7.5	4.6	0.2	0.6	1.0

Mineral abbreviations as in table II.82; Ab = albite; Misc = miscellaneous.

In conclusion we can state that the following processes are responsible for the formation of this soil: 1. cheluviation of iron; 2. differential argeluviation (kaolinite more mobile than illites and smectites); 3. termite activity and erosion (formation of a non-residual A horizon). As no parent rock was available, it is not possible to decide whether or not desilication is involved.

As already mentioned, Mediterranean soils also occur in the tropical countries. Mohr (1938), Vageler (1938), Dames (1955) and Dudal (1962) report an occurrence in the Indonesian Archipelago. The Red Mediterranean soils occupy approximately 9 per cent of the total surface of the islands of Java and Madura (Dudal, 1962) and occur predominantly on limestones and basalts. The rainfall varies from 800 to 2500 mm annually, while there is a pronounced dry season with a length of 4 to 8 months. The average temperatures range from 23° to 26° C.

The depth of these soils varies strongly, viz. from 20 cm to 100 cm. Dudal (1962) described a soil from Madura, near Desa Djurangan, Sumenep District (profile 22). It was situated on a locally dissected plateau at an elevation of 105 m and with a slope of approximately 5 per cent. The area was planted to coconut and the parent material is limestone. Annual precipitation amounts to 1800 mm approximately and there are six pronounced dry months. The description reads as follows:

Horizon	Depth (cm)	
A_p	0–17	Dark reddish brown (5YR3/6:m) sandy clay loam; weak, fine, crumb structure; friable. Clear and wavy boundary.
B_{21}	17–60	Dark reddish brown (2.5YR3/6:m) clay; strong, medium, angular blocky structure; firm.
B_{22}	+60	Dark reddish brown (2.5YR3/6:m) to dark red (10R3/6:m) clay; weak, fine, subangular blocky structure; firm; boulder of limestone imbedded in unconsolidated material; clay coatings on ped surfaces; no free lime in the matrix.

The soil can be placed in the group of the Rhodoxeralfs. The subgroup cannot be established because of lack of detailed information.

The few analytical details of table II.84 are insufficient for a discussion of the soil forming processes involved.

TABLE II.84. *Some characteristics of profile 22*

Hor.	grain size distribution (%)			C (%)	pH (H₂O)
	> 50μ	50–2μ	< 2μ		
A_p	59.6	10.7	29.7	1.4	7.8
B_{21}	41.2	8.8	50.0	0.6	7.5
B_{22}	41.3	5.6	53.1	0.3	7.5

As a general conclusion we can state that the following processes are involved in the

298

formation of Mediterranean soils if erosion is left out of consideration: 1. desilication; 2. cheluviation; 3. differential clay migration. Clay destruction is not involved, so the proposal of Dudal (1966) to call these soils Red and Brown Argilluvic Soils seems quite justified.

2.3. PODZOLS (SPODOSOLS)

Podzols occur frequently in the tropics. In the lowlands they are limited to extremely acid parent materials and continually wet climates. Moreover, groundwater influences are often involved in their development, as they occur sometimes in undulating areas in association with Yellow Podzolic Soils; the Podzols occur then in the depressions and the Yellow Podzolics on the higher parts (a.o. Dames, 1955). Sometimes the lowland Podzols are very deep and are then called Giant-Podzols.

In the mountains Podzols also occur on chemically richer parent materials; the climate is continually wet, but the temperature lower due to the elevation.

Although a great amount of literature is available on the occurrences of Podzols in the tropics, only scarce analytical data are present. Fortunately, some soils have been investigated in sufficient detail to permit a discussion of the soil forming processes. A description of a Giant-Podzol by Dames (1962: profile 23) reads as follows:

Horizon	Depth (cm)	
$O_1 + O_2$	0–12	Organic matter layer. The lower 8 cm form a dark reddish brown (2.5YR3/6:m) greasy mor in a mat of roots. Some white quartz grains are present.
A_{11}	12–17	Light yellowish orange (10YR8/3:d) to black brown (10YR3/1:m) soft, humic, medium and fine sand with weak, fine crumb structure; abundant large and fine roots, mostly horizontal. Wavy boundary.
A_{12}	17–27	Light brownish grey (7.5YR7/2:d and m) medium and fine sand with single grain structure. Many roots, mostly horizontal.
A_{21}	27–127	Light brownish grey (7.5YR7/2,d; 5YR7/1:m) to white (2.5YR8/0:d; 7.5YR8/0:m) medium and fine sand; fairly loose; fair number of vertical roots. Abrupt boundary.
A_{22}	127–267	White medium and fine sand; more compact than A_{21}; few roots; the larger roots are surrounded by a ring of pinkish-grey similar in colour to the A_{12} horizon; the soil becomes wetter with depth; at a depth of 180 cm the soil is wet and dark brown; humus water seeps from the sides, deeper some brown, organic splotches.
B_h	267–412	Dark brown cemented humus-sand pan, breakable by hand. Water stagnates on top of this horizon; some root remnants are present.
B_{ir}	412–413	Reddish-yellow ferruginous layer of variable thickness (5 to 10 mm); more or less hardened. In places there is, directly below the brown B_h, a very thin, but sometimes up to 15 cm thick, lens of greyish-yellow silty clay.
C	+413	White, loose sand with prominent, coarse, yellowish-red mottles.

In terms of the 7th Approximation (Supplement 1967) the soil should be classified as a Tropaquod.

The profile description shows that podzolization is associated with very slow decomposition of the organic material and by the formation of brown colloidal solutions that seep into and out of the soil, so draining water in these areas frequently has a dark brown colour (Klinge, 1966).

The presence of lenses of silty clay points to migration or new-formation of clay. An iron band in the lower part of the spodic horizon at great depth (412 cm) suggests that the thickness of Podzol profiles depends amongst others on the sesquioxide content of the parent material.

A well-investigated profile is a Podzol from the island of Banka, Indonesia (Hardon, 1937). The soil (profile 24) is situated on a padang (Malayan word for plain) near Aer Lajang, about 10 m above sea level (see fig. II.38, p. 271). After heavy rains it is inundated, but during periods of droughts the loose white sandy soil is very dry. The annual average temperature is approximately 26° C with only slight fluctuations. The rainfall on the island of Banka varies from 3100 mm in the north-west to 2500 mm in the southeast annually. The lowest monthly rainfall is 110 mm. The vegetation never forms a compact mass or sod. Groups of low and high shrubs, generally with higher shrubs or small trees in the middle, alternate with a lower vegetation, which is always limited to separate spots or clumps, so that the white sand shows everywhere and in many places is predominant. Characteristic plant species are: *Drosera Burmanni* in the dampest parts; *Fimbristylis sp., Rhynchospora sp., Xyris microcephala, X. bancana* and *Baeckia frutescens*, the latter reminding one much of the *Calluna* of the European heaths. The parent material is quartz sand. The profile description reads as follows:

Horizon	Depth (cm)	
A_{11}	0–10	Black cover of half decomposed organic material intermixed with coarse quartz sand.
A_{12}	10–25	Loose greyish black humic quartz sand.
A_2	25–40	Loose greyish white quartz sand.
B_h	40–70	Dark brown very compact quartz sandy hardpan. Org. matter content 5.2%.
B_{ir}	70–100	Loose light brown quartz sand.

In terms of the 7th Approximation this soil should be classified as a Typic Tropohumod.

Analytical details of table II.85 show that the A horizon is practically completely deprived of clay-sized minerals, whereas there is an accumulation in the B horizon. This clay distribution can be the result of 1) clay destruction in the A horizon; 2) clay migration; 3) new-formation of clay in the B horizon; and 4) combinations of the three possibilities. These possibilities will be discussed on page 300. Furthermore table II.85 shows that organic matter has accumulated in the B_h horizon. Combining the data of table II.86 (giving the chemical composition of the clay fraction) with that of table II.85, it can be deduced that the B_h horizon is also the horizon of maximum alumina accumulation, so there seems to be a relationship between alumina and humus accumulation. Iron is distributed in equal amounts in the B_h and B_{ir} horizons and accumulated in these horizons. Cheluviation processes are therefore very important in podzol formation.

The pH value of the A_2 horizon is very high as compared with the other horizons. As clay and organic colloids are practically absent, the buffering capacity of the A_2

TABLE II.85. *Some characteristics of profile 24*

Hor.	grain size distribution (%)			pH (H₂O)	O.M. (%)
	> 50μ	50–2μ	< 2μ		
A_1	95.0	3.8	1.2	2.7–3.9	n.r.[1]
A_2	94.0	5.7	0.3	6.1	0.1
B_h	86.9	6.6	6.5	3.9	5.2
B_{ir}	92.9	3.1	4.0	4.6	n.r.[1]

[1] n.r. = not reported.

suspension is very low; consequently, the pH cannot be measured adequately.

In order to decide whether clay transformation, or destruction, or new-formation takes place, it is necessary to investigate the clay fraction. Fortunately, Hardon (1937) made a chemical analysis of the colloidal fraction of the horizons (table II.86). The

TABLE II.86. *Chemical composition of the colloidal fractions of profile 24* (weight percentages)

Hor.	SiO_2	Al_2O_3	Fe_2O_3	CaO	MgO	Na_2O	K_2O	TiO_2
A_{11}	48.9	18.8	6.4	5.3	3.4	5.5	0.5	10.1
A_{12}	60.6	12.3	3.1	4.7	2.5	1.8	0.1	14.2
A_2	65.2	10.1	4.2	4.6	4.4	2.1	0.3	8.6
B_h	18.2	70.8	4.4	2.0	0.0	1.0	0.2	2.7
B_{ir}	14.0	73.2	6.5	1.0	0.1	1.2	0.2	2.7

TABLE II.86a. *Derived molar ratios of the colloidal fractions of profile 24*

Hor.	SiO_2/R_2O_3	SiO_2/Al_2O_3	SiO_2/Fe_2O_3	Al_2O_3/Fe_2O_3
A_{11}	3.6	4.4	20	4.6
A_{12}	7.2	8.3	53	6.4
A_2	8.7	11	42	3.8
B_h	0.4	0.4	11	15
B_{ir}	0.3	0.3	5.8	18

result shows a very peculiar distribution of the various oxides. Firstly, the alkaline earths and alkalies are exceptionally high, especially in the A horizon. This is caused by the manner in which the colloidal fraction is separated from the soil (Hardon, 1936). The result of the procedure is that a considerable part of the organic material is accumulated in the small amount of clay present. As the contents are given in percentages of organic free material all data is too high, especially for those elements which have a great affinity for organic matter, such as Ca. The data cannot be used for the calculation of the normative mineralogical composition. However, as the changes in SiO_2, Al_2O_3, and TiO_2 (apart from CaO and MgO), are very prominent, the calculation will be based on these elements and on Fe_2O_3, using average values for the A and the B horizon, as the change is very abrupt between these horizons.

Secondly, titania is stable and enriches residually in the A horizon. This, together with the tremendous increase in alumina in B horizon, points to clay destruction. Of the clay minerals present, kaolinite will be most important as the K_2O content is very low. As we have already seen (p. 210, Chapter 1 of this Part) titania is not always enriched residually and it seems advisable to investigate the conditions under which titanium becomes mobile. This problem will be discussed in Chapter 5 of Part III.

For the calculation of the normative mineralogical composition we shall use the following data (derived from table II.86):

A horizon: 63.0% SiO_2; 11.2% Al_2O_3; 3.7% Fe_2O_3; and 11.4% TiO_2
B horizon: 16.1% SiO_2; 72.0% Al_2O_3; 5.5% Fe_2O_3; and 2.7% TiO_2

Table II.87 gives the result of the goethite-norm calculation of the clay fraction. It is evident, that clay destruction has taken place, kaolinite being decomposed into silica and alumina; the latter is leached from to the A to the B horizon; in this way titania is

TABLE II.87. *Approximate normative mineralogical composition of the clay separates of profile 24* (equivalent percentages)

Hor.	Q	Kaol	Gibb	Go	Ru
A	56.8	30.3	–	3.2	9.8
B	–	48.3	42.2	6.4	3.2

Q = silica; Kaol = kaolinite; Gibb = gibbsite; Go = goethite; Ru = rutile (anatase).

accumulated residually. Iron is not so mobile as usual in Podzols.

Examples of upland Podzols in the tropics can be found in publications of Hardon (1936), Tan and Van Schuylenborgh (1961), and of Reynders (1964). Only the investigation of Reynders will be discussed.

The profile (profile 25) is located in West-Irian (Indonesia) on the Temnomabe Sigin at an elevation of 2060 m. It occurred on a gently sloping terrain on top of the mountain. The effective drainage water (precipitation minus evapotranspiration) was calculated to be approximately 3000 mm. The temperature is approximately 10° C. Vegetation: subzone of moss forest, primary medium to low forest, climbing bambu (*Chloothamnus*), mosses and *Zingiberaceae*. Parent material: residue of limestone-weathering. The profile description reads shortly as follows:

Horizon	Depth (cm)	
A₁	0–5	Humic, grey brown silty loam with weak subangular blocky structure; medium rooted. Merges into:
A₂	5–10	White to light yellow brownish grey (10YR8/2:w) silty loam with

angular blocky structure and with scattered grey brown mottles;
poorly rooted. Merges into:

B_h 10–40   Strong yellowish brown (10YR7/6:w) and light yellow brownish grey (10YR7/2:w) mottled silty loam; massive. Merges gradually into:

B_{ir} 40–80   Strong yellowish brown (10YR6/8:w) silty clay with yellow mottles; massive.

Reynders postulates that the podzol profile has been developed in a brown soil on limestone. This is very well possible, but not necessarily true. The soil may have developed directly from the material obtained after dissolution of the limestone.

TABLE II.88. *Analytical details of profile 25*

Hor.	grain size distribution (%)			pH (KCl)	C (%)	c.e.c. (m.e./ 100g)	base sat. (%)
	$>50\mu$	$50–2\mu$	$<2\mu$				
A_1	30	57	13	3.3	4.3	16.8	13
A_2	23	58	19	3.5	1.1	10.4	5.6
B_h	9	65	26	3.5	2.1	28.8	2.5
B_{ir}	5	45	50	3.7	1.5	37.0	3.6

Table II.88 shows a tremendous increase in clay from the top to the bottom of the profile and, as no mention is made of the presence of clay skins in the B-horizon, this strongly points to clay destruction in the surface layers. Cation exchange capacity, base saturation data and the decreasing SiO_2/Al_2O_3-ratio (table II.89a) are in accordance with this assumption. There is also accumulation of organic matter in the B horizon with the maximum in the B_h; table II.89 shows an accumulation of alumina and iron in the B horizon. Organic matter migration and cheluviation therefore are acting in the formation of this profile. Aluminium and iron are equally mobile, as their ratio is practically constant.

TABLE II.89. *Partial chemical composition of profile 25* (weight percentages; after Reynders, 1964)

Hor.	SiO_2	Al_2O_3	Fe_2O_3	CaO	K_2O	TiO_2
A_1	85.8	1.0	0.6	0.1	0.1	0.6
A_2	91.4	1.5	1.2	0.1	0.1	0.6
B_h	76.3	6.9	5.3	0.1	0.4	0.7
B_{ir}	68.4	12.6	9.9	0.1	0.7	0.8

The analysis of the clay fraction also indicates that clay destruction is very probably the reason for the low clay content in the surface layers. Although the data are not complete, it is possible to calculate its normative mineralogical composition, as the presence of only quartz, montmorillonite and anatase are reported. As kaolinite was found in calculation of the goethite-norm of the clay, whereas this mineral was not

TABLE II.89a. *Derived molar ratios of profile 25*

Hor.	SiO_2/R_2O_3	SiO_2/Al_2O_3	SiO_2/Fe_2O_3	Al_2O_3/Fe_2O_3
A_1	105	147	369	2.5
A_2	105	147	369	2.5
B_h	13	19	39	2.1
B_{ir}	6.2	9.2	19	2.0

TABLE II.90. *Partial chemical analysis of the clay fractions* (profile 25; weight percentages; after Reynders, 1964)

Hor.	SiO_2	Al_2O_3	Fe_2O_3	CaO	K_2O	TiO_2
A_1	84.0	3.5	0.7	0.1	0.3	1.2
A_2	79.6	7.1	1.6	0.1	0.4	1.3
B_h	67.2	14.1	5.2	0.1	0.8	1.2
B_{ir}	54.4	17.3	8.7	0.1	1.2	1.0

TABLE II.90a. *Derived molar ratios of clay fractions* (profile 25)

Hor.	SiO_2/R_2O_3	SiO_2/Al_2O_3	SiO_2/Fe_2O_3	Al_2O_3/Fe_2O_3
A_1	36	40	329	8.1
A_2	17	19	129	6.8
B_h	6.5	8.1	34	4.2
B_{ir}	4.1	5.4	17	3.1

present, the montmorillonite variant has been calculated. The result is shown in table II.91. It is clearly demonstrated that montmorillonite has been decomposed and free silica formed. The alumina, which must have been set free, has apparently dissolved

TABLE II.91. *Normative mineralogical composition of the clay fractions* (profile 25; weight percentages)

Hor.	Q	Ms	Sm	Go	Ru
A_1	87.0	2.6	8.2	0.9	1.3
A_2	75.1	3.6	17.9	1.9	1.5
B_h	49.6	7.5	35.2	6.4	1.3
B_{ir}	32.1	11.6	43.9	11.2	1.2

Q = silica; Ms = muscovite (illite); Sm = smectite; Go = goethite; Ru = anatase.

and leached away. Although not reported by Reynders, illite also occurs in the clay and appears to be unstable. Finally, cheluviation is very evident.

In conclusion, it can be stated that all processes which are characteristic for podzolization can be traced in this profile.

2.4. THE SOIL FORMING PROCESSES

The profiles discussed in the sections of this Chapter show that the processes summarized in the beginning are actually present, although in varying grades. The desilication process will be discussed in detail in Chapter 1 of Part III. The podzolization processes, viz. cheluviation (chilluviation), organic precipitation, and argeluviation (argilluviation) will be examined in Chapters 3 and 4 of Part III.

In temperate humid climates iron migration and clay migration seem to be closely related in the genesis of Grey Brown Podzolic Soils (Schlichting and Blume, 1962), although a more independent migration of both components seems to be possible too (Barshad, 1964; Van Schuylenborgh, 1966). Under warmer conditions however, this does not seem to be generally the case, as was indicated in many of the discussed profiles.

As in soils in the warm and humid or sub-humid countries kaolinite is the dominant clay mineral, and as iron oxide seems to be preferentially adsorbed on the kaolinite surface (see p. 222, Chapter 1 of this Part; Follett, 1965), it is of interest to see whether there is a correlation between kaolinite and iron oxide migration. This is the more interesting as it was shown that kaolinite is often more mobile than illite or montmorillonite. To investigate such a correlation it is appropriate to calculate the kaolinite/goethite ratio in the clay separates as well as in the horizons. Table II.92 presents the ratios of the profiles discussed earlier. It shows that only the clay fractions of the Mediterranean soils have a fairly constant kaolinite/goethite ratio. Although a certain proportion of iron oxide can migrate with kaolinite, they migrate for the greater part independently.

TABLE II.92. *Kaolinite/goethite ratios in the clay fractions and the horizons of the soils discussed*

Hor.	Lateritic Soils					Podzolic Soils (Red and Yellow)					Mediterranean Soils				
	Prof. 11	prof. 12		prof. 14		prof. 16		prof. 17		1	prof. 19	prof. 20		prof. 21	
	soil	soil	clay	soil	clay	soil	clay	soil	clay	clay	clay	soil	clay	soil	clay
A₁	10.8	1.4	3.6	3.1	5.2	1.8	6.3	1.2	5.7	4.0	1.2	0.8	2.0	3.9	5.5
A₃	5.1	0.6	3.5	4.9	4.8					3.5	1.4	0.9	2.2	5.4	5.3
B₂₁	8.9	1.2	3.8	3.8	3.6	3.4	4.6	3.2	4.6	3.6	1.5	1.7	2.0	5.2	5.4
B₂₂	9.4	0.7	2.9					2.6	4.8					5.1	5.6
B₃										3.8	1.4	1.0	2.4	4.8	6.1
C	19.3	0.8	3.1	3.5	3.8	2.0	5.9			4.4				4.7	6.4

[1] Fine clay fraction 0.2–0.08µ of p. 281.

The migration of aluminium oxide is caused for the greater part by clay migration. The SiO_2/Al_2O_3 ratio decreasing with depth often indicates clay migration. However, it can also indicate weathering of minerals into their constituent parts with the subsequent leaching of one of the products, aluminium hydroxide, and its deposition in the sub-soil. This process occurs especially if the reaction is acid (lower than pH 4.5: see fig. II. 22 on p. 213). A careful examination of the clay fraction has then to be carried out to decide which of the two processes is dominant. The most precise approach to this problem would be the fractionation of the soil sample into sand, silt, and clay fractions followed by the chemical and mineralogical analysis of these fractions. Therefore those examples from literature which gave analyses of the soil sample as a whole, of its clay fraction and of its texture were mainly discussed. The composition of the sand + silt fraction can then be calculated by difference. Applying this method in our own investigations proved to give a very useful approximation.

LITERATURE CITED

ANDERSON, M.S. and BYERS, H.G. 1931 Character of colloidal materials in the profiles of certain major soil groups. *U.S. Dept. Agric. Techn. Bull.*, 228: pp. 24.

BARSHAD, I. 1964 In F.E. Bear: The chemistry of the soil. Chapter I. Chemistry of soil development: 1–70.

BROWN, I.C. and BYERS, H.G. 1932 The fractionation, composition and hypothetical constitution of certain colloids derived from the great soil groups. *U.S. Dept. Agric. Techn. Bull.* 319: pp. 43.

BURINGH, P. 1968 Introduction to the study of soils in tropical and subtropical regions. Wageningen; pp. 118.

BURRI, C. 1964 Petrochemical calculations based on equivalents. *Translated from German. Jerusalem.*

DAMES, T. W. G. 1955 The soils of east-central Java. *Bogor.*

— 1962 Soil research in the economic development of Serawak. *FAO Report No. 1512:* pp. 83. Rome.

DUDAL, R. 1962 Soil survey and its application in Indonesia. *ETAP Report No. 1509:* pp. 71.

— 1968 Definitions of soil units for the soil map of the world. *FAO, Rome.*

ENGLAND, C. B. and PERKINS, R. P. 1959 Characteristics of three Reddish Brown Lateritic Soils of Georgia. *Soil Sci.*, 88 : 294–302.

FOLLETT, E. A. C. 1965 The retention of amorphous, colloidal 'ferric hydroxide' by kaolinites. *J. Soil Sci.*, 16: 334–341.

GRAGERA, P. and GUERRA, A. 1966 Excursion guide of the Conference on Mediterranean Soils. *Madrid,* 7–15.

HALLSWORTH, E.G. 1963 An examination on some factors affecting the movement of clay in an artificial soil. *J. Soil Sci.*, 14: 360–371.

HARDON, H.J. 1936 Podzol-profiles in the tropics. *Natuurk. Tijdschr. Ned.-Indië*, 96: 25–41.

— 1937 Padang soil, an example of podsol in the tropical lowlands. *Proc. Kon. Akad. Wet.,* 40: 530–538.

HARDY, F. and FOLLETT-SMITH, R.R. 1931 Studies in tropical soils II. Some characteristic igneous rock soil profiles in British Guiana, South America. *J. agric. Sci.*, 21: 739–761.

— and RODRIGUEZ, G. 1939 The genesis of Davidson clay loam. *Soil Sci.*, 48: 483–495.

HARRADINE, F. 1966 Comparative morphology of lateritic and podzolic soils in California.

Soil Sci., 101: 142–151.

KLINGE, H. 1966 Tropische Podsole und Schwarzwässer. *Umschau.*

KREBS, R.D. and TEDROW, J.C.F. 1958 Genesis of Red-Yellow Podzolic and related soils in New Jersey. *Soil Sci.*, 85: 22–37.

KUBIENA, W.L. 1956 Rubefizierung und Laterisierung. *Trans. 6th Int. Cong. Soil Sci.*, E: 247–249.

— 1962 Die taxonomische Bedeutung der Art und Ausbildung von Eisenoxydhydratmineralien in Tropenböden. *Z. Pflern. Düng. Bodenk.*, 98: 205–213.

LAMOUREUX, M. 1967 Contribution à l'étude de la pédogénèse en sols rouges méditerranéens. *Science du Sol.*, No. 2: 55–85.

— and SEGALEN, P. 1969 Etude comparée des produits ferrugineux dans les sols rouges et bruns méditerranéens du Liban. *Science du Sol*, No. 1: 63–75.

MANCINI, F. 1966 On the elimination of the term 'mediterranean' in soil science. *Trans. Conf. Medit. Soils (Madrid)*: 413–417.

MARBUT, C.F. 1935 Atlas of American Agriculture. Part III. Soils of the United States. *U.S. Dept. Agric.*, *Advance Sheets*, No. 8: pp. 85.

MCCALEB, S.B. 1959 The genesis of the Red-Yellow Podzolic Soils. *Soil Sci. Soc. Am. Proc.*, 23: 164–168.

MIDDLETON, H.E. 1930 Properties of soils which influence soil erosion. *U.S. Dept. Agric. Techn. Bull.*, 178: pp. 16.

MOHR, E.C.J. 1938 De bodem der tropen in het algemeen en die van Nederlandsch-Indië in het bijzonder. Deel II. *Amsterdam.*

NYUN, M.A. and MCCALEB, S.B. 1955 The reddish Brown Lateritic Soils of the North Carolina Piedmont region: Davidson and Hiwassee series. *Soil Sci.*, 80: 27–41.

PEARSON, R.W. and ENSMINGER, L.E. 1949 Types of clay minerals in Alabama soils. *Soil Sci. Soc. Am. Proc.*, 13: 153–156.

— 1957 Southeastern Uplands. In: *The Yearbook of Agriculture 1957*: 579–594.

REIFENBERG, A. 1952 The soils of Syria and the Libanon. *J. Soil Sci.*, 3: 68–90.

REYNDERS, J.J. 1964 A pedo-ecological study of soil genesis in the tropics from sea level to eternal snow. *Thesis Utrecht*: pp. 159.

RICH, C.I. and OBENSHAIN, S.S. 1955 Chemical and clay mineral properties of a Red-Yellow Podzolic Soil derived from muscovite schist. *Soil Sci. Soc. Am. Proc.*, 19: 334–339.

SCHLICHTING, E. and BLUME, H.-P. 1962 Art und Ausmasz der Veränderungen des Bestandes mobiler Oxyde in Böden aus jungpleistozänen Geschiebemergel und ihren Horizonten. *Z. Pflern. Düng. Bodenk.*, 96: 144–157.

SIMONSON, R.W. 1950 Genesis and classification of Red-Yellow Podzolic soils. *Soil Sci. Soc. Am. Proc.*, 14: 316–319.

SLAGER, S. and VAN SCHUYLENBORGH, J. 1970 Morphology and geochemistry of three clay soils of a tropical coastal plain (Surinam). *Agric. Res. Rep. 734*, pp. 34.

SOIL SURVEY STAFF U.S.A. 1960 Soil classification. A comprehensive system. *U.S. Dept. of Agriculture.*

— 1967 Supplement to the soil classification system. *U.S. Dept. of Agriculture.*

STORIE, R.E. and HARRADINE, F. 1958 Soils of California. *Soil Sci.*, 85: 207–227.

SWINDALE, L.D. and JACKSON, M.L. 1956 Genetic processes in some residual podzolized soils of New Zealand. *Trans. 6th Int. Cong. Soil Sci.*, E: 233–239.

TAN, K.H. and VAN SCHUYLENBORGH, J. 1961 On the classification and genesis of soils developed over acid volcanic material under humid tropical conditions II. *Neth. J. agric. Sci.*, 9: 41–54.

VAGELER, P.W. 1938 Grundrisz der tropischen und subtropischen Bodenkunde. *2nd. Ed.*

Berlin.

VAN BAREN, F.A. 1941 De mineralogische achtergrond van de bodemvruchtbaarheid in Nederlandsch-Indië. *Landbouw (Buitenzorg)*, 17: 520–541.

VAN DER MERWE, C.R. 1962 Soil groups and sub-groups of South Africa. *S. Afr. Dept. Agric. and Forestry, Sci. Bull.*, 356: pp. 355.

VAN DER PLAS, L. and VAN SCHUYLENBORGH, J. 1970 Petrochemical calculations applied to soils (with special reference to soil formation). *Geoderma*, 4:357-385.

VAN SCHUYLENBORGH, J. 1956 Investigations on the classification and genesis of soils, derived from acid tuffs under humid tropical conditions. *Neth. J. agric. Sci.*, 5: 195–210.

— 1966 Die Verlagerung von Sesquioxiden in Parabraunerden, Podsolen und sauren Braunerden. *Z. Pflern. Düng. Bodenk.*, 114: 9-12.

YAALON, D.H., NATHAN, H., KOYUMDJINSKY, H. and DAN, J. 1966 Weathering and catenary differentiation of clay minerals in soils on various materials in Israel. *Proc. Int. Clay Conf.*, I: 187–198.

CHAPTER 3

VERTISOLS

This chapter deals with the dark clay soils. They occur all over the world (from 45°S to 45°N latitude), but concentrate especially in warm-temperate, sub-tropical and tropical areas. Dudal (1965) wrote a very comprehensive monograph on the dark clays containing a world map of the Vertisols (fig. II.39) and a list of surfaces of the occurrences in the various continents. Tabele II.93 gives a rough estimation of the

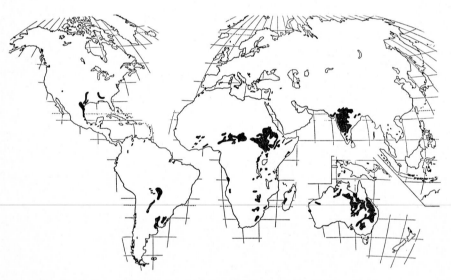

FIG. II.39. *Vertisol areas of tropical and sub-tropical regions (after Dudal, 1965)*

surface areas involved in North and South America, Africa, Asia, and Australia. It is a concise summary of Dudal's review.

Various names were and still are used for the black clay soils, such as Regur (India), Black Cotton Soil (India, Africa), Margalitic Soils (Indonesia), Black Earth and Black and Red Clays of Heavy Texture (Australia), Smonitza (Yugoslavia) and Grumusol (U.S.A.). The U.S. Soil Survey Staff (7th Approximation, 1960, 1967) proposed the name Vertisol, which is now generally adopted, also in this textbook.

Vertisols occur frequently in association with other soils such as Mediterranean-like

TABLE II.93. *Coverage* (in millions of hectares of Vertisols in the five continents)

Continent	Coverage
North America	5.6
South America	16.5
Africa	98.0
Asia	63.2
Australia	70.5

soils in the Sudan and Indonesia, with Saline soils in Chad and Turkey, with Hydro-morphic soils in South Africa, with Oxisols in Nigeria and India, with Prairie soils in Argentine, etc.

3.1. GENERAL FEATURES

One of the most conspicuous characteristics of the Vertisols is their capacity to shrink and swell enormously upon change in moisture content. During shrinking fissures of considerable width (up to 25 cm) and extending many feet into the soil are known to be formed. In the dry state the soils often show a hexagonal pattern of cracks (see fig. II. 40), the macrostructure is prismatic. On wetting the material expands again and the cracks close. This process of shrinking and swelling is reversible.

A consequence of this phenomenon is that in the dry state surface material frequently falls into the fissures, filling them partly. When the soil is subsequently wetted, this material is forced upward, often forming a typical microrelief of low hillocks and shallow depressions, called 'gilgai'.

The combined effect of cracking, partly filling up of the cracks with surface material and swelling also causes the churning of the whole soil mass to the depth of the

FIG. II.40. *Cracks in Vertisol area (photo W. A. Blokhuis)*

fissures, an effect sometimes called 'self-swallowing' or, more often but incorrectly 'self-mulching'. Another result of this mechanism is the production of polished and grooved faces, called 'slickensides' caused by the sliding of one soil mass past the other.

Owing to the intense churning the soil profile morphology is remarkably uniform in depth (see tables II.94, 97 and 98) although exceptions do occur as has been observed in the Sudan (see p. 320). The colour is generally dark to very dark, a characteristic not to be ascribed to a high content of organic matter (see table II.100). This is, contrary to expectation, mostly low to very low. The dark colour originates at least in part, in the clay fraction in which carbon occurs in a form which is not oxidizable with H_2O_2. Apparently organic matter is chemisorbed by the clay minerals, an assumption supported by a recent study of Dudas and Pawluk (1969) who found the fraction 0.2–0.08µ to be the main carrier of organo-clay complexed carbon.

TABLE II.94. *Physical and chemical characteristics of a Black Cotton Soil of Bundelkhand, United Provinces, India* (after Agarwal and Mukerji, 1949)

	depth of samples in cm					
	0–30	30–70	70–105	105–140	140–150	150–180
sand[1]	27.6	24.9	26.5	29.2	31.4	33.0
silt	24.0	28.0	28.0	23.8	22.8	24.0
clay	40.5	36.3	35.3	33.5	33.0	31.5
pH (KCl)	7.8	7.3	7.8	8.2	8.4	8.4
SiO_2	44.0	43.9	44.3	45.1	44.9	44.9
Al_2O_3	21.3	23.4	19.6	20.1	22.2	n.r.[2]
Fe_2O_3	9.2	9.6	10.0	10.4	10.8	n.r.
MgO	2.5	2.5	2.2	2.6	3.2	3.8
K_2O	2.4	2.0	2.9	2.6	2.8	2.8
Free Fe_2O_3	7.2	8.0	8.8	8.8	8.8	8.8
SiO_2/Al_2O_3	3.5	3.2	3.8	3.8	3.4	–

[1] granulometric data on air-dry basis;
[2] n.r. = not reported.

3.2. SOIL FORMING FACTORS

a) *Climate*

Dudal (1965) concluded from a study of 140 meteorological stations located in the Vertisol regions, that the average annual temperature under which the soils occur, ranges generally between 15.5° to 26.5° C. The summer temperatures are occasionally lower than 20° C. The difference between lowest and highest mean monthly temperatures is not more than 3° C near the equator but may increase to 15° C at higher latitudes.

The mean annual rainfall is generally between 500 and 1000 mm (after Dudal, 1965), although areas occur with 150 mm (e.g. Sudan) and with 2000 mm (Indonesia). The distribution of the rainfall is always seasonal. A dry period of 4 to 8 months is most common for Vertisol areas.

For agricultural purposes the climates are subdivided into phases characterized by a water balance where rainfall is related to evapotranspiration. For Australia, India, and Sudan the desertic, arid, semiarid, monsoon tropical, monsoon equatorial, semiarid temperate, dry Mediterranean, and subhumid temperate phases occur (Dudal, 1965). In the countries mentioned the Vertisols occur predominantly in the arid to semiarid areas with a high mean annual temperature, a rainfall varying between 250 and 750 mm, and a dry period varying from 6 to 12 months.

The characteristics of the climate phases can be summarized as follows. Desertic phase: all months are dry, but rainfall during one or more months covers more than 25% and the mean annual rainfall covers less than 22% of the potential evapotranspiration; occasional frosts occur. Arid phase: one or two months are non-dry, but no month is humid. Semiarid phase: two or three months are humid and the annual rainfall covers less than 44% of the annual potential evapotranspiration; the dry period is very long; occasional frosts may occur. Monsoon tropical phase: rainfall covers more than 44% of the annual potential evapotranspiration and the dry season is long; occasional frosts may occur. Monsoon equatorial phase: humid season is three to four months and the dry season four to five months; average monthly minimum temperature

TABLE II.95. *Comparative data on black cotton soils of India* (after Basu and Sirur, 1938)

	A	B	C	D	E	F	G	H
Depth of layer	15–30	25–50	15–30	15–30	15–30	20–25	15–30	25–50
Colour	black	dark grey	deep black	dark grey	grey-black	grey-brown	dark brown	choc. brown
Clay in % on $CaCO_3$ free basis	35.6	64.7	23.0	65.1	68.3	55.5	58.9	52.5
Silt in % on $CaCO_3$ free basis	22.3	13.2	31.7	18.1	11.5	21.8	9.9	13.5
$CaCO_3$ %	6.8	8.9	5.4	11.7	8.9	2.3	6.3	1.5
pH-H_2O	8.8	8.3	9.0	8.8	8.6	8.1	8.2	8.1
Humus %	1.4	0.3	1.5	1.3	1.6	0.5	0.7	0.4
C.e.c. in m.e./ 100 g of soil	81.4	47.8	66.2	65.9	79.2	66.7	66.7	61.4
Ca in % of cec.	86	65	66	75	89	93	83	85
Mg in % of cec.	6	21	27	18	9	4	9	7
K in % of cec.	6	5	1	4	1	2	7	7
Na in % of cec.	2	9	6	3	1	1	1	1

is always above 19° C. Semiarid temperate phase: no month is humid but the winter is non-dry and cool. Dry Mediterranean phase: winter months are humid and the summers hot and dry. Subhumid temperate phase: not more than two dry months; only winter is humid.

A few examples of Vertisols in India and in the Sudan may illustrate this climatic review. The region of the well-known Bombay-Deccan trap falls into the semi-arid phase.

According to Bal (1935) these soils reveal considerable variations in depth and clay content but generally speaking, no marked horizon is developed in their profiles. This is substantiated by the detailed investigations of the Deccan Canal soils conducted by Basu and Sirur (1938).

Table II.95 shows the features and properties of some of the numerous profiles which are studied. This data is based on the second layer of each profile, the depth being almost consistent so that contaminating anthropogenic influences which might have disturbed the surface layer are eliminated.

Samples of profiles A-E (see fig. II.41) were collected along the Nira Right Bank Canal, south-west of Poonah, and F-H along the Pravara Left Bank Canal, north of Ahmednager, Bombay-Deccan. This region is characterized by a mean total annual rainfall of only 470 mm, which is poorly distributed and precarious; the average number

FIG. II.41. *Black cotton soil (type A) Padegaon Farms, Nira Right Bank Canal, India (after Basu and Sirur, 1938)*

FIG. II.42. *Black cotton soil (type D) Akluj, Nira Right Bank Canal, India (after Basu and Sirur, 1938)*

of rainy days in one month calculated over a period of 15 years, reaches a maximum in July with a total 10.7. The homogeneous black, greyish and brownish soils which, under these circumstances, have been developed on or owe their origin to, the Deccan trap may vary in their clay content and percentage of calcium carbonate, but they have a high base exchange capacity in common, B being the lowest with 47.8 m.e. Calcium is the most prominent adsorbed ion, magnesium is generally a poor second and potassium and sodium are relatively unimportant.

The lack of horizon differentiation, to which Basu (l.c.) drew attention, is illustrated by i.a. profile D (see fig. 11.42), which may be regarded as a representative example. It is a dark grey soil with a brownish shade, loose and granular, with faint structure in lower horizons from 30 cm downwards, with distinct lamination in the lowest layer. Below 75 cm, a dirty white lime band of varying depth (15 to 150 cm) lies between the upper horizon and the decayed rock below. Five samples of this profile were collected and they all show a remarkable consistency in the principal features, as shown in table 11.96.

TABLE 11.96. *Principal features of a black cotton soil profile near Akluj, Nira Right Bank Canal, Bombay-Deccan, India* (after Basu and Sirur, 1938)

Depth of horizon in cm	0–15	15–30	30–45	45–60	60–75
Clay %	55.8	57.5	56.8	54.5	56.0
Silt %	15.8	16.0	14.5	11.8	20.5
CaCO$_3$ %	9.4	11.7	8.9	7.9	6.2
pH-H$_2$O	8.9	8.8	9.0	9.0	9.0
Humus %	1.3	1.3	1.2	1.2	1.2
Cec in m.e./100 g of soil	65.3	65.9	63.2	53.1	66.3
Ca in % of cec.	80	75	77	74	67
Mg in % of cec.	14	18	18	20	22
K in % of cec.	4	4	2	3	2
Na in % of cec.	2	3	3	4	9

A second example are the black soils occurring in the District of Jalam, Bundelkhand, United Provinces. This region has a monsoon-tropical climate. The mean yearly rainfall, calculated over a period of 47 years, is 791 mm; June 82 mm, July 268 mm, August 259 and September 120 mm. The other 62 mm fall in the remaining 8 months.

Agarwal and Mukerji (1949) provide the following information on these soils. They are friable, calcareous soils, and very water-retentive; they expand and contract to a remarkable degree, opening into large fissures at frequent intervals. The origin of these soils is ascribed to the sub-aqueous decomposition of trap rocks, although it has also been attributed to sub-areal denudation of basaltic rocks and the impregnation of certain argillaceous soils by organic matter, this combined with iron imparting the black colour (see, however, p. 338). A representative profile has the following morphology:

Horizon	Depth (cm)	
I	0–30	Black sticky soil tending to become ash grey on drying; massive and compact; non-calcareous. Depth of sample 0–30 cm.
II	30–105	Same as above; slightly calcareous. Depth of samples 30–70 and 70–105 cm.
III	105–150	Ash grey tending to appear white; less compact; less clayey than above; calcareous. Depth of samples 105–140 and 140–150 cm.
IV	150–180	Calcareous; loosely held calcareous material. Depth of sample 150–180 cm.

This profile reveals a most striking uniformity of both physical and chemical features in the horizons from which samples were taken. This was clearly illustrated by the collected data given already in table II.94. The figures show that practically no dislocation of weathered material occurred.

TABLE II.97. *Physical and chemical data* (weight percentages) *of a Vertisol from Seinat, Gedaref area, Sudan* (after Blokhuis, 1972)

	horizon depth in cm			
	0–30	30–90	90–150	150–180+
sand	1.9	2.1	1.4	0.7
silt	20.0	19.4	17.4	19.9
clay	77.8	78.5	81.2	79.4
pH (0.01M CaCl$_2$)	6.6	7.2	7.3	7.3
CaCO$_3$	0.7	1.2	1.2	1.5
C	0.9	0.9	0.7	0.4
SiO$_2$	52.4	52.4	51.9	52.0
Al$_2$O$_3$	17.0	17.0	16.8	17.2
Fe$_2$O$_3$	9.3	9.3	9.3	9.5
FeO	0.8	0.6	0.7	0.6
MnO	0.1	0.1	0.2	0.1
CaO	3.0	3.1	3.5	3.2
MgO	0.9	0.9	0.9	0.8
Na$_2$O	0.4	0.6	0.6	0.7
K$_2$O	0.3	0.3	0.2	0.3
P$_2$O$_5$	0.1	0.1	0.1	0.1
H$_2$O+	8.9	8.4	8.4	8.8
Free Fe$_2$O$_3$	5.1	6.2	5.7	5.3
SiO$_2$/Al$_2$O$_3$	5.2	5.2	5.3	5.2
SiO$_2$/Fe$_2$O$_3$	15	17	15	15
Al$_2$O$_3$/Fe$_2$O$_3$	2.9	2.9	2.8	2.8

The Sudan profile, the third example, occurs in the neighbourhood of Gedaref and represents the arid phase of the dark clay soils. The analytical details can be found in table II.97. The normative mineralogical composition, calculated from the data of fig. ii.97 is listed in table ii.98. It is evident that the mineralogical composition is fairly constant.

TABLE ii.98. *Normative mineralogical composition of the Seinat profile, Gedaref area, Sudan* (equivalent percentages)

mineral	horizon depth in cm			
	0–30	30–90	90–150	150–180+
Q	28.1	28.0	27.2	27.0
Plg	4.5	6.5	6.5	7.5
Sm	37.3	33.9	35.6	33.4
Ms	3.1	3.1	1.8	2.8
Kd	16.0	16.9	15.3	17.5
Zo	0.8	1.2	3.1	0.8
Go	8.0	8.0	8.0	8.2
Cc	0.5	0.5	0.8	0.9
Ru	1.3	1.3	1.3	1.3
Misc	0.4	0.5	0.4	0.6

Q = free silica; Plg = plagioclases; Sm = smectites; Ms = muscovite (illite); Kd = Kandites; Zo = zoisite; Go = goethite; Cc = calcite; Ru = rutile (anatase); Misc = miscellaneous (phosphates + manganese oxides).

These three examples reveal clearly the homogeneous build-up of the Vertisol profiles. That some differences can still be observed may be deduced from the normative mineralogical composition of the Sudan soil. Minerals of the smectite group show a distinct dominance in the 0–30 cm surface layer, a fact which coincides with the lowest content in plagioclases.

The early investigations of Hardon (1939) of the clay fractions of Vertisols of Indonesia confirm that even when the origin of the black tropical clays may be different and the parent material has been mixed with detrital material of adjacent dacites and silicified andesites, the composition and quality of the fraction smaller than 2μ are similar (see tables ii.99 and 100). In these tables the numbers 12843 and 30277 represent autochtonic soils, whereas the calcareous vertisols are probably sedimentary lake deposits.

The analyses reveal that the vertisolic soils are characterized by a SiO_2/Al_2O_3 ratio of at least 3.4, a very high cation exchange capacity of over 70 m.e./100 grams of clay, and montmorillonite as clay mineral. Calcite was only encountered in one case in any appreciable amount, viz. 2.1% of the quartz-bearing variety No. 30277. The low organic matter content which might have been presumed to be considerably higher in these black clays, confirms the statement made on page 310.

b) *Physiography, topography, and drainage*
Vertisols occur most commonly in the lowlands up to 300 m from sea level but also at

TABLE II.99. *Denomination and sample location of vertisolic soils of Java* (after Hardon, 1939)

Sample No.	Soil type	Location		Annual rainfall (mm)	dry months 60 mm
		Village	Residency		
12843	Black, old, tuffaceous margalitic soil	Grudo	Madiun	2000	4
12461	Black, old, calciferous margalitic soil	Gamping	Surakarta	2400	3
33193	ibid.	Sumberredjo	do.	2400	3
30277	Greyish, old, quartziferous marg. soil	Kunduran	Japara	2000	3

TABLE II.100. *Chemical composition of the clay fraction of some vertisolic soils* (after Hardon, 1939)

Sample number	12843	12461	33193	30277
Quartz	n.d.	n.d.	n.d.	n.d.
SiO_2	42.8	36.8	40.6	38.9
Al_2O_3	19.0	17.1	20.2	17.7
Fe_2O_3	8.7	12.2	11.0	5.5
TiO_2	tr	0.6	0.8	0.7
MnO	tr	tr	0.1	tr
CaO	1.7	2.2	2.4	4.6
MgO	1.8	1.8	1.1	0.7
K_2O	0.1	0.2	0.2	0.4
Na_2O	0.8	3.4	0.5	0.5
P_2O_5	0.1	tr	0.1	0.1
CO_2	–	–	0.1	1.0
H_2O ($-105°$)	15.5	15.6	12.8	13.6
H_2O ($+105°$)	8.7	8.0	9.0	9.4
Organic matter	0.9	1.3	1.6	1.5
SiO_2/R_2O_3 ratio	3.0	2.5	2.5	3.1
SiO_2/Al_2O_3 ratio	3.8	3.7	3.4	3.7
Cation exchange capacity in m.e./100 grams of clay	85.7	81.8	74.5	69.7

Clay minerals:
No. 12843   montmorillonite
No. 12461   montmorillonite + trace of kaolinite
No. 33193   montmorillonite + trace of kaolinite
No. 30277   montmorillonite + quartz + calcite + kaolinite

higher elevations up to 2,200 metres. The Regurs of India are situated mainly at elevations between 300 and 700 m.

The landforms in which Vertisols occur are similar to those of the Oxisols with plinthite. They occur on broad, level plateaus, coastal plains, basins, former flood plains, alluvial plains, marine and river terraces. They are also found in gently sloping areas such as peneplains and the lower slopes of volcanoes, the inclination generally not exceeding 5 %.

The gilgai microrelief consists of patterns of various forms and sizes, such as lattice, network, striped, wavy, and tank gilgai (Hallsworth et al., 1955, 1969). Sometimes the gilgai microrelief is absent (see also: p. 331).

In the absence of drainage channels as in broad, level areas, the drainage is poor and, because of the low permeability of the soils, water may stand on the surface after the rainy period for a considerable period.

c) *Parent material*
The most favourable parent materials for the formation of Vertisols are clays, either obtained by sedimentation (alluvial, colluvial, marl, etc.) or by weathering of hard or unconsolidated rocks. Amongst these the more basic rocks are most common, such as limestone, marls shale, gabbro, diabase, dolerite, serpentine, basalt, volcanic ash and tuff. This is also similar to the parent materials which are favourable for the formation of Oxisols, although Oxisols are also found on acidic rocks. Vertisols can be formed on acidic parent materials whether enriched or not with foreign materials or by flood waters.

d) *Vegetation*
The vegetation is generally a medium to tall grass savannah with scattered trees and shrubs of fire-resistent species. The ratio grass to trees depends on the local circumstances such as rainfall and burning.

Amongst the grasses *Cymbopogon*, *Setaria*, *Brachiaria*, *Hyparrhenia*, and *Sorghum* are frequently occurring genera. Common trees are *Acacia* species: *Acacia mellifera* in the more arid regions and *Acacia seyal* in the less arid regions. (For details, see: Dudal, 1965.)

3.3. PHYSICAL AND CHEMICAL CHARACTERISTICS AND SOME REMARKS ON SOIL FORMING PROCESSES

3.3.1. CALCIUM CARBONATE CONCRETIONS

One of the more typical features of Vertisols is the presence of nodules or concretions of lime which sometimes occur throughout the entire soil mass, or in other cases are accumulated at a certain depth, approaching hardpan formation. The concretions occurring in the black soils of India have been studied in detail by Singh and Lal (1946). They investigated not only the amount of concretions or 'kankar' in various sieve fractions of the coarser soil material, but also the chemical composition of these nodules. They found 'kankar' in a great variety of shapes, sizes, colours, and degrees of hardness. The hardness appeared to vary with the age of the profile and with the pore space of the concretions, as shown in table II.101. The hardness is determined in accordance with Mohs' scale, and pore space with the appropriate data on real and apparent density. The stage of development of the soil profile was estimated by taking into account the extent of the leaching of calcite in the profile.

TABLE II.101. *Relation between age of soil and hardness and pore space of kankar in Indian soils* (after Singh and Lal, 1949)

Age of soil	Hardness of kankar	Pore space of kankar	Content (%) of SiO_2 in kankar
Young	0.8	19.5	–
Immature	3.8	12.6	29.8
Semi-Mature	7.0	3.8	30.1
Mature	7.0	3.6	28.5

A classification of the lime concretions as they have been encountered in Vertisols of the Sudan, has been given by Blokhuis et al. (1969). These authors paid special attention to the microscopic build-up by studying thin sections of soils with the concretions enclosed in the soil mass. Seven samples of pedogenic carbonate were X-rayed. They showed dominant calcite with admixtures of montmorillonite and quartz. The chemical analysis of one sample revealed the presence of only 5.0 % of SiO_2.

3.3.2. PROFILES WITH ANALYTICAL DETAILS

Four more or less arbitrarily chosen profiles will be examined in this section. The first profile, although not a tropical one, is a brown Vertisol, which has been studied by Johnson, Cady and James (1962). Brown Vertisols occur in Arizona (U.S.A.) at elevations of 600 m or less to 2,300 m with average annual rainfall varying from 280 mm up to 1020 mm. Mean annual temperatures vary from 16.7° to 9.4° C. The soils have been mostly derived from basalts or other basic igneous rocks, including volcanic cinders and agglomerates. They occur on undulating or rolling plains with occasional reefs of basalt rock breaking the surface. Surface drainage is poor with much of the runoff collecting in small intermittent lakes or basins that occupy depressions between the lava flows or the volcanic calderas. The vegetation is dominated by grasses. In the dry and warmer environments of lower elevations the major species are *Hilaria mutica*, *Sporobolus cryptandrus*, and *Muhlenbergia torreyi*. In the cooler and moister areas of higher elevations the grasses are *Muhlenbergia torreyi*, *Agropyron smithii* and *Bouteloua gracilis*. Few to many juniper trees grow but these are believed to have invaded the areas in fairly recent times.

The profile under consideration here (profile 26) is located in Black Mesa, Yavapai County, Arizona at an elevation of 1,430 m, with an average annual precipitation of 360 to 410 mm and a mean annual temperature of 13.3° C. The profile description reads as follows:

Horizon	Depth (cm)	
A₁	0–10	Brownish grey (7.5YR3/2:d) to black brown (7.5YR3/2:m) stony silty clay. Granular structure in the top 2.5 cm and blocky in the lower part. Extremely hard, very firm, very plastic and very sticky. Noncalcareous.
C₁	10–89	Brownish grey (7.5YR3/2:d) to black brown (7.5YR3/2:m) silty clay. Very coarse parallelepiped aggregates because of many intersecting slickensides. Extremely hard, very firm, very plastic and very sticky. Slightly calcareous with few small hard lime concretions.
C_gg	89–99	Same colour as C₁, but with white mottles. Silty clay. Coarser parallelepiped aggregates because of intersecting slickensides. Extremely hard, very firm, very plastic and very sticky. Moderately calcareous with abundant soft lime concretions.
R	99+	Hard, dark grey basalt.

The boundaries are diffuse or gradual and wavy. Wide vertical cracks are present in the dry soil. Plant roots extend down to the bedrock, but are sparse below about 60 cm.

The analytical details can be summarized as follows. The clay percentage ranges from 43 % at the surface to 52 % at the bottom of the profile. The corresponding data for organic matter content are 0.9 % and 0.5 %. Bulk density ranges from 1.74 in top granular layer to 1.98 at the bottom of the profile. The dominant exchangeable cation is Ca^{2+} occupying approximately 70 % of the c.e.c. and the Ca/Mg ratio is between 3 and 4. Exchangeable $K^+ + Na^+$ is low and does not exceed 2 m.e./100 g of soil.

The clay mineral is dominantly well-crystallized montmorillonite. Glycol solvation shows that 001-spacings are commonly 20 Å, rather than 18 Å, indicating that the clay is complexed with organic matter (see p. 310). Thin sections show that montmorillonite replaces feldspars and augite, whilst olivine is replaced by a mixture of goethite and some layer silicate. Weathering and clay mineral formation occur when the rock decomposes and no important mineralogical changes take place in the soil. Sodium appears to be lost, but magnesium and some calcium remain as constituents of the clay and as concretions. Quartz and microcline are not normally constituents of basalt but they are found throughout the profile. It was noted that the quartz content at the bottom of the profile is much lower than in the upper horizons. It is thought that some of the quartz is residual from material interbedded or mixed with the basalt flows, or is a windblown deposit from the post-Tertiary period or both.

Several examples of Vertisols can be found in the work of Blokhuis (1972). Two profiles will be selected from his work; one of these has formed in colluvial material derived from basalt-weathering; the other has developed '*in situ*' from rock of the Basement Complex. The first of these profiles (profile 27) is situated 7 km south-west of Er Rawashda village on the road to Gedaref (Sudan). The mean daily minimum and maximum temperatures are approximately 19° and 35° C. Most rains fall during July and August. Average annual rainfall is approximately 600 mm. The average annual rainfall deficit amounts to some 1700 mm. The surface is very uneven, almost gilgai with a wavelength of 2 to 3 m and an amplitude of 15 cm. Cracks occur with a width of 5 to 15 cm and are sometimes sinkhole-like. The cracks are obscured by a 2 to 3 cm thick surface mulch of hard, granular peds of 2 to 5 mm diameter. The mulch layer again is covered by a thin very brittle, flaky crust, which is generally broken, probably due to grazing. Many light grey-coloured lime nodules and rock fragments occur on the surface, probably due to churning.

The profile description reads as follows:

Horizon	Depth (cm)	
A_{11}	0–35	Yellow brownish grey (10YR4/1:d) to black brown (10YR3/1:m) clay with subangular blocky, with depth changing to angular blocky structure. Abundant $CaCO_3$ nodules varying in colour from white to light bluish grey and in size from smaller than 1 to 5 mm. Diffuse boundary to
A_{12}	35–75	Black brown (10YR3/1:d and m) clay with weak angular blocky structure. Distinct, fine tilted wedges. Abundance, size, and colour of the $CaCO_3$ nodules as in A_{11}. Fibrous roots. Diffuse boundary to
A_{13}	75–120	Black brown (10YR3/1:d and m) clay with moderate angular blocky structure. Medium to coarse tilted wedges defined by 'meso' and 'macro' slickensides. Abundance, size, and colour of $CaCO_3$ nodules as in A_{11}. Many fibrous roots. Diffuse boundary to
C	120–150	Black brown (10YR3/1:d and m) clay with strong angular blocky structure. Tilted wedges, defined by common, distinct slickensides, which have roots and rootprints. Less abundant $CaCO_3$ nodules of the same size and colour as in A_{11}. Abrupt and wavy boundary to
R	150+	Unweathered basalt boulders.

Wide cracks occur up to a depth of 1 m. Slickensides increase from 35 to 150 cm. Classification: Typic Pellustert.

The granulometric analysis shows a homogeneous profile; $CaCO_3$ content decreases with depth, the pH varies between 6.5 and 7.0 and c.e.c. is constant. Exchangeable Ca^{2+} and K^+ are constant too, whereas exchangeable Mg^{2+} and Na^+ increase with depth (see table II.102). The chemical composition and the derived molar silica/sesquioxide ratios are presented in tables II.103 and 103a. As the solum is certainly derived from material weathered from the underlying rock it can be decided whether or not desilication has occurred during weathering. It appears that this is not the case as the SiO_2/R_2O_3 ratio of the solum (except the A_{11} horizon) is higher than that of the rock. This is in marked contrast to the profiles so far discussed. Of the alkaline earth and alkali metals only Mg and Na have undergone considerable loss. The surface

TABLE II.102. *Physical and chemical characteristics of profile 27* (after Blokhuis, 1972)

Hor.	grain size (%) distribution			pH (0.01 M CaCl₂)	C (%)	CO₂ (%)	cation exchange characteristics (m.e./100 g of soil)				
	> 50μ	50–2μ	< 2μ				c.e.c.	Ca^{2+}	Mg^{2+}	K^+	Na^+
A_{11}	1.1	19.5	79.3	6.8	0.2	7.0	45.2	33.2	11.8	0.2	1.8
A_{12}	1.0	21.1	47.9	6.5	0.9	7.1	45.3	31.4	13.3	0.2	5.2
A_{13}	0.9	20.4	78.7	6.7	0.6	6.7	45.5	32.3	13.3	0.2	5.1
C	1.0	20.0	79.0	7.0	0.5	4.1	46.0	31.3	14.0	0.2	5.9

horizon has a composition different from that of the underlying part. This cannot be attributed to lateral removal of clay by sheet erosion or wind as in many of the previous profiles; the surface soil is too much granulated for such a process to be possible. Possibly its composition is the result of the presence of rock fragments on the surface. These fragments give fresh material upon physical weathering, which would be more important than chemical weathering as the boulders are exposed to the atmosphere

TABLE II.103. *Chemical composition of profile 27* (weight percentages; after Blokhuis, 1972)

Hor.	SiO_2	Al_2O_3	Fe_2O_3	FeO	CaO	MgO	MnO	Na_2O	K_2O	TiO_2	P_2O_5	H_2O+
A_{11}	40.8	15.9	8.4	0.5	9.2	5.1	0.2	3.0	1.6	1.2	0.2	5.9
A_{12}	54.5	14.0	8.6	0.5	9.1	4.3	0.2	1.6	0.6	1.2	0.2	6.3
A_{13}	44.5	14.5	8.9	0.3	8.4	4.3	0.2	1.5	0.6	1.1	0.2	7.2
C	49.5	15.4	9.4	0.5	5.7	4.5	0.2	1.3	0.5	1.1	0.1	7.1
R	45.7	14.5	6.5	0.4	8.9	11.7	0.1	3.3	0.5	0.9	0.1	3.0

which is usually quite dry, and to a considerable difference in day and night temperatures. However, dew may play a role in transforming the original material.

Interesting data are obtained when calculating the normative mineralogical composition of the profile. Rock composition is obtained by calculating the sericite-pyroxene-titanite variant of the katanorm. The composition of the solum was computed

TABLE II.103a. *Derived molar silica/sesquioxide ratios*

Hor.	SiO_2/R_2O_3	SiO_2/Al_2O_3	SiO_2/Fe_2O_3	Al_2O_3/Fe_2O_3
A_{11}	3.2	4.5	12	2.6
A_{12}	3.7	5.3	13	2.4
A_{13}	3.7	5.2	13	2.5
C	3.9	5.5	14	2.5
R	3.6	5.3	11	2.1

by applying the rules of the goethite norm (Van der Plas and Van Schuylenborgh, 1970) to the epinorm calculation (Burri, 1964). The result is shown in table II.104.

The high content of plagioclases (predominantly albite) in the surface horizon is striking. This is in accordance with the theory of the presence of rock fragments on the surface forming primary minerals on physical weathering. The montmorillonite content of the surface horizon is lower because of the low rate of chemical weathering; some chlorites have been formed, which was confirmed by X-raying. The illite content is higher, probably because of the addition of potassium from the weathering sericite of the rock fragments. It can be expected that also in the absence of rock fragments on the surface, the montmorillonite content would have been lower and the illite content higher than in the underlying horizons. Consequently, with regard to the geochemical aspect of weathering and soil formation, the following conclusions can be drawn:

TABLE II.104. *Normative mineralogical composition of profile 27* (equivalent percentages; after Blokhuis 1972)

Hor.	Q	Plg	Ser	Di	o-Pyr	Sm	Ill	Go	Ru	Cc	Misc
A_{11}	4.9	31.3	–	–	–	23.1	15.4	6.8	1.0	9.2	8.3[1]
A_{12}	2.8	15.0	–	–	–	56.1	6.3	7.3	1.0	9.6	1.9[2]
A_{13}	1.7	15.0	–	–	–	58.6	5.6	7.5	0.9	8.8	1.9[2]
C	4.0	11.5	–	–	–	65.3	4.6	7.7	0.9	5.5	0.5[3]
R	1.8	36.6	3.4	28.2	21.2	–	–	–	–	–	8.8[4]

Q = free silica; Plg = plagioclases; Ser = sericite; Di = diopside; o-Pyr = ortho-pyroxenes; Sm = smectites; Ill = illites; Go = goethite; Ru = rutile (anatase); Cc = calcite; Misc = miscellaneous. [1] 6.8 chlorite + 1.0 magnesite + 0.5 apatite; [2] magnesite + apatite in the ratio 3 : 1; [3] magnesite + apatite in the ratio 5 : 1; [4] 6.9 magnetite + 1.8 titanite + 0.1 apatite.

During weathering montmorillonites are formed from the feldspars and pyroxenes (similarly as in profile 26, p. 319), while illite is predominantly formed from sericite. Upon soil formation montmorillonite is transformed partly into illite.

The same conclusions can be drawn from the analyses of another profile of Blokhuis (1972), formed *in situ* from rock of the Basement Complex in Sudan (profile 28: fig. II.43). It is situated near the Khor Yabus, Blue Nile Province (Sudan), approximately 15 km east of Boing, on a very smooth, rounded hill, covered with scattered rock fragments and 'baked' soil fragments (result of burning). The surface is slightly

FIG. II 43. *The Boing-profile (profile 28)* *(photo W. A. Blokhuis)*

irregular to weak gilgai. A brittle, flaky crust, breaking to mulch covers the surface. The mulch sloughs into the cracks and obscures cracking pattern for 75 percent (sloughing is promoted by treading of cattle). Cracks are 5 cm wide. Few, very fine (2–3 mm), white $CaCO_3$ concretions and some small termite mounds occur on the surface. The climate is characterized by a mean annual temperature of approximately 28° C (similar to that of the previous example) and an average annual precipitation of approximately 900 mm, falling predominantly June to September. The average annual rainfall deficit is about 500 mm. The climate is distinctly more humid than in the area of the previous profile. Vegetation is characteristic for a shifting cultivation and grazing area. Burnt tall grasses occur with scattered *Balanites aegyptiaca*, *Combretum hartmannianum*, *Anogeissus schimperi*, and palms (*Hyphaene* and *Borassus*). The bedrock is a stromatitic epidote amphibolite with equal amounts of epidote and hornblende. The sum of both is somewhat higher than the amount of plagioclases (An 70%). Small amounts of quartz, apatite, and titanite are present. Locally, traces of carbonate occur, indicating that the sampled rock is not completely fresh. The profile description reads as follows:

Horizon	Depth (cm)	
A_{11}	0–40	Black brown (10YR3/1 :d and m) clay with columnar structure between the cracks of 2 cm width. Columns break into coarse subangular to blocky peds. Very hard. Common, fine (1–3 mm), brownish-white $CaCO_3$ nodules. Few pieces of pottery. Few sand grains. Many fibrous roots. Termite activity. Slight effervescence with HCl. Diffuse boundary to
A_{12}	40–70	Black brown (2.5YR3/1 :m) clay with moderate, medium, angular blocky structure. Tilted wedges, defined by distinct, small slickensides. $CaCO_3$ segregations as in A_{11}. Pieces of pottery and few, fine pieces of charcoal. Few sand grains. Many fibrous roots along slickensides. Termite activity. Moderate effervescence with HCl. Diffuse boundary to
A_{13}	70–100	Black brown (2.5YR3/1 :m) clay. Structure and slickensides as in A_{12}, but weaker developed. Few $CaCO_3$ nodules, generally smaller than 1 mm. Pieces of pottery and charcoal. High termite activity and some termite nests. Moderate effervescence with HCl. Diffuse to
C_1	100–125/140	Black brown (2.5YR3/2 :m) clay. Structure and slickensides as in A_{13}. $CaCO_3$ nodules as in previous horizons. Some soft Fe/Mn-nodules. Fine (1–4 mm) fragments of weathering rock. Termite nests. Clear and wavy boundary to
C_{ca}	125/140– 140/160	Weathered rock. Locally accumulations of $CaCO_3$ occur in irregular concretions of 1 to 2 cm diameter.
R	140/160+	Very slightly weathered rock (stromatitic epidote amphibolite).

Classification: Typic Pellustert.

Analytical details in table 11.105 reveal that some clay migration could have taken place. This is possible as the climate is not as dry as that of the previous profile. The pH is constant and $CaCO_3$ increases slightly with depth. Exchangeable Ca^{2+} is essentially constant and Mg^{2+} and Na^+ increase with depth as in the previous profile.

Exchangeable K^+, however, decreases with depth. C.e.c. increases with depth in accordance with the increase in clay; however, this could also be caused by a change in clay mineral composition (see later).

The geochemistry of weathering and soil formation can be studied from tables II. 106, 106a, and 107. The differences with the previous profile are from the bottom to the top: 1) increasing SiO_2 content; 2) decreasing Al_2O_3 content; 3) decreasing CaO content; and 4) constant Na_2O content after considerable initial removal.

TABLE II.105. *Physical and chemical characteristics of profile 28* (after Blokhuis, 1972)

Hor.	grain size distribution (%)			pH (0.01M CaCl2)	C %	CO2 %	cation exchange characteristics (m.e./100g of soil)				
	> 50μ	50–2μ	< 2μ				c.e.c.	Ca^{2+}	Mg^{2+}	K^+	Na^+
A_{11}	19.3	19.3	61.4	6.8	1.2	1.3	43.4	27.3	10.8	2.6	0.3
A_{12}	18.2	18.4	64.3	6.8	1.2	1.3	45.9	27.5	12.0	2.8	0.8
A_{13}	13.2	17.0	69.8	6.9	1.5	1.4	51.6	27.8	15.6	2.2	1.3
C_1	10.9	13.4	75.7	6.9	0.7	1.6	54.4	30.4	17.7	1.3	1.5
C_{ca}	43.2	12.7	44.1	7.0	0.3	1.6	32.5	25.0	13.1	0.6	1.2

Apparently, these are due to the less arid conditions under which the profile has been formed. It is interesting to notice the strong accumulation of iron whereas aluminium reduced considerably. This means that the mobility of aluminium, silicium, and iron decreases in the given order. Accumulation of iron as a result of lateral transportation

TABLE II.106. *Chemical composition of profile 28* (weight percentages; after Blokhuis, 1972)

Hor.	SiO_2	Al_2O_3	Fe_2O_3	FeO	CaO	MgO	MnO	Na_2O	K_2O	TiO_2	P_2O_5	H_2O+
A_{11}	54.5	12.9	11.1	0.3	2.3	2.0	0.2	1.1	1.4	1.4	0.4	6.2
A_{12}	54.0	13.2	10.4	0.3	3.1	2.0	0.2	0.9	1.0	1.3	0.3^5	6.6
A_{13}	53.2	13.4	10.9	0.3	2.9	2.1	0.2	0.8	0.8	1.3	0.2	6.5
C_1	53.5	14.2	11.3	0.5	2.5	2.3	0.2	0.8	0.4^5	1.4	0.3	7.3
C_{ca}	49.9	14.0	11.1	0.8	7.8	4.3	0.2	0.9	0.1	1.2	0.3	4.8
R	50.2	20.9	4.6	2.3	15.4	3.8	0.1	2.2	tr	0.4	0.4	1.0

of iron-rich groundwater is impossible because of the high position of the profile in the area. The order of mobility mentioned could be understood if aluminium hydroxide had been formed as an intermediate product of weathering (see fig. II.22). Upon further weathering and soil formation the SiO_2/Al_2O_3 ratio increases from the bottom to the top. This can occur because of: 1) downward translocation of a component with low SiO_2/Al_2O_3 ratio; 2) addition of free silica from outside sources; 3) upward transportation of soil solution rich in dissolved silica with the subsequent resilication of the surface layers. The latter process is thought to be of minor importance as shortly after the rainy season the surface layers dry out so that water can only move in the gas phase, thus stopping solution transport; also the high position of the profile in the area minimizes upward movement. A possible downward movement of clay (see table II.105) is assumably supported by the fact that the SiO_2/Al_2O_3 ratios of the clay fractions of the A_{11}, A_{12}, A_{13}, C, and C_{ca} are, respectively: 4.2, 4.2, 4.1, 3.9, and 4.1,

TABLE II.106a. *Derived molar silica/sesquioxide ratios*

Hor.	SiO_2/R_2O_3	SiO_2/Al_2O_3	SiO_2/Fe_2O_3	Al_2O_3/Fe_2O_3
A_{11}	4.6	7.1	13	1.8
A_{12}	4.6	6.9	13	1.9
A_{13}	4.4	6.8	13	1.9
C_1	4.2	6.4	12	1.9
C_{ca}	3.9	6.1	11	1.8
R	3.4	4.1	19	4.6

suggesting accumulation of a clay mineral with low SiO_2/Al_2O_3 ratio in the C horizon. However, this can also be explained by process 2.

As it is to be expected that more information can be gathered from a mineralogical analysis of the profile, the normative mineralogical composition was calculated in the same way as was done for profile 27. The results are shown in table II.107.

TABLE II.107. *Normative mineralogical composition of profile 28* (equivalent percentages; after Blokhuis, 1972)

Hor.	Q	Plg	Ho	Epi	Sm	Ill	Kand	Tit	Ru	Go	Cc	Misc
A_{11}	25.5	11.8	–	–	34.4	14.3	0.9	–	1.1	9.4	1.3	1.3[1]
A_{12}	22.9	10.0	–	–	41.8	10.1	2.9	–	1.1	8.9	1.8	0.7[2]
A_{13}	21.5	9.0	–	–	44.6	8.1	3.5	–	1.1	9.3	2.3	0.5[2]
C_1	18.6	8.8	–	–	47.9	4.2	7.5	–	1.1	9.5	1.6	0.7[2]
C_{ca}	18.6	9.3	–	19.3	29.0	0.9	–	–	1.0	6.5	2.4	13.0[3]
R	3.3	41.9	26.7	26.5	–	–	–	0.9	–	–	–	tr[4]

Q = free silica; Plg = plagioclases; Ho = hornblende; Epi = epidote; Sm = smectite; Ill = illite; Kand = kandite; Tit = titanite; Ru = rutile (anatase); Go = goethite; Cc = calcite; Misc = miscellaneous. [1] 0.5 magnesite + 0.8 apatite; [2] apatite; [3] 9.2 chlorite + 3.1 serpentine + 0.7 apatite; [4] trace K-feldspar.

The table shows that the normative composition of the rock agrees well with its mode (see p. 323). Weathering of the rock produces montmorillonite, serpentine, chlorite, free silica, and a small amount of illite. Upon further weathering serpentine and chlorite disappear in favour of the formation of montmorillonite. Soil formation is characterized, from the viewpoint of geochemistry, by transformation of montmorillonite into illite and kaolinite. Kaolinite decreases when going upward in the profile. The latter fact is also shown by some analyses of Ferguson (1954), Nelson et al. (1960) and Maignien (1961). The kaolinite content, which increases with depth, explains the above reported decrease of the silica/alumina ratio of the clay fraction. However, it cannot be decided whether this is caused by downward movement of kaolinite or re-silication of kaolinite to some other mineral. This problem will be discussed in more detail in section 3.4.1.

The increase in content of plagioclases from the B to A_{11} horizon could again be attributed to the presence of rock fragments on the surface (see also profile 27).

It can be concluded that profile 28 is in a more advanced stage of soil formation as profile 27. The reason for this is undoubtedly the higher humidity.

The last profile that will be discussed is an example of the subtropical black clays, investigated by Van der Merwe (1962). They occur in the Transvaal, South Africa, at elevations between 800 m and 1350 m on undulating plateaus dissected by well-defined watercourses. The soils are known as 'Black Turf' soils. The summers are very hot and the winters mild: average annual temperature is approximately 19° C. The rainfall, usually accompanied by thunder occurs in heavy downpours and falls mainly during the summer. The winters are generally dry. The mean annual precipitation varies from 560 mm to 800 mm. The dominant vegetation is grass (a.o. *Aristida bipartita, Setaria gerrardia, Bothriochloa glabra, Cymbopogon excavatus*). Small shrubs and deciduous trees and bush grow on the rock outcrops and shallow soils e.g. 'kareeboom' and *Acacia* trees. The parent rock consists of norite, a medium to coarse-grained dark, heavy rock with varying mineralogical composition, but containing plagioclases with rhombic and monoclinic pyroxenes. Where bands of magnetite occur in this geological formation a red soil is practically always formed.

The selected profile (profile 29) is situated approximately 1 km east of Losperfontain Post Office on the crest of a very gently undulating ridge. Elevation is 1150 m above sea level. Annual rainfall is 675 mm. The vegetation is grass. The land is virgin and the parent rock norite. The profile description reads as follows:

Horizon	Depth (cm)	
A_{11}	0–23	Blackish brown (5YR2/1:d) clay with strong medium to coarse blocky structure breaking into strong coarse granules. Hard, firm, very plastic and sticky. Abundant grass roots. Few $CaCO_3$ nodules. Gradual boundary to
A_{12}	23–66	Blackish brown (5UR2/1:d) clay. Macrostructure is slightly columnar with wide cracks penetrating the soil layer. Columns break into moderate medium to coarse blocky peds when moist, and strong coarse granules when dry. Very hard, very firm, very plastic and very sticky. Few $CaCO_3$ nodules and common grass roots, the latter decreasing and the former increasing with depth. Gradual boundary to
A_{13}	66–112	Blackish brown (5UR2/1:d) clay similar to A_{12} but with few grass roots.
B_{ca}	112–117	Light brownish grey (5YR8/1:d) clay with soft and nodular $CaCO_3$. Clear boundary to
C	117–137	Light brown gravelly sandy clay loam (partly decomposed norite). Tongues of blackish brown clay and veins of $CaCO_3$ nodules. Few patches of gypsum crystals scattered in the layer.

Cracks extend down through A_{13} horizon in the dry season. Classification: Typic Pelloxerert or Pellustert.

The very detailed analyses are represented in tables II.108, 109, 109a, and 110. The determination of CO_2 in the clay separates (lime was not removed before separation of the clay fraction) was omitted, so that it was not possible to calculate the normative mineralogical compositions.

TABLE II.108. *Physical and chemical composition of profile 29* (after Van der Merwe, 1962)

Hor.	texture (%)			pH (H₂O)	C %	CO₂ %	exch. cations (me./100g)			
	> 50μ	50–2μ	< 2μ				Ca²⁺	Mg²⁺	K⁺	Na⁺
A_{11}	21.9	17.6	60.1	8.1	1.6	2.6	58.8	7.6	1.0	0.9
A_{12}	19.2	15.9	64.9	8.1	1.2	3.2	57.1	7.6	0.4	0.9
A_{13}	17.4	16.4	66.3	8.3	1.1	3.9	58.3	9.2	0.5	1.6
B_{ca}	39.6	17.9	43.4	8.4	1.0	9.4	42.0	6.4	0.4	1.3
C	73.6	14.5	12.6	8.2	0.2	5.5	37.4	6.0	0.2	1.3

The soil differs from the other soils in that it has a definite calcic horizon. As in the other profiles exchangeable magnesium and sodium increase with depth in the upper part of the soil, exchangeable potassium decreases and calcium remains constant.

Tables II.109 and 109a reveal that the solum has been enriched in silica in contrast to the rock, which indicates that desilication has not occurred. Aluminium is more mobile than iron pointing to translocation of clay. Table II.110 shows that the clay fraction is slightly desilicated and deferritisized in the upper layers, the silica and iron

TABLE II.109. *Chemical composition of profile 29* (after Van der Merwe, 1962; weight percentages)

Hor.	SiO₂	Al₂O₃	Fe₂O₃	FeO	CaO	MgO	Mn₃O₄	Na₂O	K₂O	TiO₂	P₂O₅	H₂O+[1]
A_{11}	53.3	15.3	5.9	–	7.2	1.9	0.2	0.6	0.4	0.5	tr	9.8
A_{12}	53.9	15.4	5.1	–	7.5	2.6	0.3	0.6	0.4	0.4	tr	8.2
A_{13}	53.4	16.2	4.0	–	8.1	2.6	0.3	0.6	0.5	0.4	tr	7.4
B_{ca}	41.1	15.7	4.0	–	16.7	2.8	0.2	0.9	0.3	0.3	tr	7.7
C	45.1	18.9	5.2	–	13.8	2.9	0.1	2.4	0.5	tr	tr	6.3
R	52.2	18.9	–	7.1	13.4	4.2	0.2	2.4	0.3	0.3	tr	0.2

[1] Loss on ignition — (CO_2 + org. matter).

being segregated in the silt and sand fraction, as both enrich from the bottom to the top of the profile. It seems therefore that mineral transformation has taken place, which can actually be demonstrated by the result of the calculation of the normative mineralogical composition. Table II.111 is obtained by calculating the smectite

TABLE II.109a. *Derived molar silica/sesquioxide ratios of profile 29* (after Van der Merwe, 1962)

Hor.	SiO$_2$/R$_2$O$_3$	SiO$_2$/Al$_2$O$_3$	SiO$_2$/Fe$_2$O$_3$	Al$_2$O$_3$/Fe$_2$O$_3$
A$_{11}$	4.7	5.9	24	4.0
A$_{12}$	4.8	5.9	26	4.4
A$_{13}$	4.8	5.6	32	5.7
B$_{ca}$	3.8	4.4	27	6.3
C	3.4	4.1	23	5.6
R	3.6	4.7	15	3.1

TABLE II.110. *Molar silica/sesquioxide ratios of the clay fractions of profile 29* (after Van der Merwe, 1962)

Hor.	SiO$_2$/R$_2$O$_3$	SiO$_2$/Al$_2$O$_3$	SiO$_2$/Fe$_2$O$_3$	Al$_2$O$_3$/Fe$_2$O$_3$
A$_{11}$	3.3	3.7	26	6.7
A$_{12}$	3.5	4.1	26	6.2
A$_{13}$	3.5	4.2	19	4.7
B$_{ca}$	3.4	4.3	16	3.9
C	3.3	4.3	15	3.6

TABLE II.111. *Normative mineralogical composition of profile 29* (equivalent percentages)

Hor.	Q	Plg	Di	o-Pyr	Sm	Ill	Go	Cc	Mgs[1]	Misc
A$_{11}$	23.0	6.5	–	–	56.6	4.5	5.0	2.7	1.0	0.7[2]
A$_{12}$	23.0	6.3	–	–	56.8	4.3	4.3	2.7	2.0	0.6[2]
A$_{13}$	20.8	7.3	–	–	58.9	3.8	3.7	2.8	2.1	0.6[2]
B$_{ca}$	3.9	10.0	–	–	64.1	3.3	3.5	12.7	2.0	0.5[2]
C	–	26.9	–	–	51.2	2.4	4.1	6.5	1.3	7.6[3]
R	2.1	60.7	22.1	11.9	–	–	–	–	–	3.4[4]

Q = free silica; Plg = plagioclases; Di = diopside; o-Pyr = orthopyroxenes; Sm = smectite; Ill = illite; Go = goethite; Cc = calcite; Mgs = magnesite; Misc = miscellaneous. [1] The presence of magnesite is in accordance with data of Van der Merwe (1962), who found a varying amount of magnesium in the CaCO$_3$ nodules. [2] Rutile (anatase) + hausmannite; [3] Zoisite (7.4) + serpentine (0.1) + hausmannite (0.1); [4] sericite (2.4) + titanite (0.6) + hausmannite (0.2).

variant of the epinorm of the solum and by calculating the sericite variant of the katanorm of the rock. The table shows that this profile occupies an intermediate position between profiles 27 and 28 with respect to mineral transformation. Montmorillonite is partially transformed to illites, but kaolinite has not yet been formed.

This is in accordance with the climatic conditions as profile 29 stands between profiles 27 and 29 with respect to humidity.

In conclusion, it seems that during the formation of Vertisols some of the montmorillonitic clay minerals are transformed into illites and sometimes chlorites and kaolinite. This transformation depends primarily on humidity.

3.4. SOIL FORMING PROCESSES

3.4.1. MINERAL TRANSFORMATIONS

The examples discussed in the previous section demonstrate clearly that weathering proceeds in a way quite different from that of the soils, examined in Chapters 1 and 2 of this Part. The main difference lies in the fact that silica is conserved and not leached which is quite understandable when considering the climatic conditions. As mineral transformations depend strongly on the activity of dissolved silica (see Chapter 1 of Part III), and as transformations do occur, another factor has to be active. This is the ratio of cation activities in soil moisture. This can be seen from the reaction equation, demonstrating the transformation of montmorillonite into muscovite (illite):

$$3Ca_{.19}Mg_{.40}Al_{1.71}Si_{3.93}O_{10}(OH)_2 + 1.71K^+ + 11.16H_2O + 1.74H^+ \rightleftharpoons$$
$$1.71KAl_3Si_3O_{10}(OH)_2 + 0.57Ca^{2+} + 1.20Mg^{2+} + 6.66H_4SiO_4 \quad - - - - - - \quad (4)$$

or, simplified:

$$5.3Mm + 3K^+ + 19.6H_2O + 3H^+ \rightleftharpoons 3Ms + Ca^{2+} + 2Mg^{2+} + 11.7H_4SiO_4 \quad - \quad (4a)$$

The montmorillonite composition was taken from Reesman and Keller (1968), as these authors determined its standard free-energy of formation. The thermodynamic equilibrium constant is given by:

$$\lg K_{4a} = \lg \frac{[Mg^{2+}]^2}{[K^+]^3} + \lg \frac{[Ca^{2+}]}{[H^+]^3} + 11.7\lg [H_4SiO_4] \quad - - - - - - - - - - \quad (5)$$

where brackets denote the activities of the species mentioned in the equilibrium solution.

Using formulas (8) and (9) of Chapter I of Part III, lgK can be calculated, if standard free-energies of formation of the species involved are known. Taking the data of Reesman and Keller (1968) for Mm and H_4SiO_4, of Barany and Kelley (1962) for Ms, and of Rossini et al. (1952) for H_2O, K^+, Ca^{2+}, and Mg^{2+}, the value of lgK was computed to be -54.4.

As the soils generally contain $CaCO_3$ and as the pH in the solum varies only a little, $\frac{[Ca^{2+}]}{[H^+]^3}$ can be considered as constant. According to equation (72a) in Chapter 4 of Part III (p. 463) $[Ca^{2+}]$ depends strongly on the partial CO_2 pressure, ςCO_2. In the dry season ςCO_2 will be close to that of the atmosphere (presence of deep and wide cracks, near-absence of biological activity), and in the rainy season it will be considerably higher (e.g. 2×10^{-2} atm., equivalent to 2% by volume). As an average ςCO_2 will be assumed to fluctuate around a value of 10^{-2} atm. As the examples of the Sudan soils (profiles 27 and 28) have a pH value of approximately 7, $\lg [Ca^{2+}]$ will fluctuate around a value of -2.2. Equation (5) then reduces to:

$$\lg \frac{[Mg^{2+}]^2}{[K^+]^3} + 11.7\lg [H_4SiO_4] = -73.2 \quad\text{-----------------}\quad (5a)$$

The stability fields of Mm and Ms can now be constructed in a two-dimensional figure with $\lg \dfrac{[Mg^{2+}]^2}{[K^+]^3}$ as one axis and $\lg [H_4SiO_4]$ as the other. Fig. II.44 is then obtained.

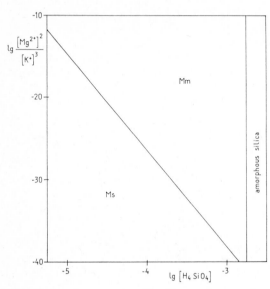

FIG. II.44. *Stability fields of montmorillonite and muscovite at 25°C, I atm. total pressure, $[Ca^{2+}] = 10^{-2.2}, \varsigma CO_2 = 10^{-2}$ atm., and pH = 7*

This shows that montmorillonite can be transformed into muscovite (illite) by decreasing the ratio of $[Mg^{2+}]$ and $[K^+]$ and decreasing $[H_4SiO_4]$ in the soil solution. As the latter does not happen under the climatic conditions of the tropical Vertisols, only the ratio $\dfrac{[Mg^{2+}]^2}{[K^+]^3}$ is the determining factor for the transformation. The Vertisols,

discussed in this Chapter and those collected by Dudal (1965) show the ratio of adsorbed Mg^{2+} to adsorbed K^+ increasing with depth. This means that the ratio of the activities of Mg^{2+} and K^+ in soil moisture also increases. Consequently, montmorillonite becomes increasingly unstable passing from the bottom to the top of the profile, which results in its transformation into illite.

The reason why the ratio Mg (adsorbed)/K (adsorbed) increases downwards is not quite clear. Presumably, this is the result of vegetation activity. This vegetation consists predominantly of grasses. Monocotyledons absorb K^+ in preference to Ca^{2+} and Mg^{2+} from the soil solution. Upon decomposition of the plant debris the surface soil layers are supplied with a greater amount of potassium than of magnesium. Hence, the ratio $[Mg^{2+}] / [K^+]$ decreases in the surface soil layers. If this mechanism does actually occur, the transformation of montmorillonite into illites in these soils would be an excellent example of the effect of vegetation on soil forming processes.

Another reason could be that foreign minerals such as quartz and mica are blown in, as was supposed to have happened in the Arizona Vertisols (profile 26: Johnson et al.,

1962). But then it has to be assumed that a similar process has occurred in the discussed examples of the Sudan and South Africa. Of course, this could be true, but the former theory is thought to be more logical. Moreover, it is known that the grasses of the savannah vegetation also accumulate silica in their tissues (see Chapter 1 of this Part: p. 223), which is returned to the soil upon decomposition of the plant debris. The frequently higher free silica content of the surface layers could be explained in this way.

On page 325 it was reported that the kaolinite content of profile 28 decreased from the C_1 to the A_{11} horizon. This could be explained by downward movement of kaolinite. However, as the ratio $[K^+]/[H^+]$ of the soil-solution increases in the surface layers kaolinite can also be transformed into illite (see Part III, Chapter 1), as the activity of dissolved silica would be high enough for this process because of the presence of amorphous silica supplied by the vegetation.

Fur further details on weathering the reader is referred to Part III, Chapter 1.

3.4.2. SHRINKING AND SWELLING

Although geochemical changes do occur during the formation of Vertisols, the most important changes are caused by shrinking and swelling of the clays. One of the most spectacular results is the formation of the 'gilgai' land surface.

Different types of gilgai are recognized (Hallsworth et al., 1955; Hallsworth and Beckmann, 1969):

a. *Normal or round gilgai.* The complex is composed of near-circular mounds (frequently called puffs) with crumbly structure and depressions (shelves) in varying proportions. The degree of development varies greatly. Cases occur with no perceptible undulation; in these cases the formation is seen by the change in colour of the surface soil and the presence of lime concretions on the mounds. However, the vertical interval may also be 2.75 m with a wave-length up to 12 m. Normal gilgai occur predominantly on flat land or land with less than 1 % slope.

b. *Melon-mole gilgai.* Large mounds and wide shelves alternate. In the center of the latter are holes of varying shapes. The holes vary in width from 0.90 to 2.70 m and in depth from 1.80 to 2.70 m. The mounds are 0.90 to 1.80 m high and 3.50 to 5.50 m wide. In contrast to normal gilgai the mounds are compact and massive and large, abrupt sink-holes occur. This type of gilgai occurs in Australia under tropical and subtropical conditions with higher rainfalls. The areas are often described locally as swamps.

c. *Wavy or linear gilgai.* The puffs and shelves are continuous and occur in rows more or less at right angles to the contour. They form parallel waves which may extend for considerable distances. The vertical interval is between 0.60 and 2.40 m. Wavy gilgai occur on sloping areas with slopes varying between 15′ and 3°.

d. *Lattice gilgai.* This type is intermediate between a and c. The mounds may be discontinuous, up to 4.50 to 6.00 m long and 1.80 m wide, arranged in rows parallel to the direction of the greatest slope. The mounds may also form semi-continuous lines of irregular direction forming an almost continuous network (network gilgai). Lattice gilgai occur in slightly sloping areas.

e. *Tank gilgai.* The mounds and depressions form a large, roughly rectangular pattern. The vertical interval is 0.60 to 1.20 m, the mounds up to 9 m wide, and the depressions 12 to 18 m long and 6 to 12 m wide.

f. *Stony gilgai*. The complex may have the form of a, c, and d. The whole mound, however, is covered by stones of varying size. The shelves may also be covered by stones; if no stones are present at the surface, they occur in the profile. This type of gilgai is restricted to arid parts of Vertisol areas.

As the mentioned classification suggests that the perturbations of the land surface in a Vertisol area has something to do with mass flow, it is thought that the hypothesis of Edelman and Brinkman (1962) is worth while mentioning here. They assume that originally gilgai areas have been a lake, sea or swamp bottom. The proposed mechanism of gilgai formation can then be explained in the following way: Sedimentary deposits rich in clay and formed under water have a very high water content. As long as the deposit remains under water its upper meters of sediment are loose and soft. It is best termed mud and is generally rich in organic matter (see fig. II.45).

Natural processes and/or human activity cause the water level of the muddy clay deposits to fall below the surface. The moisture tension in the deposit then increases from nearly zero to pF 1.5 to 2.

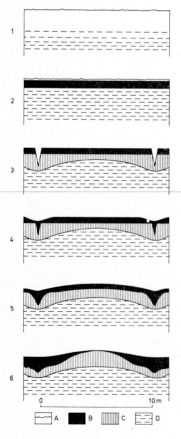

FIG. II.45. *Formation of gilgai relief. (A) water surface; (B) dark humous clay; (C) more or less consolidated (firm) clay; (D) non-consolidated (soft) sediment. (1) Soft mud is deposited in lake; (2) When the lake is filled with mud or the water level has gone down a dark-coloured topsoil is formed by a swamp vegetation; (3) The first (irreversible) desiccation through evapotranspiration with a still lower water table causes some very large cracks; near the cracks the soil dries out to a greater depth; (4) Topsoil fills in the cracks in a dry season; (5) After some cycles of drying and rewetting with movement of topsoil into the temporary cracks, the soil is compressed by swelling when rewetted and bulges upward in the weakest places where the depth of consolidation is least, that is between the cracks; (6) Topsoil is eroded from the micro-elevations and accumulated in the depressions with continued cyclic wetting and drying (after Edelman and Brinkman, 1962)*

In this situation desiccation of the mud does not yet take place. By evapotranspiration the moisture tension increases to pF 3 to 5 and the unstable spacious clay deposit collapses and consolidates. As long as the clay is plastic the loss of volume is one-dimensional; only the thickness of the deposit decreases. After consolidation continued loss of water results in a combination of settling and cracking, a three-dimensional process.

When the mud dries, and because Ca saturation is generally high, the soil between the cracks crumbles. Gradually the cracks formed during the early stage of the process partly fill up with small soil fragments. The soil fragments expand during wet seasons by adsorption of water but not to the original volume. Only physical influences such as soil erosion followed by deposition, can cause the clay to return to the state of a structureless mud.

Thus, it is assumed that where gilgai is found outside former lakes, seas or swamps, its presence is caused by colluvial transport during which the clay is transformed into a mud. The process as described above and in fig. 11.45 can then be repeated in the colluvial deposit.

The essential presence of muddy conditions is supported by the observation of Costin (1955) on the similarity between gilgai and certain periglacial phenomena. As most periglacial processes are closely connected with periodically muddy conditions, this might explain the similarity in features (see also Holmes, 1964, p. 406).

Although the process developed by Edelman and Brinkman (1962) may be helpful in explaining gilgai formation of lake, sea, and swamp deposits and some types of gilgai, it cannot explain the formation of stony gilgai in the Vertisol developed *in situ* from basic rock, as in the Boing-profile (profile 28). Here, it was shown that chemical weathering produced a montmorillonitic clay. Assuming that the clays are washed down into the cracks formed by physical weathering of the rock, repeated cycles of drying and wetting may contribute to the upheaval of stone fragments. Springer (1958) attributed this upward translocation of stones to repeated swelling and shrinkage of clay. The clay content of the washed-in material should then be at least 40%, as was shown by Jackson (1958).

It can be expected that surface perturbations will be more intense where soil moisture differences between wet and dry seasons are most marked and where the initial water content is high (Yong and Warkinton, 1966). It is also to be expected that exchangeable cations will affect the cracking pattern. It seems that desiccation of Ca-dominated montmorillonitic clay with free lime, results in the formation of few, wide and deep cracks (Smith, 1959; Sleeman, 1963). Hallsworth et al. (1955) showed that gilgaied soils had a higher Na saturation than the non-gilgaied soils of the same origin.

Vegetation also seems to affect cracking and gilgai formation. Tree roots seem to be able to hold the soil material together and consequently cracks are formed between the trees. Actually, trees are frequently found on the puffs (Hallsworth et al., 1955); but on stony gilgai the puffs are bare and the vegetation is confined to the shelves; this is probably the result of the higher moisture content in the shelves.

Another typical feature of Vertisols is the structure. In most cases there is a thin (1 to 10 cm thick) surface horizon consisting of very fine to medium granular aggregates. It develops from a brittle surface crust which forms at the surface immediately after the rainy season. Upon further drying this crust breaks apart into fine fragments.

Other Vertisols develop a surface crust which is hard and persists during the dry season. Such a crust may develop when the sand fraction is considerably higher than normal for Vertisols (Blokhuis, 1972). The sand grains form a skeleton, thus resisting shrinkage and modifying swelling. As a result aggregates are not formed or are weakly developed. Other factors may also cause the development of a hard crust, such as salinity or alkalinity.

Beneath the surface mulch Vertisols have a compound structure: large prismatic blocks between cracks, subdivided into subangular (near the surface) or angular blocky elements; these elements again are composed of smaller aggregates of the same type. The blocky peds and specially the smaller ones are often flattened and wedge-shaped. In a profile pit they protrude obliquely from the wall, more or less parallel to each other and superimposed like the tiles of a roof. The individual peds have triangular or trapezoidal faces tapering to points at each end in the form of a 'double wedge' (De Vos t.N.C. and Virgo, 1969). Several names were given to these units, such as lentils (Krishna and Perumal, 1948), wedge or parallelipiped peds (U.S. Soil Survey Staff, 1960) or 'cuneate' structural elements (Brewer, 1964). De Vos t.N.C. and Virgo (1969) proposed the use of the term 'bicuneate' in order to define the double wedge shape. The ped surfaces of all wedge-shaped peds appear to be polished and grooved; these are small slickensides.

With increasing depth and below the zone of wide cracking, the wedge-like structure becomes the dominant form; it consists of larger tilted wedges which are subdivided into smaller ones. When weakly developed the smallest wedges are difficult to separate, but they remain visually evident in a profile wall.

Still deeper in the profile the size of the wedge-shaped elements increases and the structure is no longer compound or the substructure is weakly developed. The large ped-faces appear as polished and grooved surfaces, i.e. as slickensides. These are inclined to the horizontal at angles varying from $20°$ to $60°$.

At a depth which is no longer subjected to variations in moisture content and where consequently churning of the soil mass no longer exists, the soil is massive or weakly blocky. This depth divides the solum from the substratum (Blokhuis, Slager, and Pape, 1968/1969; De Vos t.N.C. and Virgo, 1969). In some cases however – and notably described for a number of Vertisol profiles in the Sudan (De Vos t.N.C. and Virgo, 1969) – the substratum contains large slickensides, up to 50 or 60 cm in length. They have been regarded as relic colluvial features of the parent material. In other Vertisols (Blokhuis, 1972) developed in unconsolidated sediments, the substratum showed many of the structural characteristics of the solum. This is a relic feature too, probably inherited from a period in which the substratum had the position of a solum.

The genesis of this bicuneate structure is not clear. The most recent and detailed analysis of the process is given by De Vos t.N.C. and Virgo (1969). These authors write that after desiccation, 'it is probable that the rewetting cycle of Sudan clays is dependent upon the penetration of water into the cracks, with the second horizon becoming remoistened early in the cycle. For the cracks to have developed initially, the soil moisture content must have fallen to well within the range over which three-dimensional volume changes occur. Consequently, during the initial rewetting considerable horizontal and vertical pressure will develop. The vertical component is partially relieved by the upward movement of the overlying horizon, but downward expansion is limited by the soil mass. The horizontal component will be absorbed by the width of the vertical cracks. However, under normal conditions the cracks become loosely infilled with mulch material. This will restrict the horizontal expansion, causing considerable pressures within the second horizon. Depending upon the mass and the ease with which the upper horizon may be raised, a restriction to the upward vertical movement will develop. The probable forces resulting from these pressures are illustrated in fig. II.46. The resultant forces within this second horizon will be resolved at an oblique angle (r) dependent upon the relative values of the component

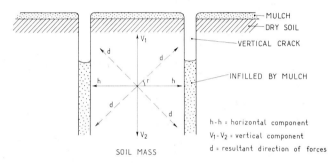

FIG. II.46. *Idealized stress diagram. Soil at three-dimensional expansion stage (after De Vos t.N.C. and Virgo, 1969)*

horizontal (h) and vertical (v_1, v_2) forces. As the moisture content rises beyond the limits of three-dimensional expansion, so the vertical component will predominate. However, at this stage the increasing plasticity of the surface horizon is likely to reduce the restriction to vertical expansion. We presume that it is during the phase of three-dimensional volume changes that the bicuneate structure is formed, with slickensided ped faces developing along the lines of stress within the soil. Unless the soil becomes completely saturated, it is probable that this structure remains, only slightly modified, during succeeding wetting and drying cycles. Expansion and contraction forces would be relieved by the displacement of peds relative to one another along the slickenside faces'.

Micromorphologically slickensided ped surfaces are characterized by an orientation of the clay domains parallel to the ped surface; the percentage of plasma which is orientated decreases gradually from the surface towards the interior of the ped. This vosepic plasmic fabric (Brewer, 1964) differs clearly from a clay skin (argillan) which occurs on the ped surface. The latter has sharp inner and outer boundaries, has distinct extinction patterns and is often finely layered. The shiny surfaces of Vertisol peds – which can hardly be distinguished from a clay coating with the naked eye – are often referred to as stress cutans or pressure faces.

The structural sequence from surface to substratum, and the depth to which cracks penetrate depend largely on the climate. With increasing rainfall cracks are generally deeper and the development of the Vertisol profile – at least the structural profile – is stronger and the solum deeper.

It is realized that the above discussion on gilgai and structure formation is unsatisfactory. Exact data and experiments on the mechanism of the processes are scarce. As the process is the result of ununiform wetting of material with subsequent development of shears and stresses in the soil the problem is one for specialists in soil mechanics.

3.5. AFFINITIES AND ASSOCIATIONS

It was mentioned in the introduction to this chapter that Vertisols often occur associated with other soils. Prescott (1941) indicated that there might be some similarity between tropical black earths and chernozems. He stated that Australian black earths such as those encountered in New South Wales and Queensland are developed for the most part on rocks of basaltic origin, although they have also been observed on granodiorite near Charter Towers (20° S). Prescott also suggested that soils with similarities with the black earths of Russia and North America and the regur of India may be found in the eastern part of Australia between Burdekin River (Queensland) in the north and Liverpool Plains (New South Wales) in the south. In the same treatise reference is made to black soils derived from marls, which remain well supplied with lime even under reasonably wet conditions. These were classified as rendzinas, a type of soil developed on limestone in many parts of Australia. In an earlier account Prescott (1931) had already stated that a definite distinction must be drawn between these rendzinas and black earths, but it is interesting to read in the new Handbook of Australian Soils (Stace et al., 1968) that black earths, rendzinas, and chernozems are all very similar to each other. It was stated that rendzinas have a general morphological similarity to shallow black earths; some fine-textured variants are virtually indistinguishable from them, except on the basis of their specific parent material, and should be classified as black earths. The same assumedly holds also for the chernozems, the latter however having a much lower clay content, finer and more porous structural units, and characteristically soft consistence when dry and very friable when moist. As only the black earths are characterized by the typical features of cracks and slickensides, the present authors are inclined to doubt the correctness of these observations. This holds the more as the clay mineralogy shows some marked differences with regard to the percentage of crystallized compounds of the fraction $< 2\mu$, as the following data indicates:

clay minerals	Black earth	Rendzina	Chernozem
Montmorillonite	50–65	–	–
Randomly interstratified material	–	–	50–65
As above with montmorillonite	–	40–50	–
Illite	–	30–40	20–30
Kaolinite	20–30	5–10	30–40
Quartz	20–30	–	–

Prescott (1941) stated that dark clay soils of Australia are restricted to a broad zone with relatively uniform distribution of effective rainfall throughout the year, as was shown on the new soil map of Australia (1968). Dudal's map (1965) of climatic phases of Australian Vertisols however shows that they are found under desertic, semi-arid, monsoon tropical, semi-arid temperate, and dry Mediterranean climates. Only the last two types are characterized by a uniform rainfall of 25 and 50 mm per month respectively but with a strong negative water balance that is specifically conspicuous from September through April. This is in common with the phases mentioned, with the exception of the monsoon tropical phase which shows a strong excess of rainfall over potential evaporation from December to March inclusive. Dudal draws special attention to the fact that his map shows the predominant distribution of the 'black earths' and the 'grey and brown soils of heavy texture', but that only a portion of the latter soils fit the definition of the 'dark clay soils'. The recent conception and understanding of these soils now being classified as 'grey, brown, and red clays' without the addition 'of heavy texture', is in accordance with Dudal's definition. Cracking, slickensides, and gilgai microrelief are dominant phenomena (Stace et al. 1968). However the clay mineralogy of most of the examples in the Handbook of Australian Soils poses a problem. Contrary to the Vertisols of Arizona, Sudan, South Africa (pages 318-329) and Uganda (Martin, 1938), which show a predominance of montmorillonite in the clay fraction with illite as a compound of the second order of magnitude, the Australian counterparts have kaolinite as a clay component which in all but one case is greater than montmorillonite or they have randomly interstratified minerals. In a few instances illite has the highest percentage but then this can be related to the recent alluvial origin of the parent material. An example of this is the Yooroobla clay from New South Wales. It is developed from quaternary alluvium, occurs in a level plain with gilgai relief, has slickensides (although at a depth of 150 cm) and a clay mineral association of 50–65% illite, 10–20% interstratified minerals, and 30–40% kaolinite. The profile was sampled on the top of a mound in the gilgai landscape and was found to be 'self-mulching'; it is therefore a Vertisol. d'Hoore (1964) remarks that recently a number of African soils have been studied that have all the morphological characteristics of Vertisols, but have a clay fraction with few minerals of the swelling type, and predominantly composed of amorphous gels. Wayland and Brasnett (1938) observed that kaolin is the basis of the clay of 'cotton soils' of Karamajo (Uganda). They pointed out that the soils crack excessively when subjected to long drought, forming fissures of considerable length and up to 10 metres deep.

Apparently the type of clay mineral is unimportant in determining whether or not a soil is a Vertisol. The degree of crystallinity seems to be more important. Nevertheless there must be differences between Vertisols with different types of clay minerals and the present authors wonder whether, at some further stage in our knowledge of Vertisols, more importance should be attached to their clay mineralogy.

An interesting association is described by Milne (1936). Drawing a distinction between calcareous and non-calcareous subgroups, which further are sub-divided into low-ground and high-ground varieties, he adds that there is no sharp division between the calcareous and non-calcareous black clays, the latter passing imperceptibly through greyish-black and grey types to soils having podzolic characteristics. This observation induces the question of whether black soils can be converted into other, possibly red ones, or whether these two types of profile, which are so unlike in colour, may show some sort of interrelationship. As regards the first possibility Sen (1939), who made a comparative study of the black and red soils of India, made the assumption that in specific cases the black soil was originally red. This had been transported from elevated regions and was subsequently converted to black after its deposition at the bottom of the valley, the iron in the soil playing the principal part in this colour change. A similar suggestion has been made by Viswanath (quoted by Raychaudhuri, 1941), who stated among other things that granite and gneiss give rise to black soils in some places and to red in others. The red ones usually occur close to the hills and cover a thin layer of decomposed granite and highly kaolinized feldspar. As one goes further away from the hills black soil of increasing depth occurs overlying a thicker layer of decomposed and kaolinized material. Ramiah and Raghvendrachar (quoted by Raychaudhuri et al., 1943) on the other hand, do not believe that where black and red soils occur side by side, the former is developed from the latter. In their opinion the black soils were probably formed from rocks containing lime and sodalime feldspars, while the red soils are the weathering products from rocks containing potash feldspar. The following comparative data (table II.112) was supplied by Raychaudhuri et al. (1943).

If the SiO_2/Al_2O_3 ratios and the exchange capacities are taken as guiding characteristics, it may be concluded that these two soils belong to different genetic classes. More difficult to explain however are the results of the investigations by Agarwal and Mukerji (1946) who, reporting on the genetic soil types of Bundelkhand, India, published the foregoing data (table II.113).

One may be inclined to assume in this case a conversion from red to black. That the

TABLE II.112. *Comparative data of a black and a red soil of Coimbatore, Southern India* (after Raychaudhuri et al., 1943)

	Black cotton soil		Red soil		
	1	2	1	2	3
Depth in cm	0–60	60–120	0–50	50–80	80–120
SiO_2/Al_2O_3 ratio	4.5	4.9	2.7	3.0	3.0
Free Fe_2O_3 in %	6.1	5.5	2.2	4.5	4.6
Carbon in %	0.8	0.5	0.4	0.5	0.3
C/N ratio	14.7	11.8	10.3	10.1	7.0
C.e.c. in m.e./100 g of clay	80.8	76.0	33.8	34.4	36.0
Hornblende in g/1000 g of soil	41.7	23.7	32.3	24.0	51.8
Garnet in g/1000 g of soil	53.1	36.2	12.4	6.8	8.1

TABLE II.113. *Some analytical data of the clay of a black and a red soil of Bundelkhand, India* (after Agarwal and Mukerji, 1946)

	Black soil		Red soil	
	Top	Bottom	Top	Bottom
SiO_2/Al_2O_3 ratio	3.1	2.7	3.2	3.9
MgO in %	2.5	3.1	4.2	6.4
K_2O in %	1.5	1.0	1.8	1.8
H_2O+ in %	16.7	2.3	15.5	17.1
C.e.c. in m.e./100 g	79.0	68.0	69.5	81.5

reverse could, in principle, be the case may be deduced from a comparative study by Raychaudhuri (1941) of black and red soils of Nyassaland. This author reports that the black soils have a c.e.c. value of 21.1 and 14.0 m.e. per 100 grams of soil and the red ones of 14.1 and 17.0 at a depth of, respectively, 70–90 and 150–180 cm, while the clay content of all the samples is about 50%.

An indication that Vertisols may acquire diverging qualities through admixture with quartz-sandy airborne material can be found in the study of Harmse (1967) of the soils of the Highveld Region of South Africa.

All this leads to the conclusion that some soil genetic problems still merit further detailed study.

LITERATURE CITED

AGARWAL, R.R. and MUKERJI, P. 1946 Studies on Bundelkhand soils of the United Provinces. II. Chemical composition of the clay fractions in relation to the process of soil formation. *Ind. J. agric. Sci.*, 16: 483–491.

— 1949 Studies on Bundelkhand soils of the United Provinces. III. Pedochemical characteristics of the black soils of the plains. *Ind. J. agric. Sci.*, 19: 31–40.

BAL, D.V. 1935 Some aspects of black cotton soils of the Central Provinces, India. *Emp. J. Expt. Agric.*, 3: 261–268.

BARANI, R. and KELLY, K. K. 1961 Heats and free-energies of formation of gibbsite, kaolinite, halloysite, and dickite. *U. S. Bur. Mines, R. I.* 5825.

BASU, J. K. and SIRUR, S.S. 1938 Soils of the Deccan Canals. I. Genetic soil survey and soil classification: Nira Right Bank and Pravara Canals. *Ind. J. agric. Sci.*, 8: 637–697.

BLOKHUIS, W.A. 1972 Vertisols of the Central Sudan clay plain. Ph. D. thesis Wageningen.

—, PAPE, TH. and SLAGER, S. 1969 Morphology and distribution of pedogenic carbonate in some Vertisols of the Sudan. *Geoderma*, 2: 173–200.

BREWER, R. 1964 Fabric and mineral analysis of soils. *New York and London.*

BURRY, C. 1964 Petrochemical calculations based on equivalents. *Translated from German. Jerusalem.*

COSTIN, A.B. 1955 A note on gilgaies and frost soils. *J. Soil Sci.*, 6: 32–34.

DE VOS t.N.C., J.H. and VIRGO, K.J. 1969 Soil structure in Vertisols of the Blue Nile clay plains, Sudan. *J. Soil Sci.*, 20: 189–206.

D'HOORE, J. L. 1964 Soil Map of Africa. *Expl. Monograph. Comm. Techn. Coop. Afr. Publ.* 93.

DUDAL, R. 1965 Dark clay soils of tropical and subtropical regions. *FAO Development Papers*, No 83: pp. 161.

DUDAS, M.J. and PAWLUK, S. 1969 Naturally occurring organo-clay complexes of orthic black chernozems. *Geoderma*, 3: 5–17.

EDELMAN, C.H. and BRINKMAN, R. 1962 Physiography of gilgai soils. *Soil Sci.*, 94: 366–370.

FERGUSON, J.A. 1954 Transformations of clay minerals in Black Earths and Red Loams of basaltic orgin. *Austr. J. agric. Res.*, 5: 98–108.

HALLSWORTH, E.G. and BECKMANN, G. G. 1969 Gilgai in the Quaternary. *Soil Sci.*, 107: 409–420.

—, ROBERTSON, G.W. and GIBBONS, F.R. 1955 Studies in pedogenesis in New South Wales. VII. The 'gilgai' soils. *J. Soil Sci.*, 6: 1–31.

HARDON, H.J. 1939 Onderzoek naar de samenstelling van de kleifractie van de voornaamste grondtypen van Nederlandsch-Indië. *Landbouw (Bogor)*, 15: 513–537.

HARMSE, H.J. VON M. 1967 Soil genesis in the Highveld Region, Sough Africa. *Ph. D. Thesis*

340

University Utrecht: pp. 201.

HOLMES, A. 1964 Principles of physical geology. *London and Edinburgh.*

JACKSON, E.A. 1958 A study of the soils and some aspects of the hydrology of Yudnapinna Station, South Australia. *C.S.I. R.O. Soils and Land Use*, Ser., No. 24.

JOHNSON, W.M., CADY, J.G. and JAMES, M.S. 1962 Characteristics of some Brown Grumusols of Arizona. *Soil Sci. Soc. Am. Proc.*, 26: 389–393.

KRISHNA, P.G. and PERUMAL, S. 1948 Structure in Black Cotton Soils of Nisamsagar project area, Hyderabad, India. *Soil Sci.*, 66: 29–38.

MAIGNIEN, R. 1961 Sur les sols d'argiles noires tropicales d'Afrique occidentale. *Bull. A.F.E.S., Paris*: 131–144.

MARTIN, W.S. 1938 Soil and soil erosion in Karamoja. *Geol. Surv. Uganda, Mem.*, IV : 82–85.

MILNE, G. et al. 1936 A provisional soil map of East Africa (Kenya, Uganda, Tanganyika, and Zanzibar) with explanatory memoir. *Amani Memoirs*, pp. 34.

NELSON, L.A., KUNZE, G.W. and GODFREY, C.L. 1960 Chemical and mineralogical properties of San Saba clay, a Grumusol. *Soil Sci.*, 89 : 122–131.

PRESCOTT, J.A. 1931 The soils of Australia in relation to vegetation and climate. *Bull. Sci. Res. Austr.*, No. 52: pp. 82.

— 1941 The soils of Tropical Australia. *Austr. Geol.*, 4: 16–19.

RAYCHAUDHURI, S.P. 1941 Studies on the physico-chemical properties of associated black and red soils of Nyasaland Protectorate, British Central Africa. *Ind. J. agric. Sci.*, 11: 100–109.

—, SULEIMAN, M. and BHUIYAN, A.B. 1943 Physicochemical and mineralogical studies of black and red soil profiles near Coimbatore. *Ind. J. agric. Sci.*, 13: 264–272.

REESMAN, A.L. and KELLER, W.D. 1968 Aqueous solubility studies of high-alumina and clay minerals. *Am. Min.*, 53 : 929–942.

ROSSINI, F.D. et al. 1952 Selected values of chemical thermodynamica properties. *Nat. Bur. Standards*, Circ. 500.

SEN, A. 1939 Definition of laterite soil. *Bull. Indian Soc. Soil Sci.*, 2 : 9–13.

SINGH, D. and LAL, G. 1946 Kankar composition as an index of the nature of soil profile. *Indian J. agric. Sci.*, 16 : 328–342.

SLEEMAN, J.R. 1963 Cracks, peds, and their surfaces in some soils of the riverine plain, N.S.W. *Austr. J. Soil Res.*, 1 : 91–102.

SMITH, R.M. 1959 Some structural relationships of Texas Blackland soils, with special attention to shrinkage and swelling. *U.S.D.A.*, ARS 41-28.

SOIL SURVEY STAFF, U.S.A. 1960 Soil Classification. A comprehensive system.

SPRINGER, M.E. 1958 Desert pavement and vesicular layer of some soils of the Lahontan Basin, Nevada. *Soil Sci. Soc. Am. Proc.*, 22: 63–66.

STACE, H.C.T. et al. 1968 Handbook of Australian Soils. *Adelaide:* pp. 435.

VAN DER MERWE, C.R. 1962 Soil groups and sub-groups of South Africa. *Dep. Agric. Techn Serv., Chemistry series No. 165, Sci. Bull.*, No. 356: pp. 355.

VAN DER PLAS, L. and VAN SCHUYLENBORGH, J. 1970 Petrochemical calculations applied to soils. *Geoderma*, 4 : 357–385.

WAYLAND, E.J. and BRASNETT, N.V. 1938 Soil erosion and water supplies in Uganda. *Geol. Surv. Uganda, Mem.*, 4, pp. 89.

YONG, R.N. and WARKINTON, B.P. 1966 Introduction to soil behaviour. *New York and London.*

CHAPTER 4

PADDY SOILS
AND
ACID SULPHATE SOILS

4.1. PADDY SOILS

The total world rice production area amounts to some 125 millions of hectares (FAO, 1965). Nearly all rice is cultivated on soils that are flooded during the greater part of the growing season. Inundation and various management practices associated with the wet cultivation of rice may lead to the development of several soil characteristics, ranging from the accentuation of development of hydromorphic features to the formation of a compact 'plough pan' and iron-manganese accumulation horizons. The soils are a typical example of man-made soils.

In the literature the term 'paddy soils' has often been used to indicate all soils utilized for wet rice cultivation. However, some authors restrict this term to soils with an iron-magnanese accumulation horizon (Tan, 1968). Others characterize paddy soils as soils that have undergone some changes due to irrigation practices (Dudal, 1958). Others define paddy soils as 'artificial hydromorphic soils' (Kanno, 1962) or 'hydromorphic associates of uncultivated soils' (Sivarajasingham, 1963), and thus disregard the fact that rice is often, if not mostly grown on soils that already possess hydromorphic characteristics as a result of their climatic and physiographic position.

This chapter deals with paddy soils in a broad sense, including e.g. seasonally flooded river basin soils that are planted to rice as well as soils of irrigated rice terraces in hilly areas.

4.1.1. GEOGRAPHICAL AND TOPOGRAPHICAL DISTRIBUTION OF PADDY SOILS

Although rice is cultivated as far north as 49° in Tchechoslovakia and as far south as 35° in Australia, it is primarily a tropical and subtropical crop (Moomaw and Vergara, 1964). Table II.114 gives an indication of the distribution of rice producing areas over the world, and it shows that the most important rice growing countries are found in tropical Asia.

The distribution of rice growing areas within the countries, mentioned in table II. 114, largely depends on climatic and topographical factors.

The estimated minimum of water used for one rice crop is approximately 1000 mm. Where water availability is mainly determined by the amount of rain, the crop requires a precipitation of at least 1200–1500 mm per year (in monsoon areas) or per growing season (Moomaw and Vergara, 1964). This occurs in most monsoon areas, as here the annual precipitation generally exceeds 2000 mm.

TABLE II.114. *Acreages of paddy soil areas in different parts of the world*

Country	acreage in 10^6 hectares	Country	acreage 10^6 hectares
Asia	114.1	South America	4.5
China (mainland)	31.5	Brasil	3.7
Japan	3.3	Columbia	0.3
Pakistan	9.9	Africa	2.9
Southeast Asia	64.2	Madagascar	0.8
India	34.8	U.A.R.	0.3
Indonesia	7.3	Europe	0.4
Thailand	6.2	Italy	0.1
Vietnam	4.7	Oceania	0.04
Burma	4.7		
Philippines	3.2		
Cambodja	2.2		

The topographical distribution is mainly governed by the fact that rice must be grown on level terrains. By far the most important rice areas are found in the basins of the deltas and flood plains of rivers (Mekong, Irrawaddy, Chao Phraye, Brahmaputra,

FIG. II.47. *Sawah-area on Mount Mala-bar, Java*

Ganges, Indus, and Amazon). If sufficient water is available, higher plateaus can also be used for rice cultivation as for instance in the North-East of Thailand. The same applies for hilly or mountainous regions where terraces are built (e.g. Indonesia: see fig. II.47). By means of ingenious techniques, such as applied in the Mountain Province of the Philippines, even slopes with gradients up to 40° or 45° are terraced (Van Breemen et al., 1968).

4.1.2. SOILS AND MANAGEMENT FACTORS

Any paddy soil profile reflects both the properties of the original uncultivated soil and the influence of cultural practices such as irrigation, terracing, and soil preparation. These factors will be discussed before entering into details concerning the characteristics of paddy soils.

Dudal and Moorman (1964) reviewed the major soils of South-East Asia in relation to their agricultural use. The great group names (according to the 1949 USDA classification) of these soils typically used for paddy cultivation and the major Japanese paddy soils (according to the classification of Oyama, 1962) are given in table II.115. The right column of this table shows the approximate equivalents according to the 7th Approximation (1967).

TABLE II.115. *Soils used for paddy cultivation in South-East Asia and Japan*

South-East Asia	Japan	7th Approximation
Great soil groups:	Great soil groups:	Orders:
Alluvial soils	gley soils	Entisols
	muck soils	
Alluvial soils	gley soils	
	grey soils	Inceptisols
Andosols	volcanic ash soils	
Regosols	–	
Grumusols	–	Vertisols
Low humic gley soils	yellowish brown soils	Alfisols
Grey hydromorphic soils	yellowish brown soils	
Non calcic brown soils	–	Ultisols
Red Yellow Podzolic soils	–	
Dark red latosols	–	
Reddish brown latosols	–	Oxisols
Organic soils	peat soils	Histosols
	muck soils	

In Japan and in South-East Asia, approximately 80% of the rice-growing areas are found in low-land regions where Entisols and Inceptisols dominate. Mostly, these soils are seasonally flooded, and drainage rather than water supply is an important problem. Where sufficient water is available and the relief is flat or gently sloping, Vertisols, Ultisols, and Alfisols are often used for paddy growing. The presence of a textural B horizon may help to minimize water losses, and therefore low humic gley and grey hydromorphic soils (approximate 7th Approximation equivalents: Aquult and Aqualf) are especially important in those regions. Oxisols, which occur mainly in hilly areas, are well suited for terracing as was done intensively in Java (Indonesia) (Dudal and Moorman, 1964). Organic soils, although covering fairly large areas in some South-East Asian countries, are used only locally for rice cultivation and the same applies to volcanic ash soils.

Though the résumé given above only deals with the situation in S.E. Asia and Japan, similar use of alluvial lowland soils for rice cultivation is probably found in the other rice producing areas in the world.

Rice fields are submerged during the whole or the greater part of the growing season, depending on such factors as water supply and cultivation practices. The soil may be either just water-saturated or may carry a waterhead ranging in thickness from several centimeters to several meters (floating rice). Controlled irrigation is the exception rather than common practice and according to Grist (1959) only 10 % of the world rice area can be classified as irrigated. This percentage was compiled from statistics mainly from countries with a highly developed agriculture (Japan, Taiwan, parts of China, U.A.R., Spain, Italy, U.S.A.) and from rice terrace areas in Java, China, and the Philippines. Wild flooding by river water during the rainy season occurs in the large flood plains in most S.E. Asian countries. On higher plateaus where river water is not easily available, rainwater is generally impounded by means of small contour bands in the fields.

In flat regions, paddy soil characteristics are merely superimposed on the original soil profile as a result of irrigation and cultivation practices. The case of terraced fields is more complicated, as the 'original' soil profile is either absent or at least largely disturbed.

Two principally different methods of terrace construction can be observed. The first involves controlled sedimentation behind earth or rock embankments by using an artificially guided stream of water mixed with soil material from upstream locations. The second method consists of back-slope digging and fore-slope filling (cf. Spencer and Hale, 1961). In the first case the soil body can be built up at the constructers' choice. Generally coarse-textured material is used for the subsoil and humus-rich, clayey material for the top soil. Outstanding examples of these truly man-made soils can be found in the Ifugao region of the Mountain Province in the Philippines (Van Breemen et al., 1968) where refined terracing and irrigation techniques have been developed in the course of many centuries.

Terracing of the second kind dominates in areas covered with thick soil mantles of erosion-resistant material. Well-known are the 'sawah' fields in Java (Indonesia) constructed on volcano slopes where red and reddish brown latosols occur (Dudal and Moorman, 1964).

Some characteristics peculiar to paddy soils may be brought about by the specific methods of soil preparation applied in the major rice areas in S.E. Asia. Important in this respect is the special method of plowing and harrowing the inundated fields ('puddling') that results in the breakdown of soil aggregates and the formation of a 10 to 20 cms thick layer of an intensively mixed soil-water slurry.

4.1.3. GENERAL CHARACTERISTICS OF PADDY SOILS

A feature common to all paddy soils is the presence of hydromorphic characteristics as a result of the periodic water saturation of the upper part of the profile.

The appearance of the soil material depends on the drainage condition at that moment. The surface soil is during the dry season, whether fallow or cultivated, generally mottled with brownish, yellowish or black concentrations of ferric and manganese compounds in a greyish matrix. On inundation these mottles may disappear (Iri et al., 1958) and tube-like accumulations of oxidized iron and manganese compounds develop around the O_2-secreting roots of rice and other aquatic plants.

The appearance of the soil below the mottled zone depends mainly on the local over-all drainage condition. Poorly drained alluvial soils, by far the most important soils used for paddy cultivation, generally show a permanently reduced subsoil immediately below the mottled horizon due to the presence of groundwater near to the surface.

In paddy soils of many rice terraces, the subsoil remains oxidized throughout the year, and the influence of irrigation is only reflected in the upper 30 to 50 cms of the profile (Koenigs, 1950; De Gee, 1950). Similar conditions are found in alluvial rice lands, where the groundwater table has been lowered by artificial drainage, but a predominantly aerobic zone remains between the water-saturated surface horizon and the permanently reduced subsoil, probably throughout the irrigation period (Kawaguchi and Matsuo, 1957; Kanno et al., 1964). It is therefore possible to distinguish three types of drainage conditions in paddy soils (fig. II.48). The separation of strongly hydromorphic and oxidized horizons in the upper part of the profile can be made by a structural B horizon (Van der Kevie, 1965), by a calcic horizon (Gupta et al., 1957) or

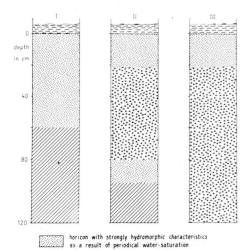

horizon with strongly hydromorphic characteristics as a result of periodical water-saturation

predominantly oxidized horizon, eventually showing weak hydromorphic characteristics

permanently reduced horizon

FIG. II.48. *Three different types of drainage conditions in paddy soils*

merely by the impermeability of the soil material itself as has been observed in heavy montmorillonitic clay soils (Briones and Cagauan, 1964; Moormann et al., 1964).

Wet rice cultivation may induce the formation of a compact, massive horizon at a depth of 10 to 20 cm (Koenigs, 1950; Dudal, 1958; Phillis, 1963; Moormann and Dudal, 1965) especially in well-drained soils, which are neither very sandy nor deep-cracking. This so called 'plough pan' has been estimated to develop within 50 to 100 years under favourable conditions (Grant, 1964), and can strongly reduce the water permeability. In this way it may be the separation between the water-saturated surface horizon and the aerobic subsoil. Ferric and manganese compounds are liable to accumulate underneath such an impervious horizon. In well-drained and acid soils high in easily reducible iron and manganese and high in organic matter, this may lead to the formation of strongly mottled horizons, concretionary layers or even well-developed iron-manganese pans (Dudal, 1958). A common feature in such horizons is the separation between iron and manganese, the latter being accumulated nearest to the aerated horizon (figs. II.49 and 50, p. 271).

In a personal communication Moormann stated that Mn-Fe-accumulations also occur frequently in Low Humic Gley soils under natural forest vegetation, so he believes that soils similar to typical paddy soils have already existed before cultivation to rice.

Fig. II.51 shows the percentages of 'active' Fe_2O_3 and Mn_3O_4 and total Fe_2O_3 at different depths in well-drained paddy soils, empoldered at different times (Kawaguchi and Matsuo, 1957). Manganese appears to be accumulated at two levels: below the surface horizon that is water-saturated during the growing season and above the permanently reduced subsoil. With increasing age, the two accumulation horizons approach each other, growing in thickness and eventually merging together.

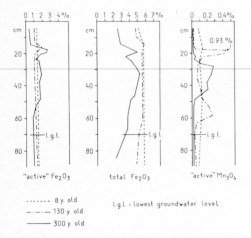

FIG. II.51. *Distribution of iron and manganese in well drained paddy soils at different stages of development (after Kawaguchi and Matsuo, 1957)*

One fairly pronounced accumulation layer of iron is found below the surface horizon and just above the corresponding manganese concentration. A weaker developed second iron concentration occurs over a considerable depth between the surface soil and the lowest groundwater level.

The deeper horizons, enriched in iron and manganese, can be considered as features common to most hydromorphic soils that have a zone of fluctuating groundwater, where oxygen-induced depositing of dissolved ferrous and manganous compounds takes place. In well-drained paddy soils a similar process may result in the formation of a second accumulation zone below the water-saturated surface soil.

The soils represented in fig. 11.51 show only a residual accumulation of iron; actual iron enrichments can be observed in similar soils elsewhere (Kanno et al., 1964). The migration of iron and manganese may lead to a serious depletion of these elements in the furrow slice, inducing the formation of so-called 'degraded' paddy soils (Mitsui, 1964). Severe 'degradation' occurs mainly in the case of acid and sandy soils.

It should be stressed that the accumulation of iron and manganese below the furrow slice can still take place in the absence of any detectable water-supporting layer. This is in fact what occurred in the examples given by Kawaguchi and Matsuo (1957) and Kanno et al. (1964). In the homogeneous profiles under consideration the concentration of iron and manganese took place within a few decades. A compact, more or less impermeable plough pan could only be observed in soils that had been cropped to rice for more than 300 years.

Finally, the development of an iron-manganese accumulation at the interface of a reduced surface horizon and a predominantly oxidized subsoil is not restricted to paddy soils only. The 'placic' horizon (7th Approximation, 1967) occurring in some Spodosols with a periodically water-saturated surface soil, probably has a similar genesis (Crompton, 1952).

Other characteristics resulting from wet rice cultivation include changes in texture. In soils irrigated with clay-containing river water, the top layer may become heavier in texture. In sandy soils a thin clayey surface layer can develop as a result of resedimentation of soil material that has been brought in suspension repeatedly during the wet soil preparation (Oldeman, 1967). On the other hand the clay content of the surface horizon may decrease in the course of many years of rice cultivation probably by runoff of mud-containing water after puddling (see section 4, profiles 30 to 33).

An increase in clay content throughout the profile after a long period of rice cultivation has been ascribed to strong weathering of silt and sand-sized minerals under alternating reduced and oxidized conditions (Kang and Markert, 1959; Raymundo et al., 1962). Some authors (Grant, 1964; Raymundo et al., 1962) believe that the formation of a textural B horizon may be enhanced by wet rice cultivation. However, the available literature offers no clear evidence to support this assumption.

Available data on plough pans indicate that this horizon is not associated with a change in textural properties. The few published chemical and mineralogical data do not suggest that any chemical cementation is involved in the genesis of such a pan. Probably this specific paddy soil horizon has been developed as a result of compaction of the soil during the wet soil preparation (Koenigs, 1950). According to Phillis (1963) the 'plough sole' or impermeable layer forms at the base of the mud, even in the absence of any deliberate cultivation. It forms, in a less definite form, even in those soils which are subject only to disturbances when seedlings are pushed in. Phillis (1963) believes that the pan is not just a sedimentary layer formed by the settling out of clay particles from a mud suspension, for the lower surface may be some distance below cultivation

348

depths. The clay suspension produced when the soil is worked is believed to settle and to fill up all the crevices and pores of the undisturbed clay just below cultivation zone forming in this way the hard layer.

Another effect of the wet soil preparation is the development of a temporarily 'separate particle structure' (Grant, 1964) that may allow the reduction processes to speed up, because the interaction between the soil solution and the solid phases can take place rapidly. Partly as a result of the growth of algae, the surface of the mud layer may become firm after some time. Gases developed under anaerobic conditions, will accumulate below this layer especially in heavy soils as may be seen from the frequent occurrence of gasbubble-shaped voids in the mud (Van Breemen et al., 1967).

After the field is drained, dessication of the topsoil encourages the formation of a platy surface layer. The development of this platy structure is probably accentuated by the horizontal textural differentiation brought about by the sedimentation of suspended soil particles after puddling.

In poorly drained soils the decomposition of organic matter proceeds much slower than in well-drained conditions, as a result of the comparatively low intensity of anaerobic microbial respiration. This is probably the main reason why the organic matter content may increase from 1 or 2% to 2 or 3% after some 50 years of rice cultivation (Kang and Markart, 1959; Raymundo et al., 1962). Depression of the soil temperature as a result of flooding and heavy organic manuring, applied in many rice growing areas, may also play an important role in this accumulation process.

Humus accumulation in the subsoil of old paddy soils has been observed in N. Korea (Kang and Markart, 1959) and in the Kiangsi province of China (Tsao, 1964). The accumulation has been attributed to the migration of humus particles, and seems to be only rarely encountered.

4.1.4. SOME EXAMPLES OF PADDY SOIL PROFILES

The available literature contains few examples of well-analyzed paddy soils. Only two cases will be discussed here, viz. 1) a chronosequence of paddy soils in empoldered marine sediments in southern Japan (Kanno et al., 1964) and 2) two latosolic 'sawah' soils and two comparable upland soils from western Java (Indonesia). The profile descriptions and samples of the latter soils were provided by Dr. K. H. Tan of the Bogor Institute of Agricultural Sciences.

4.1.4.1. *Alluvial paddy soils in Kyushu, Japan*
The soils described by Kanno et al. (1964) were empoldered from shallow sediments in the Ariake Bay (Shiroishi area, Saga Prefecture, Kyushu) by different reclamations, carried out between approximately 1560 and 1952. The mineralogical composition of the sediment indicates that the material originates from volcanic deposits and Tertiary sediments in the periphery of the Ariake Bay. The climate of the region is characterized by a mean annual precipitation of approximately 1900 mm (with highest rainfall in winter) and mean temperatures of 26° C in summer and 6° C in winter.

In summer one crop of rice is grown; wintercrops include barley, wheat, and beans. Upland crops were cultivated on ridges until the early 1950's, when the drainage (very poor in winter) was improved by the construction of drainage ditches. In the present state the water table lies between 80 and 100 cms below the surface.

The short profile descriptions, horizon designation and descriptive terms in acccordance with the 7th Approximation, read as follows:

Profile No. 30. Ariake Polder, reclaimed in 1951. Paddy grown since 1956.

Horizon	Depth (cm)	
A_{pg}	0–9	Dark grey brown (2.5Y4/2) silty clay with moderate subangular blocky structure; common red-yellowish brown and dark brown mottles and root rust; clear smooth boundary
AC_g	9–29	Grey brown (2.5Y5/2) silty clay with bluish grey (5OB5/2); common dark brown and reddish yellow mottles; moderate subangular blocky; gradual, wavy boundary.
C_{1g}	29–79	Bluish grey (5OB5/2) clay; few dark brown and brown mottles; vertical fissures (prismatic structure?); very sticky, very plastic; gradual, smooth boundary.
G	+79	Bluish grey (5OB5/2) clay without mottles; some shell fragments of *Phaxas attenuates* Dunker.

Profile No. 31. Meiji Polder, reclaimed in 1855.

Horizon	Depth (cm)	
A_{pg}	0–12	Dark grey brown (2.5Y4/2) clay with moderate granular and subangular blocky structure; common, red and yellow mottles and root rust; few brown mottles; clear, smooth boundary.
AB_g	12–18	Light brownish grey (2.5Y6/2) clay with moderate subangular blocky structure; common brown and few yellowish brown mottles; fairly compact (early stage of plough sole formation); clear, smooth boundary.
B_{2g}	18–52	Grey brown (2.5Y5/2) clay; common brown mottles; vertical fissures (prismatic structure?); clear, smooth boundary.
B_{3g}	52–77	Bluish grey (5OB5/2) clay; common brown mottles; gradual, wavy boundary.
C_g	+77	Bluish grey (5OB5/2) clay without mottles; very plastic, very sticky.

Profile No. 32. Tsukikiri; polder reclaimed around 1610.

Horizon	Depth (cm)	
A_{pg}	0–15	Dark brown (7.5YR4/2) silty clay loam with many yellowish brown and few brown mottles; clear, smooth boundary.
AB_g	15–24	Olive grey (5Y5/2) silty clay loam with few reddish brown and dark brown mottles; the upper part (15–18 cm) is more compact: early stage of plough sole formation. Clear, smooth boundary.
B_{21g}	24–50	Light brownish grey (2.5Y6/2) silty clay; many, fine, brown mottles; gradual, smooth boundary.

350

B$_{22g}$	50–80	Olive grey (5Y5/2) silty clay; coarse, angular blocky; common, brown (10YR3/4) mottles; vertical fissures; gradual, smooth boundary.
B$_{3g}$	80–100	Bluish grey (10BG5/2) silty clay; common, fine, brown mottles; gradual, wavy boundary.
C$_g$	+100	Bluish grey (10BG5/2) silty clay; few, brown mottles in the upper part; unmottled below 105 cm very sticky, very plastic.

Profile No. 33. Fukuda; reclaimed around 1560.

Horizon *Depth (cm)*

A$_{p1g}$	0–14	Light olive brown (2.5Y5/3) silty clay loam; moderate granular and subangular blocky; many, fine, yellowish brown (10YR5/8) and light olive brown (2.5Y5/6) mottles; clear, smooth boundary.
A$_{p2g}$	14–19	Dark grey brown (2.5Y4/2) silty clay loam; compact (plough pan); common, brown (10YR4/3) mottles; clear, smooth boundary.
B$_{2gir}$	19–27	Dark grey brown (2.5YR4/2) silty clay; many yellowish brown (10YR5/8 and 10YR5/6) and reddish yellow (7.5YR6/8) mottles; a vertical separation of iron and manganese can be observed; abrupt, smooth boundary.
B$_{2g}$	27–77	Olive grey (5Y4/2) silty clay; vertical fissures; many brown mottles in the lower part; gradual, smooth boundary.
B$_{3g}$	77–87	Bluish grey (10BG5/2) silty clay; few mottles; gradual, wavy boundary.
C$_g$	+87	Bluish grey (10BG5/2) silty clay; unmottled.

Chemical and mechanical characteristics of the soils, together with similar data on a sample of the fresh marine sediment from the Ariake Bay ('parent material') and a sample of an A$_p$ horizon of an unirrigated soil from Tsukikiri, are summarized in tables II.116 and 117.

The changes in the soil profiles in the course of time include the formation of a rather weakly developed plough pan, which is mainly characterized by a slightly higher compaction of the soil between 15 and 25 cm. The development of a B horizon is shown by the appearance of more, larger, and darker mottles between the furrow slice and the permanently reduced groundwater zone. The drainage condition of the older soil is represented in fig. II.48.

Table II.117 shows that both iron and manganese have been accumulated in a pattern similar to the one described by Kawaguchi and Matsuo (1957: see fig. II.51).

The fresh marine sediment has a lower clay content than the soils investigated; these soils have obviously been developed from heavier material (table II.116). The clay content of the surface soil decreases on ageing. Kanno et al. (1964) attribute this to eluviation. However, the deeper horizons do not show any clay accumulation; apparently, this is to be ascribed to the lateral wash-out of the finest particles, brought into suspension during the wet soil preparations. The decrease in c.e.c., which is especially notable in the upper horizons of the soils 32 and 33, is mainly the result of this loss of clay. Also base saturation decreases with growing age of the soils and the soluble salts become progressively leached. In general, however, paddy soils have a

TABLE II.116. *Mechanical composition, pH, and base saturation of the four paddy soils*

Profile	Horizon	grain size distribution (%)			C (%)	pH (H_2O)	pH (MKCl)	c.e.c. (m.e./ 100 g)	base[1] sat. (%)
		$> 20\mu$	$20-2\mu$	$< 2\mu$					
No. 30	A_{pg}	6.4	45.0	47.2	1.2	6.8	5.4	34.2	95
	AC_g	6.9	39.2	52.6	0.9	6.6	5.3	39.3	90
	C_{1g}	4.6	37.8	54.1	1.1	7.0	6.3	44.0	87
	C_{2g}	7.4	35.7	51.8	1.0	8.2	7.4	42.5	> 100
parent material		23.8	42.1	28.9	0.9	8.2	7.6	31.8	> 100
No. 31	A_{pg}	5.6	38.1	53.7	1.5	6.3	4.2	33.8	76
	AB_g	5.5	38.2	55.0	0.6	7.6	5.5	39.5	89
	B_{2g}	6.4	39.8	52.6	0.4	7.8	5.5	38.2	93
	B_{3g}	4.5	38.4	55.1	0.7	7.8	5.8	40.8	90
	C_g	6.2	37.8	51.8	0.8	8.3	7.1	40.4	> 100
No. 32	A_{pg}	7.5	56.0	33.1	1.7	6.1	4.4	25.2	94
	AB_g	6.5	55.0	36.9	0.7	6.8	4.9	25.4	89
	B_{21g}	2.7	40.1	56.9	0.4	7.2	4.9	36.1	94
	B_{22g}	2.1	41.0	56.4	0.3	7.6	5.4	40.6	91
	B_{3g}	2.2	40.8	56.4	0.7	7.6	5.6	40.4	100
	C_g	2.4	40.5	52.7	0.8	8.2	6.6	41.8	100
upland soil	A_{pg}	11.2	60.3	27.1	1.6	6.0	3.9	20.8	73
No. 33	A_{p1g}	7.2	50.6	36.0	2.3	5.5	4.1	28.8	69
	A_{p2g}	6.6	51.3	39.8	1.0	6.6	4.8	27.3	87
	B_{2gir}	5.2	47.9	47.8	0.3	6.9	4.9	31.9	86
	B_{2g}	3.6	42.9	53.8	0.3	7.1	4.9	35.3	86
	B_{3g}	2.5	39.2	55.7	0.6	7.6	5.4	38.6	99
	C_g	2.7	39.7	54.7	0.6	7.8	5.8	39.9	100

[1] In some cases base saturation exceeds 100%. This has to be attributed to the presence of soluble salts.

higher base saturation than comparable upland soils (Kang and Markert, 1960) and the difference between profile 32 and its unirrigated counterpart with respect to base saturation indicates that this is also true for the paddy soils under investigation.

Total chemical analyses of the clay separates from the A_{pg} and C horizons are shown in table II.118. This data has been used to calculate the mineralogical composition according to the standard goethite norm (Van der Plas and Van Schuylenborgh, 1970). The results have been summarized in table II.119. X-ray diffraction and D.T.A. studies of the clay fractions showed smectites to be the dominant clay minerals, followed by kandites (predominantly halloysite) and mica (illite). This corresponds with the calcul-

TABLE II.117 *Contents of Si, Fe, Mn in the four paddy soils* (weight percentages)

Profile	Hor.	water soluble SiO_2	total Fe_2O_3	free Fe_2O_3	total MnO	water soluble salts $(+SiO_2)$
No. 30	A_{pg}	0.04	6.8	2.5	0.15	0.2
	AC_g	0.05	6.7	2.6	0.19	0.5
	C_{1g}	0.06	6.7	2.0	0.18	0.9
	C_{2g}	0.06	6.6	1.8	0.19	2.3
parent material		0.05	7.1	1.5	0.17	2.9
No. 31	A_{pg}	0.02	6.7	2.4	0.14	0.1
	AB_g	0.03	7.0	2.9	0.20	0.1
	B_{2g}	0.04	6.9	2.7	0.15	0.1
	B_{3g}	0.06	6.9	2.2	0.12	0.2
	C_g	0.06	6.8	1.3	0.20	0.8
No. 32	A_{pg}	0.01	5.3	1.1	0.10	0.0[5]
	AB_g	0.01	5.8	1.0	0.11	0.1
	B_{21g}	0.03	6.9	1.7	0.28	0.1
	B_{22g}	0.04	6.7	2.0	0.28	0.2
	B_{3g}	0.06	6.8	2.3	0.14	0.1
	C_g	0.04	6.8	1.3	0.18	0.4
upland soil	A_{pg}	0.01	4.5	1.2	0.19	0.1
No. 33	A_{p1g}	0.01	4.5	0.7	0.08	0.1
	A_{p2g}	0.01	5.8	0.8	0.09	0.1
	B_{2gir}	0.02	7.4	1.5	0.15	0.1
	B_{2g}	0.03	7.0	1.7	0.32	0.1
	B_{3g}	0.04	6.5	1.7	0.10	0.1
	C_g	0.04	6.6	1.7	0.13	0.2

ated normative mineralogical composition (table II.119). The X-ray analyses did not reveal significant quantitative differences in the clay mineralogy of the investigated samples. However, the results of the norm calculation indicate that the smectite content decreases with ageing of the soils, whilst the amounts of kandites and free silica increase simultaneously. The differences in the smectite contents are also reflected in the c.e.c. values of the clay separates (compare tables II.118 and 119). Probably smectites are desilicated and partly transferred into kandites, whereas free silica accumulates residually. Indications of the same process occurring in similar Japanese polder soils have also been found by Kawaguchi et al. (1957). The desilication is most pronounced in the unirrigated soil from Tsukikiri and is faster in the surface soils than in the permanently reduced subsoils.

The most important factors involved in desilication can be examined by considering the composition of the soil solution in relation to the stability of kaolinite and mont-

TABLE II.118. *Chemical composition (weight percentages) and c.e.c. of the clay separates of the A_{pg} and C horizons of the paddy soils from the Shiroishi area* (Ca clays, fraction $< 1.6\mu$)

	profile 30		parent mat.	profile 31		profile 32		unirr. soil A_{pg}	profile 33	
	A_{pg}	C_g		A_{pg}	C_g	A_{pg}	C_g		A_{pg}	C_g
SiO_2	51.2	50.6	50.7	50.9	52.1	53.5	52.4	53.8	52.8	52.3
Al_2O_3	22.9	23.7	23.5	23.9	23.5	22.3	23.4	23.0	23.3	22.3
Fe_2O_3	9.7	8.4	8.5	9.2	8.4	9.4	8.7	9.1	9.1	9.7
MnO	0.1	0.2	0.2	0.1	0.2	0.1	0.2	0.2	0.1	0.1
MgO	2.2	2.1	2.2	1.8	2.0	1.6	2.0	1.3	1.2	1.8
CaO	1.1	1.0	1.1	1.2	1.3	1.3	1.3	1.3	1.4	1.3
Na_2O	0.5	0.5	0.5	0.5	0.5	0.5	0.6	0.5	0.5	0.5
K_2O	1.3	1.2	1.2	1.4	1.3	1.3	1.3	1.3	1.3	1.3
$H_2O +$	10.7	11.3	11.4	10.7	10.7	9.7	9.9	9.3	9.8	10.5
TiO_2	0.8	0.9	0.8	0.9	0.8	1.0	0.9	0.8	1.1	0.8
c.e.c. (m.e./ 100 g)	48.0	49.6	47.8	46.2	50.3	46.6	50.8	46.2	47.9	49.8

morillonite. Fig. II.52 represents the stability-diagram of a number of phases in the SiO_2–Al_2O_3–MgO–CaO–H_2O system at $25°$ C, I atmosphere total pressure, and Ca^{2+}-activity of 5×10^{-4} (for explanation of the figure see text). The crosses in this diagram represent the values of $\lg \frac{[Mg^{2+}]}{[H^+]^3}$ and $\lg [H_4SiO_4]$ in the soil solution, which have been estimated from pH data and analyses of water-soluble salts given by Kanno

TABLE II.119. *Normative mineralogical composition of the clay fractions of the paddy soils from the Shiroishi area* (expressed in equivalent percentages)

	profile 30		parent mat.	profile 31		profile 32		unirr. soil A_{pg}	profile 33	
	A_{pg}	C_g		A_{pg}	C_g	A_{pg}	C_g		A_{pg}	C_g
age[1]	12		0	88		350		350	400	
Sm	58.3	57.7	58.3	50.1	52.8	46.2	52.7	40.0	38.8	50.2
Kand	19.3	22.6	21.9	24.7	23.2	23.7	22.6	28.4	29.8	22.1
Ms	12.1	11.5	11.5	13.5	12.7	11.9	12.1	11.9	12.2	12.2
Q	2.8	1.6	1.6	4.6	4.9	10.8	5.8	12.7	11.9	8.1
Go	6.8	5.7	5.9	6.3	5.7	6.5	5.9	6.2	6.3	6.7
Ru	0.6	0.7	0.6	0.7	0.6	0.8	0.7	0.6	0.9	0.6
Misc	0.1	0.2	0.2	0.1	0.1	0.1	0.1	0.2	0.1	0.1

[1] expressed in years. Sm = smectites; Kand = kandites; Ms = muscovite (illites); Q = free silica; Go = goethite; Ru = rutile; Misc = miscellaneous.

et al. (1964). These figures are average for the whole profile, the activity coefficients of Mg^{2+} and $H_4SiO_4^0$ have been assumed to be 0.5 and 1, respectively.

In the case of the parent material, the composition of the soil solution falls within

Boundary montmorillonite/kaolinite:

$2 Ca_{.19} Mg_{.40} Al_{1.71} Si_{3.93} O_{10} (OH)_2 + 2.36 H^+ + 9.15 H_2O \rightleftharpoons$
$1.71 Al_2 Si_2 O_5 (OH)_4 + 4.44 H_4SiO_4 + .80 Mg^{2+} + .38 Ca^{2+} .....$ *(6)*

$lg K_1 = lg \frac{[Mg^{2+}]}{[H^+]^2} + .48 lg [Ca^{2+}] + 5.55 lg [H_4SiO_4]$

Boundary montmorillonite/gibbsite:

$2 Ca_{.19} Mg_{.40} Al_{1.71} Si_{3.55} O_{10} (OH)_2 + 2.36 H^+ + 17.70 H_2O \rightleftharpoons$
$1.71 Al_2O_3 \cdot 3 H_2O + 7.86 H_4SiO_4 + 8.0 Mg^{2+} + .38 Ca^{2+} ....$ *(7)*

$lg K_2 = lg \frac{[Mg^{2+}]}{[H^+]^2} + .48 lg [Ca^{2+}] + 9.84 lg [H_4SiO_4]$

Boundary kaolinite/gibbsite:

$Al_2 Si_2 O_5 (OH)_4 + 5 H_2O \rightleftharpoons Al_2O_3 \cdot 3 H_2O + 2 H_4 SiO_4$ .... *(8)*

$lg K_3 = 2 lg [H_4 SiO_4]$

From the ΔF_f^--values of montmorillonite, kaolinite, H_4SiO_4 (according to Reesman and Keller, 1968), gibbsite (Barany and Kelley, 1961), H_2O, Mg^{2+} and Ca^{2+} (Rossini et al, 1952) the values of lg K were calculated to be: lg $K_1 = -0.6$, lg $K_2 = -24.4$, and lg $K_3 = -11.2$

Boundary muscovite/kaolinite:

$2 K Al_3 O_{10} (OH)_2 + 2 H^+ + 3 H_2O \rightleftharpoons 3 Al_2 Si_2 O_5 (OH)_4 + 2 K^+ .....$ *(9)*

$lg K_4 = 2 lg \frac{[K^+]}{[H^+]}$

Boundary muscovite/gibbsite:

$2 K Al_3 O_{10} (OH)_2 + 2 H^+ + 12 H_2O \rightleftharpoons 3 Al_2O_3 \cdot 3 H_2O + 2 K^+ + 6 H_4 SiO_4^0 ....$ *(10)*

$lg K_5 = 2 lg \frac{[K^+]}{[H^+]} + 6 lg [H_4 SiO_4]$

Boundary kaolinite/gibbsite:

$Al_2 Si_2 O_5 (OH)_4 + 5 H_2O \rightleftharpoons Al_2O_3 \cdot 3 H_2O + 2 H_4 SiO_4$ ...... *(11)*

$lg K_6 = 2 lg [H_4 SiO_4]$

From the ΔF_f^--data of muscovite (Barany, 1964), gibbsite (Barany and Kelley, 1961), $H_4 SiO_4$, kaolinite (Reesman and Keller, 1968), H_2O, and K^+ (Rossini et al, 1952), the lg K-values were calculated to be: lg $K_4 = 12.2$; lg $K_5 = -21.2$ and lg $K_6 = -11.2$

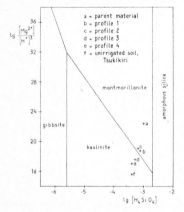

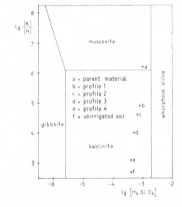

FIG. II.52. *Stability field of gibbsite, kaolinite and montmorillonite in the system $SiO_2-Al_2O_3-MgO-CaO-H_2O$ at 25°C and 1 atm. total pressure. $[Ca^{2+}] = 5 \times 10^{-4}$. The crosses refer to the composition of the soil solution in the soils of the Shiroishi area*

FIG. II.53. *Stability field of muscovite, kaolinite, and gibbsite in the system $K_2O-Al_2O_3-SiO_2-H_2O$ at 25°C and 1 atm. total pressure. The crosses refer to the composition of the soil solution in the soils of the Shiroishi area*

the stability field of montmorillonite. But after reclamation, the values of $lg \frac{[Mg^{2+}]}{[H^+]^3}$ and, to a lesser extent, lg $[H_4SiO_4]$ decrease and with growing age of the soils, kaolinite becomes progressively more stable than montmorillonite. The transformation of montmorillonite into kaolinite is probably mainly stimulated by leaching, leading to a lowering of the pH and a decrease of the Mg^{2+} activity in the soil solution. Comparison between the composition of the soil solution of profile 32 (d in fig. II.52) and its un-irrigated counterpart (f in fig. II.52) indicates that this phenomenon is an 'upland' process rather than typical for paddy soils (see also Chapter 2 of this Part).

Plotting the estimated $\lg \dfrac{[K^+]}{[H^+]}$ and $\lg [H_4SiO_4]$ values (obtained from the soluble salt analyses of Kanno et al. (1964) assuming that the activity coefficient of K^+ is 0.8) in a stability diagram for mica, kaolinite, and gibbsite (fig. II.53) shows that after reclamation muscovite also becomes increasingly unstable in relation to kaolinite. However, it follows from the calculated mineralogical composition (table II.119) that the mica content is nearly equal in the Shiroishi paddy soils. Apparently, the transformation of mica proceeds at a much slower rate than the montmorillonite-kaolinite transformation. This may be partly ascribed to the fact that muscovite occurs mainly in the coarse clay fraction ($0.2–1.6\mu$), whereas montmorillonite is concentrated in the $< 0.2\mu$ fraction. The data of Kanno et al. (1964) indicate a slight decrease of the K content in the fraction $< 0.2\mu$ with increasing age of the soils; obviously, a small portion of the mica is actually transformed. Chang (1961, cited by Grant, 1964) also reported a mica-kaolinite transformation during paddy soil development, but in view of the considerations given above, this process is also probably more typical in upland than in paddy soils.

In table II.119 'goethite' refers to amorphous ferric oxides because X-ray analysis did not reveal the presence of any α–FeOOH. Comparison of the Fe_2O_3 contents in the fine earth and clay fractions (tables II.117 and 118) shows that the accumulation of ferric oxides takes place in the sand fraction only.

X-ray analysis also indicated that the quartz content is approximately the same in all clay separates. The large differences between quartz ($+$amorphous silica) contents of the older and younger soils should probably be attributed to the production of amorphous silica or to the residual enrichment of silica in the older soils.

The mineralogical composition of the sand fraction is nearly the same in all samples, the only difference being the higher content of iron concretions in the older soils (Kanno et al. 1964).

In the case of a similar chronosequence of paddy soils (Kojima Basin, Japan; Kawaguchi et al., 1957) the amounts of pyroxenes, chlorite, and biotite appeared to have decreased in the furrow slice after 130 to 240 years of rice cultivation. The rapid weathering of these minerals has been ascribed to the alternation of oxidation and reduction processes.

4.1.4.2. *Paddy soils on reddish brown and red latosols in Western Java (Indonesia)*

Reddish brown and red latosols developed on andesitic volcanic material, cover large areas in Western Java. The mineralogical and chemical characteristics of these soils have been described by Van Schuylenborgh (1958). Reddish brown latosols are found mainly on Pleistocene volcanic deposits in rolling to hilly areas at altitudes between 100 and 300 m above sea level. Texture is generally uniform with depth. The soils have high percentages of clay (50–85 %) and the sand fraction largely consists of concretions. The clay fraction contains mainly kanditic minerals and smaller amounts of amorphous compounds (allophane), smectites, gibbsite, and quartz. The pH varies between 5.0 and 6.5. Soil structure is generally strongly granular. Climate is characterized by mean annual temperatures of approximately $25°$ C and yearly precipitation totals of some 4000 mm; the distribution pattern is such that in the wet period from October to

356

April a monthly rainfall occurs of 400 mm and in the less wet period from July to August a monthly precipitation of 200 mm.

Red latosols occur in Western Java mainly on Tertiary volcanic deposits at elevations below 100 m in the gently rolling plains near the coast. These soils are mineralogically quite similar to the reddish brown latosols, but the clay content is generally higher. The average temperature is 26° C and the yearly precipitation approximately 3000 mm.

Both types of soil are used for wet rice cultivation, mainly terraced (sawah). The 'sawah' soils differ considerably from the comparable unirrigated upland soils, mainly because of the presence of a well-developed plough pan and a pronounced Fe-Mn accumulation horizon (Koenigs, 1950; Tan, 1968).

Profile descriptions of two paddy soils (profiles 34 and 36) and their unirrigated equivalents (profiles 35 and 37) read as follows:

Profile No. 34. Paddy soil in a 'sawah' field on a reddish brown latosol near Bogor. The field was cropped with rice until three years ago, and has been planted with cassave since then. Elevation 250 m above sea level. Classification: Ochraquox.

Horizon	Depth (cm)	
A_{p1}	0–23	Dark yellowish brown (10YR3/4:m) clay with strong, fine, granular structure. Friable, abrupt, smooth boundary.
A_{p2}	23–26	Dark brown (7.5YR4/4:m) clay with weak, coarse, subangular blocky structure; yellowish coatings on cleavage planes; very compact (plough pan); abrupt, smooth boundary.
B_{21}	26–48	Dark reddish grey (5YR4/2:m) clay with weak, fine to medium, granular structure; many coarse iron-manganese streaks and mottles on cleavage planes; few, discontinuous clay coatings on the faces of compound aggregates. Gradual, smooth boundary.
B_{22}	48–62	Dark reddish grey (5YR4/2:m) clay with weak, fine to medium granular structure; very faint, fine Fe/Mn streaks and mottles.

At greater depth the profile is very similar, but the Fe/Mn mottles decrease.

Profile No. 35. Unirrigated reddish brown latosol. Located in a rubber garden near Bogor, approximately 1 km from profile 34. Physiography: flat. Elevation: 250 m above sea level. Classification: Tropeptic Haplorthox.

Horizon	Depth (cm)	
A_1	0–16	Dark yellowish brown (10YR3/4:m) clay with strong, fine to medium, granular structure; friable; many roots; intensive termite activity. Gradual, smooth boundary.
B_{21}	16–33	Dark brown (7.5YR4/2:m) clay with strong, fine, granular structure; friable; many roots and intensive termite activity. Gradual, smooth boundary.
B_{22}	33–57	Dark yellowish brown (10YR4/3:m) clay with weak, fine, granular structure; friable; more compact than B_{21}. Gradual, smooth boundary.
B_{23}	+57	Brown (7.5YR4/4:m) clay with weak, fine, granular structure; very faint Fe/Mn mottles; clay coatings in pores and on ped faces.

Profile 36. Red latosol in a sawah field near Tjibinung, normally used for paddy growing; at present planted with upland rice. Elevation: 90 m above sea level. Classification: Tropeptic Haplorthox.

Horizon	*Depth (cm)*	
A_{p1}	0–16	Reddish brown (5YR4/3:m) clay with strong, fine, crumb to granular structure; friable; many roots and intensive termite activity. Abrupt, smooth boundary.
A_{p2}	16–21	Reddish brown (5YR4/3:m) clay with strong, medium, blocky structure; many, faint, Fe/Mn mottles and streaks along cleavage planes; very compact (plough pan). Abrupt boundary.
B_{21}	21–26	Black (5YR2/1:m) clay with strong, fine to medium, subangular blocky structure; friable. Gradual, smooth boundary.
B_{22}	26–43	Dark red (2.5YR3/6) clay with fine granular structure; slightly firm to friable. Few fine black Fe/Mn streaks. Some clay coatings in pores.

Profile 37. Red latosol in a village fruit garden. Located some 200 m from profile 36. Flat area. Elevation: 90 m above sea level. Classification: Tropeptic Haplorthox.

Horizon	*Depth (cm)*	
A_p	0–13	Dark reddish brown (5YR3/4:m) clay with strong, fine, granular structure; friable; many roots and intensive termite activity; clear, smooth boundary.
B_{21}	13–29	Reddish brown (2.5YR4/4:m) clay with strong, medium, subangular to angular blocky structure; friable; few, small, black Fe/Mn mottles; some clay coatings on cleavage planes. Gradual, smooth boundary.
B_{22}	29–53	Reddish brown (2.5YR4/4:m) clay with strong, coarse subangular blocky structure; friable; very faint Fe/Mn mottles and iron coatings on ped faces; clay coatings in pores. Gradual, smooth boundary.
B_{23}	+53	Reddish brown (2.5YR4/4:m) clay with weak, coarse, subangular blocky structure; slightly firm to friable.

With respect to the classification of the profiles, it should be remarked that the typical paddy soil characteristics (plough pan and Fe/Mn accumulations) are not recognized as diagnostic features in the USDA classification scheme (7th Approximation). Hence, paddy and upland soils may be classified in the same taxa, in spite of important differences between both groups of soils.

The morphology of the profiles clearly reflects the effect of paddy cultivation on the soil characteristics. Both paddy soils have a well-developed, compact plough pan underlain by an Fe and an Mn accumulation horizon. The iron accumulation horizons and the plough pans have not been sampled separately, which accounts for the high Fe_2O_3 contents of the two A_{p2} horizons. Because the paddy soils have not been irrigated for some time, the surface horizon does not show hydromorphic characteristics; normally, however, mottles are present in, and immediately above the plough pan during fallow (Koenigs, 1950; Tan, 1968).

Apart from the data on iron and manganese, the analyses (tables II.120 and 121) do not reveal significant differences between the paddy and upland soils. The same applies to the mineralogical composition (table II. 122), calculated by means of the standard goethite norm for the clay fractions of all soils and a hypersthene variant of the epinorm for the non-clay fraction of the samples of profiles 34 and 35 and the parent material (Van der Plas and Van Schuylenborgh, 1970).

The dominant mineral in all soils is kaolinite. Associated minerals in the clay fraction include goethite and small amounts of quartz and rutile. The presence of kaolinite, poorly crystallized goethite and quartz has been confirmed by X-ray analysis. The same applies to some of the minerals of the coarse fractions, viz. hypersthene and plagioclases. The comparatively large amounts of feldspars in the surface horizons of the profiles 34 and 35 can be attributed to recent depositions of volcanic dust. It is remarkable that in these soils, just as in the alluvial paddy soils discussed earlier, iron and manganese have accumulated almost exclusively in the sand and silt fractions, whereas the Fe_2O_3 and MnO contents of the clay fractions are approximately the same in all horizons of each profile.

In the examples discussed in this section, plough pan formation and translocation

TABLE II.120. *Some data on the profiles 34, 35, 36 and 37*

Prof.	Hor.	grain size distribution (%)			C (%)	Fe_2O_3 (%)	MnO (%)	c.e.c. (m.e./100 g)
		> 50μ	50–2μ	< 2μ				
34	A_{p1}	4.3	18.6	77.1	1.8	12.0	0.1	9.5
	A_{p2}	6.1	21.7	72.2	1.3	16.7	0.1	8.2
	B_{21}	4.1	13.7	82.2	0.6	13.4	0.5	8.8
	B_{22}	3.8	12.6	83.6	0.6	12.2	0.1	7.5
35	A_1	16.3	27.3	56.4	2.6	12.3	0.1	8.8
	B_{21}	17.1	27.6	55.3	1.8	12.7	0.1	8.8
	B_{22}	11.5	32.9	55.5	1.1	12.9	0.2^5	8.8
	B_{23}	16.4	22.7	60.9	0.4	12.7	0.2	9.5
36	A_{p1}	3.2	10.2	86.5	1.6	11.7	0.2	8.2
	A_{p2}	2.6	11.3	86.1	1.1	12.1	0.3	10.0
	B_{21}	1.6	9.4	89.0	0.9	12.0	1.3	8.2
	B_{22}	1.0	7.4	91.6	0.9	11.3	0.3	9.5
37	A_p	5.2	16.6	78.1	2.1	11.7	0.4	8.8
	B_{21}	1.1	5.5	93.3	1.2	11.1	0.2	8.2
	B_{22}	1.1	6.2	92.7	1.1	11.2	0.2	11.1
	B_{23}	0.8	6.2	93.0	0.8	11.5	0.2	11.1
	C^1	72.0	13.3	14.7	0.4	5.9	0.2	–

[1] parent material: partly weathered andesitic ash.

of iron and manganese appear to be the most typical processes, differentiating paddy soils from comparable upland soils. Most paddy soils, viz. those of the alluvial lowlands (section 4.1) are either poorly drained or too young to show this type of profile development. Special attention should be given here to the short-term reduction and oxidation processes as a result of alternating flooding and drying, which may lead to the development or enhancement of hydromorphic characteristics. These processes are also of paramount importance in understanding the formation of Fe/Mn accumulation horizons, and will be discussed in the next section.

4.1.5. SHORT TERM PROCESSES IN PERIODICALLY FLOODED SOILS

4.1.5.1. *Processes initiated by flooding*
As the diffusion of gases in water is approximately $10^{-4} \times$ that in air, the exchange of gases between the soil and the atmosphere is cut down immediately after flooding. Consequently, the soil deeper than a few millimeters below the soil-water interface becomes depleted of oxygen, because the oxygen is rapidly consumed by the aerobic micro-organisms and cannot be replenished. Within one or two days, virtually all oxygen has disappeared (Takai et al., 1956) and the activity of facultative and obligate anaerobic micro-organisms increases. As a result of the metabolic activity of these organisms, many compounds with high oxidation states can be reduced, either directly by acting as electron acceptors in the anaerobic dissimilation process, or indirectly by forming organic decomposition products with reducing properties.

The most important processes taking place upon flooding (Ponnamperuma, 1964) include: (1) accumulation of gases such as CO_2, H_2, and CH_4; (2) reduction of nitrate to e.g. N_2; (3) reduction of manganese and iron oxides to Mn^{2+} and Fe^{2+}; (4) reduction of sulfates to sulfides; (5) considerable increase of the concentrations of Ca^{2+}, Mg^{2+}, K^+, Na^+, $H_2PO_3^-$ and HCO_3^- in the interstitial water; (6) production of ammonia and soluble organic compounds (fatty acids, amino acids and mercaptans) as a result of the anaearobic decomposition of fresh organic matter; (7) stabilization of the pH between 6.5 and 7.0 and decrease of redox-potential.

These effects of flooding develop not only in the presence of a water layer above the soil surface but also where the soil is saturated (IRRI, 1964). Percolation of the soil with water rich in oxigen does not prevent soil reduction to any extent (Ponnamperuma, 1955) because at normal percolation rates all oxygen is consumed in the oxidized thin toplayer below the soil-water interface. According to Uchiyama and Onikura (1956), percolation at a rate of 3 cm/day can even intensify the reduction in the subsoil by illuviating easily decomposable organic matter.

4.1.5.1.1. *Changes in the gas phase*
The production of CO_2 is mainly a result of microbial dissimilation processes. Shortly after flooding the partial CO_2 pressure (ςCO_2) increases to maximum values between 0.2 and 0.9 atmosphere and declines to values between 0.05 and 0.3 atm. after 2 to 6 weeks (IRRI, 1964). High ςCO_2 peaks are typical for acid soils with high amounts of organic matter and low manganese content. In neutral and calcareous soils the peak values are lower and the decline more gradual.

TABLE II.121. *Chemical composition of the fine earth and clay fractions of the profiles 34–37 and of the partly weathered andesitic ash* (weight percentages)

Prof.	Material	SiO_2	Al_2O_3	Fe_2O_3	FeO	MnO	MgO	CaO	Na_2O	K_2O	TiO_2	P_2O_5	H_2O+
34	Ap1 hor.	39.8	28.8	12.0	0.4	0.1	0.1	0.1	0.6	–	1.5	0.3	16.5
	clay sep.	39.0	31.0	12.5	0.4	0.1	tr	–	0.2	tr	1.4	0.3	14.9
	Ap2 hor.	36.6	28.0	16.7	0.6	0.1	0.1	0.1	0.4	–	1.4	0.2	15.9
	clay sep.	38.5	30.4	14.0	0.3	0.1	tr	–	0.2	tr	1.4	0.3	15.0
	B21 hor.	37.1	30.7	13.5	0.5	0.5	0.1	0.1	0.3	–	1.3	0.3	15.3
	clay sep.	30.7	32.4	11.1	0.3	0.1	tr	–	0.2	tr	1.1	0.4	15.1
	B22 hor.	37.7	29.7	12.1	0.3	0.1	0.1	0.2	0.2	–	1.2	0.3	14.6
	clay sep.	39.8	32.5	11.2	0.3	0.1	tr	–	0.2	tr	1.1	0.3	15.2
35	A1 hor.	38.5	26.2	13.2	0.7	0.1	0.4	0.3	0.3	–	1.4	0.3	17.0
	clay sep.	39.6	31.3	12.7	0.3	0.1	0.1	–	0.2	tr	1.3	0.4	14.6
	B21 hor.	40.0	26.8	12.7	0.4	0.1	0.3	0.4	0.3	–	1.4	0.3	15.7
	clay sep.	39.3	30.9	12.8	0.3	0.1	0.1	—	0.3	tr	1.3	0.4	14.6
	B22 hor.	39.1	27.8	12.9	0.3	0.2	0.3	0.3	0.1	–	1.4	0.4	14.8
	clay sep.	38.7	31.7	11.9	0.3	0.1	–	–	0.6	0.2	1.2	0.4	14.4
	B23 hor.	40.2	28.8	12.7	0.7	0.2	0.2	0.3	0.1	–	1.4	0.3	14.2
	clay sep.	38.9	31.5	11.8	0.3	0.1	–	–	0.5	0.1	1.1	0.3	14.5
36	Ap1 hor.	39.1	28.8	11.7	0.7	0.2	0.2	0.4	–	–	1.5	0.2	15.4
	clay sep.	40.6	32.6	11.4	0.2	0.1	–	–	0.7	0.1	1.4	0.3	13.8
	Ap2 hor.	39.7	28.6	12.2	0.6	0.4	0.2	0.4	–	–	1.5	0.2	14.8
	clay sep.	40.5	32.7	11.4	0.1	0.1	–	–	0.2	0.1	1.4	0.3	13.9
	B21 hor.	38.4	29.4	12.0	0.2	1.3	0.2	0.3	–	–	1.4	0.1	15.4
	clay sep.	41.0	33.0	11.1	0.2	0.1	–	–	tr	tr	1.3	0.3	14.2
	B22 hor.	39.4	29.7	11.3	0.6	0.3	0.1	0.6	–	–	1.4	0.1	14.8
	clay sep.	40.1	33.1	11.0	0.3	0.1	–	–	tr	tr	1.3	0.3	13.7
37	Ap1 hor.	39.6	27.4	11.6	0.6	0.4	0.3	0.4	–	–	1.5	0.1	15.9
	clay sep.	40.3	32.0	11.2	0.3	0.1	–	–	tr	0.1	1.4	0.4	13.7
	B21 hor.	38.9	30.1	11.1	0.3	0.2	0.1	0.2	–	–	1.4	tr	15.1
	clay sep.	40.7	32.0	11.1	0.3	0.1	–	–	tr	0.1	0.3	0.3	13.5
	B22 hor.	39.1	30.5	11.2	0.2	0.2	0.1	0.1	–	–	1.4	tr	14.9
	clay sep.	40.5	32.2	11.0	0.3	0.1	–	–	tr	tr	1.3	0.2	13.6
	B23 hor.	39.3	30.9	11.5	0.2	0.2	0.1	0.1	–	–	1.3	tr	14.3
	clay sep.	41.2	32.3	11.1	0.3	0.1	–	–	tr	tr	1.5	0.2	13.8
	C mat.	36.0	30.2	5.9	2.2	0.2	1.3	2.9	2.5	0.3	0.7	0.1	12.2
	clay sep.	33.9	32.6	11.2	n.d.	tr	–	0.6	0.8	0.4	n.d.	n.d.	n.d.[1]

[1] n.d. = not determined.

The pH effect on the CO_2 formation follows from the equilibrium:
$$H^+ + HCO_3^- \rightleftharpoons H_2O + CO_2 \text{ (g)} - - - - - - - - - - - - - - - - \quad (12)$$
for which: $\lg K = \lg \varsigma CO_2 + pH - \lg [HCO_3^-] = 7.9 - - - - - - - - - - - \quad (12a)$

The main factors responsible for the decline of ςCO_2 after several weeks are a) the escape of CO_2 as gasbubbles; b) microbial reduction of CO_2 to CH_4; c) precipitation of poorly soluble carbonates as e.g. $MnCO_3$ (rhodochrosite); and 4) the effect of leaching (IRRI, 1964).

TABLE II.122. *Normative mineralogical composition of profiles 34 to 37 and of the partly weathered andesitic ash* (equivalent percentages)

Prof.	material	Kd	Sm	Ms	Go	Plg	Pyr + Amph	Gibb	Q	Ru	Str	MnO
34	Ap1 hor.	84.6	3.5	–	10.1	6.4	0.8	–	2.6	1.3	0.5	0.2
	clay sep.	82.0	4.5	–	10.5	–	–	–	1.1	1.2	0.6	0.1
	Ap2 hor.	73.6	2.5	–	14.8	3.9	1.7	0.3	1.4	1.2	0.4	0.2
	clay sep.	80.9	3.5	–	11.9	–	–	–	1.9	1.1	0.6	0.1
	B21 hor.	77.4	2.9	–	11.7	2.7	1.1	1.6	0.3	1.2	0.6	0.5
	clay sep.	85.3	3.5	–	9.1	–	–	–	0.3	1.0	0.7	0.1
	B22 hor.	80.4	2.9	–	10.9	1.6	0.8	–	1.7	1.1	0.6	0.1
	clay sep.	85.1	3.5	–	9.3	–	–	–	0.5	1.0	0.5	0.1
35	A1 hor.	70.1	2.9	–	10.9	5.0	2.5	–	6.6	1.3	0.6	0.1
	clay sep.	81.5	5.1	tr	10.5	–	–	–	1.0	1.1	0.7	0.1
	B21 hor.	70.9	3.0	–	11.1	2.9	1.7	–	8.3	1.3	0.6	0.2
	clay sep.	80.9	5.4	tr	10.6	–	–	–	1.2	1.1	0.7	0.1
	B22 hor.	74.1	1.8	1.0	11.2	2.1	2.0	–	5.5	1.3	0.7	0.3
	clay sep.	83.1	3.3	1.8	10.0	–	–	–	–	1.0	0.7	0.1
	B23 hor.	75.4	1.9	0.6	10.8	2.4	1.6	–	5.2	1.2	0.6	0.3
	clay sep.	83.5	3.2	1.0	9.9	–	–	–	0.7	1.0	0.6	0.1
36	Ap1 clay sep.	84.1	2.6	1.0	9.3	–	–	–	1.3	1.1	0.5	0.1
	Ap2 clay sep.	85.1	1.0	1.0	9.4	–	–	–	1.8	1.1	0.5	0.1
	B21 clay sep.	85.3	2.6	–	9.1	–	–	–	1.3	1.1	0.5	0.1
	B22 clay sep.	86.1	3.1	–	9.1	–	–	–	–	1.1	0.5	0.1
37	Ap clay sep.	83.1	3.1	1.0	9.2	–	–	–	1.7	1.1	0.7	0.1
	B21 clay sep.	82.9	3.1	1.0	9.2	–	–	–	2.1	1.1	0.5	0.1
	B22 clay sep.	84.5	3.1	–	9.1	–	–	–	1.6	1.1	0.5	0.1
	B23 clay sep.	83.9	3.1	–	9.2	–	–	–	2.2	1.1	0.4	0.1
	C mat.	26.0	0.8	3.0	5.0	42.5	8.3	13.4	–	0.6	0.1	0.3
	clay sep.	72.6	5.3	3.9	9.7	–	–	6.9	0.1	0.9	0.6	–

Kd = kandites; Sm = smectites; Ms = muscovite (illite); Go = goethite; Plg = plagioclases; Pyr + Amph = pyroxenes + amphiboles; Gibb = gibbsite; Q = silica; Ru = rutile (anatase); Str = strengite.

The kinetics of CO_2 in paddy soils are very important in controlling the pH and the Mn^{2+} activity and will be discussed later.

Besides CO_2 and CH_4, small quantities of N_2 (denitrification), H_2 (mainly by decomposition of fatty acids) and H_2S (sulfate reduction) can be produced. H_2 generally accumulates after several weeks (Takai et al., 1956), but it can be rapidly formed on flooding of soils that contain appreciable amounts of easily decomposable carbohy-drates. In this case the redox-potential (E_h) suddenly drops to very low values (down to $-0.4V$) which can be explained in terms of the H_2/H^+ redox-couple (Yamane and Sato, 1968).

The conversion of NO_3^- to N_2 starts immediately after flooding because this reduction occurs at comparatively high E_h levels and because many micro-organisms are able to use NO_3^- as electron acceptor. Denitrification is generally not very im-portant in soil formation, but when NO_3^- is present in large amounts the reduction of manganese and ferric oxides can be delayed (Ponnamperuma, 1955).

The production of the gases mentioned above probably accounts for the develop-ment of the gasbubble-like structure in the soil, described in section 4.1.3.

4.1.5.1.2. *Reduction of iron and manganese*
Mn(IV), Mn(III), Mn(II, III) and Fe(III) oxides can all be reduced to yield Mn_2^+ and Fe_2^+ ions. The reduction can be the result of metabolic processes of anaerobic bacteria (Mann and Quastel, 1946; Kumura et al., 1963) but the reducing effect of organic decomposition products such as hydroxy fatty acids and polyphenolic substances is probably more important and certainly in the case of iron (Bloomfield, 1951, 1956; Bromfield, 1954).

The concentrations of Mn^{2+} and Fe^{2+} show a distinct increase during the first weeks

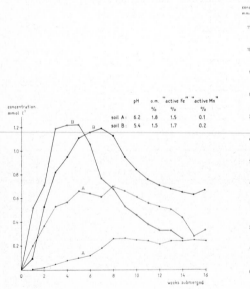

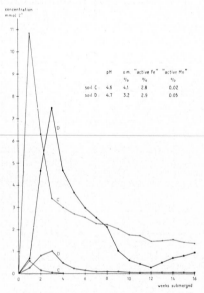

FIG. II.54a. *Kinetics of Fe^{2+} (•) and Mn^{2+} (o) in the soil solution of two flooded soils high in active manganese and low in organic matter (data from IRRI, 1964)*

FIG. II.54b. *Kinetics of Fe^{2+} (•) and Mn^{2+} (o) in the soil solution of two flooded soils high in active Fe and or-ganic matter and with low pH (data from IRRI, 1964)*

after the onset of reduction and decrease gradually to a fairly constant level afterwards. As can be seen from figs. II.54a and 54b (data taken from IRRI, 1964) the
kinetics of Mn^{2+} and Fe^{2+} are strongly influenced by such soil characteristics as pH,
organic matter content and the amounts of easily reducible iron and manganese present. The peaks of the graph are steeper and higher as the pH is lower and the organic
matter content higher. Manganese appears to be more readily reduced than iron if the
ncrease in the concentrations of both ions is comparatively slow, such as in soils A and
B (fig. II.54a).

An interpretation of the redox systems that account for the kinetics of iron and
manganese in flooded soils is difficult. Many attempts to correlate data on E_h, pH,
$[Fe^{2+}]$, and $[Mn^{2+}]$ with several well-established ferric-ferrous and manganese-
manganous redox systems were not successful (IRRI, 1964; Bohn, 1968). One disadvantage is that the E_h measurement in the soil is often inconsistent.

Ponnamperuma and co-workers (IRRI, 1964, 1965; Ponnamperuma et al., 1967)
made E_h–pH measurements in the soil solution of paddy soils. The solution was
drawn by gravity through a sintered glasstube from a pot with water-saturated soil and
transferred into a N_2-filled cell constructed for E_h–pH determinations. The 'solution
E_h' values were highly consistent, positive throughout the inundation period and, in the
last stages of reduction, 0.1 to 0.3 V higher than the redox potentials measured in the
soil. For soils low in manganese the following equilibria have been established:

$$Fe^{2+} + 3H_2O \rightleftharpoons Fe(OH)_3 \text{ (s)} + 3H^+ + e \quad - - - - - - - - - - - - - - - - - - \quad (13)$$

$$E_{h\,13} = 1.06 - 0.059 \lg [Fe^{2+}] - 0.177\,pH - - - - - - - - - - - - - - - - - - \quad (13a)$$

$$Fe_3(OH)_8 \text{ (s)} + H_2O \rightleftharpoons 3Fe(OH)_2 \text{ (s)} + 8H^+ + e \quad - - - - - - - - - - - \quad (14)$$

$$E_{h\,14} = 0.43 - 0.059\,pH - \quad (14a)$$

$$3Fe^{2+} + 8H_2O \rightleftharpoons Fe_3(OH)_8 \text{ (s)} + 8H^+ + 2e \quad - - - - - - - - - - - - - - \quad (15)$$

$$E_{h\,15} = 1.37 - 0.089 \lg [Fe^{2+}] - 0.236\,pH - - - - - - - - - - - - - - - - - - \quad (15a)$$

Equation (13a) appeared to hold throughout the inundation period, whereas the
equations (14a) and (15a) were closely followed after the maximum in water-soluble
iron had been reached.

Similarly, data on the 'solution E_h', pH, $[Mn^{2+}]$, and ςCO_2 for flooded soils high in
active manganese, indicated the participation of $Mn(OH)_3$, hydrous Mn_3O_4 and
$MnCO_3$ during the dissolution and precipitation of Mn^{2+}. However, it was necessary
to estimate again ΔF_f° values for $Mn(OH)_3$ and Mn_3O_4, as the values given by Garrels
and Christ (1965) were not adequate. The values used by Ponnamperuma were –197.6
for $Mn(OH)_3$ and –325 kcal/mol for Mn_3O_4.

It can be argued that the redox systems shown by Ponnamperuma and co-workers to
be present, are produced by the oxidation of O_2 adsorbed on the surface of the Pt
electrodes or by very small impurities in the N_2 gas that was used during and after the
collection of the soil solution. This can have occurred in the following manner:
Suppose a solution with pH 6.5 and $[Fe^{2+}] = 10^{-3}$; in this case only 4×10^{-10} moles
O_2/l are necessary to increase the E_h from –0.22 to +0.08 V (which are normal values
for 'soil E_h' and 'solution E_h' respectively), causing the precipitation of $Fe(OH)_3$. At a
higher pH or lower $[Fe^{2+}]$, $Fe_3(OH)_8$ is precipitated. After the precipitation of an
immeasurably small quantity of $Fe(OH)_3$ or $Fe_3(OH)_8$, the E_h no longer depends on
the labile $[Fe^{3+}]/[Fe^{2+}]$ ratio and is fairly stable. In fact Doyle (1968) found evidence

for an E_h-determining ferric oxide coating on the Pt-electrode in ferrous sulfate solutions under laboratory conditions.

Preliminary experiments on E_h measurements in the soil solution of two flooded
soils (Van Breemen, 1969) indicated that the calculated E_h° in the equation:

$$E_h = E_h^\circ - 0.059 \lg [Fe^{2+}] - 0.177 \, pH \quad - \quad (16)$$

showed a gradual decrease from values near to $+1.06$ V (E_h° for the $Fe^{2+} - Fe(OH)_3$
couple: equation 13a) just after flooding to values near $+0.72$ V (E_h° for the $Fe^{2+}/$
$\alpha-FeOOH$ couple: see Part III, Chapter 1). This suggests that a series of indefinite,
hydrated ferric oxides ('limonite'), that probably form a continuous thermodynamic
sequence, participate in the 'solution reduction' of iron in flooded soils. The existence
of such a sequence has been discussed by Garrels (1959) in connection with the ageing
of an amorphous $Fe(OH)_3$ precipitate.

A fraction of the ferric oxides in most soils consists of amorphous $Fe(OH)_3$ precipitate (Bohn, 1967) and hydromorphic soils may contain more amorphous iron hydroxides than comparable upland soils. Therefore one may expect the Fe^{2+} activity to be
regulated by $Fe(OH)_3$ as long as only a small amount of Fe^{2+} enters into solution. This
may be the case in soils with a low organic matter content and/or a high pH value. For
example, 10 out of 29 paddy soils with a high pH (6.5 ± 0.6[1]) and a low organic matter
content (2.7 ± 1.3 %[1]) had, two weeks after flooding, soil E_h values differing less than
0.05 V from the E_h value that could be expected on the basis of the $Fe^{2+}/Fe(OH)_3$
system. At the same time, the 19 other soils with lower pH values (5.7 ± 0.7[1]) and
more organic matter (3.8 ± 1.8[1]) showed soil E_h values that were $0.15 - 0.10$ V lower
than that expected for the $Fe^{2+}/Fe(OH)_3$ redox system (derived from data given in
IRRI, 1964). In this second group of soils, the ferrous/ferric oxide equilibrium obviously had already adjusted to the presence of oxides of higher stability. Of these
compounds $\gamma-FeOOH$ (lepidocrocite) may be important, because this mineral has
been shown to dominate the crystalline fraction of the ferric oxides in the hydromorphic
soils and in paddy soils (Brown, 1953, 1954; Kamoshita and Iwasa, 1959).

According to Ponnamperuma and co-workers, the values of $[Fe^{2+}]$, 'solution E_h',
and pH correspond with the equations (14a) and (15a) from the peak in water-soluble
Fe^{2+} onwards. Therefore:

$$0.43 - 0.059 pH = 1.37 - 0.089 \lg [Fe^{2+}] - 0.236 pH$$

or: $$\lg [Fe^{2+}] + 2pH = 10.66$$

Hence, in the precipitation stage, the Fe^{2+} activity does not conform to any measured
E_h value and is only determined by the pH. By using experimentally determined E_h
values instead of the theoretical ones of 0.43 and 1.37 V, $\lg [Fe^{2+}] + 2pH$ appeared to
be 10.1 ± 0.5, rather than 10.66, for 32 soils with widely different characteristics
(derived from data of Ponnamperuma et al., 1967). It seems as if Fe^{2+} is precipitated to
form $Fe(OH)_2$:

$$Fe^{2+} + 2H_2O \rightleftharpoons Fe(OH)_2 (s) + 2H^+ \quad - - - - - - - - - - - - - - - - - - \quad (17)$$

$$-\lg K_{17} = +10.1 = \lg [Fe^{2+}] + 2pH \quad - - - - - - - - - - - - - - - - - - - \quad (17a)$$

or: $$K_{so} = [Fe^{2+}][OH^-]^2 = 1.3 \times 10^{-18} \quad - - - - - - - - - - - - - - - - - \quad (17b)$$

However, figures published on the solubility product of $Fe(OH)_2$ are almost 10^3 times

[1] The figures refer to mean values and standard deviations.

lower (e.g. 8×10^{-16}; Sillén and Martell, 1964) and it is therefore very improbable that the precipitate really consists of $Fe(OH)_2$. Possibly, the equilibrium is determined by a $Fe(II)Fe(III)$-hydroxide with a high $Fe(II)/Fe(III)$ ratio, e.g. $Fe_4(OH)_{10}$ (Arden, 1950; Ponnamperuma et al., 1967). The equilibrium between Fe^{2+} and such a compound is mainly governed by the pH and is little effected by E_h.

The assumption, however, that only the pH determines Fe^{2+} activity in the presence of a hypothetical '$Fe(OH)_2$' according to equation (17a), allows a fairly good approximation of the quantity of $[Fe^{2+}]$ in flooded soils after the peak in water-soluble iron content has been reached.

If the partial CO_2 pressure exceeds $10^{-2.6}$ atmosphere, which is almost invariably the case in flooded soils even after prolonged submergence (IRRI, 1964), '$Fe(OH)_2$' is actually metastable with respect to $FeCO_3$ (siderite):

$$FeCO_3\,(s) + 2H^+ \rightleftharpoons Fe^{2+} + CO_2\,(g) + H_2O ------------------ \quad (18)$$
$$\text{for which: } \lg [Fe^{2+}] + 2pH = 7.5 - \lg_{\varsigma}CO_2 ---------------- \quad (18a)$$

(Garrels and Christ, 1965). Huber and Garrels (1953) have shown in laboratory experiments that siderite formation is slow compared to the precipitation of amorphous iron hydroxides; obviously, kinetic factors must account for the supersaturation with respect to $FeCO_3$ in the interstitial solution of most paddy soils. However, siderite concretions have been found in very poorly drained paddy soils high in organic matter, where reduced conditions and high CO_2 pressures may persist over long periods (Yamasaki and Yoshizawa, 1961; Ponnamperuma et al., 1967).

Summarizing, the 'solution reduction' of ferric oxides and the subsequent precipitation of ferrous iron in flooded soils can be formulated by the equations (16) (with E_h varying from 1.06 to 0.72 V) and (17a). An E_h–pH diagram, based on these relationships and calculated for $[Fe^{2+}]$ of 10^{-3}, is given in fig. II.55. In the first stages of

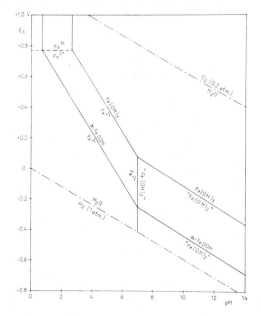

FIG. II.55. E_h–pH diagram, showing the possible equilibrium relationships between iron compounds in flooded soils; $[Fe^{2+}] = 10^{-3}$; 25°C; 1 atm. total pressure

solution-reduction of iron, the E_h–pH values drop near the $Fe(OH)_3/Fe^{2+}$ boundary and move towards the α–$FeOOH/Fe^{2+}$ boundary as the ferric oxides of lower stability disappear. In the course of this process, both pH and $[Fe^{2+}]$ increase and '$Fe(OH)_2$' is formed when the value of lg $[Fe^{2+}]$ + 2pH approaches 10.1.

The assumption that the presence of $Mn(OH)_3$ and hydrous Mn_3O_4 governs the manganese equilibria in flooded soils (IRRI, 1965) can be criticized on the same grounds as the hypothesis on the iron redox systems put forward by Ponnamperuma et al. (1967). Also in the case of manganese, a thermodynamic sequence of Mn–(hydr)-oxides should probably be considered. Recently, Ponnamperuma et al. (1969) suggested the presence of mixed iron-manganese oxides which have much lower apparent free-energies of formation than the pure Mn oxides (see also p. 444).

In whatever form the reducible manganese is present, Mn^{2+} will be liberated at a higher E_h–level than Fe^{2+} in flooded soils. This can be seen in fig. 11.56, where the hatched areas represent the E_h–pH stability fields of manganese oxides (with stabilities between $Mn(OH)_3$ and MnO_2, $MnOOH$, and Mn_3O_4) and iron oxides (between $Fe(OH)_3$ and α–$FeOOH$) in equilibrium with Mn^{2+} and Fe^{2+}, both at an activity of 10^{-3}. The figure shows that manganese will be dissolved more readily than iron in the course of the drop in E_h upon flooding.

The decrease in the manganese concentration after prolonged flooding has been attributed to the formation of $MnCO_3$ (IRRI, 1965). The following equation can be formulated based on $\Delta F^\circ_{fMnCO_3} = -194.8$ kcal/mole (Morgan, 1967) and the ΔF°_f values for the other compounds as given by Garrels and Christ (1965):

$$Mn^{2+} + 2\,H_2O \rightleftharpoons MnOOH + 4\,H^+ + 2e$$
$$E_h = 1.225 - 0.030\ \text{lg}\ [Mn^{2+}] - 0.118\ \text{pH}$$

$$Mn^{2+} + 2\,H_2O \rightleftharpoons MnO_2 + 3\,H^+ + e$$
$$E_h = 1.47 - 0.059\ \text{lg}\ [Mn^{2+}] - 0.177\ \text{pH}$$

$$3\,Mn^{2+} + 4\,H_2O \rightleftharpoons Mn_3O_4 + 8\,H^+ + 2e$$
$$E_h = 1.82 - 0.089\ \text{lg}\ [Mn^{2+}] - 0.236\ \text{pH}$$

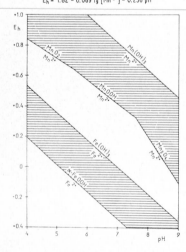

FIG. 11.56. E_h–pH diagram, showing the environments where Mn^{2+} and Fe^{2+} at an activity of 10^{-3} are in equilibrium with the various indicated oxides

$$Mn^{2+} + H_2O + CO_2(g) \rightleftharpoons MnCO_3(s) + 2H^+ - - - - - - - - - - - - - \quad (19)$$

and: $-lgK_{19} = 7.75 = lg[Mn^{2+}] + lg_{\varsigma}CO^2 + 2pH \quad - - - - - - - - - - - - \quad (19a)$

From data on five submerged paddy soils high in manganese (0.20–0.35% 'active' Mn: IRRI, 1965) the value of lg $[Mn^{2+}] + lg_{\varsigma}CO_2 + 2pH$ has been calculated to be 9.45 $\pm$ 0.23 from the peak in content of water-soluble Mn onwards. As complexing of Mn^{2+} (e.g. as $MnHCO_3^+$: Morgan, 1967) can hardly account for the difference between the observed and the theoretical values of lgK, the soil solution is supersaturated with respect to $MnCO_3$, probably due to its slow formation (IRRI, 1965). Another possibility is the formation of a metastable carbonate, e.g. $Mn_2(OH)_2CO_3$ (Morgan, 1967).

The effects of certain soil characteristics on the mobility of these elements can be easily imagined considering the above theoretical discussion of iron and manganese equilibria. For example, a pH drop of one unit is accompanied by an increase of $[Fe^{2+}]$ and $[Mn^{2+}]$ with 10^3 or 10^2 for equilibria with Fe(III) and Mn(III) oxides or 'Fe(II)hydroxide' and Mn(II)carbonate if other variables are kept constant. Hence, high concentrations of iron and manganese can be expected in slightly acid soils, especially during the first weeks of reduction.

The content of easily decomposable organic matter is also important. A large quantity of such matter induces intensive reduction shortly after flooding, leading to a rapid accumulation of Fe^{2+} and Mn^{2+} in the soil solution.

The effect of these factors can be observed in, e.g., the near-absence of mottling in calcareous paddy soils (Gupta et al., 1957), or the frequent occurrence of Fe–Mn accumulation horizons in well-drained paddy soils with a low pH level and/or considerable quantities of organic matter.

4.1.5.1.3. *The effect of flooding on the concentrations of other soluble compounds*

Mortimer (1941) observed an increase in water-soluble SiO_2 from 30 to 100 ppm in anaerobically incubated lake mud. A similar effect on the silica concentration was found by Ponnamperuma (1964) when flooding paddy soils. Here, the highest increase in the silica concentration (from 25 ppm SiO_2 directly after submergence to 30 or 40 ppm after 60 days) took place in soils rich in organic matter ($> 6\%$), whereas flooding hardly affected the silica concentration in soils with less than 2% organic matter.

As the concentration of dissolved silica (H_4SiO_4) in equilibrium with solid SiO_2 (either quartz or amorphous silica) is independant of pH if the latter is lower than 8 to 9 (Krauskopf, 1967), the correlation between the release of silica and the organic matter content can be understood in two ways: a) release of SiO_2 from organic matter by its decomposition; this effect will be pronounced if organic matter content is high; b) organic matter induced reduction of ferric hydroxides; these are able to adsorb H_4SiO_4 (McKeague and Cline, 1963) and upon dissolution of ferric hydroxide by reduction, silicic acid is released (Ponnamperuma, 1964).

Most substances dissolving upon flooding tend to disappear after prolonged submergence as a result of precipitation, adsorption, leaching and microbial decomposition, but no such effect has been noted in the case of silica (Ponnamperuma, 1964). The eluviation of easily soluble ('active') silica from the furrow slice of paddy soils (Kawaguchi and Matsuo, 1957; Kanno et al., 1964) probably reflects the long-term

effect of the dissolution of SiO_2 under flooded conditions. However, it is still questionable whether the eluviation of SiO_2 is more pronounced in paddy soils than in comparable upland soils (see table II.117).

The increase in the concentration of other substances upon flooding can be dealt
with in short (for details see: Ponnamperuma, 1964). The release of ammonia is a
result of the mineralization of organic matter under anaerobic conditions. The increase
in the concentration of cations such as Na^+, K^+, Ca^{2+}, etc., can be attributed mainly to
ion-exchange processes involving the adsorption of Fe^{2+} and Mn^{2+}. The $H_2PO_4^-$ concentration is raised, partly as a result of the reduction of ferric phosphates especially if
much organic matter is present.

Finally, flooding may result in the accumulation of a variety of soluble organic
compounds. Acetic, buteric, propionic, and formic acids are quantitatively most
important (Mottomura, 1962; IRRI, 1965). The effect of these and other organic compounds on the mineral equilibria, e.g. by complex formation, may be of interest, but
the available literature gives no information on this subject.

4.1.5.1.4. *The effects of flooding on redox potential and pH*

Under aerobic conditions, the redox potential in the soil (solution) is probably regulated by the O_2/H_2O_2 couple (Sato, 1960), and generally falls between $E_h = 0.86–0.059$
pH (V) and $E_h = 0.68–0.059$ pH (V) (see also: Michard, 1967). Under the pH conditions
of most soils (pH 4–7), the E_h lies between 0.6 and 0.8 volts. Upon flooding, reduction
induces an abrupt drop in the E_h and within one week E_h values between 0.2 and –0.2
volts can be found. In soils high in active manganese and/or low in organic matter, E_h
may remain positive for almost six months. The E_h in soils that contain much iron
and organic matter undergoes a steeper decline and may finally attain lower values
(Ponnamperuma, 1964).

Following inundation the pH increases in acid soils and decreases in calcareous
soils. After 4 to 12 weeks the pH reaches fairly stable values between 6.5 and 7.0 in a
wide variety of soils (Ponnamperuma et al., 1966). The increase in pH is mainly the
result of the uptake of H^+ ions during reduction of iron and manganese oxides, e.g.:

$$Fe_2O_3.nH_2O + 6H^+ + 2e \rightleftharpoons 2Fe^{2+} + (3+n)\,H_2O \quad ------------- \quad (20)$$

Stabilization of the pH between 6.5 and 7.0 takes place when Fe^{2+} and Mn^{2+} begin
to precipitate, when sufficient amounts of CO_2 and HCO_3^- are formed, and when the
Fe and Mn precipitates come into equilibrium with the soil solution (Ponnamperuma
et al., 1966). In calcareous (and alkali) soils the pH is too high to permit a significant
solution-reduction of iron and manganese oxides. Here the acidifying effect of CO_2
accumulation:

$$CO_2 + H_2O \rightleftharpoons HCO_3^- + H^+ \quad ---------------------------- \quad (21)$$

induces a lowering of the pH. H^+ ions are buffered as long as Ca and Mg carbonates
are present, and, if equilibrium is maintained, the following relationship should be
valid:

$$CaCO_3 \text{ (s:calcite)} + 2H^+ \rightleftharpoons Ca^{2+} + CO_2 \text{ (g)} + H_2O \quad -------- \quad (22)$$

with: $\lg K_{22} = \lg [Ca^{2+}] + \lg \varsigma CO_2 + 2pH = 9.8 \quad ----------- \quad (22a)$

(the value of $\lg K_{22}$ has been calculated from standard free energy values listed by
Garrels and Christ, 1965).

In calcareous paddy soils the actual pH values were slightly higher than those predicted by equation (22a) (Ponnamperuma et al., 1966). This was attributed to the presence of Mg carbonates or to Ca carbonates being less stable than calcite (Ponnamperuma et al., 1969).

4.1.5.2. *Processes accompanying oxidation*

During the fallow period, oxidative conditions will prevail in the greater part of the top soil. However, in the flooded soils oxidation may also occur locally, viz. in the upper 0.1 to 2 cms of the profile, where some O_2 may penetrate the soil and, in the case of well-drained paddy soils, in the zone below the water-saturated topsoil.

As gas diffusion in standing water is extremely slow, thermally induced water movement and O_2 produced by the photosynthetic activity of e.g. algae are probably the main factors involved in the development of the thin oxidized toplayer in which the redox potential can show a drop from 0.6 to 0.1 V (De Gee, 1950). In soils with a well-developed iron-manganese accumulation horizon, E_h may increase with depth from 0.0 V in the water-saturated furrow slice to +0.5 V below the Fe-Mn pan (De Gee, 1950).

The presence of an oxidized subsoil in flooded fields can easily be possible if an impermeable horizon is present, but also in well-drained paddy soils without a textural B horizon, a well-developed Fe/Mn layer, or an impervious plough pan, the E_h in the subsoil may remain as high as 0.3 V throughout the inundation period (Aomine, 1962). Perhaps in some soils an oxidized zone may be sandwiched between the ground-water table and the furrow slice if air is trapped after rapid sheet flooding (Grant, 1964), but it is difficult to imagine this to be possible in excessively drained lowland paddy soils and in deep permeable latosols that do not yet show plough pans or Fe-Mn accumulation horizons (see: Mitsuchi, 1968).

E_h measurements in soil samples taken at different depths from one paddy soil and

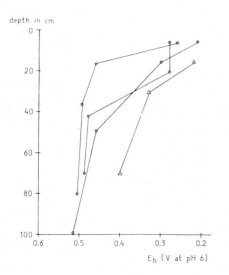

FIG. II.57. *Redox potentials of paddy soil samples from different dephts, that have been inundated separately in the laboratory for 14 days (○) and 30 days (△) respectively; ○: red soils from Kiangsi, China (Yu and Li, 1956); △: averages of 5 Japanese paddy soils (Shiori and Tanada, 1954)*

submerged separately in the laboratory, show that the material from the subsoil may remain in a comparatively high state of oxidation (E_h = 0.4 to 0.5 V) for considerable time (fig. II.57), so even if water-saturated, the subsoil may remain in an oxidized condition for 2 to 4 weeks and probably longer. The difference in the kinetics of reduction in the surface and subsoil is undoubtedly the result of the difference in organic matter content (Mitsui, 1964).

At the interface of predominantly reduced and predominantly oxidized horizons, Fe^{2+} and Mn^{2+} can be oxidized and precipitated as Fe(III) and Mn(III, IV) oxides. The concentration gradient that develops as a result of this process, stimulates the diffusion of Fe^{2+} and Mn^{2+} and a distinct accumulation may occur. The effect may be seen clearly in the upper few cms of a flooded soil where a bleached layer, depleted of oxidizable compounds develops just below the thin oxidized layer that is characterized by the presence of accumulated ferric hydroxides (Shiori and Tanada, 1954). This is only temporary because of frequent disturbances during soil preparation. During the fallow a similar process can take place at the groundwater level, but here capillary rise of water containing Fe^{2+} and Mn^{2+} will stimulate the accumulation of hydroxides. The lower accumulation horizons in fig. II.51 may have been developed in this way.

The enrichment of iron and manganese below the furrow slice of well-drained paddy soils with oxidized subsoils may be helped by mass transport of Mn^{2+} and Fe^{2+} through water percolation, at least initially. Once such an accumulation horizon is fairly well developed it may become impermeable to water, leading to a more pronounced differentiation between the reduced topsoil and the oxidized subsoil, and adding to the possibilities for future accumulation.

Finally, local accumulations of ferric and manganic compounds in the form of mottles and concretions may develop in horizons where oxidized and reduced conditions alternate. Such mottles may also develop in the neighbourhood of the oxidized rhizosphere of rice or other aquatic plants in an otherwise reduced matrix.

Because accumulation will be further stimulated if the reduced phase of the soil contains large quantities of dissolved iron and manganese, alternate flooding and drying, leading to a rapid building up of high Fe^{2+} and Mn^{2+} concentrations after each flooding (see figs. II.54a and 54b) is important. This may partly explain why iron and manganese are accumulated more strongly underneath the furrow slice than above the permanently reduced subsoil (see fig. II.51).

Irrespective of the type of oxide that is formed, iron will be precipitated more readily than manganese upon oxidation, as can be seen from fig. II.56 and Part III, Chapter I. This accounts for the separation between iron and manganese commonly observed in accumulation zones. Probably the oxidation products consist mainly of somewhat amorphous, metastable hydroxides, especially when oxidation is rapid (Huber and Garrels, 1953; Morgan, 1967). However, the crystalline fraction of the iron oxides in hydromorphic soils is generally dominated by lepidocrocite, as has been mentioned above. This accords with the fact that lepidocrocite can be most easily prepared from ferrous iron, especially in the presence of organic matter (Van Schuylenborgh, 1964). On the other hand, certain organic substances present in the soil tend to inhibit the crystallization of amorphous iron oxides (Schwertmann et al., 1968) and possibly also prevent the formation of crystalline iron oxides during oxidation.

After several weeks of submergence, reduced iron and manganese are mainly present in the form of precipitated hydroxides and carbonates. In short-term processes, e.g. in the formation of mottles, the oxidation of these solid compounds may be more important than the oxidation and precipitation of dissolved iron and manganese. Therefore, besides diffusion and oxidation of dissolved Fe^{2+} and Mn^{2+}, local precipitation of Fe(II) and Mn(II) compounds may be important in the formation of mottles upon drainage. Other factors that can play a rôle here probably include adsorption phenomena and irregular distribution of reducing environments as a result of local concentrations of organic materials.

LITERATURE CITED

AOMINE, S. 1962 A review of research on redox potentials of paddy soils in Japan. *Soil Sci.* 94: 6-13.

ARDEN, T.V. 1950 The solubility product of ferrous ferrosic hydroxides. *J. chem. Sic.:* 882-885.

BARANY, R. 1964 Heat and free-energy of formation of muscovite. *U.S. Bur. Mines, Rep. Invest. 6356:* pp. 13.

— and KELLEY, K.K. 1961 Heats and free-energies of formation of gibbsite, kaolinite, halloysite, and dickite. *U.S. Bur. Mines, Rep. Invest. 5825:* pp. 13.

BLOOMFIELD, C. 1951 Experiments on the mechanism of gley formation. *J. Soil Sci.*, 2: 196-211.

— 1956 The solution reduction of ferric oxide by aqueous leaf extracts. The role of certain constituents of the extracts. *6th Int. Cong. Soil. Sci.* B: 427-432.

BOHN, H.L. 1967 The (Fe) (OH)^3 ion product in suspensions of acid soils. *Soil Sci. Soc. Am. Proc.*, 31: 641-644.

— 1968 Electromotive force of inert electrodes in soil suspensions. *Soil Sci. Soc. Am. Proc.*, 32: 211-215.

BRIONES, A.A. and CAGAUAN, B.G. 1964 Moisture retention of some paddy soils in Laguna. *The Phill. Agriculturist*, 48: 61-81.

BROMFIELD, S.M. 1954 The reduction of iron-oxide by bacteria. *J. Soil Sci.*, 5: 129-139.

BROWN, G. 1953 The occurrence of lepidocrocite in some British soils. *J. Soil Sci.*, 4: 220-228.

— 1954 Soil morphology and mineralogy. A quantitative study of some gleyed soils from north-west England. *J. Soil Sci.*, 5: 145-155.

CROMPTON, E. 1952 Some morphological features associated with poor soil drainage. *J. Soil Sci.*, 3: 277-289.

DE GEE, J.C. 1950 Preliminary oxidation potential determination in a 'sawah' profile near Bogor (Java). *Trans. 4th Int. Cong. Soil Sci.*, 1: 300-301.

DOYLE, R.W. 1968 The origin of the ferrous ionferric oxide Nernst potential in environments containing dissolved ferrous ion. *Am. J. Sci.*, 266: 840-859.

DUDAL, R. 1958 Paddy soils. *Int. Rice Comm. News letter, VII No. 2:* 19-27.

— and MOORMANN, F.R. 1964 Major soils of Southeast Asia. *J. trop. Georg.:* 54-80.

FAO 1965 The world rice economy in figures. *Comm. Ref. series 3*, FAO, Rome, pp. 134.

GARRELS, R.M. 1959 Rates of geochemical reactions at low temperatures and pressures. In: *Researches in Geochemistry*, I: 25-37.

— and CHRIST, CH.L. 1965 Solutions, minerals, and equilibria. *Tokyo*, pp. 450.

GRANT, C.J. 1964 Soil characteristics associated with the wet cultivation of rice. – The mineral Nutrition of the rice plant. *Proc. Symp. Int. Rice Res. Inst. Los Banos:* 15-28.

GRIST, D.H. 1959 Rice. *3rd Ed. Longmans Green*, London, pp. 472.

GUPTA, R.N., AGARWAL, R.R. and MEHROTRA, C.L. 1957 Genetics and pedochemical characteristics of Dhankar: grey hydromorphic soils in the lower Gangetic plains of Utta Pradash. *J. Int. Soc. Soil Sci.*, 5: 5–12.

HUBER, M.K. and GARRELS, R.M. 1953 Relation of pH and oxidation potential to sedimentary iron formation. *Econ. Geol.*, 48: 337–357.

IRI, H., MARUTA, I., TAKAHASHI, I. and KUBOTA, M. 1958 The variation of ferrous iron content in soil profiles under flooded condition of rice field (I). *Soil and Plant Food*, 3: 36–47.

IRRI 1964 Annual Report 1964. *Int. Rice Res. Inst.*, Los Banos. The Philippines.

— 1965 Annual Report 1965 *Int. Rice Res. Inst.*, Los Banos. The Philippines.

KAMOSHITA, Y. and IWASA, Y. 1959 On the rusty mottles in paddy field soils. *J. Soil Sci. and Man. Japan*, 30: 185–188.

KANG, S.H. and MARKART, S. 1959 Ein Beitrag zur Kenntnis nord-ost koreanischer Reisböden. I. und II. *Albr. Thaer Arch.*, 4: 268–292; 405–435.

KANNO, J. 1962 A new classification system of rice soils in Japan. Trans. Joint *Meeting Comm. IV and V, Int. Soc. Soil Sci.*, New Zealand: 617–624.

KANNO, J., HONJO, Y., ARIMURA, S. and TOKUDOME, S. 1964 Genesis and characteristics of rice soils, developed on polder lands of the Shiroishi area, Kyushu. *Soil Sci. Pl. Nutr.*, 10: 1–20.

KAWAGUCHI, K. and MATSUO, Y. 1957 Movements of active oxides in dry paddy soil profiles. *Trans. 6th Int. Cong. Soil Sci.*, 1: 300–301.

—, HATTORI, T., and WAKI, K. 1957 Some chemical and mineralogical studies on profiles of dry rice fields of polder lands in Kojima Basin, Okayama Pref. Japan. *Soil and Pl. Food*, 3: 7–13.

KOENIGS, F.F.R. 1950 A 'sawah' profile near Bogor (Java). *Trans. 4th Int. Cong. Soil Sci.*, 1: 297–300.

KRAUSKOPF, K.B. 1967 Introduction to geochemistry. New York, pp. 771.

KUMURA, T., TAKAI, T. and ISHIKAWA, K. 1963 Microbial reduction mechanism of ferric iron in paddy soils (I). *Soil Sci. Pl. Nutr.*, 9: 171–175.

MANN, P.J.G. and QUASTEL, J.H. 1946 Manganese metabolism in soils. *Nature*, 1958: 171–175.

MCKEAGUE, J.A. and CLINE, M.G. 1963 Silica in soils. *Adv. in Agron.*, 15: 339–396.

MICHARD, G. 1967 Significance of redox potentials in natural waters. Conditions for applications of E_h-pH diagrams. *C.A.*, 68: 33045a.

MITSUCHI, M. 1968 Profile differentiation of surface water type paddy soils under different drainage conditions. *Soil Sci. Pl .Nutr.*, 14: 207.

MITSUI, S. 1964 Inorganic nutrition, fertilisation and soil amelioration for lowland rice. 4th Ed. *Yokende Ltd.*, pp. 107.

MOOMAW, J.C. and VERGARA, B.S. 1964 The environment of tropical rice production. *Min. Nutr. Rice Plant, IRRI Symp.*, Baltimore: 3–13.

MOORMANN, F.R., MONTRAKUN, S. and PANICHAPONG, S. 1964 Soils of Northeastern Thailand, a key to their identification and survey. *Soil Survey Div., Land Dev. Dept.*, Bangkok: pp. 32.

MORGAN, J.J. 1967 Chemical equilibria and kinetic properties of manganese in natural waters. In: *Principles and Applications of Water Chemistry by S. D. Faust and J. V. Hunter*, New York: 561–624.

MORTIMER, C.H. 1941 The exchange of dissolved substances between mud and water in lakes. *J. Ecol.*, 29: 280–329.

MOTOMURA, S. 1962 Effect of organic matters on the formation of ferrous iron in soil. *Soil Sci. Pl. Nutr.*, 8: 20–29.

OLDEMAN, L.R. 1967 De studiekartering Magenta, Suriname. *Student Rep.*, Wageningen: pp. 27.

OYAMA, M. 1962 A classification system of paddy rice field soils, based on their diagnostic horizons. *Bull. Nat. Inst. Agr. Sci.*, *Series B*, No. 12: 360–372.

PHILLIS, E. 1963 Profiles and permeability in Malayan padi soils. *The Malayan agric. J.*, 44: 3–17.

PONNAMPERUMA, F.N. 1955 The chemistry of submerged soils in relation to the growth and yield of rice. *Thesis Cornell Univ.*: pp. 208.

— 1964 Dynamic aspects of flooded soils. In: The mineral nutrition of the rice plant, IRRI. *Baltimore:* 295–328.

—, CASTRO, R.U. and VALENCIA, C.M. 1969 Experimental study of the influence of the partial pressure of carbon dioxide on the pH values of aqueous carbonate systems. *Soil Sci. Soc. Am. Proc.*, 33: 239–241.

—, LOY, T.A. and TIANCO, E.M. 1969 Redox systems in flooded soils: II. The manganese oxide systems. *Soil Sci.*, 108: 48–57.

—, MARTINEZ, E. and LOY, T. 1966 Influence of redox potential and partial pressure of carbon dioxide on pH values and the suspension effect of flooded soils. *Soil Sci.*, 101: 421–431.

—, TIANCO, E.M. and LOY, T. 1967 Redox equilibria in flooded soils. I. The iron hydroxide system. *Soil Sci.*, 103: 374–382.

RAYMUNDO, M.E. PANTASTICO, E.B. and MANARPAAC, V.T. 1962 Some physical and chemical properties of an upland soil and its associated paddy soils. *Phil. Agricst.*, 46: 560–569.

REESMAN, A.L. and KELLER, W.D. 1968 Aqueous solubility studies of high-alumina and clay minerals. *Am. Min.*, 53: 929–942.

ROSSINI, F.D. et al 1952 Selected values of chemical thermodynamic properties. *U.S. Nat. Bur. Stand. Circ. 500.*

SATO, M. 1960 Oxidation of sulfide ore bodies. 1. Geochemical environments in terms of E_h and pH. *Econ. Geol.*, 55: 928–961.

SCHWERTMANN, U., FISCHER, W.R. and PAPENDORF, H. 1968 The influence of organic compounds on the formation of iron oxides. *Trans. 9th Int. Cong. Soil Sci.*, I: 645–655.

SHIORI, M. and TANADA, T. 1954 The chemistry of paddy soils in Japan. *Min. Agric. and Forestry*, Japan: pp. 45.

SILLÉN, L.G. and MARTELL, A.E. 1964 Stability constants of metal ion complexes. *The Chemical Society*, London.

SIVARAJASINGHAM, S. 1963 Classification of rice field soils. *Agron. Trop.*, 18: 769–772.

SPENCER, J.E. and HALE, G.A. 1961 The origin, nature, and distribution of agricultural terracing. *Pac. Viewpoint*, 3: 1–39.

TAKAI, Y., KOYAMA, T. and KAMURA, T. 1956 Microbiological studies on the reduction process of paddy soils. *Trans. 6th Int. Cong. Soil Sci.*: 527–531.

TAN, K.H. 1968 The genetics and characteristics of paddy soils in Indonesia. *Soil Sci. Pl. Nutr.*, 14: 117–122.

TSAU, S.K. 1964 The peculiarity of soil formation of the paddy soils derived from red earth in Kiangsi, China. *Acta Pedol. Sin.*, 12: 155–163.

UCHIAMA, N. and ONIKURA, Y. 1956a Some considerations in profile investigations of paddy soils. *Trans. 6th Int. Cong. Soil Sci.*: 493–497.

— 1956b Clay minerals in certain paddy soils in Japan. *Trans. 6th Int. Cong. Soil Sci.*: 515–520.

VAN BREEMEN, N. 1969 The effect of ill-defined ferric oxides on the redox characteristics of flooded soils. *Neth. J. agric. Sci.*,

—, OLDEMAN, L.R., PLANTINGA, W.J. and WIELEMAKER, W.G. 1968 The Ifugao rice terraces. *Unpubl. Rep.*, Wageningen: pp. 30.

—, OLDEMAN, L.R. and WIELEMAKER, W.G. 1967 Effect of mechanized rice farming on the soil condition in the alluvial coastal plain of Surinam. *Unpubl. Rep.*, Wageningen: pp. 71.

VAN DER KEVIE, W. 1965 Report on the soil survey in the Boromdhart tract. *Soil Surv. Rep. No. 3₁. Land Dev. Dept.*, Bangkok: pp. 15.

VAN SCHUYLENBORGH, J. 1958 On the genesis and classification of soils, derived from andesitic tuffs under humid tropical conditions. *Neth. J. agric. Sci.*, 6: 99–123.

— 1964 The formation of sesquioxides in soils. In: *Experimental Pedology*, Nottingham: 113–125.

YAMANE, I. and SATO, K. 1968 Initial drop of oxidation-reduction potential in submerged, air-dried soils. *Soil Sci., Pl. Nutr.*, 14: 68–72.

YAMASAKI, T. and YOSHIZAWA, T. 1961 Concretions of ferrous carbonate (siderite) in paddy soils in Japan. I. Occurrence, constituents of ferrous carbonate depositions and the mechanism of its formation. *Bull. Hokuriki agric. Expt. Sta.*, 2: 1–16.

YU, T.J. and LI, S.H. 1956 Studies on oxidation-reduction processes in paddy soils. 1. Conditions affecting redox-potentials. *Rep. for the 6th Int. Cong. Soil Sci. Submitted by the Soil Sci. Soc. China*, Peking: pp. 14.

4.2. ACID SULPHATE SOILS

Acid sulphate soils (Chenery, 1954) also called cat-clays (Van der Spek, 1950) are soils which have been strongly acidified upon aeration, either as a result of natural processes (regression of the sea, land upheaval) or of artificial drainage (empoldering). They are most commonly soils of marine floodplains. The acidification is the result of the oxidation of sulphides or polysulphides which have been accumulated during and after the deposition of the marine sediments. A specific characteristic of these soils is the occurrence of pale-yellow mottles and streaks of basic ferric sulphates, such as jarosite, $KFe_3(SO_4)_2(OH)_6$, natrojarosite $NaFe_3(SO_4)_2(OH)_6$, and carphosiderite, $Fe_3(SO_4)_2(OH)_5H_2O$ (Schwertmann, 1961; Clark et al., 1961; Fleming and Alexander, 1961; Horn et al., 1967; Bloomfield et al., 1968). The yellow mottles occur as coatings over the peds, especially where cracks are evident, or in the form of tubes around old roots and other plant remains. The presence of the yellow material seems closely connected with the presence of organic matter accumulations.

The cat-clays are formed from mud-clays (Edelman and Van Staveren, 1958), which are high in organic matter and sulphides, and have pH values varying from 6 to 7.5. These clays are formed by sedimentation of suspended materials on tidal flats with mangrove vegetation and a constant sea level (Pons, 1966; Brinkman and Pons, 1968). Two types of mangrove vegetations are distinguished, a western and an eastern type. The former occurs along the west-coast of Africa and the coast of South-America and is poor in plant varieties (*Rhizophora Mangle, Laguncularia racemosa, Avicennia nitida,* and *Avicennia tomentosa*). The latter grows along the coasts of the Indian Ocean and eastwards and contains 6 to 7 times as many plant varieties, of which the nipah palm (*Nipa frutescens*) is an important species (Bloomfield et al., 1968).

During deposition varying amounts of sulphate are reduced to sulphides. The sediments under some *Avicennia* species (e.g. *Avic. nitida*) contain practically no sulphides, whereas those under other *Avicennia* species contain great amounts. In sediments with a *Rhizophora* vegetation sulphates are always reduced to sulphides, a process related to the presence of organic matter. Pons and Zonneveld (1965) found a positive correlation between the sulphide and organic matter content in many coastal sediments.

A specific characteristic of the mangrove vegetation is its system of pneumatophores. These grow upwards with the rising mudflat, thus providing the trees with oxygen under extremely wet conditions. The channels formed by these pneumatophores can be found as yellow or brown tubes when the sediments have turned into cat-clays.

During sedimentation the mud is constantly homogenized by crabs (Slager, 1966), thus preventing the formation of stratified sediments.

Upon uninterrupted deposition the mangrove zone widens and the trees gradually die on the landinward side. The sediment then is a nearly totally reduced, unconsolidated, homogeneous mud with varying amounts of lime and sulphides and with a varying number of channels depending on the density of the pneumatophores during sedimentation.

The sulphide (usually pyrites) accumulated during this stage of mud formation is sometimes called secondary pyrites to distinguish it from primary pyrites brought in with the sediment.

When the mangrove vegetation disappears, a brackish herbaceous and shrub swamp vegetation with *Phragmites* species takes over. Also the nipah palm comes into existence under slightly brackish conditions. Under these conditions sulphides (tertiary pyrites) are accumulated in a peaty surface layer. Such swamps may periodically dry out to some depth or may be wet throughout the year. In the first case part of the pyrites will oxidize. This does not result in a strong acidification of the soil, but the mud consolidates to some extent due to irreversible loss of water. Peptisation and mass-illuviation of clay may then compact the subsurface horizon, as some biopores are filled with clay, but new and finer biopores are formed by the swamp vegetation. Further oxidation of iron compounds may take place and iron hydroxides precipitate around rootchannels, giving rise to rather rigid tubes, which ensure rapid permeability. If the swamp remains wet throughout the year, sulphides continue to be accumulated in the peaty surface soil and new, fine rootchannels are also formed. Consolidation of the mud, mass-illuviation of clay and oxidation of ferrous compounds are then hindered.

Gradually the brackish swamp changes to a fresh-water swamp. Naturally, any appreciable accumulation of sulphides ceases due to the low concentration of sulphates. If the sediment formed in this stage becomes thick enough, cat-clays will not be formed upon reclamation provided the drainage depth is not lower than the sulphide-rich subsoil. However, if the soils are empoldered in the brackish stage, the clays sedimented in the mangrove vegetation in particular will give rise to the formation of real cat-clays if the pyrite content is high and lime content low. High lime content and silicate minerals which can be easily hydrolysed (Slager and Van Schuylenborgh, 1970) may weaken acidification, and stimulate the formation of gypsum.

Summarizing, it may be stated that during sedimentation, the dominant chemical and biochemical processes are the reduction of sulphate and ferric compounds to form ferrous polysulphides. The oxidation of ferrous sulphides and formation of sulphuric acid and basic ferric sulphates are the most important results of drainage with the frequent formation of gypsum.

4.2.I. THE PROFILE OF AN ACID SULPHATE SOIL

No detailed descriptions of tropical acid sulphate soil profiles can be found in literature. Fairly detailed descriptions of non-tropical cat-clays in British Columbia are
given by Clark et al. (1961). Bloomfield et al. (1968) describe some characteristics of
Malayan soils in the undrained and drained states. The former have been classified
predominantly in the Linau series (Panton et al., 1965) and consist of a very dark
greyish brown organic clay horizon on top of brown mucks with considerable contents
of buried organic matter of half-decayed *Rhizophora* or *Nipa frutescens* roots. The
subsoil is a massive dark bluish grey, unconsolidated silty clay, often with an H_2S
smell.

After a reclamation period of 30 years, with intense drainage in the last 5 to 6 years,
acid sulphate soils have been developed as three variants of the Salangor series
(Bloomfield et al., 1968). One variant has a surface horizon (25 cm thick) of well-
decomposed peat on top of an organic clay horizon with pale yellow (2.5Y8/4)
deposits (cat-clay). The second has an irreversibly dried peaty top horizon (7.5 to 15
cm thick) on top of clay in which the acid sulphate horizon occurs between 60 and 90
cm. The third variant is the normal clay soil with the acid sulphate horizon at 50 to 75
cm. The pale yellow deposits of jarosite occur as large blotches on ped faces and around
old root channels or other buried organic matter. The jarosite is sometimes covered
with a reddish brown material. There are numerous reddish brown tubes of 5 to 7.5 cm
length with a diameter of half a centimeter occurring locally. According to Bloomfield
et al. (1968) the acid layers are nearly always associated with material sedimented in the
nipah palm swamps.

In the drained soils very strong prismatic structures are formed to a depth of 60 cm,
with a massive greasy clay underneath. Many of the cracks do not close upon wetting
due to irreversible shrinkage of the peaty clay.

A detailed description of an acid sulphate soil profile was obtained from W. van der
Kevie (personal information). The soil occurs in the Central Plain of Thailand,
Ayutthaya Province, District Wang Noi. It is situated on an old tidal flat at an elevation
of 2 m above sea level; the slope is nil. The land is used for broadcast 'floating rice'.
No fertilizers are used and ploughing is done by waterbuffaloes.

The climate is a tropical savannah climate with the highest temperature in April
(30° C) and the lowest in December (25.5° C). Total annual rainfall is 1400 mm, of
which 85 % falls during the period May to October. The parent material is a brackish
heavy clay and the drainage is poor. The land is flooded by rain and river water for 7
to 8 months annually. At the time the description was made groundwater was at 120
cm and the surface was cracked to 20 cm; the cracks were 1 cm wide. The profile
description is as follows:

Horizon	*Depth (cm)*	
A_{pg}	0–27	Black (10YR2/1:m) heavy clay with common, fine, prominent, strong brown (7.5YR4/8) and reddish brown (5YR4/8) mottles. Moderate, medium and coarse angular blocky structure. Hard. Few, very fine, tubular and few, very fine, interstitial pores. Common, fine roots. Clear and smooth boundary.

B$_{1g}$	27–48	Brownish grey (7.5YR5/2:m) heavy clay with many, medium and coarse, prominent, reddish orange (10R4/6) and common, medium, distinct, light brown (7.5YR5/8) mottles. Some black (10YR2/1) inclusions. Moderate, fine, angular blocky structure. Firm. Few, small slickensides. Few, very fine and fine tubular, and few, very fine, interstitial pores. Black cutans along some fine pores. Very few, fine gypsum crystals. Few, very fine roots. Clear and smooth boundary.
B$_{2g}$	48–64	Brownish grey to yellow brownish grey (8.5YR5/2:m) heavy clay with common, medium, prominent, reddish orange (10R4/8) and many, medium, prominent, strong orange brown (7.5YR6/8) mottles. Some large, black (10YR2/1) inclusions, probably old cracks filled up with surface material. Weak, fine and medium, angular blocky structure. Firm. Common, very fine, tubular and few, fine, interstitial pores. Black cutans along some fine pores. Very few, fine, gypsum crystals. Few, very fine roots. Clear and smooth boundary.
B$_{3g}$	64–93	Brownish grey to yellow brownish grey (8.5YR5/2:m) heavy clay with many, medium and coarse, strong orange brown (7.5YR6/8) and light yellow (2.5Y8/6) mottles (cat-clay horizon). Weak, fine and medium, angular blocky structure. Sticky and plastic. Many very fine, tubular and few, fine, interstitial pores. Black cutans along some fine pores. Few, very fine roots. Clear and smooth boundary.
C$_{1g}$	93–150+	Brownish grey (8.5YR4/2:m) heavy, greasy clay with slightly darker spots. Very weak, medium, angular blocky structure. Sticky and plastic. Few, very fine tubular and few, very fine, interstitial pores. Very few, very fine roots.

No analytical details of this profile are available, but fairly detailed analyses have been made of some cat-clays of Thailand, one of them (profile 38) belonging to the same series (personal information Dr L. J. Pons). The above profile represents the brown phase, and the analyzed one the yellow phase of the Rangsit series. It is a clay to silty clay with a thick A$_1$ horizon 35 cm thick on top of a horizon with brown and yellow (jarosite) mottles, the number of yellow mottles increasing and brown mottles decreasing downwards to 125 cm. The oxidation boundary lies at 150 cm; beneath this boundary the permanently reduced mud occurs. Samples were taken from 0–10 cm, 20–35 cm, 35–50 cm, 115–125 cm, 125–150 cm, and 200–230 cm; they will be indicated by the numerals 1, 2, 3, 4, 5, and 6. Some general characteristics are shown in table II.123.

It appears that the soil has been formed in a reasonably homogeneous sediment; horizon 5 is only slightly more silty than the others. The c.e.c. of the clay fraction increases with depth, which indicates that the composition changes with depth; this is probably the result of mineral transformations during soil genesis (see p. 379). The low 'free iron' content of horizon 5 and of the surface horizons 1 and 2 and the high contents in horizons 3 and 4 indicate that the layers are enriched in iron from the underlying horizons and from the topsoil. It is thought that this happens by diffusion, as the permeability of the soil is extremely low (Van Breemen: personal information). This mechanism is very similar to that responsible for the formation of the pallid and plinthite zones in plinthitic oxisols.

TABLE II.123. *Some physical and chemical characteristics of profile 38*

Hor.	texture (%)			C (%)	pH (0.01M CaCl₂)	'free iron' (%)	c.e.c. of clay (m.e./ 100 g)	SO₃ (%)
	> 50µ	50–2µ	< 2µ					
1	0.2	31.6	68.2	2.6	3.7	1.6	35	0.4
2	0.3	34.8	64.9	1.2	3.3	1.1	36	0.3
3	2.6	31.7	65.7	0.7	3.1	5.6	38	0.4
4	0.7	35.4	63.9	0.6	3.2	4.0	37	1.3
5	0.2	41.8	58.0	0.8	3.1	0.9	42	0.3
6	0.1	35.2	65.7	6.3	2.5[1]	2.2	44	4.3[2]

[1] The low pH values are the result of air-drying of the samples of the permanently reduced mud.
[2] In this sample the sulphur is present as sulphide expressed as SO_3.

The sulphides of the permanently reduced subsoil were oxidized in the fifth layer and partly moved upwards to form jarosite and/or gypsum in the horizons above, and

TABLE II.124. *Chemical composition of the soil* (weight percentages)

Hor.	SiO₂	Al₂O₃	Fe₂O₃	FeO	CaO	MgO	MnO	Na₂O	K₂O	TiO₂	P₂O₅	H₂O+[1]
1	59.5	19.3	3.6	0.2	0.4	0.3	tr[2]	0.4	1.4	0.9	0.1	7.0
2	61.8	19.5	3.2	0.1	0.2	0.3	tr	0.3	1.5	1.0	0.1	6.6
3	57.4	19.3	7.9	0.3	0.3	0.3	tr	0.4	1.7	0.9	0.1	8.3
4	61.8	17.2	6.0	0.1	0.2	0.3	tr	0.4	2.0	0.9	0.1	8.2
5	64.5	17.0	3.1	0.1	0.3	0.3	tr	0.4	1.6	1.0	0.1	5.9
6	53.0	16.9	4.2	0.6	0.3	0.6	0.1	0.5	1.5	0.8	0.1	6.3

[1] H_2O+ = loss on ignition-organic matter; [2] tr = trace.

partly leached. The content of jarosite is highest in the fourth layer and decreases upwards becoming goethite, the liberated sulphate being leached.

The total element analysis (table II.124) also reveals that iron is removed from horizon 5. The table shows that upon oxidation (6→ 5), ferrous iron and magnesium have partly disappeared, which is the result of weathering of certain ferrous-magnesian minerals. Potassium has slightly accumulated in horizons three and four, indicating the formation of K containing minerals. The aluminium content of the upper horizons is higher than that of the subsoil which indicates the formation of aluminium-rich minerals, e.g. kaolinite.

The conclusions are confirmed by the data of table II.125, showing the normative mineralogical composition of the profile. It was calculated as indicated in Part I, Chapter 3 (p. 131), with the following adaptations: As the SO_4^{2-} content in soil moisture of cat-clays is fairly constant (varying from $10^{-2.4}$ to 10^{-3} mol 1^{-1}, indicating the presence of gypsum in these soils (personal communication of N. van Breemen), SO_3 was allocated to CaO to form gypsum; remaining SO_3 was allocated to K_2O and Fe_2O_3 to form jarosite. Remaining K_2O was used for the formation of illites.

It is evident that upon oxidation (hor. 6→ hor. 5) part of the smectites are decomposed; the hydrogen ions, formed during the oxidation of pyrites liberate Mg^{2+}, Al^{3+}, and silicate ions, from the clay lattice, and form with the latter the undissociated H_4SiO_4. Hence, montmorillonite buffers the hydrogen ion. It can also be expected that the concentration of dissolved ferrous species is considerable under the conditions in horizon 5. In the wet season these diffuse upwards and form jarosite and illite in horizon 4 with potassium and sulphate ions. Mg^{2+} ions are leached as it appears that they do not form insoluble compounds with other constituents. In the upper 50 cm of the profile, jarosite appears to be unstable and is transformed into goethite; illite also becomes unstable and is partly transformed into kaolinite. It is remarkable that after the initial decomposition of smectites, they are stable in the solum. This is only

TABLE II.125. *Normative mineralogical composition of profile 38* (equivalent percentages)

Hor.	Q	Plg	Sm	Ms	Kand	Go	Pr	Jar	Gy	Ru	Misc
1	35.6	4.3	8.7	14.0	32.6	2.9	–	–	0.9	0.7	0.1
2	38.5	3.3	6.6	14.7	32.9	2.1	–	0.7	0.4	0.8	0.1
3	32.3	4.3	9.6	16.5	29.2	6.0	–	0.7	0.6	0.7	0.1
4	39.9	4.2	7.2	18.9	22.0	2.1	–	4.5	0.4	0.7	0.1
5	44.1	4.3	6.6	15.7	25.3	2.3	–	0.2	0.7	0.7	0.1
6	31.6	5.7	12.0	15.6	25.8	2.6	5.4	–	0.5	0.7	0.1

Q = free silica; Plg = plagioclases; Sm = smectites; Ms = muscovite (illite); Kand = kandites (= kaolinite); Go = goethite; Pr = pyrite; Jar = jarosite; Gy = gypsum; Ru = rutile (anatase); Misc = miscellaneous.

possible if the activity ratio of Mg^{2+}, Ca^{2+}, H^+, and Na^+ ions in the medium is favourable for the maintenance of smectite (see Chapter 3 of this Part, p.329, and Chapter 1 of Part III, p. 430).

The normative mineralogical composition of the clay fractions (table II.126) confirms the conclusions drawn above. The trend in the clay composition is reflected in the c.e.c. trend (table II.123).

In summary, it can be concluded that the following processes are involved in the formation of acid sulphate soils: 1) formation of the mud with the reduction of SO_4^{2-} and ferric iron species and the formation of pyrites; 2) oxidation of sulphides and ferrous iron compounds upon aeration, with subsequent formation of jarosite, gypsum, and iron hydroxides; 3) transformation of silicate minerals.

TABLE II.126. *Normative mineralogical composition of the clay fractions of profile 38* (equivalent percentages)

Hor.	Q	Sm	Ms	Kand	Go	Ru	Misc
1	14.0	15.4	15.8	48.3	3.6	0.7	2.2
2	14.0	15.0	17.2	47.7	3.2	0.8	2.1
3	14.2	16.0	18.9	42.2	5.3	0.8	2.6
4	16.4	15.4	19.3	40.9	5.3	0.7	2.0
5	14.1	16.4	17.9	44.6	3.6	0.8	2.6
6	11.3	19.2	18.5	42.9	4.7	0.8	2.6

Mineral abbreviations as in table II.125.

4.2.2. THE OCCURRENCE OF DISSOLVED S AND FE COMPOUNDS IN MARINE SEDIMENTS AND CAT-CLAY SOILS

Before discussing the soil forming processes, it is necessary to have some idea of the occurrences of dissolved and solid sulpfur and iron and of their distribution as function of the redox potential and pH.

4.2.2.1. *S and Fe species in aqueous solution*

Besides native (rhombic) sulpfur (S_{rh}) many dissolved S compounds (more than 40) are known in the system $S–H_2O$. Fortunately however, Valenski (1950) has shown that only native sulphur, hydrogen sulphide, sulphide, bisulphide, sulphate, and bisulphate ions occur in important quantities.

The distribution of the species mentioned depending on the redox potential and pH within the stability field of water is shown in fig. II.58. For the construction of such diagrams reference is made to Garrels and Christ (1965) and to Part III, Chapter 2.

The equations on which this diagram is based (after elimination of the metastable reactions), are the following:

$$H_2S \rightleftharpoons HS^- + H^+ \tag{23}$$

$$lgK_{23} = lg\frac{[HS^-]}{[H_2S]} - pH = -7 \tag{23a}$$

$$HS^- + 4H_2O \rightleftharpoons SO_4^{2-} + 9H^+ + 8e \tag{24}$$

$$E_{h24} = E^0_{24} + 0.01lg\frac{[SO_4^{2-}]}{[HS^-]} - 0.07pH; \quad E^0_{24} = 0.25 \text{ V} \tag{24a}$$

$$H_2S + 4H_2O \rightleftharpoons SO_4^{2-} + 10H^+ + 8e \tag{25}$$

$$E_{h25} = E^0_{25} + 0.01lg\frac{[SO_4^{2-}]}{[H_2S]} - 0.08pH; \quad E^0_{25} = 0.30 \text{ V} \tag{25a}$$

$$HSO_4^- \rightleftharpoons SO_4^{2-} + H^+ \tag{26}$$

$$lgK_{26} = lg\frac{[SO_4^{2-}]}{[HSO_4^-]} - pH = -1.90 \tag{26a}$$

$$H_2S + 4H_2O \rightleftharpoons HSO_4^- + 9H^+ + 8e \ - \quad (27)$$

$$E_{h27} = E_{27}^\circ + 0.01 lg \frac{[HSO_4^-]}{[H_2S]} - 0.08pH; \ E_{27}^\circ = 0.29 \ V \ - - - - - - - - - - - - - - \quad (27a)$$

(The values of lgK and E° were calculated from standard free-energy of formation values, listed by Garrels and Christ, 1965, and Robie and Waldbaum, 1968).

It is evident that the dominance field of SO_4^{2-} is very large and that H_2S and HS^- exist only under strongly anaerobic conditions.

Elemental S in the rhombic modification, which is the stable phase, occurs in the system $S–H_2O$ under specific conditions of E_h, pH, and total activity of dissolved S species. The stability field of rhombic S is included in fig. II.58.

The stability field of rhombic S can be delineated with the aid of the following reactions (after elimination of the metastable ones):

$$H_2S \rightleftharpoons S_{rh} + 2H^+ + 2e \ - \quad (28)$$

$$E_{h28} = E_{28}^\circ - 0.03 lg \ [H_2S] - 0.06pH; \ E_{28}^\circ = 0.14 \ V \ - - - - - - - - - - - - - - - \quad (28a)$$

$$S_{rh} + 4H_2O \rightleftharpoons HSO_4^- + 7H^+ + 6e \ - \quad (29)$$

$$E_{h29} = E_{29}^\circ + 0.01 lg \ [HSO_4^-] - 0.07pH; \ E_{29}^\circ = 0.34 \ V \ - - - - - - - - - - - - - - - \quad (29a)$$

$$S_{rh} + 4H_2O \rightleftharpoons SO_4^{2-} + 8H^+ + 6e \ - \quad (30)$$

$$E_{h30} = E_{30}^\circ + 0.01 lg \ [SO_4^{2-}] - 0.08pH; \ E_{30}^\circ = 0.36 \ V - - - - - - - - - - - - - - - - \quad (30a)$$

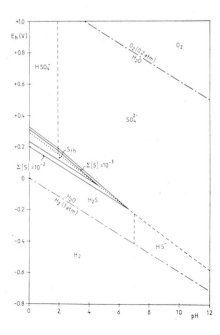

FIG. II.58. *Fields of dominance of S-species and stability field of rhombic S at 25°C, I atm. total pressure, and* $\Sigma[S]$ *of* 10^{-3} *and* 10^{-2}

382

The diagram shows that under certain conditions during oxidation H_2S may first form rhombic S, then SO_4^{2-}.

The distributions of dissolved and stable solid Fe species are represented in the figures III.10 and 11 of Part III, Chapter 2.

The above summary is valid for pure $S-H_2O$ and $Fe-H_2O$ systems. As complex formation plays an important rôle in seawater, it is necessary to determine which dissolved S and Fe species occur in seawater and in the soil solution of acid sulphate soils.

The fact that the chloride content in the neighbourhood of the mouths of large rivers is not more than 0.2 % less than that of seawater shows that the composition of seawater is fairly constant (1.9 %; Berner, 1965). The average composition of seawater and the distribution of the most important complexes are given in table II.127 (after Garrels and Thompson, 1962; Berner, 1965).

It appears that SO_4^{2-} is an important ligand; approximately half of the SO^{2-} will form the ion pairs $NaSO_4^-$, $CaSO_4^0$, and $MgSO_4^0$. Table II.128, derived from table II.127, shows that the activity of the free SO_4^{2-} ion is approximately $1/6$ of the total SO_4^- activity.

TABLE II.127. *Average composition of seawater* (1.9 % Cl; pH 8.15; ionic strength 0.7 mol/l), *the distribution of the most important complexes, and the activity coefficients of the free ions and complexes*

Ion species	total molality	distribution of free ions and complexes (% of total molality)			
		free ion	Me-SO₄	Me-HCO₃	Me-CO₃
Na⁺	0.48	99	1	–	–
K⁺	0.010	99	1	–	–
Mg²⁺	0.054	87	11	1	0.3
Ca²⁺	0.010	91	8	1	0.2
		free ion	Ca anion	Mg anion	Na anion	K anion
SO²⁻	0.028	54	3	22	21	0.5
HCO₃⁻	0.0024	69	4	19	8	–
CO₃²⁻	0.00027	9	7	67	17	–
Cl⁻	0.56	100	–	–	–	–

activity coefficients of free ions and complexes in seawater

	free ion	Me-SO₄	Me–HCO₃	Me-CO₃
Na⁺	0.76	0.55	–	–
K⁺	0.64	0.55	–	–
Mg²⁺	0.36	1.13	0.55	1.13
Ca²⁺	0.20	1.13	0.55	1.13
SO₄²⁻	0.12			
HCO₃⁻	0.55			
CO₃²⁻	0.20			
Cl⁻	0.64			

The effect of this complex formation on the distribution of the dissolved S species of fig. II.58 can be derived from redox-reaction (24) and from:

$$HS^- + 4H_2O + Mg^{2+} \rightleftharpoons MgSO_4^0 + 9H^+ + 8e \quad ---------------- \quad (31)$$

$$E_{h31} = 0.23 - 0.07pH + 0.01 \lg \frac{[MgSO_4^0]}{[Mg^{2+}][HS^-]} \quad ------------- \quad (31a)$$

As $[Mg^{2+}]$ equals approximately 2×10^{-3} mol/l (see table II.128), the boundary between $MgSO_4^0$ and HS^- ($[MgSO_4^0] = [HS^-]$) is given by the relationship:

$$E_{h31} = 0.25 - 0.07pH \quad ------------------------- \quad (31b)$$

and therefore does not deviate from the boundary between SO_4^{2-} and HS^- ($E_{h24} = 0.25 - 0.07pH$).

Corresponding calculations with other complexes give similar results, so fig. II.58 is also valid for seawater, although $NaSO_4^-$ and $MgSO_4^0$ dominate SO_4^{2-} in the SO_4–field of dominance.

TABLE II.128. *Molalities and activities of SO$_4$ species in seawater*

species	molality	activity coeff.	activity
SO_4^{2-}	0.015	0.12	0.002
$MgSO_4^0$	0.006	1.13	0.007
$CaSO_4^0$	0.001	1.13	0.001
$NaSO_4^-$	0.006	0.55	0.003
KSO_4^-	nil		

Berner (1963) showed that $[S^{2-}]$ in most reduced seabottom sediments lies between 10^{-8} and 10^{-14} mol/l. As under marine conditions HS^- is the dominant dissolved species (see fig. II.55), it is possible to calculate its activity from the dissociation constant of HS^- ($HS^- \rightleftharpoons S^{2-} + H^+$; $\lg \frac{[S^{2-}]}{[HS^-]} - pH = -14$); i.e. it varies between $10^{-1.5}$ and $10^{-7.5}$ mol/l.

According to James (1966) the iron concentration in aerobic seawater is largely determined by amorphous ferric hydroxide and averages 6×10^{-9} mol/l. [1] In anaerobic conditions more iron might be dissolved as Fe^{2+}. However, as soon as sulphate reduction occurs, the Fe^{2+} concentration will again decrease as a result of the formation of ferrous sulphides.

In acid sulphate soils the concentration of dissolved sulphate nearly always fluctuates between 10^{-2} and 3×10^{-2} mol/l (Nhung and Ponnamperuma, 1966; Van der Spek, 1950; Yoneda and Kawada, 1954; Horn and Chapman, 1968). Even at extremely low pH values (1.9) only a slightly higher SO_4 concentration was found (7×10^{-2} mol/l; Wind and Steeghs, 1964). In leached cat-clays (pH 4–6) SO_4 concentrations of approximately 2×10^{-3} mol/l occurred (Van der Spek, 1950). Even under reduced

[1] This statement is questionable as Gayer and Woontner (1956) found a concentration of 3×10^{-7} mol/l for a saturated Fe(OH)$_3$ solution.

conditions the SO_4^{2-} concentration remains constant over a long period (Nhung and Ponnamperuma, 1966). This phenomenon is undoubtely related to the low activity of sulphate-reducing bacteria at pH values below 5 (this will be discussed in section 3).

The concentration of dissolved iron in young acid sulphate soils is determined by the solubility of amorphous ferric hydroxide (Van Breemen, 1968). In older cat-clay soils it is controlled by some other unknown iron compound (Van Breemen, personal information). The Fe concentration is strongly dependent upon E_h and pH, and is approximately 10^{-5} mol/l at pH 3.5 under aerobic conditions. After inundation, $Fe(OH)_3$ reduces to Fe^{2+} and, as the pH remains initially relatively low extremely high concentrations of Fe^{2+} can occur in inundated cat-clay soils (up to 10^{-2} mol/l: Nhung and Ponnamperuma, 1966).

As SO_4^{2-}, and in saline or brackish medium also Cl^-, occur in excess over dissolved Fe species, it can be expected that Fe anion complexes occur in acid sulphate soils. The following complexes are known: $FeHSO_4^{2+}$, $FeH(SO_4)_2^0$, $FeSO_4^+$, $FeSO_4^0$, $Fe(SO_4)_2^-$, $FeCl^{2+}$, $FeCl_2^+$, and probably $FeCl^+$, $FeCl_2^0$ (Sillén and Martell, 1964) and $(FeOH)_2$-$(SO_4)_3^{2-}$ (Guitier, 1948). The importance of $FeSO_4^+$, $Fe(SO_4)_2^-$, $FeSO_4^0$, $FeCl^+$, and $FeCl_2^+$ can be examined as their stability constants are known (Sillén and Martell, 1964). It appears that if $\Sigma[S]$ is larger than $\Sigma[Fe]$ as occurs in cat-clay soils, $FeSO_4^+$, $Fe(SO_4)_2^-$, and $FeSO_4^0$ dominate the other dissolved species, if $[SO_4^{2-}]$ is larger than 10^{-5} (for $FeSO_4^+$), 4.5×10^{-2} (for $Fe(SO_4)_2^-$), and 5×10^{-3} (for $FeSO_4^0$) mol/l.

Assuming that the ionic strength of the soil solution in cat-clay soils varies between 0.7 (ionic strength of seawater) and 0.03 (ionic strength of the solution of an 'average' inundated soil, IRRI, 1965), the activity coefficient of SO_4^{2-} varies between 0.1 and 0.5 (Garrels and Christ, 1965, fig. 2.15). Hence, $[SO_4^{2-}]$ varies between approximately 1.5×10^{-2} and 10^{-3} mol/l in acid sulphate soils.

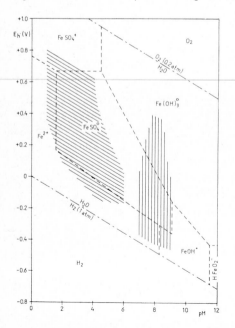

FIG. II.59. *Fields of dominance of dissolved Fe-species in cat-clay soils at 25°C, 1 atm. total pressure, and $\Sigma[S] = 10^{-2}$.* ▨ *cat-clay soils;* ▥ *marine sediments*

Calculations show that the Fe–SO₄ complexes dominate the Fe–Cl complexes, even if $[Cl^-]/[SO_4^{2-}]$ equals 36 (such as in seawater), so it can be expected that $FeSO_4^+$ and $FeSO_4^0$ or Fe^{2+} are the dominant species of dissolved iron in cat-clay soils. Distribution of the dissolved Fe species dependent on the E_h–pH, at a total activity of S species ($\Sigma[S]$) of 10^{-2} mol/l is shown in fig. 11.59. The obliquely striped area shows the variations of E_h and pH in acid sulphate soils and the vertically striped area those in marine sediments (predominantly based on data presented by Berner, 1963, 1964; Kaplan et al., 1963; Nhung and Ponnamperuma, 1966). Although the diagram is incomplete because of the absence of the acid and basic Fe–SO₄ complexes and the Fe–HS complex (Khodakovskii, 1966), the fields of $FeSO_4^0$, Fe^{2+}, $FeOH^+$, and $FeSO_4^+$ occur largely in the E_h–pH area characteristic for acid sulphate soils.

The diagram is constructed with reactions (28), (29), (33), and (34) of Chapter 2 of Part III (table III.5) and the following reactions:

$$Fe^{3+} + HSO_4^- \rightleftharpoons FeSO_4^+ + H^+ \quad - \quad (32)$$

$$lgK_{32} = 2.1 = lg\frac{[FeSO_4^+]}{[Fe^{3+}]} - lg\,[HSO_4^-] - pH \quad - - - - - - - - - - - - - \quad (32a)$$

$$Fe^{2+} + HSO_4^- \rightleftharpoons FeSO_4^+ + H^+ + e \quad - - - - - - - - - - - - - - - - - - - \quad (33)$$

$$E_{h33} = E_{33}^o - 0.06lg\frac{[FeSO_4^+]}{[Fe^{2+}]} - 0.06lg\,[HSO_4^-] - 0.06pH;\, E_{33}^o = 0.64\,V \quad - - - - - - \quad (33a)$$

$$FeSO_4^0 + 3H_2O \rightleftharpoons Fe(OH)_3^o + SO_4^{2-} + 3H^+ \quad - - - - - - - - - - - - - - - \quad (34)$$

$$lgK_{34} = -15.5 = lg\frac{[Fe(OH)_3^o]}{[FeSO_4^+]} + lg\,[SO_4^{2-}] - 3pH \quad - - - - - - - - - - - - \quad (34a)$$

$$FeSO_4^0 \rightleftharpoons FeSO_4^+ + e \quad - \quad (35)$$

$$E_{h35} = E_{35}^o + 0.06lg\frac{[FeSO_4^+]}{[FeSO_4^o]};\, E_{35}^o = 0.67\,V \quad - - - - - - - - - - - - - \quad (35a)$$

$$Fe^{2+} + HSO_4^- \rightleftharpoons FeSO_4^o + H^+ \quad - \quad (36)$$

$$lgK_{36} = 0.4 = lg\frac{[FeSO_4^o]}{[Fe^{2+}]} - lg\,[HSO_4^-] - pH \quad - - - - - - - - - - - - - - \quad (36a)$$

$$FeSO_4 + 3H_2O \rightleftharpoons Fe(OH)_3^o + SO_4^{2-} + 3H^+ + e \quad - - - - - - - - - - - - - \quad (37)$$

$$E_{h37} = E_{37}^o + 0.06lg\frac{[Fe(OH)_3^o]}{[FeSO_4^o]} + 0.06lg\,[SO_4^{2-}] - 0.18pH;\, E_{35}^o = 1.58\,V \quad - - - - - \quad (37a)$$

$$FeSO_4^o + H_2O \rightleftharpoons FeOH^+ + SO_4^{2-} + H^+ \quad - - - - - - - - - - - - - - - - - - \quad (38)$$

$$lgK_{38} = -11.1 = lg\frac{[FeOH^+]}{[FeSO_4^o]} + lg\,[SO_4^{2-}] - pH \quad - - - - - - - - - - - - - - \quad (38a)$$

$$H_2S + Fe^{2+} + 4H_2O \rightleftharpoons FeSO_4^{\circ} + 10H^+ + 8e \text{ --------------------} \quad (39)$$

$$E_{h39} = E_{39}^{\circ} + 0.01lg\frac{[FeSO_4^{\circ}]}{[Fe^{2+}]} - 0.01lg[H_2S] - 0.07pH; E_{39}^{\circ} = 0.28 V \text{ ------} \quad (39a)$$

$$HS^- + Fe^{2+} + 4H_2O \rightleftharpoons FeSO_4^{\circ} + 9H^+ + 8e \text{ -------------------} \quad (40)$$

$$E_{h40} = E_{40}^{\circ} + 0.01lg\frac{[FeSO_4^{\circ}]}{[Fe^{2+}]} - 0.01lg[HS^-] - 0.07pH; E_{40}^{\circ} = 0.19 V \text{ ------} \quad (40a)$$

4.2.2.2. *Solid S and Fe compounds*

Elemental S is frequently found in seabottom sediments and in seawater (a.o. Kaplan et al., 1963; Stokes, 1907) and is formed by oxidation of solid or dissolved sulphides. The oxidation probably proceeds via the formation of amorphous S (Ljunggren, 1960; Sato, 1960), which ages rapidly into the stable rhombic modification (Berner, 1963).

The most important iron sulphides in marine sediments are amorphous FeS, which is transformed within a few days into tetragonal FeS (mackinawite), cubic Fe_3S_4 (greigite), and cubic FeS_2 (pyrite). Other ironsulphides such as hexagonal FeS (troilite), monoclinic-hexagonal Fe_7S_8 – FeS (pyrrhotite), rhombic FeS_2 (marcasite), and rhombic Fe_3S_4 (smythite) are unimportant or do not occur in seabottom sediments. In soils pyrites, hydrotroilite ($FeS.nH_2O$), and melnikovite ($FeS_2.nH_2O$) have been found (a.o. Beers, 1962). The two latter sulphides are probably composed of one or more of the above-mentioned minerals whether or not mixed with rhombic S.

Sulphates in the solid state are absent under marine conditions. Gypsum precipitates if 80% of the water is evaporated from seawater (Krauskopf, 1967). In cat-clay soils iron and, possibly, aluminium sulphates, especially the basic ones, can occur, as these are often less soluble than gypsum.

Unfortunately, little is known about the chemistry and mineralogy of these sub-stances and: 'Numerous species still remain to be investigated, even among the simpler structures, and the constitution of the numerous hydrated and basic sulphates is not understood in even elementary regards' (Dana's System of Mineralogy: Palache et al., 1951).

According to Teodorovich (1961) and Kubisz (1964) jarosite and alunite are the most important sulphates in non-arid regions. In cat-clay soils jarosite is the dominant basic ferric sulphate and alunite, $KAl_3(SO_4)_2(OH)_6$ may also occur. A jarosite sample from Thailand showed a small deviation in the magnitude of the unit-cell (personal communication of Van Breemen). Data on isomorphic substitution in alunite-jarosite minerals (Brophy et al., 1962; Parker, 1962) indicate that in the jarosite from Thailand part of Fe(III) is replaced by Al, and of K by Na.

Besides the Fe sulphides and sulphates mentioned, various hydroxides and oxides of iron occur. Goethite (α–FeOOH) is the dominant Fe compound under marine conditions (James, 1966). In young acid sulphate soils amorphous ferric hydroxide occurs, which is the dominant form in hydromorphic soils (Ponnamperuma et al., 1967). Although this hydroxide is unstable with respect to goethite in aqueous medium, it can be formed by continually alternating oxidizing and reducing processes (Van Breemen and Oldeman, 1967). The following reactions give an idea of this process:

$$Fe(OH)_3(s) \to \alpha\text{--}FeOOH(s) + H_2O \text{ --------------------} \quad (41)$$
$$\alpha\text{--}FeOOH(s) + 3H^+ + e \to Fe^{2+} + 2H_2O \text{ ----------------} \quad (42)$$
$$Fe^{2+} + 3H_2O \to Fe(OH)_3(s) + 3H^+ + e \text{ ---------------} \quad (43)$$

If reactions (42) and (43) proceed faster than reaction (41), it is understandable that during alternating reduction and oxidation $Fe(OH)_3$ seems to be a stable phase.

Under reduced conditions an important part of the iron occurs as $Fe_3(OH)_8$ (amorphous ferric-ferrous hydroxide: Arden, 1950; Ponnamperuma, 1964), which may dominate the more stable magnetite (Fe_3O_4) as a result of alternating oxidation and reduction.

Siderite ($FeCO_3$) sometimes occurs in strongly reduced seabottom sediments (James, 1966) and hydromorphic soils rich in organic matter (Yamane and Sato, 1961).

Gypsum ($CaSO_4.2H_2O$) may be formed in acid sulphate soils, especially if the sediment was initially calcareous (Teakle and Southern, 1937; Fleming and Alexander, 1961).

Many other iron minerals, such as the silicates chamosite, greenaltite, and glauconite are often important in marine sediments (James, 1966) and may therefore play a rôle in the formation of iron sulphides (Berner, 1964).

The distribution of the different minerals in cat-clay soils as function of E_h and pH is represented in the figs. II.60 and 61. In both diagrams it is assumed that the activity

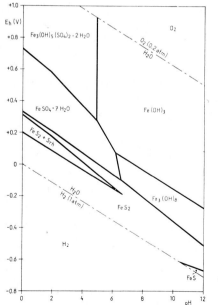

FIG. II.60. *Stability fields of stable iron sulphates and sulphides and metastable iron hydroxides at 25°C, 1 atm. total pressure, and* $\Sigma[S] = 10^{-2}$

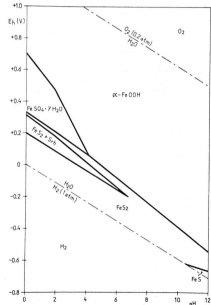

FIG. II.61. *Stability fields of the stable phases in the system Fe–S–H₂O at 25°C, 1 atm. total pressure, and* $\Sigma[S] = 10^{-2}$

388

of total dissolved S species ($\Sigma[S]$) is 10^{-2}. Fig. II.60 gives the relationship between the stable iron sulphates and sulphides and the metastable iron hydroxides. Diagram II.61 shows only the stable phases. In these diagrams, the mineral 'jarosite' is supposed to have the composition $Fe_3(OH)_5(SO_4)_2.2H_2O$, as it is chemically and crystallographically similar to the minerals of the jarosite group (Black, 1967). As Van Breemen (1968) had calculated an approximate value for its standard free-energy of formation, the construction of the figs. II. 60 and 61 was possible.

The reactions on which fig. II.60 was based, are (after elimination of the metastable reactions):

$Fe_3(OH)_5(SO_4)_2.2H_2O(s) + 2H_2O \rightleftharpoons 3Fe(OH)_3(s) + 2SO_4^{2-} + 4H^+$ – – – – – – – – (44)

$lgK_{44} = -23.7 = 2lg[SO_4^{2-}] - 4pH$ – (44a)

$3FeSO_4.7H_2O(s) \rightleftharpoons Fe_3(OH)_5(SO_4)_2.2H_2O(s) + HSO_4^- + 14H_2O + 4H^+ + 3e$ – – – (45)

$E_{h45} = 0.77 + 0.02lg[HSO_4^-] - 0.08pH$ – – – – – – – – – – – – – – – – – (45a)

$3FeSO_4.7H_2O(s) \rightleftharpoons Fe_3(OH)_5(SO_4)_2.2H_2O(s) + SO_4^{2-} + 14H_2O + 5H^+ + 3e$ – – – (46)

$E_{h46} = 0.79 + 0.02lg[SO_4^{2-}] - 0.10pH$ – – – – – – – – – – – – – – – – – (46a)

$FeSO_4.7H_2O(s) \rightleftharpoons Fe(OH)_3(s) + SO_4^{2-} + 4H_2O + 3H^+ + e$ – – – – – – – – – – (47)

$E_{h47} = 1.26 + 0.06lg[SO_4^{2-}] - 0.18pH$ – – – – – – – – – – – – – – – – – (47a)

$Fe_3(OH)_8(s) + H_2O \rightleftharpoons 3Fe(OH)_3(s) + H^+ + e$ – – – – – – – – – – – – – – – (48)

$E_{h48} = 0.43 - 0.06pH$ – (48a)

$3FeSO_4.7H_2O(s) \rightleftharpoons Fe_3(OH)_8(s) + 13H_2O + 8H^+ + 3SO_4^{2-} + e$ – – – – – – – – – (49)

$E_{h49} = 3.36 + 0.18lg[SO_4^{2-}] - 0.47pH$ – – – – – – – – – – – – – – – – – (49a)

$FeS_2(s) + 15H_2O \rightleftharpoons FeSO_4.7H_2O(s) + HSO_4^- + 15H^+ + 14e$ – – – – – – – – – (50)

$E_{h50} = 0.34 + 0.004lg[HSO_4^-] - 0.06pH$ – – – – – – – – – – – – – – – – (50a)

$FeS_2(s) + 15H_2O \rightleftharpoons FeSO_4.7H_2O(s) + SO_4^{2-} + 16H^+ + 14e$ – – – – – – – – – (51)

$E_{h51} = 0.34 + 0.004lg[SO_4^{2-}] - 0.07pH$ – – – – – – – – – – – – – – – – – (51a)

$3FeS_2(s) + 32H_2O \rightleftharpoons Fe_3(OH)_8(s) + 6SO_4^{2-} + 36H^+ + 44e$ – – – – – – – – – (52)

$E_{h52} = 0.40 + 0.01lg[SO_4^{2-}] - 0.08pH$ – – – – – – – – – – – – – – – – – (52a)

$FeS(troilite) + HS^- \rightleftharpoons FeS_2(s) + H^+ + 2e$ – – – – – – – – – – – – – – – – (53)

$E_{h53} = -0.37 - 0.03lg[HS^-] - 0.03pH$ – – – – – – – – – – – – – – – – – –·– – (53a)

and further the reactions (28), (29) and (30).

For the construction of fig. II.61 the following equations are needed, besides (50), (51), (52), (28), (29) and (30).

$Fe_3(OH)_5(SO_4)_2.2H_2O(s) \rightleftharpoons 3\alpha\text{-FeOOH}(s) + 2HSO_4^- + H_2O + 2H^+$ – – – – – – – (54)

$lgK_{54} = -2.5 = 2lg[HSO_4^-] - 2pH$ – (54a)

$FeSO_4.7H_2O(s) \rightleftharpoons \alpha\text{-FeOOH}(s) + HSO_4^- + 5H_2O + 2H^+ + e$ – – – – – – – – – – (55)

$E_{h55} = 0.82 + 0.06lg[HSO_4^-] - 0.12pH$ – – – – – – – – – – – – – – – – – (55a)

$FeSO_4.7H_2O(s) \rightleftharpoons \alpha\text{-FeOOH}(s) + SO_4^{2-} + 5H_2O + 3H^+ + e$ – – – – – – – – – (56)

$E_{h56} = 0.90 + 0.06lg[SO_4^{2-}] - 0.18pH$ – – – – – – – – – – – – – – – – – (65a)

$FeS_2(s) + 10H_2O \rightleftharpoons \alpha\text{-FeOOH}(s) + 2SO_4^{2-} + 19H^+ + 15e$ – – – – – – – – – – (57)

$E_{h57} = 0.38 + 0.01lg[SO_4^{2-}] - 0.08pH$ – – – – – – – – – – – – – – – – – – (57a)

The standard fee-energy of formation values, used to calculate the equilibrium constants and standard redox-potentials, were taken from Robie and Waldbaum (1968) for FeS_2, FeS (troilite), $FeSO_4 . 7H_2O$, SO_4^{2-}. HS^-, and H_2S, from Garrels and Christ (1965) for HSO_4^- and $Fe(OH)_3$, from Ponnamperuma et al. (1967) for $Fe_3(OH)_8$, and from Van Breemen (1968) for 'jarosite'. For the value used for goethite (α-FeOOH) see Part III, Chapter 2, p. 434.

Fig. II.60 shows that 'jarosite' is stable with respect to ferric hydroxide in an 'average' cat-clay soil ($\Sigma[S] = 10^{-2}$ mol/l) if the pH is smaller than 5. Melanterite ($FeSO_4.7H_2O$) is a stable phase up to neutrality under moderately reducing conditions. Fig. II.61 shows that 'jarosite' is stable with respect to goethite only if the pH is lower than zero. The stability field of melanterite is considerably narrowed. Even the stable counterpart of $Fe_3(OH)_8$, viz. Fe_3O_4, does not occur stably in the Fe–S–H_2O system if $\Sigma[S] = 10^{-2}$ mol/l. Comparison of both figures shows that upon ageing of $Fe(OH)_3$ into α–FeOOH, 'jarosite' disappears, which explains the fact that pale yellow jarosite mottles gradually change into brown goethite mottles or concretions.

Finally the data of figs. II.58, 59, and 60 and of figs. II.58, 59, and 61 are combined into the two composite diagrams II. 62 and II.63. Comparison of both diagrams with the corresponding diagrams in figs. II.60 and 61 shows that melanterite is easily soluble and at $\Sigma[Fe] = 10^{-3}$ it is completely dissolved. If $\Sigma[Fe]$ had been 10^{-1}, melanterite would have appeared in the diagrams; but such high Fe-activity does not

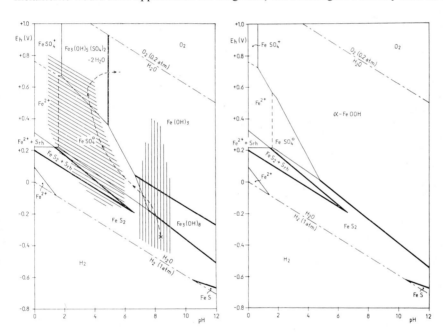

FIG. II.62. *Stability relations in the system Fe–S–H_2O between 'jarosite', the metastable phases $Fe(OH)_3$ and $Fe_3(OH)_8$, and dissolved species at $25°C$, 1 atm. pressure, and $\Sigma[S] = 10^{-2}$. Boundary between solids and dissolved iron species at $\Sigma[Fe] = 10^{-3}$*

FIG. II.63. *Stability relations between the stable phases in the Fe–S–H_2O system under the same conditions as in fig. II.62*

occur even in cat-clay soils and this sulphate would never be formed. Comparison of figs. II.62 and 63 shows again that the mobility of iron decreases considerably upon ageing of $Fe(OH)_3$ into α–FeOOH: the dominance field of $FeSO_4^0$ is greatly narrowed.

If the reduction-oxidation conditions of a potential acid sulphate soil changed to the conditions represented by the dotted line in fig. II.62, the following results could be expected: black mottles in the lower part of the profile caused by the formation of $Fe_3(OH)_8$; pale yellow mottles of jarosite at higher levels, and a coating of red Fe $(OH)_3$ stains or a complete change of jarosite into ferric hydroxide. The black patches have been observed by Van der Kevie (see p. 376), who ascribed them to surface material fallen into old cracks. The red coatings of jarosite mottles were observed by Bloomfield et. al (1968) (see p. 376).

It is thought that both diagrams clarify certain morphological characteristics of cat-clay soils, and facilitate the prediction of certain changes in the profile upon leaching and ageing.

The logical step now would be the discussion of the stability relations of the Al minerals. Some silicates have been discussed in preceeding chapters (see figs. II.44, 52, and 53) and will be treated further in Part III, Chapter I (fig. III.7). Unfortunately, little is known about the concentrations of the different ions in the solution of cat-clay soils, so that further discussion on the distribution of the Al minerals is impossible.

4.2.3. THE SOIL FORMING PROCESSES

4.2.3.1. *Sulphate reduction*

Sulphate reduction under natural circumstances is entirely a microbiological process (a.o. Starkey, 1966). The anaerobic bacteria of the *Desulfovibrio* and *Desulfotomaculum* genera are able to use SO_4^{2-}, $S_2O_3^{2-}$, and $S_{el.}$ as electron acceptors during the (energy supplying) oxidation of organic substances and/or hydrogen gas. The end product of the reduction is always H_2S or HS^-, never elemental S. The reduction of SO_4^{2-} is represented in the following example of the oxidation of glucose to pyruvic acid:

oxidation of glucose: $2C_6H_{12}O_6 \rightarrow 2CH_3COCOOH + 8H^+ + 8e$

reduction of SO_4^{2-}: $SO_4^{2-} + 10H^+ + 8e \rightarrow H_2S + 4H_2O$

net reaction: $2C_6H_{12}O_6 + SO_4^{2-} + 2H^+ \rightarrow 2CH_3COCOOH + H_2S + 2H_2O$

It is evident that pH will increase during the reduction process.

The sulphate reducing micro-organisms are especially active in neutral media and only between pH 4 and 9. The pH of seawater is approximately 8.2 and that of sea-bottom sediments slightly lower (7.5) as a consequence of CO_2 production. Under marine conditions sulphate reduction by salt-tolerant species takes place readily if the E_h is sufficiently low and if enough organic material is present. Such conditions occur in low lying tidal flats with a dense *Rhizophora* and *Phragmites* vegetation (Pons, 1964) and with a permanent supply of sulphate (see also p. 374).

Because SH groups (e.g. as cysteine) occur in living cells it appears that microorganisms are able to reduce S to sulphide.

In the surface horizons of cat-clay soils (pH < 4) it takes months before sulphate-reduction takes place (see p. 383). Nhung and Ponnamperuma (1966) found that only after 37 weeks after inundation of a cat-clay soil (pH 3.5) SO_4 reduction was noticeable. Increase of the pH of the same soil to pH 5.6 by liming caused all sulphate to disappear 24 weeks after inundation. Most soils obtain pH values between 6.0 and 7.0

within a few weeks after inundation (Ponnamperuma et al., 1966) as a result of reduction of other components (e.g. $Fe(OH)_3(s) + 3H^+ + e \rightarrow Fe^{2+} + 3H_2O$); under those conditions the sulphate is usually entirely reduced within 3 to 5 weeks (IRRI, 1964, 1965).

It is possible that elemental S can be formed by purely chemical oxidation of HS^- and H_2S (see reaction (28) and: $HS^- \rightarrow S_{rh} + H^+ + 2e$). In these cases ferric hydroxides (e.g. goethite) act as oxidants (see reaction (59)).

4.2.3.2. *Formation of iron sulphides*

Iron sulphides form under natural circumstances predominantly by reaction of H_2S or HS^- on ferric and ferrous minerals; the precipitation of Fe^{2+} as FeS is much less important (Berner, 1964a). The formation of amorphous FeS can be formulated:

$$Fe^{2+} + H_2S \rightarrow FeS + 2H^+ \quad - \quad (58)$$

and the formation of mackinawite (tetragonal FeS):

a) crystallization of amorphous FeS (within a few days), and

b) reduction of iron hydroxide by H_2S:

$$2\,\alpha\text{–FeOOH} + 3H_2S \rightarrow 2FeS_{tetr.} + S_{rh} + 4H_2O \quad - - - - - - - - - - - - - \quad (59)$$

There are many indications that pyrites can be formed by the reaction of FeS with elemental S (Verhoop, 1940; Volkov, 1961; Kaplan et al., 1963; Berner, 1967):

$$FeS_{tetr.} + S_{rh} \rightarrow FeS_2 - \quad (60)$$

The reaction is rapid in acid medium and reaction (59) changes at pH 4 into:

$$2\,\alpha\text{–FeOOH} + 3H_2S \rightarrow FeS_{tetr.} + FeS_2 + H_2O \quad - - - - - - - - - - - - - \quad (61)$$

The reaction mechanism of (60) is probably as follows (Berner, 1967):

$$FeS + H^+ \rightarrow Fe^{2+} + HS^- \quad (60a)$$

$$Fe^{2+} + HS^- + S_{rh} \rightarrow FeS_2 + H^+ - \quad (60b)$$

The first reaction (60a) seems to be 'rate determining'; this could explain why the formation of pyrites at higher pH levels, such as seabottom sediments, takes sometimes centuries (Van Straaten, 1954).

The oxidation of H_2S or HS^- to elemental S is necessary for the formation of pyrites and if no suitable oxidants (such as ferric hydroxide) are present, mackinawite will remain stable for long periods. This is the situation in the sediments on the bottom of the Black Sea, where even at considerable depths greigite and mackinawite occur predominantly (Volkov, 1961; Berner, 1967a).

4.2.3.3. *Oxidation of elemental S and iron sulphides*

As already mentioned H_2S and HS^- can be easily oxidized purely chemically (without the interference of micro-organisms). However, rhombic S will remain inert for a considerable time if strong oxidants, such as MnO_4^-, ClO^-, etc. and sulphate bacteria are absent.

Sulphate bacteria (predominantly *Thiobacilli spec.*) are aerobic, autotrophic organisms, that are able to assimilate CO_2, using energy obtained from the oxidation of dissolved sulphides, elemental sulphur thiosulphate, etc. to form SO_4^{2-}. Various species (a.o. *Th. thio-oxidans* and *Th. ferro-oxydans*) have optimal activity in very acid media (pH 2-4).

As the redox-potential in an aerobic, aqueous medium is nearly always between $E_h = 0.86 - 0.06pH$ and $E_h = 0.68 - 0.06pH$ (which is determined according to Sato

(1960a) by the H_2O_2–O_2 redox-couple: $H_2O_2 \rightleftharpoons O_2 + 2H^+ + 2e$; $E_h = 0.68 - 0.06pH + 0.03lg \frac{\varsigma\,O_2}{[H_2O_2]}$), rhombic S can occur below this zone (called: the 'weathering environment') over a wide E_h range without being oxidized to SO_4^{2-}. Only within this zone will rhombic S be oxidized according to reaction (30) under the catalytic influence of sulphate bacteria.

The first step in the oxidation of iron sulphides is probably the formation of diatomic elemental sulphur (S_{2el}: Sato, 1960b). This definitely occurs below the zone of the 'weathering environment' in the case of greigite and mackinawite. In the case of pyrites it takes place at the upper boundary of the 'weathering environment':

$$FeS_2(s) + 3H_2O \rightarrow Fe(OH)_3(s) + S_{2el} + 3H^+ + 3e \quad --------------- \quad (61)$$
$$E_{h61} = 0.86 - 0.06pH \quad ------------------------------ \quad (61a)$$

Oxidation within the 'weathering environment' is only possible if pH is so low (<3), that $Fe(OH)_3$ can be completely dissolved:

$$FeS_2 \rightarrow Fe^{2+} + S_{2el} + 2e \quad -------------------------- \quad (62)$$
$$E_{h62} = 0.76 + 0.03lg\,[Fe^{2+}] \quad ------------------------ \quad (62a)$$

Although pyrites can oxidize theoretically at much lower E_h levels to $Fe_3(OH)_8$, α–FeOOH, and $FeSO_4.7H_2O$ (see figs. ii.60 and 61), it is apparently stable (metastable) under aerobic conditions because pyrites does not oxidize directly to SO_4^{2-}, but first forms S_{2el}.

The conspicuous resistance of pyrites in fairly neutral aerobic soils is probably the result of the high E_h level of reaction (61). In acid medium pyrites oxidizes more easily; this is evident when comparing reaction (62) with the E_h values within the 'weathering environment'.

The reactions which play a rôle in the oxidation of pyrites in acid medium, are probably the following (based on data of Sato, 1960b, and Temple and Delchamps, 1953):

$$FeS_2 \rightarrow Fe^{2+} + S_{2el} + 2e \text{ (purely chemical oxidation)} \quad ----------- \quad (62))$$
$$Fe^{2+} \rightarrow Fe^{3+} + e \text{ (partly influenced by } Th.\,ferro\text{-}oxidans) \quad ----------- \quad (63)$$
$$S_{2el} + 8H_2O \rightarrow 2SO_4^{2-} + 16H^+ + 14e \text{ (microbial oxidation by } Thiobacilli) \quad -- \quad (64)$$
$$Fe^{3+} + FeS_2 \rightarrow 2Fe^{2+} + S_{2el} + e \text{ (chemical oxidation by } Fe^{3+}) \quad ------- \quad (65)$$

In this way the initially formed products Fe^{2+} and S_{2el} are oxidized microbiologically to Fe^{3+} (63) and SO_4^{2-} (64); as a result reaction (62) takes place. Fe^{3+}, formed in this way, oxidizes pyrites (65) to form Fe^{2+} and S_{2el}; these can again be oxidized according to (63) and (64). These reactions refer exclusively to oxidation of pyrites in acid media (pH 2–4). At higher pH values $[Fe^{3+}]$ is lowered by precipitation as $Fe(OH)_3$, and the effect of reaction (65) decreases.

It is, however, questionable whether or not this is the only factor that hinders pyrites oxidation in less acid media. The boundary between the FeS_2 and $Fe(OH)_3$ occurrences coincides with the upper boundary of the 'weathering environment' (see equation (61a)); this means that the E_h at pH values larger than 3 or 4 in a natural, aqueous medium will not be high enough to enable the first oxidation reaction (62). The boundary between $Fe^{2+} + S_{2el}$ lies largely within the 'weathering environment' and this is possibly one of the reasons for the readier oxidation of pyrites in acid media.

It is also possible that the effect of the acidity and of the activity of micro-organisms is nullified by the particle size. Harmsen et al. (1954) found that very finely ground pyrites oxidized rapidly in air in sterile media as well as after inoculation with *Thiobacilli* over a large pH range (pH 3 to 7) in aqueous medium. Pyrites often occurs as spherical particles (diameter 1μ) in marine sediments; these particles aggregate into clusters of 20 to 40μ diameter (Pons, 1963). It is not exactly known at which grain-size rapid oxidation can occur but it is very probable that the ball-milled pyrites used by Harmsen have a smaller grain size.

4.2.3.4. *Formation of gypsum and jarosite*

It has been shown in the foregoing discussion that on oxidation of sulphides and elemental sulphur, H^+ and SO_4^{2-} ions are formed, so if there are no buffering substances the pH of the medium will drop considerably. However, in many cases the H^+ ions are neutralized or partly neutralized either by the silicate ions set free upon decomposition of minerals, to form undissociated orthosilicic acid (see p. 379), or by lime, and buffered by exchangeable cations. Considering the simple case of neutralisation by calcite, the following reaction can take place:

$$CaCO_3(s) + 2H^+ \rightleftharpoons Ca^{2+} + CO_2(g) + H_2O \quad - - - - - - - - - - - - - - - - - \quad (66)$$
$$lgK_{66} = lg[Ca^{2+}] + lg_\varsigma CO_2 + 2H_2O = 9.8 \quad - - - - - - - - - - - - - - - - \quad (66a)$$

where $_\varsigma CO_2$ is the partial CO_2 pressure in soil-air in atmospheres and where lgK is calculated from thermochemical data, listed by Robie and Waldbaum (1968).

The partial CO_2 pressure in soil-air fluctuates between $10^{-3.5}$ atm. (which is the partial pressure in the atmosphere) and 10^0 atm. (can occur temporarily in reduced soils high in organic matter). Assuming an 'average' $_\varsigma CO_2$ in the soil of $10^{-2.5}$ atm., equation (66a) reduces to:

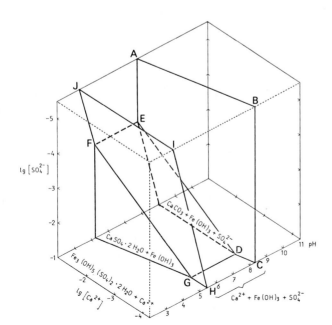

FIG. II.64. *Stability fields of $CaCO_3$, $CaSO_4.2H_2O$, $Fe(OH)_3$, and 'jarosite' as function of pH, lg$[Ca^{2+}]$, and lg$[SO_4^{2-}]$ at 25°C, 1 atm. total pressure, and $_\varsigma CO_2 = 10^{-2.5}$ atm.*

$$\lg [Ca^{2+}] + 2pH = 12.3 \quad - \quad (66b)$$

If sufficient Ca^{2+} and SO_4^{2-} (formed upon oxidation of sulphides) are accumulated to precipitate gypsum, the following reaction has to be considered:

$$CaSO_4.2H_2O \rightleftharpoons Ca^{2+} + SO_4^{2-} + 2H_2O \quad - - - - - - - - - - - - - - - - - - \quad (67)$$

$$\lg K_{67} = \lg [Ca^{2+}] + \lg [SO_4^{2-}] = -4.7 \quad - - - - - - - - - - - - - - - - - \quad (67a)$$

The stability fields of these components can be represented in a three-dimensional diagram with $\lg [Ca^{2+}]$, $\lg [SO_4^{2-}]$, and pH as the axes (see fig. II.64). Equation (66b) is represented in this diagram by plane ABCDE. As long as $CaCO_3$ is present in the system, the composition of the equilibrium solution is represented by any point in this plane. The activity of Ca^{2+} will increase by dissolution of $CaCO_3$; however, the pH only decreases to a value of 7 to 8.

Equation (67a) is represented in fig. II.64 by plane DEFG (parallel to the pH axis). It can now be stated that as long as both $CaCO_3$ and $CaSO_4.2H_2O$ are present, the composition of the equilibrium solution is given by line DE. After the complete dissolution of $CaCO_3$, the system is no longer buffered and the pH can be lowered considerably; the solution composition is then represented by plane DEFG.

The pH can again be buffered by the formation of basic ferric sulphate. Using the formula $Fe_3(OH)_5(SO_4)_2.2H_2O$, (as previously done) and considering reaction (44), equation (44a: $4pH - 2\lg [SO_4^{2-}] = 23.7$) can be represented by plane FGHIJ. As long as gypsum and $Fe(OH)_3$ are present, the composition of the equilibrium solution is given by line FG and the pH will remain practically unchanged. Only after complete dissolution of ferric hydroxide can other equilibria come into play (e.g. between SO_4^{2-} and α–FeOOH) and cause further lowering of the pH.

LITERATURE CITED

ARDEN, T.V. 1950 The solubility product of ferrous ferrosic hydroxides. *J. chem. Soc.*: 882–885.

BEERS, W.F.J. 1962 Acid sulphate soils. *Int. Inst. Land Recl. Impr.*, Bull. 3: pp. 31.

BERNER, R.A. 1963 Chemistry of hydrogen sulfide in marine sediments. *Geochim. Cosmochim. Acta*, 27: 563–575.

— 1964a Iron sulfides formed from aqueous solutions at low temperatures and atmospheric pressure. *J. Geol.*, 72: 826–834.

— 1964b Stability fields of iron minerals in anaerobic marine sediments. *J. Geol.*, 72: 826–834.

— 1965 Activity coefficients of bicarbonate, carbonate and calcium ions in seawater. *Geochim. Cosmochim. Acta*, 29: 947–965.

— 1967 Diagenesis of iron sulfide in recent marine sediments. In: Estuaries: *Amm. Ass. Adv. Sci. Publ.*, 83: 268–272.

— 1967a Thermodynamic stability of sedimentary iron sulfides. *Am. J. Sci.*, 265: 773–785.

BLACK, A.P. 1967 Electrokinetic characteristics of hydrous oxides of aluminium and iron. In: Principles and applications of water chemistry. *Proc. 4th Rudolfs Res. Conf.*, New York: 274–300.

BLOOMFIELD, C., COULTER, J.K. and KANARIS-SOTIRIOU, R. 1968 Oil palms on Acid Sulphate Soils in Malaya. *Trop. Agric. (Trinidad)*, 45: 289–300.

BRINKMAN, R. and PONS, L.J. 1968 A pedo-geomorphological classification and map of the holocene sediments in the coastal plain of the three Guianas. *Soil Survey Papers*, No. 4: pp. 40.

BROPHY, P.P., SCOTT, E.S. and SNELLGROVE, R.A. 1962 Sulfate studies II. Solid solution between alunite and jarosite. *Am. Min.*, 47: 112–126.

CHENERY, E.M. 1954 Acid sulfate soils in Central Africa. *Trans. 5th Int. Cong. Soil Sci.*, 4 195–198.

CLARK, J.S., GOBIN, C.A. and SPROUT, P.N. 1961 Yellow mottles in some poorly drained soils of the Lower Fraser Valley, British Columbia. *Can. J. Soil Sci.*, 41: 218–227.

EDELMAN, C.H. and VAN STAVEREN, J.M. 1958 Marsh soils in the United States and The Netherlands. *J. Soil and Water Cons.*, 1–1.

FLEMING, J.F. and ALEXANDER, L.T. 1961 Sulphur acidity in South Carolina tidal marsh soils. *Soil Sci. Soc. Am. Proc.*, 25: 94–95.

GARRELS, R.M. and CHRIST, CH.L. 1965 Solutions, minerals, and equilibria. New York.

— and THOMPSON, M.E. 1962 A chemical model for seawater at 25°C and one atmosphere total pressure. *Am. J. Sci.*, 260: 57–66.

GAYER, K.H. and WOONTNER, L. 1956 The solubility of ferrous hydroxide and ferric hydroxide in acidic and basic media at 25°C. *J. Phys. Chem.*, 60: 1569–1571.

HARMSEN, G.W., QUISPEL, A. and OTZEN, D. 1954 Observations on the formation and oxidation of pyrite in the soil. *Plant and Soil*, 5: 324–347.

HORN, M.E. and CHAPMAN, S.L. 1968 Clay mineralogy of some acid sulphate soils on the Guinea coast. *Trans. 9th Int. Cong. Soil Sci.*, III: 31–40.

—, HALL, V.L., CHAPMAN, S.L. and WIGGINS, M.M. 1967 Chemical properties of the coastal alluvial soils of the Republic of Guinea. *Soil Sci. Soc. Am. Proc.*, 31: 108–114.

IRRI 1964 Annual Report Int. Rice Res. Inst., Los Baños, Laguna, The Philippines.

— 1965 Annual Report Int. Rice Res. Ints., Los Baños, Laguna, The Philippines.

JAMES, H.L. 1966 Chemistry of the iron rich sedimentary rocks. *Geol. Surv. Prof. Paper 440-W*, USDI: pp. 61.

KAPLAN, I.R., EMERY, K.O. and RITTENBERG, S.C. 1963 The distribution and isotope abundance of sulphur in recent marine sediments of southern California. *Geochim. Cosmochim. Acta*, 27: 297–331.

KHODAKOVSKII, I.L. 1966 The hydrosulfide form of the heavy metal transportation in hydrothermal solutions. *Geokhimiya*, 8: 960–971 (*Chem. Abstr.*, 65: 14502).

KRAUSKOPF, K.B. 1967 Introduction to geochemistry. New York.

KUBISZ, J. 1964 Minerals of the alunite-jarosite group. *Polska Akad. Nauk. Prace Geol.*, 22: 1–85 (*Min. Abstr.*, 17 (5): 498).

LJUNGGREN, P. 1960 A sulfur mud deposit formed through bacterial transformation of fumarolic hydrogen sulfide *Econ. Geol.*, 55: 531–538.

NHUNG, M.M. and PONNAMPERUMA, F.N. 1966 Effects of calcium carbonate, manganese dioxide, ferric hydroxide and prolonged flooding on chemical and electrochemical changes and growth of rice in a flooded acid sulfate soil. *Soil Sci.*, 102: 29–41.

PALACHE, C.H., BERMAN, H. and FONDELL, C. 1951 The system of Mineralogy of J. D. and E. S. Dana. 7th Ed., Vol. II. New York – London.

PANTON, W.P., SOO, S.W. and MA'AROF, N. 1965 Reconnaissance soil survey of the Southwest Johore coconut area. *Malayan Soil Surv. Rep.*, 3/1965.

PARKER, R.L. 1962 Isomorphous substitution in natural and synthetic alunite. *Am. Min.*, 47 127–136.

PONNAMPERUMA, F.N. 1964 Dynamic aspects of flooded soils. In: The mineral nutrition of the rice plant, IRRI: 295–328.

—, MARTINEZ, E. and LOY, T. 1966 Influence of redox potential and partial pressure of carbon dioxide on pH values and the suspension effects of flooded soils. *Soil Sci.*, 101: 421–431.

—, TIANCO, E.M. and LOY, T. 1967 Redox equilibria in flooded soils. I. The iron hydroxide system. *Soil Sci.*, 103: 374–382.

PONS, L.J. 1963 Pyrites as a factor controlling 'ripening' and formation of 'cat clay', with special reference to the coastal plain of Surinam. *Agric. Expt. Sta. Bull. 82*, Paramaribo, Surinam.

— 1966 Geogenese en pedogenese in de Jong-Holocene kustvlakte van de drie Guianas. *Tijdschr. Kon. Ned. Aardr. Gen.*, 83: 153–173.

— and ZONNEVELD, I.S. 1965 Soil ripening and soil classification. *Int. Inst. Land Recl. Impr.*, No. 13.

ROBIE, R.A. and WALDBAUM, D.R. 1968 Thermodynamic properties of minerals and related substances at 298.15°K (25.0°C) and one atmosphere (1.013 bars) pressure and at higher temperatures. *Geol. Surv. Bull. 1259:* pp. 256.

SATO, M. 1960a Oxidation of sulfide ore bodies. I. Geochemical environments in terms of E_h and pH. *Econ. Geol.*, 55: 928–961.

— 1960b Oxidation of sulfide ore bodies. II. Oxidation mechanisms of sulfide minerals at 25°C. *Econ. Geol.*, 55: 1200–1231.

SCHWERTMANN, U. 1961 Über das Vorkommen und die Entstehung von Jarosit in Marschböden (Maibolt). *Die Naturwiss.*, 6: 159–160.

SILLEN, L.G. and MARTELL, A E. 1964 Stability constants of metal ion complexes. *Spec. Publ. No. 17.* The Chemical Society, London.

SLAGER, S. 1966 Morphological studies of some cultivated soils. *Thesis Wageningen.*

— and VAN SCHUYLENBORGH, J. 1970 Morphology and geochemistry of three clay soils of a tropical coastal plain (Surinam).) *Versl. Landbk. Onderz.* 734, pp. 34.

STARKEY, R.L. 1966 Oxidation and reduction of sulfur compounds in soils. *Soil Sci.*, 101: 297–307.

STOKES, H.N. 1907 Experiments on the action of various solutions on pyrite and marcasite. *Econ. Geol.*, 2: 14–23.

TEAKLE, L.J.H. and SOUTHERN, B.L. 1937 The peat soils and related soils of Western Australia. II. Soil survey of Herdsman Lake. *J. Agric. West-Austr.*, 14: 404–424.

TEMPLE, K.L. and DELCHAMPS, E.W. 1953 Autotrophic bacteria and the formation of acid in bituminous coal mines. *Appl Microbiol.*, 1 : 255–258.

TEODOROVICH, G.I. 1961 Authigenic minerals in sedimentary rocks (transl. from Russian: Consultants Bureau, New York). pp. 120.

VALENSKI, G. 1950 Contribution au diagramme potentiel-pH du soufre. *C.R. 2ieme Réunion Comm. Int. Therm. Kinetics Electrochim.* (Milan): 51–68.

VAN BREEMEN, N. 1968 Vorming en omzetting van sulfiden en sulfaten in zeebodem sedimenten en katteklei gronden. *Unpubl. Rep. Wageningen:* pp. 67.

— and OLDEMAN, L.R. 1967 Bodemvorming en bodemclassificatie van rijstgronden. *Unpubl. Rep. Wageningen:* pp. 71.

VAN DER SPEK, J. 1950 Katteklei. *Versl. Landbk. Onderz.*, No. 56.2: pp. 40.

VAN STRAATEN, L.M.J.U. 1954 Composition and structure of recent marine sediments in the Netherlands. *Leidse Geol. Meded.*, 19: 1–108.

VERHOOP, J.A.D. 1940 Chemische en microbiologische omzettingen van ijzersulfiden. *Thesis Leiden.*

VOLKOV, I.I. 1961 Iron sulfides, their interdependance and transformations in the Black Sea bottom sediments. *Tr. Inst. Okeanol.*, *Akad. Nauk. SSSR*, 50: 68–92 (*Chem. Abstr.*, 55: 13956).

WIND, G.P. and STEEGHS, B.H. 1964 Kattezand. *Landb. Tijdschr.*, 76: 150–157.

YAMANE, I. and SATO, K. 1961 Effect of temperature on the formation of gases and ammonium-nitrogen in the waterlogged soils. *Tohoku Univ. Res. Inst. Sci. Rep.*, Ser. D 12: 1–10.

YONEDA, S. and KAWADA, N. 1954 A study on polder soils in Japan. 5. A note on the forming processes of the strong acid soils found in halogenetic polders. *J. Sci. Soil Man.*, 25: 36–40.

CHAPTER 5

ANDOSOLS

The Andosols are soils developed on pyroclastic material. They occur in volcanic regions, such as those bordering the Pacific basin: on the west coast of South America, Central America, The Rocky Mountains, Alaska, The Philippine Archipelago, Indonesia, Australian New Guinea, New Zealand, and Japan. The name originated from

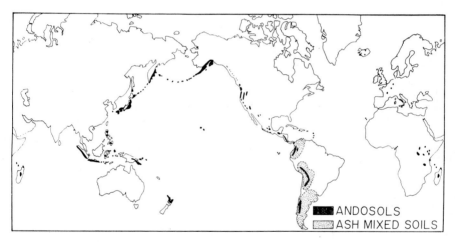

F I G. II.65. *Distribution of Andosols and Ash Mixed Soils (after various sources)*

the Japanese 'ankantsu-shoku-do' meaning dark brown soil (Thorp and Smith, 1949). Other names in literature include the Humic Allophane Soils (Kanno, 1961) and Kuroboku soils (Ohmasa, 1965) of Japan, the Trumao soils of Chile (Wright, 1960), the fresh volcanic ash soils, young volcanic ash soils, 'Brown earth', etc. soils of the Antilles (McConaghy, 1969), the Tapetate, pardo forestal, andosol, and 'latosol' of Central America (Martini, 1969); Black Dust soils, or High Mountains soils, and Andosols of Indonesia (Tan, 1965); the Alvisols or Yellow Brown Loams of New Zealand (Taylor, 1965); the Andepts and Andaquepts of the U.S.D.A. 7th Approximation (1960–1967), and the Andosols FAO/UNESCO Soils Map of the World Project.

The denomination 'Andosols' for soils derived from volcanic ash had become very popular and the Meeting on the Classification and Correlation of Volcanic Ash Soils, in Japan (FAO/Unesco, Report 14, 1965) agreed that the name was suitable.

5.1. SOIL FORMING FACTORS

a) *Climate*

Andosols are found in the temperate dry sub-humid, temperate moist sub-humid, cool temperate humid, and cool superhumid environments of Chile (Wright, 1965); in the cool humid, warm temperate, warm humid, sub-tropical humid, and tropical humid low-lands of Colombia and Ecuador; in the humid sub-tropical and humid tropical undulating to flat territory of Central America; in humid climates in Alaska and the Aleutian chain, along the coast of Washington, Oregon and northern California (Flach, 1965); in the cool semi-arid, tropical semi-arid, and tropical perhumid mountainous territory of Hawaii (Swindale and Sherman, 1965); in the flat or gently undulating land stretching from Hokkaido close to the subarctic region to the extreme southern part of Kyushu in the sub-tropical belt (Ohmasa, 1965).

Soils developed on volcanic ash such as the Regosols and other mineral soils in arid regions and the organic soils in very humid and superhumid environments, do not comply with the modal concept of Andosols.

b) *Vegetation*

A number of plant species are found. Some of the species of plants are probably typical for certain regions or environments i.e. the *Notophagus oblicua* has been associated with the Trumao soils in Chile (Besoain, 1958); *Notophagus* spp. have also been reported on volcanic ash soils in other countries of the world. Ferns are found on acid soils, xerophitic plant species under arid conditions in Peru (Zavaleta, 1969), mosses are common in superhumid climates. Soils on volcanic ash in the humid sub-tropical belt in Colombia provide most suitable conditions for coffee growing. A list of several plant species found on Andosols in several countries follows.

Chile: From south to north in the Trumao zone the plant species include, *Nothofagus oblicua, Nothofagus dombei, Nothofagus antarctica, Nothofagus pumila, Weimania spp., Saxegothea, Laurelia sempervirens, Podocarpus nubigenus* (in mountainous country), *Fittroya cupresoides, Acacia cavenia, Boldea boldus, Aristotelia spp.* (Valdes, 1969).

Colombia: According to Montenegro and Espinal (1963) the following vegetation formations are found in the Andosol zone: humid mountain forest, humid lower mountain forest, humid subtropical forest, and humid tropical forest. The plant species include, grasses, *Quercus spp., Cederela rapanea*, several species of Conifers and *Nothofagus, Ginerum sagittatum, Mimosa pigra, Erythrina glauca, Calliandria spp.*

Central America: Nothofagus spp., and several species of trees of the original vegetation still remain. Coffee, sugar cane are cultivated at below 1500 m and vegetables at higher elevations. Grasses are common in the uplands.

Mexico: Several species of Conifers, *Bromus spp., Muhlenbergia spp., Festuca spp., Agrostis spp.*, etc. (Aguilera, 1969).

U.S.A. (California): The original vegetation includes several species of Conifers, *Nothofagus spp.*, ferns and grasses.

New Zealand: Nothofagus spp., Dracophyllum tarnui, mosses, bracken ferns, grasses *(Dactylis glomerata L.)*

Japan: Several species of Conifers, *Betula spp.*, *Acer pictum*, *Magnolia abovata*, *Salix spp.*, *Quercus serrata*, *Quercus agustissima*, etc. The artificial forest includes *Latrix leptolepis*, *Quercus dentata*, *Sasa spp.*, etc.

c) *Parent material*

The parent material of the Andosols is mainly the volcanic debris which remains un-consolidated after it has been deposited. In Japan, the so called 'Humic Allophane Soils', are soils developed on comparatively recent eruptive material from the volcanos (excluding lava and welded tuff, Ohmasa, 1965). In northern Sumatera, Indonesia, soils with similar characteristics to the 'Humic Allophane Soils' are formed on andes-ito-dacitic tuffs and lahars of the Sibajak volcano (Tan, 1965).

Volcanic tuff consists of rock fragments, single mineral grains, and glass. The glass is the most important of these three components (Pettijohn, 1957) in relation to the formation of Andosols. It forms part of the fine, comminuted material of the formerly liquid magma.

In South America the bulk of the Andosols are developed on finely comminuted ejecta from a magma with a chemical composition between acidic and intermediate. Acidic ejecta mixed with sub-ordinate intermediate magma of Pleistocene times are found in northern South America (Colombia, Ecuador), and intermediate ejecta with sub-ordinate acidic magma from the Quaternary is found in the south (in Chile). In the zone of Los Angeles, Chile, basic material from the Antuco volcano is present (Valdes, 1969).

In Central America, acidic type of rocks are found in El Salvador, Guatemala, and Honduras; basic and intermediate ejecta are present in Panama, Costa Rica, and Nicaragua (Martini, 1969).

In the Antilles, the rock types range from acid dacites to basic lavas but the inter-mediate andesitic one is the most common (McConaghy, 1969).

The pyroclastic materials in Mexico include basalts rich in olivine (soils of Popo-catepetl, Poricutin), andesites (soils of the Itraccihuat), rhyolitic-andesites (soils of the Valle de Puebla), and rhyolites in the northern part of the country (Aguilera, 1969).

The widely distributed deposits in the northern United States are generally of dacitic composition about 6,600 years old (Haward and Borchardt, 1969).

In Japan seven volcanic soil groups have been classified on andesitic, dacitic, or basaltic rock types (Ministry of Agriculture and Forestry, 1964).

The Andosols in Indonesia are developed from a wide variety of parent material. They change from acidic to basic types going from west to east along the Indian Ocean.

Intermediate and rhyolitic rocks are the parent material of the soils in New Zealand (Taylor, 1965).

5.2. ANDOSOL PROFILES

5.2.1. GENERAL CHARACTERISTICS

The Andosols have:

a) AC or ABC profiles, ranging from 30 to 50 cm, and in some cases up to 100 cm depth:

b) dark colours which dominate throughout the profile, although there is a clear difference in colour between the top soil and the subsoil. In humid temperate and in humid tropical uplands (above 2500 m) the colours of the profile are darker than in the humid tropical lowlands (below 1000 m) and in the sub-tropical belt (from about 1000 to 2000 m);

c) very porous, very friable, non-plastic, non-sticky A horizons, merging clearly into the brown B or C horizons;

d) A horizons with a crumb or granular structure;

e) B horizons (if present) with weakly developed blocky structure;

f) high water holding capacity;

g) segregation of aluminium in the form of nodules of gibbsite or segregation of iron oxides in the B or C horizons;

h) 'soapy' feeling of the soil (in the field) when rubbed, becoming almost liquid;

i) sometimes irreversible granulation after air-drying;

j) an amorphous fabric (Luna, 1969), consisting of an isotropic and porous plasm.

The mineralogical properties.

a) Both the silt and fine sand fractions have volcanic glass, the amount of glass varying according to the locality. Some of the grains (particularly hypersthene) appear with a rim of volcanic glass;

b) Ferromagnesian minerals (olivine, pyroxenes, amphiboles), feldspars, and quartz are very common, the amount depending on the origin of the volcanic ash;

c) Allophanes dominate the clay fraction (more than 60 percent) in young soils; allophane and halloysite are found in more developed soils;

d) 'Phytolith' (or 'plant opal') occurs abundantly (Kanno and Arimura, 1958; Luna, 1969).

The physico-chemical properties.

a) Base saturation is low, although the pH is higher than expected.

b) C.e.c. is high when determined by the sodium acetate method at pH 7.

c) Anion exchange capacity is high.

d) The pH of 1 g of soil in 50 ml of 1N NaF exceeds 9.4 after two minutes (Fieldes, 1961).

e) C and N contents are high; the C/N ratio is low.

f) The P content is low (when extracted by 0.5M $NaHCO_3$-solution at pH 8.5) due to strong P fixation (Olsen, 1954).

h) The soils are difficult to peptize.

i) More than 20% moisture is retained at 15 bar pressure.

j) Bulk density is smaller than 0.85.

5.2.2. SOME PROFILES WITH ANALYTICAL DETAILS

Luna (1969) describes a typical profile (profile 39) of the humid subtropical belt in Colombia (S.A.). The profile is situated on the east slope of the Medellin river valley, 9 km from the city of Medellin. Elevation is 2150 m. There is a 40% convex slope. Rainfall is 2600 mm annually. The vegetation consists of grass, ferns and few trees. The parent material is volcanic ash and colluvium of amphibolites. The soil is well-drained. The morphological characteristics are:

Horizon	Depth (cm)	
A1	0–40	Moist, black 10YR2/1 (10YR3/1:d) very humic, silty loam; non-porous aggregates; very friable; non-plastic; poorly rooted; irregular and gradual boundary to
B	40–50	Moist, very dark greyish brown 10YR3/2 (10YR4/2:d) very humic, loam; moderate, medium, prismatic structure, breaking to moderate, medium aggregates; non-plastic, non-sticky; poorly rooted; regular and gradual boundary to
C	+50	Moist, dark brown 7.5YR4/4 (7.5YR5/6:d) humic loam; massive; friable and porous; non-plastic and slightly sticky; no roots.

Analytical details are given in tables 11.129, 130, and 131.

TABLE 11.129. *Some physical and chemical characteristics of profile 39* (after Luna, 1969)

Hor.	a^1	Bulk density (g cm^{-3})	pH (H$_2$O)	C (%)	C/N	h.a.^{2} f.a.	cation exchange characteristics (m.e./100 g of soil)						
							c.e.c.	Ca	Mg	K	Na	Al	H
A1	40.6	0.4	5.1	13.9	15.5	0.5	79	0.2	0.2	0.1	tr	2.5	78
B	46.5	0.5	5.8	7.3	11.0	0.4	60	0.2	0.2	tr	tr	0.4	59
C	34.3	0.4	6.4	1.9	6.9	0.5	49	0.2	0.1	tr	tr	–	48

[1] a = moisture (%) retained at 15 bar pressure. [2] h.a./f.a. = ratio humic acids/fulvic acids.

TABLE 11.130. *Chemical composition (partial) of profile 39* (After Luna, 1969; weight percentages)

Hor.	SiO$_2$	Al$_2$O$_3$	Fe$_2$O$_3$	TiO$_2$	CaO	K$_2$O	SiO$_2$/ Al$_2$O$_3$	SiO$_2$/ Fe$_2$O$_3$	Al$_2$O$_3$/ Fe$_2$O$_3$	free Fe$_2$O$_3$
A1	36.0	14.4	13.0	0.5^5	0.5	0.1	4.3	7.5	1.8	4.1
B	39.8	17.0	13.7	0.6	0.6	0.1	4.1	8.3	2.0	4.5
C	39.8	22.4	16.3	0.6	0.6	0.2	3.1	6.6	2.1	4.6

TABLE 11.131. *Mineralogical composition of the sand fraction (500–50μ) in percentages*

Hor.	l.m.^{1}	h.m.^{2}	light minerals							heavy minerals					op
			Q	Gl	Ph	Or	Ab	Mi	Misc	Epi	Ho	Oho	Py	Misc	
A1	56	44	59	2	3	11	21	–	4	2	89	5	4	–	14
B	51	49	48	3	12	12	21	tr	4	–	87	tr	10	3	17
C	62	38	51	3	–	10	31	2	3	–	93	3	4	–	35

[1] l.m. = light minerals; [2] h.m. = heavy minerals. Q = quartz; Gl = volcanic glass; Ph = phytoliths; Or = K-feldspars; Ab = acid plagioclases; Mi = mica; Epi = epidote; Ho = hornblende; Oho = oxyhornblende; Py = pyroxenes; Misc = miscellaneous; op = opaque.

The grain-size distribution in the A_1 horizon is: 21% $> 50\mu$, 55% $50-2\mu$, and 24% $< 2\mu$. The clay fraction (see fig. II.66) consists of abundant quartz followed by crystoballite, allophane, and gibbsite. Gibbsite increases, and allophane and crystoballite decrease with depth. In the C horizon some halloysite is present.

In spite of the low base saturation, soil pH is not extremely low, a well-known phenomenon in soils with allophane-loaded clay fractions. The pH-dependent charge characteristics, the amphoteric nature of exchangeable aluminium, the complex nature of the amorphous material all play a role. It is believed that some of the amorphous free silica and allophane dissolve in the extracting solution (amorphous silica solubility is constant between pH 3 and 8: see fig. II.22) and the silicic acid is titrated. The silt fraction can also be the site of the exchange reactions, but it is thought that this fraction also contains a considerable amount of amorphous and metastable components; even the sand fraction contains plant opal. Further research into this subject is necessary.

The ratio humic acids/fulvic acids is low, so the content of soluble organic acids is high; this can be expected to have some bearing on sesquioxide translocation. Aluminium hydroxide is extremely mobile (see table II.130 and the X-ray data); this cannot be explained on the basis of its solubility product. It has to be assumed that Al forms soluble complexes with the fulvic acids which are transported downwards with the percolating water and which are then hydrolysed at higher pH values, forming a deposit of aluminium hydroxide (see Part III, Chapter 3). The same process applies, though to a lesser extent, to iron oxide.

It is evident that certain aspects of podzolization, viz. deferritization or cheluviation, are present.

Another selected example (profile 40) of a volcanic ash soil (Luna, 1969) was from Chile (S.A.) from the Centinela Experimental Station of the Ministry of Agriculture (Chile) near Puerto Ocatay. It was situated on a very gently undulating old terrace surface. The parent material is volcanic ash (probably andesitic) overlying alluvial gravels. The elevation is 200 m, the vegetation a grass-forest cover, and the rainfall 2000 mm annually. The profile description is as follows:

Horizon	Depth (cm)	
A_{11}	0–8	Black (10YR2/1:m) to black brown (10YR2/2:d) silt loam; friable; moderately developed fine and very fine granular structure; non-sticky, and very slightly plastic when moist; diffuse boundary to
A_{12}	8–18	Black brown (10YR2/2:m to 10YR3/2:d) silty loam; friable, soft when dry; moderately developed, medium and fine sub-angular blocky structure; very slightly sticky and slightly plastic when moist; diffuse boundary to
B_1	18–43	Dark brown (10YR3/3:m) to grey yellowish brown (10YR4/3:d) silt loam; friable soft loam when dry; strong, medium sub-angular blocky structure, breaking to coarse granules; slightly sticky and slightly plastic when moist; clear boundary to
B_2	43–74	Dark brown (7.5YR3/4:m) to grey yellowish brown (10YR5/4:d) silt loam; moderately developed fine and very fine sub-angular blocky

structure; friable to firm; slightly sticky and slightly plastic when moist; diffuse boundary to

B₃   74–128   Dark brown (10YR3/4:m) to brown (10YR4/4:d) silt loam; firm to friable; weakly developed fine structure, breaking to very fine granules; slightly sticky and moderately plastic when moist.

The analytical details are given in tables II.132, 133, and 134. As the percentages of the other elements in the clay fraction are in the order of magnitude of 0.1 to 0.5%, the

TABLE II.132. *Some physical and chemical characteristics of profile 40*

Hor.	texture (%)			pH (H₂O)	C (%)	C/N	cation exchange characteristics (m.e./100 g of soil)				
	> 50μ	50–2μ	< 2μ				c.e.c.	Ca	Mg	K	Na
A₁₁	10	81	9	5.8	18.7	14.4	76	22.5	6.5	1.1	0.6
A₁₂	17	46	37	5.8	7.9	13.3	55	7.0	2.0	0.4	0.3
B₁	12	75	13	5.9	4.3	12.9	34	0.5	1.1	0.2	0.1
B₂	18	70	12	5.9	4.0	10.3	37	0.2	0.2	0.1	0.1
B₃	22	65	13	5.8	4.0	9.9	43	0.2	0.3	0.1	0.1

TABLE II.133. *Partial chemical composition of the clay fractions of profile 40* (weight percentages; after Luna, 1969)

Hor.	SiO_2	Al_2O_3	Fe_2O_3	SiO_2/Al_2O_3	SiO_2/Fe_2O_3	Al_2O_3/Fe_2O_3
A₁₁	26.8	15.4	8.6	3.0	8.3	2.8
A₁₂	23.0	26.0	9.8	1.5	6.3	4.2
B₁	21.9	28.3	9.8	1.3	6.0	4.6
B₂	20.9	30.1	10.2	1.2	5.4	4.5
B₃	19.8	30.8	10.2	1.1	5.2	4.7

data of table II.133 facilitates the calculation of the normative mineralogical composition assuming that allophane (composition $2SiO_2.Al_2O_3.3H_2O$: Wada, 1967) and gibbsite are the most important constituents of the clay. DTA data show that allophane is the dominant mineral and gibbsite increases with depth. The result of the calculation is given in table II.134, which confirms the DTA results (see fig. II.66). As in the previous profile it can be seen that aluminium hydroxide is mobile.

Table II.135 shows that the profile is not as strongly weathered as the previous profile, as the reserve of weatherable minerals is fairly high. The increase in volcanic glass in the surface layers points to a rejuvenation of the profile.

Profile 40 belongs to the 'trumao' type of Chilean soils, to the sub-alvic soils in New Zealand, and probably is the Typic Dystrandept of the 7th Approximation.

TABLE II.134. *Approximate normative mineralogical composition of the clay fractions of profile 40* (equivalent percentages).

Hor.	Allo	Gibb	Q	Go
A_{11}	70.6	–	17.8	12.6
A_{12}	75.4	12.5	–	12.1
B_1	69.8	18.4	–	11.8
B_2	65.4	22.7	–	11.8
B_3	62.2	25.7	–	12.1

Allo = allophane; Gibb = gibbsite; Q = free silica; Go = goethite.

TABLE II.135. *Mineralogical composition of the sand fraction (500-50μ) in percentages* (after Luna, 1969)

Hor.	l.m.[1]	h.m.[2]	light minerals							heavy minerals					
			Q	Gl	Or	Ab	Lab	An	Misc	Epi	Zo	Ho	Cpy	Opy	op
A_{11}	90	10	20	23	6	7	13	8	23	5	7	8	26	54	2
A_{12}	96	4	18	20	4	1	12	16	29	9	3	7	23	58	2
B_1	90	10	18	18	2	6	12	8	36	2	1	10	19	68	1
B_2	87	13	36	4	8	11	9	17	15	3	tr	7	26	64	9
B_3	89	11	35	2	15	7	16	12	13	5	2	9	17	67	9

[1] l.m. = light mineral fraction; [2] h.m. = heavy mineral fraction. Q = quartz; Gl = volcanic glass; Or = K-feldspar; Ab = acid plagioclases; Lab = intermediate plagioclases; An = basic plagioclases; Misc = miscellaneous; Epi = epidote; Zo = zoisite; Ho = hornblende; Cpy = clino-pyroxenes; Opy = ortho-pyroxenes; op = opaque. Many of the minerals are covered with a rim of volcanic glass.

Profile 40 is only weakly podzolized in comparison with profile 39.

The Yellow Brown Loams from New Zealand are similar to the 'trumao' soils of Chile. One example of these soils was developed on volcanic ash deposits of different ages. C_{14} determinations and the stratigraphy revealed that the age increases from 1,800 and 3,500 years in the top to roughly 10,000 years in the bottom of the profile. The profile (profile 41) is situated at an elevation of 450 m at Powe Hawe's Bay, on a convex slope of 5° in the undulating area of a wide valley. The parent material is rhyolitic volcanic ash over marine sediments. The soil is used as grassland. Rainfall is 1500 mm annually. The profile description is as follows:

Horizon	Depth (cm)	
A_1	2.5–15	Brownish black (5YR2/1) loamy sand with 3% very coarse sand; friable; moderately developed, fine, granular to crumb structure; abundant roots.
B	15–30	Dull yellowish brown (10YR4/3) sand with 3% very coarse sand; very friable; moderately developed, fine crumb structure; many roots.
II A'	30–40	Dull yellow orange (10YR6/3) coarse sand with 8% very coarse sand and gravel, many small pieces of charcoal; slightly compact; single grain structure; few roots.

II B′	40–60	Dull yellowish brown (10YR4/3) sand with 5 % very coarse sand; firm; weakly developed medium-sized subangular blocky structure.
II C′	60–70	Dull yellowish brown (10YR4/3) very coarse sand consisting of brownish yellow pumice (85–90%) and grey rhyolite (10–15%); loose and single grain structure.
III B′$_3$	70–90	Yellowish brown (10YR5/6) sandy loam with some very coarse pumice sand in the upper 30 cm; slippery non-sticky consistence; weakly developed coarse subangular blocky structure when dry.
III C′$_1$	105–120+	Light yellow (2.5Y7/4) silt loam derived from Tertiary sandstone.

Classification: Umbric Vitandrept.

TABLE II.136. *Some physical and chemical properties of profile 41*

Hor.	texture (%)			a^1	pH (H$_2$O)	C (%)	C/N	h.a.^{2} f.a.	cation exchange characteristics (m.e./100 g of soil)				
	> 50μ	50–2μ	< 2μ						c.e.c.	Ca	Mg	K	Na
A$_1$	31	66	3	11.8	5.5	4.5	12.6	1.0	23.4	2.7	0.6	0.3	0.2
B	41	57	2	6.3	5.7	1.7	10.7	0.3	11.7	0.5	0.1	0.3	0.3
II A	55	44	1	5.4	5.8	1.3	n.d.	1.0	8.6	0.3	tr	0.3	0.3
II B	66	30	4	4.6	5.9	1.1	7.6	n.d.	9.7	0.4	tr	0.2	0.2
II C	82	15	3	4.5	6.0	0.6	7.9	n.d.	6.8	0.2	0.1	0.1	0.1
III B	40	35	25	14.0	5.8	1.7	9.5	n.d.	24.3	0.5	0.7	0.2	0.2
III C$_1$	36	35	29	24.0	6.0	1.2	17.3	n.d.	28.5	0.6	0.5	0.1	0.1

^{1} a = moisture (percentages) retained at 15 atm. pressure. ^{2} h.a./f.a. = humic acid/fulvic acid ratio.

The analytical details are represented in tables II.136 and 137 and in fig. II.66. The discontinuities observed in the profile are fairly well reflected in the analyses, especially the distinct break between deposits II and III. The gradual decrease of the sand fraction and increase of the silt fraction can be attributed to increasing weathering of a homogeneous deposit. The mineralogical analysis (table II.137) also shows a distinct break

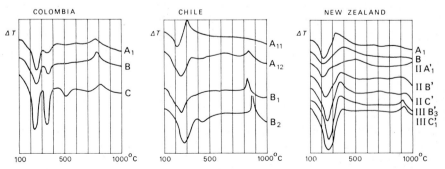

FIG. II.66. *Differential thermal curves of the Na-saturated clay fractions of the Andosol profiles 39, 40, and 41*

between deposit II and III. Apparently, the time lapse between the deposit of materials I and II has been short, and the nature of the material is very similar. This conclusion agrees with the C_{14} datings mentioned above and with the data in fig. II.66. Only the clay fraction of the two lowest horizons have allophane with an exotherm at approximately 900° C (see also section 3, p. 412), indicating that the allophane of the subsoil is better crystallized than that of the upper part of the profile.

The Colombia profile is the oldest one, followed by Chilean profile and finally by the New Zealand profile, with the same age range for the podzolic tendencies in the profiles.

TABLE II.137. *Mineralogical composition of the sand fraction (500–50μ) in percentages*

Hor.	l.m.[1]	h.m.[2]	light minerals							heavy minerals				
			Q	Gl	Or	Ab	Lab	Wp	Misc	Ho	Cpy	Opy	Alt	op
A₁	98	2	2	77	4	2	–	15	–	7	21	61	11	28
B	94	6	tr	97	–	–	–	3	–	4	24	65	7	40
IIA	98	2	–	96	tr	2	–	2	–	5	25	64	6	38
IIB	96	4	tr	89	–	–	–	--	11	–	6	18	61	15
IIC	95	5	tr	67	–	–	–	33	–	tr	6	87	7	55
IIIB	96	4	5	17	–	–	–	70	8	8	26	60	6	32
IIIC	96	4	4	9	–	2	3	78	4	2	21	74	3	17

[1] l.m. = light minerals; [2] h.m. = heavy minerals; Q = quartz; Gl = volcanic glass; Or = K-feldspars; Ab = acid plagioclases; Lab = intermediate plagioclases; Wp = weathering products; Misc = miscellaneous; Ho = hornblende; Cpy = clino-pyroxenes; Opy = ortho-pyroxenes; Alt = alterites; op = opaque. Some of the minerals have a rim of volcanic glass.

An interesting example of the influence of age on clay-mineral formation in volcanic ash soils is found in the study published by the Japanese Ministry of Agriculture and Forestry on this subject (1964). In one profile 15 volcanic deposits occurred and the nature of the clay fractions has been examined by thermal analysis.

From this data it can be seen that the younger deposits are all characterized by the presence of allophane. Kaolinite becomes prevalent from layer IX onwards with the exception of the layers XI and XII in which allophane again occurs in large quantities. One explanation might be that these layers were exposed for too short a period to the atmosphere to allow the transformation of allophane into kaolinite.

Finally two examples from Indonesia will be discussed (Van Schuylenborgh, 1958). The first profile (profile 42) is situated on a practically horizontal part of the slope of Mount Wajang (volcano of Plio-Pleistocene age: Van Bemmelen, 1949, p. 623) South-East of Pengalengan (Preanger, Java). The altitude is 1620 m above sea level. Mean annual rainfall is 2751 mm; the monthly distribution is as follows:

Jan.	Febr.	Mrch	Apr.	Mai	June	July	Aug.	Sept.	Oct.	Nov.	Dec.
332	298	349	300	217	135	88	70	99	210	309	344 mm

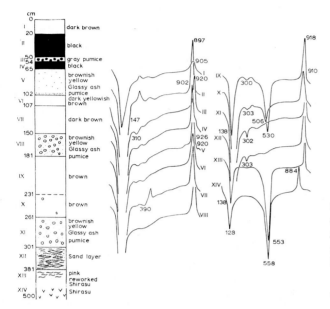

FIG. II.67. *Ash sequences of a Humic Allophane soil of Kanoya, Kagoshima and DTA curves of their clay separates (after Volcanic Ash Soils in Japan, 1964)*

Mean annual temperature is 16.4° C. Vegetation: tropical mountain rainforest with an evapotranspiration of approximately 1000 mm annually. The drainage is excessive and the parent material a basalto-andesitic tuffaceous ash. The profile description reads as follows:

Horizon	Depth (cm)	
$O_1 + O_2$	5–0	Forest litter. Lower part well-decomposed. Mulltype.
A_{11}	0–5	Brownish black (10YR2/2:m) to greyish yellow brown (10YR4/2:d) sandy loam. Well-developed granular to fine subangular blocky structure. Very friable. Abundance of roots. Clear boundary to
A_{12}	5–31	Brownish black (10YR3/2:m) to dull yellowish brown (10YR5/3:d) loam. Well-developed fine subangular blocky structure. Friable. Many roots. Clear boundary to
A_2	31–61	Dark brown (10YR3/4:m) to dull yellow orange (10YR6/4:d) loam. Thin platy structure. Friable. Roots are present. Gradual boundary to
B_1	61–80	Brown (10YR4/4:m) to bright yellowish brown (10YR6/6:d) clay loam. Moderately developed fine subangular blocky structure. Slightly firm. Prominent glassy (clay) coatings on structural units. Few roots. Clear boundary to
IIB'_2	80–95	Brownish black (7.5YR3/2:m) to dull yellowish brown (10YR5/4:d) silty clay loam. Well-developed medium subangular blocky structure. Friable. Very few roots.
$IIIA'_1$	95+	Coaled organic horizon. Old vegetation surface burnt by hot ash deposit.

The soil dehydrates irreversibly into gravel-size aggregates. Therefore it was analysed in the field-wet state. None of the common peptizing agents could be used in the granulometric analysis. However, 10^{-3}M to 10^{-4}M hydrochloric acid produced perfect peptization. Classification: Typic Hydrandept.

The analyses are given in tables II.138 and 139. Table II.139 shows that there is mineralogical difference between horizon IIB_2 and the upper part of the profile. Apparently the last eruption of the volcano consisted of a short first stage in which a basalto-andesitic ash with hypersthene-augite association was deposited, followed by a longer (dying-out) stage in which a similar ash with an olivine association was deposited. Although primary minerals are still present in the solum, glass has already been completely weathered. A considerable amount of fine iron concretions can be observed, indicating that this soil is in a fairly advanced stage of weathering. It is certainly the oldest of the profiles discussed.

Table II.138 shows that there is an accumulation of clay in the B horizon, which was also indicated in the profile description. X-ray analysis showed that the clay was predominantly composed of amorphous material, with only minor admixtures of

TABLE II.138. *Some physical and chemical characteristics of profile 42*

Hor.	texture (%)			C (%)	C/N	pH H_2O	molar ratios of clay fraction		
	> 50µ	50–2µ	< 2µ				SiO_2/Al_2O_3	SiO_2/Fe_2O_3	Al_2O_3/Fe_2O_3
A_{11}	44.4	48.8	6.8	14.6	12.8	6.3	2.2	9.3	4.1
A_{12}	26.3	55.1	18.6	7.1	9.8	6.0	1.9	8.1	4.3
A_2	31.4	45.2	23.4	4.6	8.1	6.1	1.2	5.6	4.5
B_1	28.1	43.5	28.4	3.3	7.7	6.0	1.2	5.1	4.3
IIB_2	13.2	52.2	34.6	3.5	8.8	5.9	1.1	4.5	4.2

montmorillonite, kaolinite, and gibbsite. The coatings in the B horizon do not show clay orientation, so are not considered coatings in the sense of the definition of the 7th Approximation. Nevertheless, there is movement of clay-sized particles and the B horizon is therefore the horizon of accumulation of clay-sized particles. The glassy or wax-like coatings on the structural units are undoubtedly accumulations of allophane together with gibbsite, as X-ray analysis showed an increase of gibbsite with depth.

TABLE II.139. *Mineralogical composition of the sand fraction of profile 42* (in percentages)

Hor.	total sand fraction											heavy sand fraction					
	Q	Lab	Ho	Hy	Aug	Ol	Gl	op	ic	Z	Misc	op	Ho	Hy	Aug	Ol	Z
A_{11}	–	20	tr	tr	6	1	–	2	23	1	47	9	13	26	33	26	2
A_{12}	2	18	2	1	5	2	tr	1	29	–	40	16	8	34	34	24	1
A_2	2	21	4	1	6	3	1	2	30	1	29	12	17	28	28	17	1
B_1	1	13	7	7	11	3	1	3	25	5	24	29	14	17	33	34	–
IIB_2	tr	6	5	9	3	–	1	1	68	–	7	27	32	51	17	–	2

Q = quartz; Lab = intermediate plagioclases; Ho = green hornblende; Hy = hypersthene; Aug = augites; Ol = olivine; Gl = volcanic glass; op = opaque; ic = iron concretions; Z = zircon; Misc = miscellaneous (rock fragments).

These conclusions are supported by the molar SiO_2/Al_2O_3 ratios of the clay fraction; the decrease of this ratio with depth is caused either by translocation of clay with a low SiO_2/Al_2O_3 (allophane) or by translocation of gibbsite or by both processes. The remainder of the clay in the upper horizons is then residually enriched with components of high SiO_2/Al_2O_3 ratios. This was actually found as X-ray analysis showed that kaolinite increases from the bottom to the top.

This profile represents a fairly strongly podzolized soil; translocation of clay-sized particles took place together with cheluviation of aluminium hydroxide and iron oxides (see SiO_2/Fe_2O_3 ratio in table II.138). It should be emphasized that this clay translocation was only discovered because the samples were not air-dried before analysis and a suitable peptizing agent was used.

The same tendencies can be observed in the second profile, which is slightly younger than the previous one. This profile comes from Mount Tandjungsari of the Salak-complex (Pleistocene age: Hartmann, 1938), near Leuwiliang, Tjanten tea plantation, Western Java (Indonesia). The profile (profile 43) is situated on the flattened top at an elevation of 1100 m above sea level. The mean annual temperature is 19.6° C. Average monthly rainfall and rainfall distribution are:

Total	Jan.	Febr.	Mrch	Apr.	Mai	June	July	Aug.	Sept.	Oct.	Nov.	Dec.
5420	432	420	472	538	497	350	290	338	464	583	576	460

The climate is more humid than in the previous case. The parent material is an andesitic tuffaceous ash with hypersthene-association. The vegetation is a tropical mountain rain forest and the drainage is perfect.

The profile description reads as follows:

Horizon	Depth (cm)	
$O_1 + O_2$	2.5–0	Forest litter, lower part well-decomposed. Mulltype.
A_{11}	0–15	Brownish black (10YR3/2:m) to dark brown (10YR3/3:d) loam with moderately developed granular and subangular blocky structure. Very friable. Abundance of roots. Gradual boundary to
A_{12}	15–28	Dull yellowish brown (10YR4/3:m and d) clay loam. Weakly developed fine subangular blocky structure. Friable. Many roots. Clear boundary to
B_1	28–46	Brown (10YR4/4:m and d) clay. Well-developed medium subangular blocky structure. Friable. Many roots. Gradual boundary to
B_2	46–66	Yellowish brown (10YR5/6:m) to dull yellowish brown (10YR5/4:d) clay. Well-developed fine subangular blocky structure. Pronounced wax-like coatings. Friable. Few roots. Clear boundary to
C	66+	Bright yellowish brown (10YR6/8:m) to yellow orange (10YR7/8:d) sandy clay loam. Very porous. Very friable. No roots.

As the preceding profile, the material dries irreversibly. Classification: Typic Hydrandept.

The mineralogical analysis of the sand fraction (table II.141) shows that the parent material is homogeneous. The amount of iron concretions is smaller than in profile 42, pointing to a less advanced weathering stage.

TABLE II.140. *Some physical and chemical characteristics of profile 43* (after Van Schuylenborgh, 1958)

Hor.	texture (%)			C (%)	C/N	pH (H₂O)	molar ratios clay fraction		
	> 50μ	50–2μ	< 2μ				SiO_2/Al_2O_3	SiO_2/Fe_2O_3	Al_2O_3/Fe_2O_3
A_{11}	26.2	61.6	12.2	16.6	15.9	4.9	1.8	8.4	4.8
A_{12}	20.5	54.5	25.0	10.1	14.1	5.3	0.9	5.1	5.9
B_1	20.8	46.7	32.5	5.4	14.7	5.4	0.7	5.7	7.5
B_2	28.7	31.0	40.3	2.0	14.6	5.4	0.8	6.6	8.3
C	53.8	17.0	29.2	0.7	8.0	5.6	0.9	10.0	11.5

Translocation of clay-sized particles can also be observed in this profile (see profile description and table II.140). The molar SiO_2/Al_2O_3 ratio again points to movement of allophane and gibbsite. The latter is confirmed by X-ray analysis of the clay fraction, showing an increase of gibbsite with depth. There is an abundance of amorphous material with minor admixtures of montmorillonite, kaolinite, and α-crystoballite. Kaolinite content increases slightly in the upper horizons.

Some volcanic ash soils have horizons with accumulation of clay-sized particles and others not. The allophane is predominantly a weathering product of glass and changes, under conditions of good drainage, its composition from $SiO_2.Al_2O_3.2H_2O$ in the youngest soils to $2SiO_2.Al_2O_3.3H_2O$ in older soils and finally to halloysite and kaolinite in still older soils. This process is accompanied by the separation of gibbsite, which is highly mobile because it complexes with fulvic acids, which are predominant

TABLE II.141. *Mineralogical analysis of the sand fraction of profile 43* (after Van Schuylenborgh, 1958).

Hor.	total sand fraction											heavy sand fraction			
	Q	Plg	Ho	Hy	Aug	Gl	op	ic	Gibb	Ph	Misc	op	Ho	Hy	Aug
A_{11}	2	27	1	12	1	17	4	3	6	9	17	43	8	82	10
A_{12}	3	25	2	11	2	18	3	2	8	7	19	21	8	85	7
B_1	2	29	tr	15	1	21	2	3	6	12	9	30	2	91	7
B_2	2	40	1	13	1	20	5	2	7	–	9	21	4	95	1
C	1	44	tr	9	–	18	4	1	19	–	4	39	1	96	3

Mineral abbreviations as in table II.139, Plg = plagioclases; Gibb = gibbsite, Ph = phytoliths.

in volcanic ash soils. Consequently, some soils show argeluviation and cheluviation, others only cheluviation.

Many volcanic ash soils show irreversible granulation upon air-drying, especially those which are continually moist because of the humid climate. It is therefore useless to analyse air-dried samples (Van Schuylenborgh, 1954), if it is desired to determine the grain size distribution or other physical properties. It is also possible that air-drying effects cation exchange characteristics, although exact data are not available.

5.2.3. WEATHERING AND SOIL FORMING PROCESSES

A great deal of information has been obtained in the last decade on the weathering of volcanic ash, and particularly on the formation of secondary minerals. The weathering process of volcanic ash begins with the leaching of soluble components (H_4SiO_4, Ca^{2+}, Mg^{2+}, Na^+, K^+, etc.) by rainwater (desilication: see Part III, Chapter 1). Carbonic acid accelerates the decomposition of the ash. Sesquioxides will accumulate residually, while aluminium with silicic acid forms secondary minerals. The composition of the ash and the leaching conditions determine the type of the secondary minerals. Commonly, a narrow SiO_2/Al_2O_3 ratio is characteristic for volcanic soils. When allophane predominates in the clay fraction of young volcanic soils, the ratio varies between 1 and 2 (a.o. Birrell, 1965). On increasing age the allophane is transformed into kandites and the ratio is then 2. When drainage is impeded and the parent ash contains a considerable amount of ferromagnesian minerals, smectites can be formed and the ratio is then 3 or more. Sometimes, in intermediate and basic ashes and under excessive drainage, SiO_2/Al_2O_3 ratios are smaller than 1 (see profile 43), due to the presence of free aluminium hydroxide (see also: Tan and Van Schuylenborgh, 1961).

It seems that allophane is formed from volcanic glass and plagioclases (andesine and labradorite) and that ferromagnesian minerals (olivine, pyroxenes, and amphiboles) also participate (a.o. Kanno, 1961). Besoain (1969) has constructed a time scale for the transformation of the primary minerals into the several intermediate products of the formation of kaolinite. Firstly a mixed gel of SiO_2 and Al_2O_3 is formed (called allophane B by Fieldes, 1955), then allophane (allophane A of Fieldes, 1955), then halloysite and finally kaolinite. The time-scale is as follows:

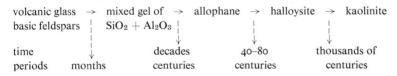

DTA data of a 10,000 years old volcanic ash layer that forms the lower part of a profile in New Zealand (fig. 11.66) indicates that the weathering of the primary minerals has reached the allophane stage. This does not tally with Besoain's scheme. As a matter of fact, such a scheme as Besoain's (1969) has little meaning, as it depends on the environmental conditions. This is clarified by the reaction:

$2NaCaAl_3Si_5O_{16}(s) + 17H_2O + 6H^+ \rightleftharpoons$
(labradorite)
$3Al_2SiO_4(OH)_2.H_2O(s) + 2Na^+ + 2Ca^{2+} + 7H_4SiO_4$ $----------$ (68)
(allophane)
$lgK_{68} = 2lg[Na^+] + 2lg[Ca^{2+}] + 7lg[H_4SiO_4] + 6pH$ $---------$ (68a)

It depends on the soluble reaction products whether the reaction will proceed to the right or not. If these are removed readily (rapid permeability), the reaction will be more complete than if the leaching process is slow. If leaching is slow it is even possible that allophane is not formed at all; if, for example, there is sufficient Mg^{2+} (set free upon weathering of ferromagnesian minerals), montmorillonite may be formed.

Several other secondary compounds have been found in the clay fraction of volcanic ash soils. They include imogolite (Yoshinaga and Aomine, 1962), palagonite (Birrell, 1965), hisingerite (Sudo and Nakamura, 1952), amorphous silica, and, of course, iron oxides (Matsui, 1959) and titanium oxide (Sherman et al., 1964). However, allophane is the most important product. Its composition (Wada, 1967) varies between SiO_2. $Al_2O_3.2H_2O$ (comparable with Fieldes' allophane B) and $2SiO_2.Al_2O_3.3H_2O$ (comparable with Fieldes' allophane A). The structure proposed by Wada for allophane with the Si/Al ratio of 1, is composed of a silica tetrahedral chain and an alumina octahedral chain joined at one corner. The addition of another alumina octahedral chain to the silica tetrahedral chain results in the formation of allophane with the Si/Al ratio of 1/2.

The DTA curves of fig. 11.66 (after Luna, 1969) indicate the presence of two types of allophane. One of them gives an endothermic reaction in the region 150° to 200° C (present in the upper horizons); the other one (present in the lower parts of the profiles) gives two thermic reactions, viz. an endotherm at 150° to 200° C and an exotherm at 850° to 900° C. The type of allophane present in the upper horizons is apparently a less organized form, the one found in the lower horizons a more ordered type. The last type could well be an intermediate stage in the formation of crystalline minerals (hydrated halloysite, kaolinite) and is possibly comparable with Wada's allophane, composition $2SiO_2.Al_2O_3.3H_2O$. Another intermediate phase to halloysite formation may be imogolite (Wada, 1967), which has an endotherm at 410° to 430° C and appears as thread-like particles of 100 to 200 Å diameter in electron micrographs (Yoshinaga and Aomine, 1962).

The most frequently cited formation mechanism of allophane is isoelectric precipitation of silica and alumina (Egawa, 1965). The mechanism of isoelectric precipitation of gels (mutual precipitation of positively and negatively charged colloids), which is inapplicable for a number of minerals (Van Schuylenborgh and Sänger, 1954), seems to be valid in the formation of allophane. It can occur if amorphous aluminium hydroxide is formed during the weathering of glass; this may be in the positively charged stage and form mixed gels with the electro-negative silica colloids.

Andosols have a much higher organic-matter content than non-volcanic soils under similar circumstances. It is believed that the decomposition of organic matter is hindered by the amorphous aluminium hydroxide in Andosols (Kosaka et al., 1962; see Part I, Chapter 4, p. 180).

Humic and fulvic acids are the most important components of the organic fraction. In Japan the humic acid/fulvic acid ratio of the Humic Allophane Soils ranges from 1 to 2; in the Red Yellow Soils the ratio is approximately 1. Similar values apply to the Andosols of Colombia (Luna, 1969). This means that the fraction of organic acids with low molecular weights is very important. As this fraction is also the most soluble, it can be expected that sesquioxides are mobile because of the formation of soluble complexes. This seems to be especially true for alumina translocation, and less so for the iron oxide. For particulars on complex formation refer to Part III, Chapter 3.

It is difficult to understand the occurrence of clay translocation, as the climate is not favourable for this process. Possibly it can be explained by dissolving in the surface layers and reprecipitation in sub-surface horizons. Coatings of clay-sized materials occur on the peds in the B horizon, so this horizon should be called an argillic horizon, although not exactly in the sense of the definition of the 7th Approximation.

When examining the soil formation on andesitic volcanic material in a continually humid climate as in the case of profiles 42 and 43, Van Schuylenborgh (1958) found the following sequence of soils, their characteristics strongly dependent on the altitude:

> 1100 m altitude: Humic Allophane Soils with accumulation of clay-sized minerals in the B horizon (profiles 42 and 43). The soils show irreversible granulation upon air-drying. Classification according to the 7th Approximation: Hydrandepts.

1100–600 m altitude: Humic Allophane Soils with no accumulation of clay-sized minerals in the B horizon, but with irreversible granulation upon air-drying. Very acid. Aluminium is mobile, iron not. Classification according to the 7th Approximation: Hydrandepts or Dystrandepts.

600–300 m altitude: Brown clay soils with no irreversible granulation upon air-drying. The amount of amorphous material is much smaller than in the soils of the higher altitudes, and is replaced by kaolinite. Argillic B horizon is present. Classification according to the 7th Approximation: Tropudalf or Tropudult.

300–0 m altitude: Reddish-brown and Red clay soils with up to 90% of clay. The clay is predominantly kaolinitic. Classification: Haplorthox.

Under very similar climatic conditions, but on rhyolitic volcanic material, the sequence was (Tan and Van Schuylenborgh, 1961):

2000–1500 m: Soils with a spodic horizon. No irreversible granulation upon air-drying. Classification: Tropohumods.

1500–500 m: Soils with a cambic horizon. Moderately acid (pH 5 to 6.5). There is no irreversible granulation. Classification: Eutropepts or Dystropepts.

500–0 m: Soils with an argillic horizon and low base saturation. Classification: Tropudults.

Under a monsoon climate (2 to 5 months dry; 10–7 months wet) and on andesitic volcanic material, the sequence was (Tan and Van Schuylenborgh, 1959):

> 2500 m: Soils with a cambic horizon, a mollic epipedon and very high contents in organic matter. There is no irreversible granulation upon air-drying. Podzolic tendencies in soil formation are fairly strong. Considerable amounts of volcanic glass and pumice particles are present. Classification: Eutrandepts.

2500–1400 m: Soils similar to the preceding ones, but with weaker podzolic tendencies; the biological activity in the soil is considerably higher. Classification: Eutrandepts.

1400–1000 m: Soils similar to the preceding ones. Podzolic tendencies are absent and biological activity is very high. Classification: Vitrandepts.

1000–300 m: Strongly weathered soils with clay percentage up to 75 %. The material is not yet oxic and the B horizon is argillic. Base saturation is higher than 35 %. Classification: Haploxeralfs.

5.3. THE CLASSIFICATION OF ANDOSOLS

The classification of Andosols is generally based on their morphological, physical and chemical properties, while the mineralogical composition of the sand, silt, and clay fractions is also taken into account. In some of the classification systems stress has been laid on profile characteristics, whereas in others the effect of the soil forming factors and processes such as climate, location, degree of weathering, composition of organic matter, have been considered.

Typical Andosols are classified in the order of Intrazonal soils because of the domination of the parent material (volcanic ash) over other zonal, pedogenic factors (climate, vegetation). Forms which can be classified into Zonal soils may occur upon ageing of the soil; the parent material no longer has weatherable minerals and the amorphous clays have been converted into crystalline clays.

A preliminary classification of Andosols or Humic Allophane soils has been made in South America (Wright, 1965). They are grouped into soils of high latitudes (Argentina and Chile), and soils of low latitudes (Colombia and Ecuador). The classification is based mainly on the degree of weathering and leaching and on organic matter content. The soils of the high latitudes include seven different environments, ranging from the temperate dry sub-humid (mesomediterranean) conditions to the cold, humid to superhumid environments. In the soils of the low latitudes, five different environments have been (provisionally) recognized, viz. the cool, temperate, tropical, humid, and equatorial lowlands.

The soils on volcanic ash in Central America have not been classified. They are known as: Andosol, suelo de Talpetate, pardo forestal, and latosol (Martini, 1969). Andosols and latosols are the most important of the group that can be used for classification purposes. The soils have mostly forest vegetation covers.

In the U.S.D.A. 7th Approximation, the group of soils developed on volcanic ash are classified in the order of the Inceptisols (the Inceptisols have diagnostic horizons which have been formed relatively recently; they show moderate weathering of the primary minerals and there is little or no eluviation of clay), in the sub-order of the Andepts and in the Great Group of the Andaquepts. The Andepts are classified as having 60 % or more of vitric volcanic ash, cinders or other vitric pyroclastic materials in the silt, sand, and gravel fractions or a bulk density of the fine earth fraction of the soil of less than 0.85 per cc in the upper part of the solum, and an exchange complex that is dominated by amorphous material. The Andepts are further sub-divided into the following Great Groups:

Cryandepts (with a mean annual soil temperature of less than 8.3° C and mean summer temperature of less than 15° C), Durandepts (with a duripan within 1 m of the surface), Hydrandepts (with clays that dehydrate irreversibly), Eutrandepts (soils with high base saturation), Dystrandepts (soils with low base saturation) and Vitrandepts.

The Andaquepts have similar characteristics as Andosols, except that these soils also have hydromorphic characteristics.

Very young ash soils with no or only slight profile development are classified in the Entisol order. Ash-derived soils in arid or semi-arid conditions, showing accumulation of organic matter and having clay minerals of the smectite group are grouped in the Aridisol order. Extremely weathered ash-derived soils fall into the Order of the Oxisols (see Part II, Chapter 1). Those with a spodic horizon are grouped in the Spodosol order and those with an argillic horizon in an andic subgroup of the Hapludalfs or Hapludults.

The profiles 42 and 43 of section 3, however, are difficult to classify. They have a horizon with accumulation of clay-sized material which dries irreversibly upon air-drying. It is therefore thought that an alfic and ultic sub-group should be made in the Hydrandepts, depending on base saturation; or an andic sub-group in the Tropudalfs or Tropudults. As the argillic horizon of the soils mentioned is not argillic in the sense of the 7th Approximation, the first suggestion is probably most logical.

In theory the separation of Andosols from Ultisols, Spodosols and Oxisols is simple, following the key to the U.S.A. classification system. However, the value of this separation from the genetic point of view depends on several factors including the composition of the pyroclastic material, time, and environmental conditions of the volcanic ash layers. Organic matter, if present in a large quantity in the profile, can influence the water holding capacity of the soil, bulk density, and can even mask some of the pedogenic processes such as eluviation and cheluviation.

In Japan the 'Kuroboku' are the typical soils derived of volcanic ash (Ohmasa, 1965) and are characterized by a dark-coloured A horizon which has 15 to 30 per cent humus content, and low stickiness and plasticity. It is suggested that the formation of the 'Kuroboku' soils is closely connected with grassland vegetation and humid climatic conditions. The soils are classified on the bases of thickness and colour of the A horizon; therefore, soils with light-coloured A horizon are known as 'light-coloured Kuroboku' (Volcanic Ash Soils in Japan, 1964). The light-coloured soils which occur under forest are grouped as Brown Forest Soils or Acid Brown Forest Soils in the Japanese classification.

In New Zealand (Taylor, 1965), the soils developed on volcanic ash are divided into three main categories, named 'skeletiform' (with regosolic profile), 'fulviform' (with profiles similar to those of the brown soils of the humid temperate regions), and 'podiform', with profiles similar to the podsols. The 'fulviform' and 'podiform' soil categories are further subdivided into 'alvic' and 'sub-alvic' according to the state of weathering of the primary minerals. A third sub-division is made on the basis of certain morphological features such as the formation of a B horizon, fragipans, etc. Other sub-divisions are concerned with the degree of leaching of the soils and the 'mellanized' A horizon.

In Indonesia (Tan, 1965), a tentative classification of Andosols into soils with low humic/fulvic acid ratio (0.2) and low variable charge (CEC_v < 30 m.e./100 g), and soils with high humic/fulvic acid ratio (0.5) and medium to high variable charge (CEC_v > 30 m.e./100 g) is proposed.

The central concept of Andosols is similar in all countries of the world. The soils are dark in colour, very porous, organic and with clay, dominantly the amorphous type (allophane, silica, alumina, iron hydroxides, etc.). However, the correlation of the soils is difficult because of the different criteria used in the several classification systems. The characterization of the organic matter by its humic acid/fulvic acid ratio, as has been done in Indonesia (Tan, 1965), is suggested by Dudal (1965) to be a satisfactory approach to the classification of the soils with respect to differences in climate, but further investigations are needed before this suggestion can be generally applied.

The study of the micromorphology of Andosols may also contribute to a better understanding of the classification problems which are still to be solved. In a recent paper Kawai (1969) provides an addition of 4 sub-groups to those of the 7th Approximation based on the specific nature of the micromorphological fabric of a

TABLE II.142. *Classification of Andosols based on micromorphological characteristics, with special reference to the 7th Approximation* (after Kawai, 1969)

Great Groups	Sub-groups	Author's sub-group	Example
Dystrandepts	Typic Cryandepts	*Entic Cryandepts*	Tokotan
	Typic Dystrandepts	Typic Dystrandepts	Kanuma
		Humic Dystrandepts	Imaichi, Kuju
			Kuroishibaru
			Hirusen
		Umbreptic Dystrandepts	Shinshiro
Eutrandepts	Typic Eutrandepts	Typic Eutrandepts	Miyagasaki
			Yatsugatake
			Miura
Durandepts	Typic Durandepts		
		Humic Durandepts	Imazato
Vitrandepts	Umbric Vitrandepts	Umbric Vitrandepts	Jönouchi

Subgroups in italics are proposed by the author.

number of Japanese Andosols (table II.142). It is indicated that micromorphological investigations may lead to a more detailed classification of Andosols.

LITERATURE CITED

AGUILERA,N. 1969 Distribución y características de los suelos derivados de ceniza volcánica de Mexico. *Suelos derivados de cenizas volcánicas de America Latina. Centro de Ensenanza e Investigación del IICC, Turrialba, Costa Rica.*
BESOAIN, E. 1958 Mineralogia de las arcillas de algunos suelos volcánicos de Chile. *Agr. Tec. Santiago*, 18: 110–167.
— 1969 Mineralogia de las argillas de suelos derivados de cenizas volcánicas de Chile. *Suelos derivados de cenizas volcánicas de America Latina. Centro de Ensenanza e Investigación del IICC, Turrialba, Costa Rica.*
BIRRELL, K.S. 1965 Some properties of volcanic ash soils. *Meeting on the classification and correlation of soils from volcanic ash. FAO Report 14*, Rome: 74–81.

EGAWA, T. 1965 Mineralogical properties of volcanic ash soils in Japan. *Meeting on the classification and correlation of soils from volcanic ash. FAO Report 14*, Roma: 89–91.

FLACH, K. W. 1965 Genesis and morphology of ash derived soils in the United States. *Meeting on the classification and correlation of soils from volcanic ash. FAO Report 14*, Roma: 111–114.

FIELDES, M. 1955 Clay mineralogy of New Zealand soils. 2. Allophane and related mineral colloids. *N.Z.J. Sci. Tech.*, B. 37: 336–350.

HARTMAN, M.A. 1938 Die Vulkangruppe im Südwesten des Salak-Vulkans in West Java. *Natuurk. Tijdschr. Ned. Ind.*, 98: 216–249.

HAWARD, M.E. and BORCHARDT, G.A. 1969 Mineralogy and trace element composition of ash and pumice soils in the Pacific northwest of the United States. *Suelos derivados de cenizas volcánicas de America Latina. Centro de Ensenanza e Investigación del IICA, Turrialba, Costa Rica.*

KANNO, I. 1961 Genesis and classification of main genetic soil types in Japan. *Bull. Kyushu Agr. Exp. Sta.*, 7: 1–185.

— and ARIMURA, S. 1958 Plant opal in Japanese soils. *Soils and Plant Food*, 4, No. 2.

—, KUMANO, Y., HONJO, I. and ARIMURA, S. 1964 Characteristics and classification of an unirrigated anthropogenic alluvial soil found in the Kumamoto Plain. *Bull. Kyushu Agr. Exp. Sta.*, 10: 11–122.

KAWAI, K. 1969 Micromorphological studies of Andosols in Japan. *Bull. Nat. Inst. Agric.*, Japan: 145–154.

KOSAKA, J., HONDA, CH. and IZEKI, A. 1962 Transformation of humus in upland soils, Japan. *Soil Sci. & Pl. Nutr.*, 8: 191–197.

LUNA, C. 1962 Minerales amorfos en suelos del Depto. de Antioquia. *Trabajo presentado al III Congreso Nacional de Químicos e Ing. Químicos, Baranquilla, Colombia.*

— 1969 Aspectos genéticos de andosoles en Colombia. *Suelos derivados de cenizasvolcánicas de America Latina. Centro de Ensenanza e Investigación del IICA, Turrialba, Costa Rica.*

MARTINI, J.A. 1969 Distribución geográfica y características de los suelos derivados de cenizas volcánicas de Centro America. *Suelos derivados de cenizas volcánicas de America Latina. Centro de Ensenanza e Investigación del IICA, Turrialba, Costa Rica.*

MATSUI, T. 1959 Some characteristics of Japanese soil clays. *Adv. Clay Sci., Tokyo*, 1: 244–259.

MCCONAGHY, S. 1969 Geographic distribution and characteristics of vocanic ash soils in the Antilles. *Suelos derivados de cenizas volcánicas de America Latina. Centro de Ensenanza e Investigación del IICA, Turrialba, Costa Rica.*

MINISTRY OF AGRICULTURE AND FORESTRY. 1964 Volcanic Ash Soils in Japan. *Jap. Govern. Tokyo*, pp. 211.

MONTENEGRO, E. and ESPINAL, S. 1963 Formaciones vegetales de Colombia Depto. Agrológico, Inst. Geogr. *Agustin Codazzi, Bogotá, Colombia.*

OHMASA, M. 1965 Scope of volcanic ash soils, their extent and distribution. *Meeting on the classification and correlation of soils from volcanic ash. FAO Report 14*, Rome: 56–60.

OLSEN, S.R. 1954 Estimation of available phosphorus in soils by extraction with sodium bicarbonate. *U.S.D.A. circ. 939*, pp. 18.

PETTIJOHN, F.J. 1957 Sedimentary rocks. 2nd. Ed. *New York-London.*

SHERMAN, G.D., MATSUAKA, Y., IKAWA, H. and HAHASA, G. 1964 The role of amorphous fraction in the properties of tropical soils. *Agrochemia*, 7: 146–162.

SUDO, T. and NAKAMURA, T. 1952 Hinsingerite from Japan. *Am. Min.*, 37: 618–621.

TAN, K.H. 1965 The andosols in Indonesia. *Meeting on the classification and correlation of soils from volcanic ash. FAO Report 14*: 30–35.

— and VAN SCHUYLENBORGH, J. 1959 On the classification and genesis of soils derived from andesitic volcanic material under a monsoon climate. *Neth. J. agric. Sci.*, 7: 1–21.

— and — 1961 On the classification and genesis of soils developed over acid vocanic material under humid tropical conditions. II. *Neth. J. agric. Sci.*, 9: 41–54.

TAYLOR, N.H. 1965 The classification of volcanic ash soils in New Zealand. *Meeting on the classification and correlation of soils derived from volcanic ash. FAO Report 14:* 101–106.

THORP, J. and SMITH, G.D. 1949 Higher categories of soil classification: Order, Suborder, and Great Soil Groups. *Soil Sci.*, 67: 117–126.

VALDES, A. 1969 Distribución geográfica y características de los suelos derivados de cenizas volcánicas de Chile. *Suelos derivados de cenizas volcánicas de America Latina. Centro de Ensenanza e Investigacion del IICC, Turrialba, Costa Rica.*

VAN BEMMELEN, J.M. 1949 The Geology of Indonesia. Vol. IA. *The Hague.*

VAN SCHUYLENBORGH, J. 1954 The effect of air-drying of soil samples upon some physical properties. *Neth. J. agric. Sci.*, 2: No. 1.

— 1958 On the genesis and classification of soils derived from andesitic tuffs under humid tropical conditions. *Neth. J. agric. Sci.*, 6: 99–123.

— and SÄNGER, A. M. H. 1949 The electrokinetic behaviour of iron- and aluminium-hydroxides and -oxides. *Rec. trav. chim. Pays-Bas*, 68 : 999–1010.

WADA, K. 1967 A structural scheme of soil allophane. *Am. Min.*, 52: 690–708.

WRIGHT, A.C.S. 1960 Observaciones sobre los suelos de la zona central de Chile. *Agr. Tec., Santiago.*

— 1965 The 'Andosols' or Humic Allophane Soils of South America. *Meeting on the classification and correlation of soils derived from volcanic ash. FAO Report 14:* 9–20.

YOSHINAGA, N. and AOMINE, S. 1962 Imogolite in some Ando soils. *Soil Sci. & Pl. Nutr.*, 8: 22–29.

ZAVALETA, A. 1969 Distribución geográfica y características de los suelos derivados de cenizas volcánicas del Peru. *Suelos derivados de cenizas volcánicas de America Latina. Centro de Ensenanza e Investigación del IICC, Turrialba, Costa Rica.*

PART III

EXPERIMENTAL AND PHYSICO-CHEMICAL STUDY OF THE SOIL FORMING PROCESSES

CHAPTER 1

DESILICATION

In Chapter 1, sections 1.1 and 1.2, of Part II it has been stated that the desilication process is one of the processes involved in the formation of Oxisols. Chapter 2 of Part II indicated that this process may also occur in the formation of Ultisols, though it may be less intense than in the genesis of Oxisols. It was also emphasized that desilication is never complete but that part of the silica dissolved is used to form secondary minerals, the clay minerals. The discussion of the mechanism of these processes is the scope of this Chapter.

Many laboratory experiments have been performed imitating the weathering reactions. Some authors have used the technique of equilibrating powdered rock or mineral material with some solution, analysing the equilibrium solution, and then again equilibrating the residue with a new portion of the solution, etc. Others have used the technique of continuous leaching of minerals or rocks with some solution and analysing the percolated solution. This procedure was followed by Correns and co-workers (Correns and Von Engelhardt, 1938; Mehmel, 1937; Krüger, 1939; Tunn, 1940; and others). Correns (1961) came to the conclusion that most silicates are completely broken down and dissolved in their constituent ions. The minerals investigated were: adular, a K-feldspar, $KAlSi_3O_8$; leucite, a feldspatoid: $KAlSi_2O_6$; tremolite, an amphibole: $Ca_2Mg_5Si_8O_{22}(OH)_2$; biotite, a mica: $K_2Mg_5(Al_3Si_5)O_{20}(OH)_4$; muscovite, a mica: $KAl_2(AlSi_3)O_{10}(OH)_2$, and olivine, a chrysolite: $(Fe,Mg)_2SiO_4$. In the first stages of the 'weathering' experiments the rates of dissolution are high; in later stages these gradually decrease until a steady rate is maintained which ultimately leads to the complete dissolution of the mineral (fig. III.1).

X-ray analysis of the weathering minerals shows, that their lattices remained unchanged. The tendency of the different constituent ions to leave the crystal depends upon the pH of the medium. Consequently, the outer layer of the particles, influenced by the leaching effect and consisting predominantly of more slowly dissolving components, has a composition which is different for each pH value. The dissolution of the more readily dissolving components is determined by their rate of diffusion through the leached layer. The thickness of the leached layer grows until there is an equilibrium between the rate of diffusion of the more readily dissolving components and the dissolution of the leached layer itself; hence, the feldspar particles are, after the first stages of weathering, surrounded by a leached layer of constant thickness. Deviations from this pattern are formed by muscovite and, partly, by olivine. In fact, if the minerals are ball-milled during the experiments to disturb the leached layer, the initial rate of

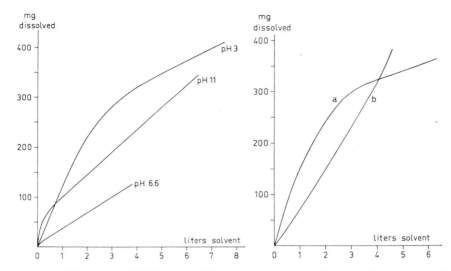

FIG. III.1. *Dissolution of K-feldspar at different pH levels (particle diameter < 1 μ)*

FIG. III.2. *Decomposition at pH 3 without (a) and with ball-milling (b)*

dissolution is maintained throughout and does not decrease (fig. III.2). The leached layer, according to Correns, is very thin, except in the case of percolation with 1 N H_2SO_4, where a residue of silicic acid remained due to its very limited solubility at low pH value.

In the case of muscovite a uniform rate of decomposition is not attained. Table III. 1 gives the experimental values and the quantities which should be present in solution if the muscovite dissolves uniformly, i.e., the theoretical values. The experimental values for SiO_2 were 5–10 times less than the theoretical ones, while for Al_2O_3 the

TABLE III.1. *Dissolution experiments on muscovite (< 1 μ) at different pH values, after Böhmeke* (from Correns, 1961)

	millimoles in solution			pH
	K_2O	Al_2O_3	SiO_2	
Found	1.37	0.38	1.56	3
Theoretical[1]	1.37	4.41	8.22	
Found	0.82	0.08	1.00	5.8
Theoretical[1]	0.82	2.46	4.92	
Found	0.88	0.14	0.59	8.5
Theoretical[1]	0.88	2.84	5.68	

[1] = millimoles in solution if the muscovite dissolved uniformly.

disparity was even greater, the factor being 10–20. Consequently, the potassium was dissolved first, whereas the octahedral sheet was more difficult to attack. Fig. III.3

shows the composition of the leached layer (together with those of the other minerals), which is almost constant over the entire pH range. The thickness of the leached layer increased in all experiments with the length of leaching. This peculiar behaviour explains the formation of micas poor in potassium, the so-called di-octahedral illites.

The olivine, which had a MgO mol-percentage of 0.22, also showed divergent behaviour. Table III.2 shows that at pH 3, 5.8, and 9 the leached layer was free from SiO_2, but very rich in iron. At pH 4.6 a layer containing very little SiO_2 and consisting essentially of iron hydroxide was obtained; also the MgO content was negligible. At pH 3, 5.8, and 9, however, there was more magnesium present than at pH 4.6. It would seem that at slightly acid reactions olivine is pseudomorphologically altered into some iron hydroxide.

The composition of the leached layers, in terms of the ratio SiO_2/R_2O_3 (or SiO_2/MgO for tremolite), as shown in fig. III.3, differ strongly depending on the pH value. With K-feldspar the ratio never reached a value common to some known clay mineral, whereas with other minerals this did occur. Whether clay minerals could have been formed is doubtful as the X-ray analyses show no transformations of the primary minerals.

TABLE III.2. *Composition and thickness of the leached layer of olivine at different pH levels, after Hoppe* (from: Correns, 1961)

pH	particle radius (μ)	volume of solution (l)	leached layer		
			MgO/FeO	SiO$_2$/FeO	thickness (μ)
3	I	4	3.77	–	[1]
4.6	I	5.2	–	0.04	0.10
5.8	I	6.8	2.74	–	[1]
9	I	4.1	5.50	–	[1]

[1] constant thickness not attained.

Correns and Schlünz (1936) and Von Engelhardt (1937) showed that also in nature the feldspars are transformed completely without leaving a residue of the original mineral. The question still remains: what happens to the ions in solution? They may be washed down into the groundwater, but under certain conditions they react to form either silicate clay minerals or boehmite, gibbsite, goethite, quartz, etc. The reactions may occur at any place where the conditions are favourable, sometimes quite near or even in the parent crystals. According to Correns (1940) the hydroxides of Al and Fe in the colloidal state cannot react with silicic acid colloids to form clay minerals.

Not only the primary minerals are subjected to alterations as a result of leaching, but also the clay minerals which are eventually formed. Heydemann (1966) subjected kaolinite, illite, and montmorillonite to leaching procedures, comparable to those described above. Pedro and Berrier (1966) used a special technique (see later) when leaching kaolinite with pure water at a temperature of approximately 65° C. Heydemann (1966) found that the kaolinite minerals were dissolved stoichiometrically in

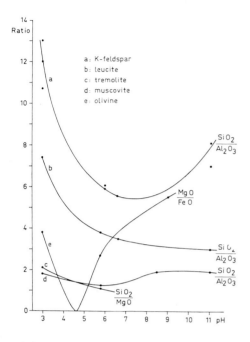

FIG. III.3. *Composition of the leached layer in dependence of pH*

acidic as well as in alkaline media, which could be concluded from the fact that the atomic ratio Si/Al in the extracting solutions was approximately 1. In the neutral region (pH 6 and 7) however, comparatively more Si was dissolved, the residues being enriched in Al. These results are consistent with those of Pedro and Berrier (1966); they found that the molar SiO_2/Al_2O_3 ratio of the residue diminished from 2.21 to 1.73 in one year of leaching.

The samples of montmorillonite never went into solution stoichiometrically. Silicium dissolved primarily and the residue became enriched in aluminium. These findings are consistent with those of Barnishel and Rich (1963), whose experience was that gibbsite was formed in the intermicellar layers, even at pH values less than 4.3.

The samples of illite occupied an intermediate position between kaolinite and montmorillonite. At pH 3 it went into solution approximately stoichiometrically, whereas at pH values of 6 and 10 more Si was dissolved, leading to a decreasing atomic Si/Al ratio of the residue.

The results with kaolinite in the neutral pH region can be easily understood on the basis of the low solubility product of Al hydroxide. In the case of montmorillonite and to some extent also of illite, the Al concentration may be appreciably affected in acidic as well as in alkaline media by effects of fixation and adsorption.

In this context we have to consider the work of Turner and Brydon (1965), who determined the solubility product of aluminium hydroxide in the presence of montmorillonite to be $10^{-33.0}$ instead of the $10^{-32.3}$ which we used for the construction of fig. II.22. The dotted pAl_t line of fig. II.22 is adapted to the solubility product of $10^{-33.0}$. It is evident that if the solubility product of $Al(OH)_3$ is lowered the pH range, in which $Al(OH)_3$ accumulates, widens.

424

The experiments show that even kaolinite, although very stable, can be decomposed by prolonged leaching. It can also be stated that in none of the experiments new-formation of lattice clays was observed. This could be ascribed to the possibility that the leaching was too fast and too profuse (see Part II, Chapter 1, p. 242).

Pedro (1960, 1961, 1964, 1966) used a quite different technique in weathering studies. A Soxhlet apparatus, filled with rock fragments of uniform size, was used to imitate the leaching effect of pure water in contact with air, of water in contact with a CO_2 atmosphere, of water in contact with H_2S gas, and finally of water with a certain content of acetic acid in contact with air. The temperature was near to $70°$ C. The rocks used were a biotite-containing granite, a trachyandesite, a basalt and a serpentine (Pedro and Bitar, 1966). The Soxhlet container was filled in such a manner, that the upper part of the rock fragments could never be soaked with water (atmospheric part). The results may be summarized as follows: The leaching of the first three rocks with pure water in contact with the atmosphere led firstly to total elimination of silica, alkalis and alkaline earths; secondly to accumulation of iron in the form of stilpnos-iderite and goethite; thirdly, to partial elimination of aluminium, the remainder being transformed to boehmite (in the upper – atmospheric – part) and gibbsite (in the lower part). It can be concluded that here an ultimate imitation of the desilication process is in play, showing that aluminium is more mobile than iron, which is generally found to be so during the formation of Oxisols. Again there was no indication of the form-ation of kaolinite or some other clay mineral.

The experiment on weathering of rocks with water in contact with a CO_2 and H_2S atmosphere resulted firstly in total elimination of silica, alkalis and alkaline earths; secondly, in partial elimination of iron; thirdly, in an almost total accumulation of aluminium in the form of boehmite (in the upper, atmospheric part) and gibbsite (in the lower part). The leachate, rich in Ca, Mg, Fe, and Si had consequently an alkaline reaction so it was not surprising that the formation of trioctahedral smectites and of carbonates could be noticed. Such processes could also occur in the pallid zone and zone of alteration of well-developed Oxisols with plinthite. Montmorillonite is some-times to be found especially in the weathering zone (a.o. Schellmann, 1964).

The simultaneous occurrence of boehmite or diaspore and gibbsite is almost in-variably noticed in nature and also in the experiments described above, even though boehmite and diaspore are metastable in pure water. Diaspore and boehmite are related to gibbsite by the reaction:

$Al_2O_3.H_2O + 2H_2O \rightleftharpoons Al_2O_3.3H_2O$

The standard free-energy change of reaction is approximately −6 kcal per mol diaspore or boehmite. This means that diaspore and boehmite should hydrate to gibbsite in the presence of pure water but the reaction is very slow at room temperature. The reason that gibbsite is found only in the lower part of the weathering rock mass of Pedro's experiments could be that in that part the temperature is considerably higher than in the upper, atmospheric part.

The effect of acetic acid completely changed the dynamics of alteration, as could be expected. All the elements of the rocks were dissolved, especially iron and aluminium. The elimination of sesquioxides was relatively much higher than that of silica, in this way explaining the corresponding accumulation of silica in the weathering residue.

The result is more or less comparable with some aspects of the effect of podzolization.

In the case of the serpentine rock (Pedro and Bitar, 1966) the velocity of elimination of silicium is greater than that of magnesium when leaching with pure and carbonated water, whilst mixed hydroxides of Mg–Fe–Al accumulated in the weathering residue. These results are consistent with those of Hoppe (cited by Correns, 1961) in the weathering experiments of olivine. When treating the serpentine with a dilute acetic acid solution the magnesium was completely eliminated, leaving behind free and amorphous silica in association with iron hydroxides.

Pedro (1964) gave the following physico-chemical picture in respect to the accumulation of sesquioxides. In an aerated medium, iron is in the trivalent state. When

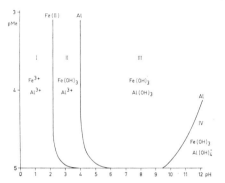

FIG. III.4. *Iron (III) and aluminium ions in equilibrium with Fe(OH)3 and Al(OH)3, respectively*

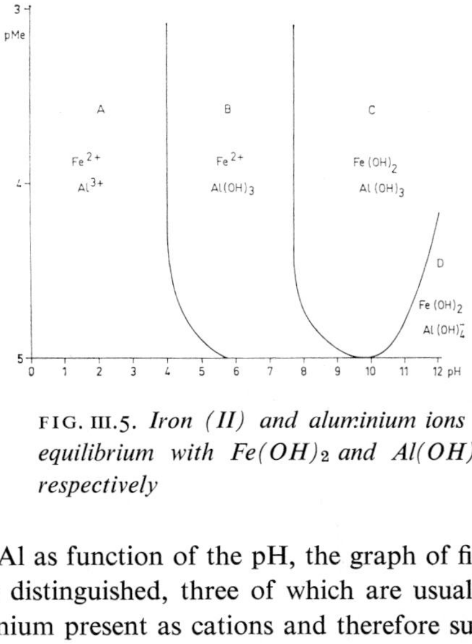

FIG. III.5. *Iron (II) and aluminium ions in equilibrium with Fe(OH)2 and Al(OH)3, respectively*

examining the occurrences of Fe(III) and Al as function of the pH, the graph of fig. III.4 can be plotted. Four zones can be distinguished, three of which are usually present in nature: zone I, iron and aluminium present as cations and therefore susceptible to leaching; zone II, iron precipitated as hydrates and aluminium still dissolved and therefore mobile; zone III, iron and aluminium both precipitated as hydroxides and therefore immobile.

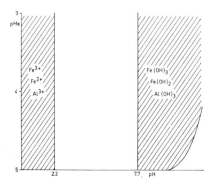

FIG. III.6. *Combination of figs. III.4 and III.5*

In a reduced medium iron is predominantly present as ferrous iron and again four zones can be distinguished when examining the occurrences of the ferrous and aluminium ions as a function of the pH (fig. III.5): zone A, both elements are present as cations and therefore susceptible to leaching; zone B, Al precipitated as hydroxide, whereas Fe (II) is still soluble; zone C (only occurring at concentrations larger than 10^{-4} M/l), aluminium and iron are both precipitated as hydroxides.

On superimposing the two diagrams (see fig. III.6) it can be concluded that both elements behave identically if the pH is lower than 2.2 or higher than 7.7, independent of the redox conditions of the medium. In all other cases ($2.2 < pH < 7.7$), which are the normal cases occurring in nature, the mobility of iron depends on the redox potential of the medium. It should be added that these conclusions are only valid if no organic acids are present, which actually is the case in the lower part of deep Oxisols.

In these experiments, as well as in those of Correns and collaborators, no kaolinite had been formed. Apparently, the leaching was too fast and too abundant and/or the temperature too high (see also: Van Baren, 1941; p. 242, Chapter I of Part II). However, the fact that almost invariably a certain vertical mineralogical zonality (see profiles I and 6 of Part II, Chapter I) can be observed in Oxisol profiles and the conception that new-formations depend on the dynamics of silica, alumina and cations (Wollast, 1961, 1963; Garrels and Christ, 1965; Hess, 1966) enabled Pedro (1966) to make the following statement: If the leaching of silica is weak, the amount of silica in the superficial horizon is such that 2 : I clay minerals (illite, montmorillonite) can be formed, which is accompanied by a partial retention of cations in the interlayer spaces.

If the elimination of silica increases, the SiO_2 concentration is only high enough to form I : I clay minerals (kaolinite, halloysite). The cations are leached completely.

Finally, if the desilication is extreme, the SiO_2 concentration is too low to form silicate minerals and only hydroxides and oxyhydroxides (boehmite, goethite, gibbsite, etc.) are synthesized.

As it is difficult to define the velocity of desilication, Pedro (1966) introduced a relative value for the evaluation of the desilication. He defined the molecular parameters:

$$\frac{\text{combined } SiO_2}{MgO + CaO + Na_2O + K_2O} = \frac{\text{combined } SiO_2}{\text{bases}} = R \text{ for the original rocks and}$$

$$\frac{\text{eliminated } SiO_2}{\text{eliminated bases}} = L \text{ for the desilication. If } L \geqslant R \text{ [or } q(SiO_2) \geqslant q \text{ (bases)] a desili-}$$
cation process and if $L \leqslant R$ [or $q(SiO_2) \leqslant q(\text{bases})$] a siallitization process is acting with the formation of 2 : I lattice clays (called bisiallitization by Pedro) or of I : I lattice clays (monosiallitization). Now, it is interesting to see whether or not it is possible to distinguish between these two processes. Assume a completely kaolinized rock; the bases have then been completely removed, whilst the eliminated silica can be represented by the combined SiO_2 content of the original rock diminished by the silica intergrated in the newly formed kaolinite ($2SiO_2.Al_2O_3.2H_2O$). This last quantity is equal to twice the molecular value of the Al_2O_3 content of the rock, if it is assumed

that the aluminium initially present is maintained *in situ* during the weathering process. At the end of the kaolinization process the molecular value of L can be represented by:

$$L_k = \frac{\text{combined } SiO_2 - 2Al_2O_3}{\text{bases}}$$

However, for every rock type a certain value for L_k can be expected, so it is necessary to establish the relation between R and L_k. Pedro (1966) calculated from numerous mineralogical and chemical analyses of different rocks that the mean value of L_k can be represented by the relation: $L_k = 0.64R$. It is now possible to state that if $0.64 \leqslant L < R$, or $0.64q(\text{bases}) \leqslant q(SiO_2) < q(\text{bases})$, monosiallitization is in process, whereas, if $L < 0.64R$, or $q(SiO_2) < 0.64q(\text{bases})$, the bisiallitization is in process.

TABLE III.3. *The zonal types of weathering* (after Pedro, 1966)

Geochemical characteristics of the percolating (vadose) water	$q(Al_2O_3) < q(SiO_2)$			$q(Al_2O_3) > q(SiO_2)$
	$L \geqslant R$ $q(SiO_2) \geqslant$ $q(\text{bases})$	$0.64R \leqslant L < R$ $0.64q(\text{bases}) \leqslant$ $q(SiO_2) <$ $q(\text{bases})$	$L < 0.64R$ $q(SiO_2) <$ $0.64q(\text{bases})$	
Mineralogical composition of the leached layer	Hydroxides of aluminium	1:1 lattice clays	2:1 lattice clays	free silica
Weathering process	desilication	monosiallitization (kaolinization)	bisiallitization	podsolization
Climate	← tropical humid zone arid zone →			temperate zone

When using the geochemical parameters mentioned above we can distinguish between four zonal types of weathering. These are shown in table III.3.

In a similar way it possible to distinguish vertically mineralogical zones (Pedro, 1964) in Oxisol profiles. This is shown in table III.4.

TABLE III.4. *Zonality in the tropical weathering process*

Geochemical characteristics of the vadose waters	Mineralogical composition of the horizons	Decrease of percolation
Free infiltration	aluminium hydroxide (top soil + plinthite horizon)	
Water excess with circulation Stagnant water	1:1 lattice clays (mottled clay) 2:1 lattice clays (pallid + weathering zone)	↓

It is interesting to discuss the above-mentioned weathering reactions from a thermo-dynamic viewpoint. As an example the conversion of K-feldspars into muscovite (illite), pyrophyllite, kaolinite, gibbsite, and dissolved silica, or in other words, the stability relationships in the system $K_2O–Al_2O_3–SiO_2–H_2O$ will be discussed. The following reactions represent this conversion (Wollast, 1961, 1963; De Keyser, 1964; Garrels and Christ, 1965; Slager and Van Schuylenborgh, 1970):

$$3\ Or + 2\ H^+ + 12\ H_2O \rightleftharpoons Ms + 2\ K^+ + 6\ H_4SiO_4 \quad ----------- \quad (1)$$

$$K_1 = \frac{[Ms]\ [K]^2\ [H_4SiO_4]^6}{[Or]^3\ [H]^2\ [H_2O]^{12}},$$

where brackets denote activities. The charges on the ions are omitted for the sake of convenience. As, by convention, the activities of solid substances are taken to be unity, and as, in dilute solutions, the activity of water is also unity, the expression for K_1 reduces to:

$$K_1 = \frac{[K]^2\ [H_4SiO_4]^6}{[H]^2}, \text{ or}$$

$$\lg K_1 = 2\ \lg\frac{[K]}{[H]} + 6\ \lg [H_4SiO_4] \quad -------------------- \quad (1a)$$

Similarly:

$$2\ Or + 2\ H^+ + 4\ H_2O \rightleftharpoons Pyr + 2\ K^+ + 2\ H_4SiO_4 - ----------- \quad (2)$$

$$\lg K_2 = 2\ \lg\frac{[K]}{[H]} + 2\ \lg [H_4SiO_4] \quad ------------------- \quad (2a)$$

$$2\ Ms + 2\ H^+ + 6\ H_4SiO_4 \rightleftharpoons 3\ Pyr + 2\ K^+ + 12\ H_2O \quad ---------- \quad (3)$$

$$\lg K_3 = 2\ \lg\frac{[K]}{[H]} - 6\ \lg [H_4SiO_4] \quad ------------------ \quad (3a)$$

$$2\ Ms + 2\ H^+ + 3\ H_2O \rightleftharpoons 3\ Kaol + 2\ K^+ \quad ---------------- \quad (4)$$

$$\lg K_4 = 2\ \lg\frac{[K]}{[H]} \quad ------------------------ \quad (4a)$$

$$Pyr + 5\ H_2O \rightleftharpoons Kaol + 2\ H_4SiO_4 \quad ----------------- \quad (5)$$

$$\lg K_5 = 2\ \lg [H_4SiO_4] \quad ------------------------ \quad (5a)$$

$$2\ Ms + 2H^+ + 18\ H_2O \rightleftharpoons 3\ Gibb + 2\ K^+ + 6\ H_4SiO_4 - --------- \quad (6)$$

$$\lg K_6 = 2\ \lg \frac{[K]}{[H]} + 6\ \lg [H_4SiO_4] \quad ------------------ \quad (6a)$$

$$Kaol + 5\ H_2O \rightleftharpoons Gibb + 2\ H_4SiO_4 \quad ----------------- \quad (7)$$

$$\lg K_7 = 2\ \lg [H_4SiO_4] - ------------------------ \quad (7a)$$

The symbols, used in the equations, have the following meaning: Or = K-feldspar, $KAlSi_3O_8$; Ms = muscovite, $KAl_3Si_3O_{10}(OH)_2$; Pyr = pyrophyllite, $Al_2Si_4O_{10}(OH)_2$; Kaol = kaolinite, $Al_2Si_2O_5(OH)_4$; Gibb = gibbsite, $Al_2O_3.3H_2O$.

In order to calculate the thermodynamic equilibrium constants, the following relationships have to be used:

$$\ln K = -\Delta F_r^{\circ}/RT \quad \text{or} \quad \lg K = -\Delta F_r^{\circ}/1.364 - -------------- \quad (8)$$

and

$$\Delta F_r^\circ = \Sigma \; \Delta F_f^\circ \; \text{products} - \Sigma \; \Delta F_f^\circ \; \text{reactants} \; - - - - - - - - - - - - - - - - - \quad (9)$$

where K = the equilibrium constant, ΔF_r° = standard free-energy change of the reaction, ΔF_f° = standard free-energy of formation, R = gas constant (0.001987 kcal/deg), and T = absolute temperature (298.15° K). All reactions are considered to proceed at 1 atmosphere pressure.

The values, used for the standard free-energies of formation, are $\Delta F_{f\,Or}^\circ = -893.8$ (Kelley, 1962); $\Delta F_{f\,Ms}^\circ = -1330.1$ (Barany, 1964); $\Delta F_{f\,Pyr}^\circ = -1258.7$ (Reesman and Keller, 1968); $\Delta F_{f\,Kaol}^\circ = -904.0$ (Reesman and Keller, 1968); $\Delta F_{f\,Gibb}^\circ = -547.0$ (Barany and Kelley, 1961); $\Delta F_{f\,H_4SiO_4}^\circ = -312.7$ (Reesman and Keller, 1968); $\Delta F_{f\,K^+}^\circ = -67.5$ (Rossini et al., 1952); $\Delta F_{f\,H_2O}^\circ = -56.7$ (Rossini et al., 1952); $\Delta F_{f\,H^+}^\circ = 0$; all values in kcal mol^{-1}. With (9) and (8) the following values for lg K were obtained: lg $K_1 = -15.4$; lg $K_2 = +3.3$; lg $K_3 = +40.5$; lg $K_4 = +12.2$; lg $K_5 = -9.4$; lg $K_6 = -21.2$; lg $K_7 = -11.2$.

With the aid of these data the stability fields of the minerals mentioned can be delineated in a two-dimensional diagram with lg $\dfrac{[K]}{[H]}$ as one axis and lg $[H_4SiO_4]$ as the other. The results are given in fig. III.7. In this figure the line of highest content of dissolved silica is obtained from the data of Siever (1962), which is $10^{-2.8}$ mol l^{-1}. At the right side of this line we have therefore the field of K-feldspar + amorphous silica.

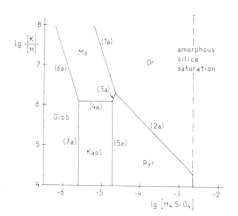

FIG. III.7. *Stability relations of some phases in the system $K_2O-Al_2O_3-SiO_2-H_2O$ at 25°C and 1 atm. total pressure (numbers at the boundary lines refer to the equations above)*

The figure shows that if the H_4SiO_4 activity is kept low (and consequently also the activities of the dissolved ions), e.g. when permeability is rapid and drainage perfect, the stable end product of weathering is gibbsite. This in agreement with the findings of Herbillon and Gastuche (1962), who stated that elimination of extraneous ions promotes the formation of crystalline gibbsite.

At higher H_4SiO_4 activities and in neutral or alkaline media (high $\dfrac{[K]}{[H]}$ ratios) as may occur under slow permeability and poor drainage conditions, muscovite (illite) will be formed. At lower $\dfrac{[K]}{[H]}$ pyrophyllite (montmorillonite) can be formed. At later stages, when the cations of the decomposing feldspars have been removed and when the reaction has become acid, both minerals are transformed into kaolinite. Muscovite (illite) can therefore expected to be present in the weathering zone of acid rocks, whereas kaolinite is the common product in the middle zone.

A study of the system $Na_2O–K_2O–Al_2O_3–SiO_2–H_2O$ at 25° C and 1 atm. was made by Hess (1966). The various phase equilibria in this system could be described as functions of the $\frac{[Na^+]}{[H^+]}$ and $\frac{[K^+]}{[H^+]}$ ratios and the activity of dissolved silica. This study was especially interesting with regard to the occurrence of montmorillonite, which can sometimes be found in the weathering zone immediately above the rock. It appeared that this mineral was stable at low values of $\lg \frac{[K^+]}{[H^+]}$, whilst the value of $\lg \frac{[Na^+]}{[H^+]}$ can vary considerably. It is important that the activity of dissolved silica be very high. These statements are illustrated in fig. III.8 where the phases occurring at $\lg \frac{[K]}{[H]} = 4$ are represented. It appears that the phases albite, phillipsite, K-feldspar, and a part of the montmorillonite occurrence are metastable under these conditions. This confirms that montmorillonite predominantly forms under conditions of poor drainage, a fact noticed by Schellmann (1964), who found montmorillonite at a depth of approximately 8 meters below the surface in the weathering zone of a serpentinite and in many other situations which are described in Chapter 3 of Part II.

The most important conclusion to be drawn from this is that at the beginning of the weathering process products will be formed different from those at more advanced stages, merely as a consequence of the change in drainage conditions.

It is evident from the discussion, that silica is removed as silicic acid. However, silica is frequently found to be present as a solid phase, especially in the profiles that show the transformation of montmorillonite (in our hypothetical case: pyrophyllite) into kaolinite. We have to conclude that in these soils silica occurs metastably or is

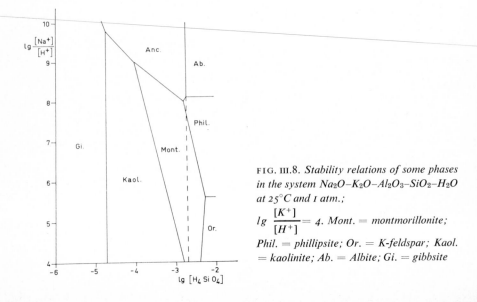

FIG. III.8. *Stability relations of some phases in the system $Na_2O–K_2O–Al_2O_3–SiO_2–H_2O$ at 25°C and 1 atm.;*

$\lg \frac{[K^+]}{[H^+]} = 4$. *Mont. = montmorillonite;*

Phil. = phillipsite; Or. = K-feldspar; Kaol. = kaolinite; Ab. = Albite; Gi. = gibbsite enriched residually. The metastable occurrence of silica is probably caused by the dehydration of the silicic acid in dry periods to form amorphous silica; upon rewetting the formed silica does not dissolve rapidly and appears as a metastable phase. It will disappear, however, in the end. It would have been very interesting to see what would have occurred if Correns (1961) and Pedro (1964) had included several drying cycles in their experiments.

In discussions of this kind it is necessary to take into account the reaction rates. It is, for example, possible that the formation of Pyr into Kaol is much faster than that of Ms into Kaol. This could lead to the conclusion that Ms occurs stably, although the solution composition predicts its instability. In this way the maintenance of illite (muscovite) in some profiles could be explained. It will be clear that old soils will conform more to theory than young soils, as the former system will be closer to equilibrium than the latter.

Actually, thermodynamic studies of the stability of minerals in relation to their environment assist in explaining mineral transformations, if handled very carefully. However, much more information is necessary in this field before all possible mineral transformations can be so explained.

Finally, attention should be given to an unusual suggestion, made by Lovering (1959) with respect to the desilication process (see also: Davis, 1964). He suggested that desilication could be effected to a considerable extent by the accumulation of silica by tropical vegetation and the removal of fallen litter by erosion before the silica is released. Considering a tropical forest of silica accumulating trees averaging 2.5 % SiO_2 and approximately 40 tons dry weight growth per ha per year, he calculated that in 5000 years, approximately 5000 tons of silica would be removed from one ha of soil by the forest. This amount of silica is, according to Lovering, equivalent to the silica in a volume of basalt of 1 ha and 30 cm thickness. As there was no data available on the amount of litter removed by erosion, he was not able to calculate the amount of silica removed in this way relative to the amount of silica returned to the soil by decaying vegetation.

LITERATURE CITED

BARANY, R. 1964 Heat and free-energy of formation of muscovite. *U.S. Bur. Mines*, R.I. 6356.
— and KELLEY, K.K. 1961 Heats and free-energies of formation of gibbsite, kaolinite, halloysite, and dickite. *U.S. Bur. Mines*, R.I. 5825.
BARNISHEL, R.I. and RICH, C.I. 1963 Gibbsite formation from aluminium interlayers in montmorillonite. *Soil Sci. Soc. Amer. Proc.*, 27: 632–635.
CORRENS, C.W. 1940 Die chemische Verwitterung der Silikate. *Die Naturwissenschaften*, 28: 369–376.
— 1961 The experimental chemical weathering of silicates. *Clay Min. Bull.*, 4: 249–265.
— and VON ENGELHARDT, W. 1938 Neue Untersuchungen über die Verwitterung des Kalifeldspates. *Chem. d. Erde*, 12: 1–22.
— and SCHLÜNZ, F.K. 1936 Mineralogische Untersuchungen dreier mecklenburgischer Böden. *Z. Pfl. ern. Düung. Bodenk.*, 44: 316.
DAVIES, S.N. 1964 Silica in streams and groundwater. *Am. J. Sci.*, 262: 870–891.
DE KEYSER, W.L. 1964 Contribution à l'étude du système silice-alumine. *Bull. Soc. fr. Céram.*, 62: 19–34.

GARRELS, R.M. and CHRIST, CH.L. 1965 Solutions, minerals, and equilibria. *New York*.

HERBILLON, A. and GASTUCHE, M.C. 1962 Synthèse et génèse de l'hydrargyllite. *C.R. Séances Acad. Sci. Paris*, 254: 1105–1107.

HESS, P.C. 1966 Phase equilibria of some minerals in the $K_2O-Na_2O-Al_2O_3-SiO_2-H_2O$ system at 25°C and 1 atmosphere. *Am. J. Sci.*, 264: 289–309.

HEYDEMANN, A. 1966 Über die chemische Verwitterung von Tonmineralen (Experimentelle Untersuchungen). *Geochim. Cosmochim. Acta*, 30: 995–1035.

KELLEY, K.K. 1962 Heats and free-energies of formation of anhydrous silicates. *U.S. Bur. Mines*, R.I. 5901: pp. 32.

KRÜGER, G. 1939 Verwitterungsversuche am Leuzit. *Chem. d. Erde*, 12: 236–264.

LOVERING, T.S. 1959 Significance of accumulator plants in rock weathering. *Bull. Geol. Soc. Am.*, 70: 781–800.

MEHMEL, M. 1937 Ab- und Umbau am Biotit. *Chem. d. Erde*, 11: 307–333.

PEDRO, G. 1960 Premier résultats sur la génèse des laterites par voie expérimentale. *Int. Geol. Cong. Rep.*: 108–111.

— 1961 An experimental study on the geochemical weathering of crystalline rocks by water. *Clay Min. Bull.*, 4: 266–281.

— 1964 Contribution à l'étude expérimentale de l'altération géochimique des roches crystallines. *Thesis Paris*.

— 1966 Essai sur la caractérisation géochimique des différents processus zonaux résultant de l'altération des roches superficielles (cycle aluminosilicique). *C.R. Acad. Sci. Paris*, 262: 1828-1831.

— and BERRIER, J. 1966 Sur l'altération expérimentale de la kaolinite et sa transformation en boehmite par lessivage à l'eau. *C.R. Acad. Sc. Paris*, 262: 729–732.

— and BITAR, K.E. 1966 Sur l'influence du type chimique de la roche mère dans le développement des phénomènes de l'altération superficielle: Recherches expérimentales sur l'évolution des roches ultrabasiques (serpentinites). *C.R. Acad. Sc. Paris*, 263: 313–316.

REESMAN, A.L. and KELLER, W.D. 1968 Aqueous solubility studies of high-alumina and clay minerals. *Am. Min.*, 53: 929–942.

ROSSINI, F.D. et al. 1952 Selected values of chemical thermodynamic properties. *Nat. Bur. Standards*, Circ. 500.

SCHELLMANN, W. 1964 Zur lateritischen Verwitterung von Serpentinit. *Geol. Jahrb.*, 81: 645–679.

SIEVER, R. 1962 Silica solubility, 0°-200°C., and the diagenesis of siliceous sediments. *J. Geol.*, 70: 127–150.

SLAGER, S. and VAN SCHUYLENBORGH, J. 1970 Morphology and geochemistry of three clay soils of a tropical coastal plain (Surinam). *Agric. Res. Rep.* 734: pp. 34.

TUNN, W. 1940 Untersuchungen über die Verwitterung des Tremolits. *Chem. d. Erde*, 12: 275–304.

TURNER, R.C. and BRYDON, J.E. 1965 Factors affecting the solubility of $Al(OH)_3$ precipitated in the presence of montmorillonite. *Soil Sci.*, 100: 176–181.

VAN BAREN, F. A. 1941 De mineralogische achtergrond van de bodemvruchtbaarheid in Nederlandsch-Indië. *Landbouw (Buitenzorg)*, 17: 520–541.

VON ENGELHARDT, W. 1937 Mineralogische Beschreibung eines mecklenburgischen Bodenprofils. *Chem. d. Erde*, 11: 17–37.

WOLLAST, R. 1961 Aspect chimique du mode de formation des bauxites dans le bas Congo. *Bull. Acad. Roy. Sc. d'Outre-Mer*, 7: 468–489.

— 1963 Confrontation des données thermodynamiques et expérimentales. *Bull. Acad. Roy. Sc. d'Outre-Mer*, 9: 392–412.

(As considerable time has elapsed between the delivery of the manuscript of this book by the authors, January 1970, and its appearance, the end of 1972, and as important progress has been made in the theoretical treatment of weathering processes, the publishers consented in the addition of a concise report on certain aspects of the fundamental work of Helgeson (1968), Helgeson, Garrels and Mackenzie (1969) and Garrels and Mackenzie (1971). This was thought to be essential and should be included.)

As all processes are irreversible, their theoretical treatment should be one for irreversible reactions. Or, in other words, the thermodynamics of reversible reactions should be adapted to irreversible ones. One way to achieve this is the assumption of the occurrence of reversible reactions, or partial equilibria, during certain stages of the irreversible overall-process (Helgeson, 1968; Helgeson a.o., 1969; Garrels and Mackenzie, 1971). Obviously, it requires the knowledge of all equilibrium states (metastable as well as stable) that might arise. As an example the weathering of albite by pure water will be chosen. The conditions are constant pressure (1 atm.) and temperature (25°C) and the system is a closed one.

The first reaction that occurs when very small portions of the feldspar react with water is its congruent dissolution, according to:

$$NaAlSi_3O_8(s) + 8H_2O \rightarrow Na^+ + Al(OH)_4^- + 3H_4SiO_4 \ - - - - - - - - - - \quad (9a)$$

Of the various possible dissolved Al-species, $Al(OH)_4^-$ will be formed dominantly as the pH of pure water is 7 at 1 atm. and 25°C. In this irreversible reaction equilibrium (partial equilibrium) is supposed to be present between all dissolved species.

As reaction (9a) proceeds the solution approaches saturation with respect to gibbsite and at a definite moment gibbsite precipitates according to:

$$Al(OH)_4^- \rightleftharpoons Al(OH)_3(s) + OH^- \ - \quad (9b)$$

The position of this point can be calculated exactly and represented by point A in fig. III.8a, constructed in the way as described on p. 428 and showing the stability relationships between albite, nepheline, Na-montmorillonite, kaolinite and gibbsite (Helgeson a.o., 1969) in the system $Na_2O-Al_2O_3-SiO_2-H_2O$ at 1 atm. and 25°C. From this moment on the congruent dissolution of additional small amounts of albite changes into its incongruent dissolution with the production of gibbsite, according to:

$$NaAlSi_3O_8(s) + 8H_2O \rightarrow Al(OH)_3(s) + Na^+ + OH^- + 3H_4SiO_4 \ - - - - - \quad (9c)$$

This reaction represents the irreversible dissolution of albite, whereas a partial equilibrium is maintained between gibbsite and the solution. The reaction path is given by A → B, the slope being determined by eq. (9c).

If the system is assumed to be opened at a point somewhere between A and B, and when it is assumed that the removal of the dissolved reaction products keeps pace with their production by dissolution of the albite, so that the solution composition does not change ("steady state") the reaction will proceed until all albite has been dissolved and replaced by gibbsite. This seems to happen often in nature as the pseudomorphic replacement of feldspars by gibbsite is frequently observed (see pp. 193 and 194, and

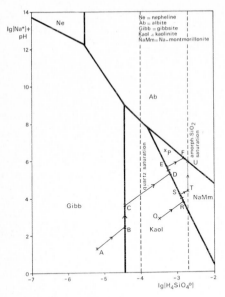

FIG. III.8a. *Stability relationships in the system* Na_2O–Al_2O_3–SiO_2–H_2O *at* 25° *C and* 1 *atm. as function of the equilibrium – solution composition.*
(*Ne* = $NaAlSiO_4$; *Ab* = $NaAlSi_3O_8$; *Gibb* = $Al(OH)_3$; *Kaol* = $Al_2Si_2O_5(OH)_4$; *NaMm* = $Na_{.33}Al_{2.33}Si_{3.67}O_{10}(OH)_2$)

fig. II.5). This process is similar to the "early formation of gibbsite" as a stage in the laterization process.

Returning to the closed system it can be stated that at B gibbsite is in danger to become unstable, whereas kaolinite occurs stably. A new equilibrium will be established between kaolinite and the solution. If all partial equilibrium states are maintained and small amounts of albite continue to dissolve, the reaction proceeds from B to C, according to:

$$2NaAlSi_3O_8(s) + 4Al(OH)_3(s) + H_2O \rightarrow 3Al_2Si_2O_5(OH)_4(s) + 2Na^+ + 2OH^- \quad (9d)$$

Eq.(9d) represents the irreversible dissolution of albite, whereas a partial equilibrium is maintained between kaolinite, gibbsite and the solution until all gibbsite, produced between A and B, has been consumed. The position of C can be calculated from the equations (9c) and (9d). From C onwards kaolinite is produced as the result of the continuous incongruent dissolution of small amounts of albite, according to:

$$2NaAlSi_3O_8(s) + 11H_2O \rightarrow Al_2Si_2O_5(OH)_4(s) + 2Na^+ + 2OH^- + 4H_4SiO_4 \quad (9e)$$

The slope of CD is determined by eq.(9e). At D kaolinite is in danger to become unstable, whereas Na-montmorillonite starts to occur stably. A new partial equilibrium is established between kaolinite, Na-montmorillonite and the solution. The reaction proceeds now from D to E until all kaolinite, produced from B to D, has been consumed, according to:

$$2.3NaAlSi_3O_8(s) + 2.8Al_2Si_2O_5(OH)_4(s) + 10^{-3}H_4SiO_4 \rightarrow$$
$$3.4Na_{.33}Al_{2.33}Si_{3.67}O_{10}(OH)_2(s) + 1.2Na^+ + 1.2OH^- + 1.7H_2O \quad ------ \quad (9f)$$

Finally the reaction proceeds from E to F, where the overall-equilibrium is established between albite, montmorillonite and the solution, according to:

$$2.3NaAlSi_3O_8(s) + 8.6H_2O \rightarrow Na._{33}Al_2._{33}Si_3._{67}O_{10}(OH)_2(s) + 2Na^+ +$$
$$2OH^- + 3.3H_4SiO_4 \quad - \quad (9g)$$

In this way a stability diagram, representing equilibrium states in a multi-component system can be used to predict reaction pathways in irreversible processes such as the weathering of primary minerals.

It is interesting to see what happens if albite would be brought into contact with a solution of composition Q in fig. III.8a. It is clear that kaolinite is produced according to equation (9e). From R onwards the reaction proceeds according to eq.(9f) until all kaolinite has been consumed at S. Then the reaction is determined by eq.(9g) until at T the solution becomes saturated with respect to amorphous silica. From T onwards the dissolution of new small amounts of albite is governed by the new partial equilibrium:

$$am.SiO_2(s) + 2H_2O \rightleftharpoons H_4SiO_4 \quad - \quad (9h)$$

and proceeds according to:

$$2.3NaAlSi_3O_8(s) + 2H_2O \rightarrow Na._{33}Al_2._{33}Si_3._{67}O_{10}(OH)_2(s) + 2OH^- +$$
$$3.3SiO_2(s) \quad - \quad (9i)$$

along TU. Arrived at U overall-equilibrium is settled between albite, montmorillonite amorphous silica, and the solution.

An example of this case can be found in profile 6 of Chapter I of Part II, although representing essentially a weathering sequence in the system $MgO–Al_2O_3–SiO_2–H_2O$. Here the presence of chlorite, smectite, and amorphous silica can be observed in horizon C_2 inmmediately above the rock. In horizon C_1, the silica is practically absent whereas the smectites and chlorites are dominant. The upper horizons finally show the disappearance of smectites and chlorites and the formation of kaolinite and gibbsite.

Finally it should be remarked that the reaction path C → D is only possible if the precipitation of quartz from the solution does not occur or is an extremely slow process. Otherwise the reaction path would have been along the dotted line at $lg[H_4SiO_4] = -4$ upwards until at the interception with the line, representing the equilibrium state between albite, kaolinite, and the solution, overall-equilibrium is attained. The soil solution, however, is practically ever supersatured with respect to quartz as quartz precipitation is an extremely slow process.

It is clear, as already mentioned earlier (pp. 219 and 220) that the weathering of rocks when present at the interface earth/atmosphere will be different from the reaction sequence if the rock has been weathered to a certain depth. In the first case the rock will be in contact with rainwater and in the latter with a solution which contains a certain concentration of silicic acid and other constituents. Consequently it is impossible to calculate the losses and gains of respectively the A- and B-horizon by comparison with the C-material. Such calculations can only be made if the composition of the original rock is known and if a mineral is present that is unaffected by the weathering process. Such situations will be found rarely.

LITERATURE CITED

GARRELS, R.M. and MACKENZIE, F.T. 1971 Evolution of sedimentary rocks. Appendix B: Mineral Chemistry, p. 345–377. Norton & Cy, Inc., New York.

HELGESON, H.C. 1968 Evaluation of irreversible reactions in geochemical processes involving minerals and aqueous solutions. I. Thermodynamic relations. *Geochim. Cosmochin. Acta*, 32: 853–877.

—, BROWN, Th.H., and LEEPER, R.H. 1969 Handbook of theoretical activity diagrams depicting chemical equilibria in geologic systems involving an aqueous phase at one atm. and 0° to 300°C. Freeman, Cooper & Cy, San Francisco.

—, GARRELS, R.M. and MACKENZIE, F.T. 1969 Evaluation of irreversible reactions in geochemical processes involving minerals and aqueous solutions. II. Applications. *Geochim. Cosmochim. Acta*, 33: 455–481.

CHAPTER 2

PLINTHIZATION
Reduction-oxidation

In Part II, Chapter 1, it was stated that alternating reduction and oxidation as result of the fluctuating groundwater table causes redistribution of iron and manganese into mottles, leading eventually to the formation of plinthite. It was also remarked (p. 231) that the simultaneous oxidation of ferrous and manganous ions and their deposition as oxides at the same spot creates a problem which is rather difficult to explain.

To achieve a good insight into this problem, the stability relations of the various phases and dissolved species in the systems $Fe - O_2 (g)^1 - H_2O$ and $Mn - O_2(g) - H_2O$ have to be studied. The standard conditions under which this will be performed are a temperature of $25°$ C and total pressure of one atmosphere, unless otherwise stated.

The system $Fe - O_2(g) - H_2O$ can contain the following components: Fe, FeO, $Fe(OH)_2$, Fe_3O_4, α–FeOOH, γ–FeOOH, α–Fe_2O_3, γ–Fe_2O_3, and $Fe(OH)_3$ as solid phases, and (neglecting for convenience the notation of hydrational water and omitting the presence of polymers) Fe^{2+}, $FeOH^+$, $HFeO_2^-$, Fe^{3+}, $FeOH^{2+}$, $Fe(OH)_2^+$, and $Fe(OH)_3^0$ as dissolved species. Some of these are stable and others metastable under the above-mentioned conditions. To decide which phases are stable, it is necessary to examine the following reactions (for details, see Garrels and Christ, 1965):

$$4FeO(s)^2 \rightleftharpoons Fe_3O_4(s) + Fe(s) - \quad (10)$$

From the listed standard free-energies of formation (Garrels and Christ, 1965; Robie and Waldbaum, 1968), the standard free-energy change of reaction can be calculated, using equation (9). It is for reaction (10) : –2.7 kcal, which means that magnetite and iron are stable with respect to FeO.

The next reaction to be examined is:

$$3Fe(OH)_2(s) \rightleftharpoons Fe_3O_4(s) + H_2(g) + 2H_2O - - - - - - - - - - - - - - - - - - \quad (11)$$

$\Delta F_r^o = -9.7 \, kcal$

Equation (8) shows that $\lg K = -9.7/-1.364 = 7.1$. Hence, $\lg \varsigma H_2 = 7.1$ and $\varsigma H_2 = 10^{7.1}$ atm., ςH_2 being the partial hydrogen pressure. It is evident, that $Fe(OH)_2$ is unstable with respect to its decomposition into magnetite, water, and hydrogen gas. Therefore, $Fe(OH)_2$ should eventually decompose under 1 atmosphere total pressure to yield magnetite and hydrogen gas.

It is fairly difficult to decide which of the phases in the highest oxidation state are stable, as the ΔF_f^o values of some of them (goethite, lepidocrocite, and maghemite) are not accurately known. Schmalz (1959) reports for α–FeOOH a value of $-117.0 \pm$

---

[1] g means gas; [2] s means solid.

1.0 kcal/mole whereas for γ–FeOOH and γ–Fe$_2$O$_3$ no data are available as far as known. Our own determinations (see also later) have produced the values -117.7 ± 0.3, and -114.0 ± 0.1 kcal/mole for natural goethite and synthetic lepidocrocite, respectively. Using the values of -177.7 ± 0.3 kcal/mole for hematite (Robie and Waldbaum, 1968) and -166.0 kcal/mole for amorphous Fe(OH)$_3$ (Latimer, 1964), the following reactions can be examined:

$$\gamma\text{–FeOOH(s)} \rightleftharpoons \alpha\text{–FeOOH(s)} \quad \text{---------------------} \quad (12)$$
$$\Delta F^\circ_r = -3.7 \text{ kcal}$$

$$2\text{Fe(OH)}_3\text{(s)} \rightleftharpoons \alpha\text{–Fe}_2\text{O}_3\text{(s)} + 3\text{H}_2\text{O} \quad \text{-----------------} \quad (13)$$
$$\Delta F^\circ_r = -15.8 \text{ kcal}$$

$$\text{Fe(OH)}_3\text{(s)} \rightleftharpoons \alpha\text{–FeOOH(s)} + \text{H}_2\text{O} \quad \text{------------------} \quad (14)$$
$$\Delta F^\circ_r = -8.4 \text{ kcal}$$

$$\alpha\text{–Fe}_2\text{O}_3\text{(s)} + \text{H}_2\text{O} \rightleftharpoons 2\alpha\text{–FeOOH(s)} \quad \text{-----------------} \quad (15)$$
$$\Delta F^\circ_r = -1.0 \text{ kcal}$$

These results mean that 1) goethite is stable with respect to lepidocrocite; 2) amorphous ferric hydroxide is unstable with respect to hematite and goethite + water; 3) goethite is stable with respect to hematite + water; and 4) that no conclusion can be drawn on the stability of maghemite. The third conclusion is in accordance with results of Schmalz (1959), but disagrees with Berner (1969), who found a standard free-energy change for relation (15) of $+0.40$ kcal. The discrepancy is possibly caused by the poor crystallinity of the goethite used by Berner. Our own ΔF°_f determinations of well-crystallized synthetic goethite, extremely well-crystallized natural goethite, well-crystallized synthetic hematite, and extremely well-crystallized natural hematite yield the following values, respectively: -117.3 ± 0.3; -117.7 ± 0.3; -177.1 ± 0.5; and -177.7 ± 0.2 kcal/mole. It depends therefore on the degree of crystallinity of the phases, whether or not goethite is stable with respect to hematite + water. Reaction (15) for the transformation of very well-crystallized hematite into well-crystallized goethite has a change in free-energy of -0.2 kcal, indicating that goethite is the stable phase. The water activity at which these types of goethite and hematite will be in equilibrium, is given by:

$$\lg\frac{1}{[\text{H}_2\text{O}]} = \lg K = \frac{-0.2}{-1.364} \approx 0.17$$
$$\lg [\text{H}_2\text{O}] \approx -0.17$$
$$[\text{H}_2\text{O}] \approx 0.68$$

As $[\text{H}_2\text{O}] = \dfrac{\varsigma\text{H}_2\text{O}}{\varsigma^*\text{H}_2\text{O}}$ at moderate pressures, where $\varsigma\text{H}_2\text{O}$ is the vapour pressure of water and $\varsigma^*\text{H}_2\text{O}$ the saturated water vapour pressure, it can be concluded that at a relative humidity of approximately 70% goethite and hematite may be in equilibrium. At higher relative humidities goethite is the stable phase and at lower relative humidity hematite is. If the reported values of ΔF°_f are accepted to be reliable values for naturally occurring hematite and goethite, it must be concluded that hematite can only occur in soils if relative humidities of the soil atmosphere reach values as low as 70 % and if the reaction rates of (15) in both directions are equal.

Experimental evidence for this conclusion can be found in the work of Schellmann (1959) and Schwertmann (1959, 1965, 1966). They found that amorphous iron hydroxides always age in dilute solutions of 1-1-electrolytes to form goethite, if goethite is not formed directly. On the contrary, in the presence of Ca and Mg salts (Schellmann, 1959) or of Al salts (Gastuche et al., 1964), hematite was formed. Apparently the salts had reduced water activity to a level that only hematite could be formed. It can therefore be expected that hematite is sometimes formed in the weathering zone of basic rocks high in calcium and magnesium. This was confirmed by Taylor and Gradey (1967), who observed that Tasmanian soils formed from basalt showed near sea level (slow drainage) a low goethite/hematite ratio and at elevated areas (rapid drainage) high ratios. This was correlated with the (Ca + Mg) content of the soils; the content was high at low goethite/hematite ratios and low at high ratios.

The conclusion is drawn that Fe, Fe_3O_4, and α–FeOOH are the stable solid phases in the system $Fe - O_2(g) - H_2O$.

It is common use to express the stability relations in such systems as function of E_h (redox-potential) and pH. To examine these, the stability field of water has to be established. This can be achieved by considering the oxidation reactions (see Garrels and Christ, 1965):

$$2H_2O \rightleftharpoons O_2(g) + 4H^+ + 4e \quad - \quad (16)$$

and

$$H_2(g) \rightleftharpoons 2H^+ + 2e - \quad (17)$$

For (16) holds: $E_{h16} = E^o_{16} + \dfrac{RT}{nF}\ln \varsigma O_2 + \dfrac{RT}{F}\ln [H^+] - - - - - - - - - \quad (16a)$

E_h is the redox-potential of an O_2 electrode immersed in water which contacts a gas mixture with a certain partial oxygen pressure, ςO_2; E^o is the standard redox-potential or the voltage of the O_2 electrode if all substances involved are at unit activity; R is the gas constant (0.001987 kcal/deg); T is the absolute temperature in $^\circ K$; n is the number of electrons involved; F is the Faraday (23.06 kcal/volt-gram equivalent); and [] denotes activity.

Substitution and converting to Briggian logarithms lead to:

$$E_{h16} = E^o_{16} + 0.015 \lg \varsigma O_2 - 0.06pH \quad - - - - - - - - - - - - - - - - - \quad (16b)$$

E^o can be calculated from ΔF^o_r using the relation:

$$E^o = \frac{\Delta F^o_r}{nF} = \frac{F^o_r}{n \times 23.06} \quad - \quad (18)$$

For half-cell reaction (16), E^0_{16} is 1.23 V.

Assuming that ςO_2 in soil-air never exceeds 0.2 atmospheres, the upper boundary of water stability can be characterized by $\varsigma O_2 = 0.2$ atm. Substituting the values for E^0_{16} and ςO_2, (16b) gives:

$$E_{h18} = 1.22 - 0.06pH \quad - \quad (16c)$$

The lower boundary of water stability can be obtained from (17a) by substituting

$$E_{h17} = E^o_{17} - 0.03 \lg \varsigma H_2 + 0.06 \lg [H^+] \quad - - - - - - - - - - - - - - - - \quad (17a)$$

for ςH_2 the value 1 and for E^0_{17} 0 V. Hence,

$$E_{h17} = -0.06pH \ - \quad (17b)$$

The stability field of water on a E_h–pH plot is therefore situated between the lines represented by equations (16c) and (17b).

To delineate the stability fields of the various stable iron species, the following equations have to be used:

$$3Fe(s) + 4H_2O \rightleftharpoons Fe_3O_4(s) + 8H^+ + 8e \ - - - - - - - - - - - - \quad (19)$$

with $\quad E_{h19} = -0.09 - 0.06pH \ - - - - - - - - - - - - - - - - - - - \quad (19a)$

$$Fe_3O_4(s) + 2H_2O \rightleftharpoons 3\alpha\text{–FeOOH}(s) + H^+ + e \ - - - - - - - - - - \quad (20)$$

with $\quad E_{h20} = 0.15 - 0.06pH \ - \quad (20a)$

The boundaries between magnetite and the metastable phases are derived from:

$$2Fe_3O_4(s) + H_2O \rightleftharpoons 3Fe_2O_3(s) + 2H^+ + 2e \ - - - - - - - - - - - \quad (21)$$

with $\quad E_{h21} = 0.21 - 0.06pH \ - \quad (21a)$

$$Fe_3O_4(s) + 2H_2O \rightleftharpoons 3\gamma\text{–FeOOH}(s) + H^+ + e \ - - - - - - - - - - \quad (22)$$

with $\quad E_{h22} = 0.63 - 0.06pH \ - \quad (22a)$

$$Fe_3O_4(s) + 5H_2O \rightleftharpoons 3Fe(OH)_3(a, s) + H^+ + e \ - - - - - - - - - - \quad (23)$$

with $\quad E_{h23} = 1.24 - 0.06pH \ - \quad (23a)$

Fig. III.9 represents the result of these relations. It shows that the Fe/Fe_3O_4 boundary is situated below the lower boundary and the $Fe_3O_4/Fe(OH)_3$ boundary above the upper boundary of the stability field of water. Hence, the stability field of iron and of metastable $Fe(OH)_3$ cannot be reached in the presence of water if equilibrium is maintained. This is only possible if water is present metastably. The table also shows

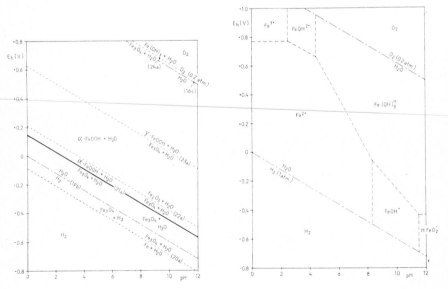

FIG. III.9. *Stability relationships of iron oxides and hydroxides as function of E_h and pH at 25°C and 1 atm. total pressure*

FIG. III.10. *Fields of 'dominance' of various dissolved iron species as function of E_h and pH at 25°C and 1 atm. total pressure*

that goethite is the common iron mineral in practically all circumstances. The other minerals are metastable under aerated conditions and will age to goethite. Magnetite exists only under strongly reducing conditions and high pH values.

It is not possible to delineate true stability boundaries for the dissolved species; however fields of 'dominance' can be drawn. This follows from table III.5, representing the hydrolytic and redox equilibria of various iron species[1].

The first equation of the table shows that at pH 2.5 the activities of $FeOH^{2+}$ and Fe^{3+} are equal. At higher pH values $FeOH^{2+}$ dominates, at lower Fe^{3+}. The table also shows that $Fe(OH)_2^+$ cannot occur stably as it is hydrolysed to $Fe(OH)_3^0$ at a lower pH value than that at which it is formed from $FeOH^{2+}$, so $Fe(OH)_2^+$ is not included in the redox-equilibria of the table.

The various fields of 'dominance' are drawn in fig. III.10. It shows that in the pH range occurring in soils, only Fe^{2+}, $Fe(OH)_3^0$, and $FeOH^{2+}$ may be of importance. In very acid soils (e.g. acid sulphate soils) Fe^{3+}, in very alkaline soils and under strongly reducing conditions $FeOH^+$ may occur.

A decision must be made about the activity of the solutes at which the solids become unstable in order to construct boundaries between the various solid phases and the solutes. Garrels and Christ (1965) stated that for geological purposes a value of 10^{-6} had been chosen: in other words, if the sum of the activities of the dissolved species in equilibrium with a solid is less than 10^{-6}, the solid will behave as an immobile constituent in its environment. Van Schuylenborgh and Bruggenwert (1965) showed that from the viewpoint of soil formation the sum of the activities of the dissolved species has to be at least 5×10^{-6}; in the following discussions a value of 10^{-5} is taken.

This means that $Fe(OH)_3^0$ can be omitted in the discussion as its activity in a saturated solution of amorphous ferric hydroxide is $10^{-6.54}$ (Gayer and Woontner, 1956) and only Fe^{3+}, $FeOH^{2+}$, Fe^{2+}, and $FeOH^+$ remain to be examined.

The equilibria of these ions with the stable solid phases in the stability field of water are as follows:

Reactions with Fe^{3+}:
$$\alpha\text{--}FeOOH(s) + 3H^+ \rightleftharpoons Fe^{3+} + 2H_2O \quad ------ \quad (35)$$
$$lg\,[Fe^{3+}] = -1.3 - 3pH \quad -------------- \quad (35a)$$
$$Fe_3O_4(s) + 8H^+ \rightleftharpoons 3Fe^{3+} + 4H_2O + e \quad ------ \quad (36)$$
$$E_{h36} = 0.42 + 0.18\,lg\,[Fe^{3+}] + 0.48pH \quad ------ \quad (36a)$$

Reactions with $FeOH^{2+}$:
$$\alpha\text{--}FeOOH(s) + 2H^+ \rightleftharpoons FeOH^{2+} + H_2O \quad ----- \quad (37)$$
$$lg\,[FeOH^{2+}] = -3.7 - 2pH \quad ------------ \quad (37a)$$
$$Fe_3O_4(s) + 5H^+ \rightleftharpoons 3FeOH^{2+} + H_2O + e \quad ----- \quad (38)$$
$$E_{h38} = 0.81 + 0.18\,lg\,[FeOH^{2+}] + 0.30pH \quad ---- \quad (38a)$$

Reactions with Fe^{2+}:
$$Fe^{2+} + 2H_2O \rightleftharpoons \alpha\text{--}FeOOH(s) + 3H + e \quad ----- \quad (39)$$
$$E_{h39} = 0.69 - 0.06\,lg\,[Fe^{2+}] - 0.18pH \quad ------- \quad (39a)$$
$$3Fe^{2+} + 4H_2O \rightleftharpoons Fe_3O_4(s) + 8H^+ + 2e \quad ----- \quad (40)$$
$$E_{h40} = 0.97 - 0.09\,lg\,[Fe^{2+}] - 0.24pH \quad ------- \quad (40a)$$

---

[1] The values for lgK and E° were calculated from the ΔF_f° values listed by Garrels and Christ (1965). ΔF_f° of molecular dissolved ferric hydroxide was calculated from data on the solubility of amorphous ferric hydroxide, presented by Gayer and Woontner (1956).

438

TABLE III.5. *Hydrolytic and redoxequilibria for dissolved iron species*

Hydrolytic equilibria

$Fe^{3+} + H_2O \rightleftharpoons FeOH^{2+} + H^+$ $- -$ (24)

$lg*K_1 = -2.5 = lg\{[FeOH^{2+}]/[Fe^{3+}]\} - pH$ $- - - - -$ (24a)

$FeOH^{2+} + H_2O \rightleftharpoons Fe(OH)_2^+ + H^+$ $- -$ (25)

$lg*K_2 = -4.7 = lg\{[Fe(OH)_2^+]/[FeOH^{2+}]\} - pH$ $- - - - -$ (25a)

$Fe(OH)_2^+ + H_2O \rightleftharpoons Fe(OH)_3^0 + H^+$ $- - - - - - - - - - - - - - - - - - - -$ (26)

$lg*K_3 = -4.2 = lg\{[Fe(OH)_3^0]/[Fe(OH)_2^+]\} - pH$ $- - - - -$ (26a)

$FeOH^{2+} + 2H_2O \rightleftharpoons Fe(OH)_3^0 + 2H^+$ $- - - - - - - - - - - - - - - - - -$ (27)

$lg\beta_3 = -8.9 = lg\{[Fe(OH)_3^0]/[FeOH^{2+}]\} - 2pH$ $- - - -$ (27a)

$Fe^{2+} + H_2O \rightleftharpoons FeOH^+ + H^+$ $- -$ (28)

$lg*K_1 = -8.3 = lg\{[FeOH^+]/[Fe^{2+}]\} - pH$ $- - - - -$ (28a)

$FeOH^+ + H_2O \rightleftharpoons HFeO_2^- + 2H^+$ $- -$ (29)

$lg*K_3 = -23.0 = lg\{[HFeO_2^-]/[FeOH^+]\} - 2pH$ $- - - - - - - - -$ (29a)

Redox equilibria

$Fe^2 \rightleftharpoons Fe^{3+} + e$ $- -$ (30)

$E_{h30} = 0.77 + 0.06 lg\{[Fe^{3+}]/[Fe^{2+}]\}$ $- - - - - - - - - - - - - - - - - - -$ (30a)

$Fe^{2+} + H_2O \rightleftharpoons FeOH^{2+} + H^+ + e$ $- - - - - - - - - - - - - - - - - - - -$ (31)

$E_{h31} = 0.92 + 0.06 lg\{[FeOH^{2+}]/[Fe^{2+}]\} - 0.06pH$ $- - - - - - -$ (31a)

$Fe^{2+} + 3H_2O \rightleftharpoons Fe(OH)_3^0 + 3H^+ + e$ $- - - - - - - - - - - - - - - - - -$ (32)

$E_{h32} = 1.44 + 0.06 lg\{[Fe(OH)_3^0]/[Fe^{2+}]\} - 0.18pH$ $- - - - -$ (32a)

$FeOH^+ + 2H_2O \rightleftharpoons Fe(OH)_3^0 + 2H^+ + e$ $- - - - - - - - - - - - - - -$ (33)

$E_{h33} = 0.95 + 0.06 lg\{[Fe(OH)_3^0]/[FeOH^+]\} - 0.12pH$ $- - - - -$ (33a)

$HFeO_2^- + H_2O \rightleftharpoons Fe(OH)_3^0 + e$ $- -$ (34)

$E_{h34} = -0.43 + 0.06 lg\{[Fe(OH)_3^0]/[HFeO_2^-]\}$ $- - - - - - - - - - - - -$ (34a)

Reactions with $FeOH^+$: $FeOH^+ + H_2O \rightleftharpoons \alpha-FeOOH(s) + 2H^+ + e$ $- - - -$ (41)

$E_{h41} = 0.20 - 0.06lg[FeOH^+] - 0.12pH$ $- - - - - -$ (41a)

$3FeOH^+ + H_2O \rightleftharpoons Fe_3O_4 + 5H^+ + 2e$ $- - - - - -$ (42)

$E_{h42} = 0.23 - 0.09lg[FeOH^+] - 0.15pH$ $- - - - - -$ (42a)

Combining these data with those used for the construction of figs. III.9 and III.10, the stability diagram of fig. III.11 was constructed. It appears that the dissolved species $FeOH^{2+}$ and $FeOH^+$ can never contribute to the mobility of the stable phases goethite and magnetite. It also appears that the ferric ion has a very restricted field of predominance. Only at strongly acid and oxidizing conditions does the activity of the ion contribute to the dissolution of goethite. The great stability of goethite is very striking. Only under very acid or strongly reducing conditions is it mobile.

The conclusion can be drawn that goethite can only be rendered soluble at oxidizing conditions, if some agent is present that forms strong complexes with Fe^{3+} or Fe^{2+}.

The system $Mn-O_2(g)-H_2O$ can be examined in a similar manner. The system may contain many solid phases (Bricker, 1965): manganosite, MnO; pyrochroite, $Mn(OH)_2$;

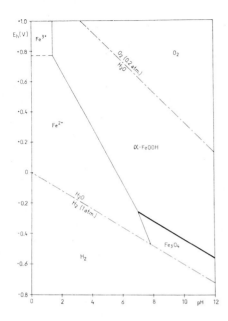

FIG. III.11. *Stability fields of goethite and magnetite in water. Boundaries of the solids at the total activity of dissolved species of 10^{-5}; $25°C$; I atm. total pressure*

hausmannite, Mn_3O_4; groutite, α–$MnOOH$; manganite, γ–$MnOOH$; bixbyite, Mn_2O_3; birnessite, δ–MnO_2; nsutite, γ–MnO_2; pyrolusite, β–MnO_2; and ramsdellite, MnO_2. As manganosite and bixbyite are unstable in supergene environment, thermo-chemical data are not available for groutite and ramsdellite, and birnessite and nsutite are unstable with respect to pyrolusite (ΔF_f^o values respectively: −108.3, −109.1, and −111.3 kcal/mole), the discussion will be confined to the remaining phases within the stability field of water.

The following redox couples have to be examined then[1]:

$3Mn(OH)_2(s) \rightleftharpoons Mn_3O_4 + 2H_2O + 2H^+ + 2e$ – – – – – – – – – – – – – – – (43)

$E_{h43} = 0.47 - 0.06pH$ – (43a)

$Mn_3O_4(s) + 2H_2O \rightleftharpoons 3\gamma$–$MnOOH(s) + H^+ + e$ – – – – – – – – – – – – – (44)

$E_{h44} = 0.85 - 0.06pH$ – (44a)

γ–$MnOOH(s) \rightleftharpoons \beta$–$MnO_2(s) + H^+ + e$ – – – – – – – – – – – – – – – – – (45)

$E_{h45} = 0.95 - 0.06pH$ – (45a)

For delineating the boundary between the solids and the dissolved species, it is only necessary to consider Mn^{2+}, as this ion dominates. The relations are:

$Mn^{2+} + 2H_2O \rightleftharpoons Mn(OH)_2(s) + 2H^+$ – – – – – – – – – – – – – – – – – – (46)

$lg[Mn^{2+}] = 15.2 - 2pH$ – (46a)

$3Mn^{2+} + 4H_2O \rightleftharpoons Mn_3O_4(s) + 8H^+ + 2e$ – – – – – – – – – – – – – – – – (47)

$E_{h47} = 1.80 - 0.09lg[Mn^{2+}] - 0.24pH$ – – – – – – – – – – – – – – – – – – – (47a)

[1] The standard redox potentials and the values for lg K were calculated from the thermo-chemical data listed by Mah (1960), Latimer (1964), Bricker (1965), Krauskopf (1967), Robie and Waldbaum (1968). The values used are: $Mn(OH)_2$, −147.1; Mn_3O_4, −306,1; γ–$MnOOH$, −133.3; β–MnO_2, −111.3; MnO, −86.7; Mn_2O_3, −209.8; Mn^{2+}, −54.4 kcal/mole.

$$Mn^{2+} + 2H_2O \rightleftharpoons \gamma\text{-}MnOOH(s) + 3H^+ + e \text{ -- -- -- -- -- -- -- -- -- -- --} \quad (48)$$
$$E_{h48} = 1.45 - 0.06\lg[Mn^{2+}] - 0.18pH \text{ -- -- -- -- -- -- -- -- -- -- --} \quad (48a)$$
$$Mn^{2+} + 2H_2O \rightleftharpoons \beta\text{-}MnO_2(s) + 4H^+ + 2e \text{ -- -- -- -- -- -- -- -- --} \quad (49)$$
$$E_{h49} = 1.25 - 0.03\lg[Mn^{2+}] - 0.12pH \text{ -- -- -- -- -- -- -- -- -- -- --} \quad (49a)$$

The various stability fields are represented in fig. III.12. It shows that the Mn^{2+} field is very wide and much wider than the corresponding Fe^{2+} field in the Fe–O_2(g)–H_2O system (fig. III.11). It means that manganese oxide is more easily reduced than ferric oxide; and in reverse, ferrous ions are more readily oxidized than manganous. Hence, the simultaneous precipitation of iron and manganese oxides remains difficult to explain. Consequently, it is necessary to investigate if certain constituents in the soil

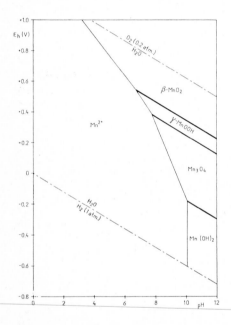

FIG. III.12. *Stability fields of the stable phases in the system Mn–O_2 (g) –H_2O. Boundary between solids and Mn^{2+} at $[Mn^2]^+ = 10^{-5}$; 25°C, 1 atm. total pressure*

affect both systems. Such a constituent could be silica as, in fact, opal and chalcedony (p. 195) are frequently found in Oxisols with plinthite. Unfortunately, thermochemical data are scarcely available for most of the manganese containing minerals. Data are only listed for rhodonite, $MnSiO_3$, and tephroite, Mn_2SiO_4 (Mah, 1960; Kelley, 1962; Krauskopf, 1967; Robie and Waldbaum, 1968). Another possible constituent is CO_2. The partial CO_2 pressure varies strongly in soils as already mentioned in Part I, Chapter I, p 67; A partial CO_2 pressure, $_\varsigma CO_2$, of $10^{-1.7}$ atm. (2% by volume) and tephroite as the Mn silicate will be selected for the examination of the system Mn – O_2(g) – SiO_2(a, s) – H_2O – CO_2(g).

Whether Mn_2SiO_4 or $Mn(OH)_2$ is stable in the presence of amorphous silica can be deduced from:

$$Mn_2SiO_4(s) + 2H_2O \rightleftharpoons 2Mn(OH)_2(s) + SiO_2(a,s) \text{ -- -- -- -- -- -- --} \quad (50)$$
$$\Delta F_r^\circ = +4.3 \text{ kcal -- -- -- -- -- -- -- -- -- -- -- -- -- -- -- -- --} \quad (50a)$$

which means that tephroite occurs stably with respect to pyrochroite plus amorphous silica in the presence of pure water.

Rhodochrosite, $MnCO_3$, can occur if CO_2 is present in the system:

$$Mn_2SiO_4(s) + 2CO_2(g) \rightleftharpoons 2MnCO_3(s) + SiO_2(a, s) \quad - - - - - - - - - - - - \quad (51)$$

$$lgK = -2lg\ _\varsigma CO_2 = +11.2 \quad - \quad (51a)$$

$$\therefore\ _\varsigma CO_2 = 10^{-5.6}\ atm.$$

Hence, at $_\varsigma CO_2 = 10^{-1.7}$ atm., rhodochrosite is the stable phase. The next step to consider is the oxidation of $MnCO_3$ to Mn_3O_4:

$$3MnCO_3(s) + H_2O \rightleftharpoons Mn_3O_4(s) + 3CO_2(g) + 2H^+ + 2e \quad - - - - - - - - - \quad (52)$$

$$E_{h52} = 1.15 + 0.9lg\ _\varsigma CO_2 - 0.06pH \quad - - - - - - - - - - - - - - - - - \quad (52a)$$

At $_\varsigma CO_2 = 10^{-1.7}$ atm., (52a) turns into:

$$E_{h52} = 1.00 - 0.06pH \quad - \quad (52b)$$

Hence the boundary between $MnCO_3$ and Mn_3O_4 falls above that of Mn_3O_4 and γ-MnOOH (see eq. 44a). As Mn_3O_4 cannot be oxidized to γ-MnOOH, because $MnCO_3$ is not yet oxidized to Mn_3O_4, the latter is metastable with respect to $MnCO_3$.

The oxidation of $MnCO_3$ to γ-MnOOH can be examined from:

$$MnCO_3(s) + H_2O \rightleftharpoons \gamma\text{-}MnOOH(s) + CO_2(g) + H^+ + e \quad - - - - - - - - - \quad (53)$$

$$E_{h53} = 1.06 + 0.06lg\ _\varsigma CO_2 - 0.06pH \quad - - - - - - - - - - - - - - - - - \quad (53a)$$

At $_\varsigma CO_2 = 10^{-1.7}$ atm.: $E_{h53} = 0.96 - 0.06pH \quad - - - - - - - - - - - - - - \quad (53b)$

Thus, the boundary between $MnCO_3$ and γ-MnOOH plots above that of γ-MnOOH and β-MnO$_2$ (see eq. 45a). Consequently, rhodochrosite and pyrolusite are the stable phases in the system $Mn - O_2(g) - SiO_2(a, s) - CO_2(g) - H_2O$ at $_\varsigma CO_2 = 10^{-1.7}$ atm. The boundary is found from:

$$MnCO_3(s) + H_2O \rightleftharpoons \beta\text{-}MnO_2(s) + CO_2(g) + 2H^+ + 2e \quad - - - - - - - - - \quad (54)$$

$$E_{h54} = 1.01 + 0.03lg\ _\varsigma CO_2 - 0.06pH \quad - - - - - - - - - - - - - - - - - \quad (54a)$$

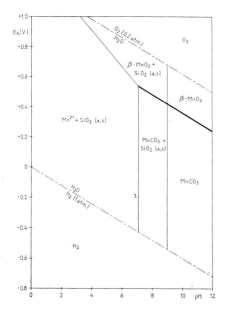

FIG. III.13. *Stability fields in the system* $Mn-O_2\ (g) - SiO_2\ (a,s)-H_2O-CO_2\ (g)$ *at* $_\varsigma CO_2 = 10^{-1.7}$ *atm.,* $25°C$, *and 1 atm. total pressure. Boundary of solids at total activity of dissolved species of* 10^{-5}; *activity* H_4SiO_4 *is* $10^{-2.7}$.

At $_cCO_2 = 10^{-1.7}$ atm.: $E_{h54} = 0.96 - 0.06pH$ — — — — — — — — — — — — — — (54b)

The boundary between the solids and dissolved species (activity 10^{-5}) is given by (49a) and by:

$$MnCO_3(s) + 2H^+ \rightleftharpoons Mn_2^+ + CO_2(g) + H_2O \quad — — — — — — — — — — — — — (55)$$

$$lg\,[Mn^{2+}] = 7.4 - lg_cCO_2 - 2pH \quad — — — — — — — — — — — — — — — — — (55a)$$

At $_cCO_2 = 10^{-1.7}$ atm.: $\quad lg\,[Mn_2^+] = 9.1 - 2pH$ — — — — — — — — — — — — (55b)

The thus derived relations are graphically shown in fig. III.13. It is evident that the predominance field of Mn^{2+} has been considerably narrowed by the introduction of CO_2.

As the silicic-acid activity in systems with amorphous silica is approximately $10^{-2.7}$ and as the dissociation constant of H_4SiO_4 into $H_3SiO_4^-$ and H^+ ions is $10^{-9.9}$ (Krauskopf, 1967), amorphous silica is unstable at pH values of approximately 9 and higher. Therefore a line parallel to the E_h axis has been drawn at pH 9 to indicate the boundary of $SiO_2(a, s)$.

A similar analysis of the system $Fe - O_2(g) - SiO_2(a, s) - H_2O - CO_2(g)$, using fayalite as the Fe silicate (although rarely present in rocks), can be made in the following way:

$$Fe_2SiO_4(s) + 2CO_2(g) \rightleftharpoons 2FeCO_3(s) + SiO_2(a, s) \quad — — — — — — — — — — — — (56)$$

The standard free-energy change of reaction (56) is -7.1 kcal (calculated from the ΔF_f^o-values listed by Robie and Waldbaum, 1968). This means that at equilibrium

$$_cCO_2 = 10^{-2.6} \text{ atm. (from } lgK = -2lg_cCO_2 = \frac{-7.1}{-1.364} = 5.2\text{)}.$$ Consequently, siderite will occur stably with respect to fayalite at $_cCO_2 = 10^{-1.7}$ atm.

The boundary between $FeCO_3$ and Fe_3O_4 can be found from:

$$3FeCO_3(s) + H_2O \rightleftharpoons Fe_3O_4(s) + 3CO_2(g) + 2H^+ + 2e \quad — — — — — — — — — (57)$$

$$E_{h57} = 0.30 + 0.09lg_cCO_2 - 0.06pH \quad — — — — — — — — — — — — — — (57a)$$

At $_cCO_2 = 10^{-1.7}$ atm.: $\quad E_{h57} = 0.15 - 0.06pH$ — — — — — — — — — — — (57b)

Hence, the boundary is just situated at the boundary of Fe_3O_4 and α–$FeOOH$. It means that under the chosen conditions only the phases siderite and goethite are stable. This conclusion can be checked by considering:

$$FeCO_3(s) + H_2O \rightleftharpoons \alpha\text{–}FeOOH(s) + CO_2(g) + H^+ \quad — — — — — — — — — — — (58)$$

$$E_{h58} = 0.25 + 0.06lg_cCO_2 - 0.06pH \quad — — — — — — — — — — — — — — (58a)$$

At $_cCO_2 = 10^{-1.7}$ atm.: $\quad E_{h58} = 0.15 - 0.06pH$ — — — — — — — — — — — — (58b)

Finally, the boundary between $FeCO_3$ and dissolved Fe^{2+} (activity $\geqslant 10^{-5}$) can be found from:

$$FeCO_3(s) + 2H^+ \rightleftharpoons Fe^{2+} + CO_2(g) + H_2O \quad — — — — — — — — — — — — — (59)$$

$$lg\,[Fe^{2+}] = 7.6 - lg_cCO_2 - 2pH \quad — — — — — — — — — — — — — — — — — (59a)$$

At $_cCO_2 = 10^{-1.7}$ atm. and $[Fe^{2+}] = 10^{-5}$, the boundary is found at pH $= 7.15$.

The results are summarized in fig. III.14. As could be expected, the field of dominance of Fe^{2+} is only slightly narrowed because of the disappearance of Fe_3O_4. Comparing figs. III.13 and 14, it is evident that the field of dominance of Mn^{2+} is still considerably greater than that of the dissolved iron species. Therefore it is necessary to seek another explanation for the simultaneous precipitation of iron and manganese as their oxides. One possibility could be the formation of intermediary, unstable iron hydroxides during the reduction-oxidation processes. Frequently, lepidocrocite is found in the bright orange mottles of pseudo-gley or gley soils (Schwertmann, 1959).

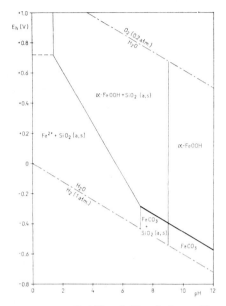

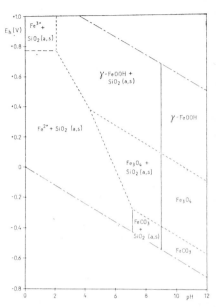

FIG. III.14. *Stability fields of the stable phases in the system Fe(s)–O₂(g)–CO₂(g)– SiO₂(a,s)–H₂O at ςCO₂ = 10⁻¹·⁷ atm., 25° C, and 1 atm. total pressure. [Fe²⁺] ⩾ 10⁻⁵. Activity H₄SiO₄ = 10⁻²·⁷*

FIG. III.15. *Stability fields of FeCO₃, Fe₃O₄, and metastable γ–FeOOH in the presence of amorphous silica, at 25°C and 1 atm. total pressure. Boundary of solids at activities of dissolved Fe species = 10⁻⁵; activity dissolved H₄SiO₄ = 10⁻²·⁷*

If it is thought that this hydroxide has been formed a stability diagram can be constructed under the same conditions as the latter two diagrams (presence of amorphous silica and $ςCO_2 = 10^{-1.7}$ atm.). The boundaries $FeCO_3/Fe_3O_4$ and $Fe_3O_4/γ–FeOOH$ are given by the equations (57b) and (22a). The boundaries between the solids and dissolved species are characterized by equations (59a), (40a), and by:

$$Fe^{2+} + H_2O \rightleftharpoons γ–FeOOH(s) + 3H^+ + e \quad - - - - - - - - - - - - - - - - \quad (60)$$

$$E_{h\,60} = 0.86 - 0.06 lg\,[Fe^{2+}] - 0.18pH \quad - - - - - - - - - - - - - - - - \quad (60a)$$

$$Fe^{3+} + 2H_2O \rightleftharpoons γ–FeOOH(s) + 3H^+ \quad - - - - - - - - - - - - - - - - \quad (61)$$

$$lg\,[Fe^{2+}] = 1.4 - 3pH \quad - \quad (61a)$$

The results (fig. III.15) show that the field of predominance of Fe^{2+} has grown considerably, but even so is not comparable in size to that of Mn^{2+}. The conclusion seems justified that a separation between manganese and ferric deposits is unavoidable. In fact, this is frequently observed in paddy soils (Part II, Chapter 4) and pseudogley and gley soils (Bouma et al., 1968).

A second possibility is the formation of stable ferrous complexes, as suggested earlier. The presence of such complexes, especially with reducing organic ligands (e.g. polyphenols) was suggested by Bloomfield (1957, 1958), but little is known about their nature and stability in soils. If such a mechanism occurs it is necessary that the Fe^{2+} ions form stabler complexes with the ligands than Mn^{2+} ions do. This was actually found by Irving and Williams (1948). It has to be stipulated here, however, that the magnitude of the stability constants of the complexes is not the one criterion for their stability. Also the solubility products of the hydroxides of the metals are important. The higher the stability constants of the metal complexes and the larger the solubility products of the metal hydroxides, the stabler the complexes are and consequently, the stronger they resist oxidation. More exactly, the smaller the overall hydrolysis constant of the complexes, the higher the stability and the stronger the oxidation resistance. The relation

$$K_{h\,ML} = \frac{I}{K_{ML}\,K_{so}}$$

where K_{hML} is the hydrolysis constant of the metal complex, ML; K_{ML} is the stability constant of the complex, and K_{so} is the solubility product of the metal hydroxide, predicts what will happen on raising the pH of the environment. If it is smaller than 1, the complex is stable in neutral or weakly alkaline media, if larger than 1 it is stable only in acid media (see Chapter 3, Part III, p. 456). The solubility products (calculated from free-energy values) of $Fe(OH)_2$ and $Mn(OH)_2$ are respectively, $10^{-14.7}$ and $10^{-13.0}$. Hence, if K_{FeL} is larger than $10^{14.7}$ the Fe(II) complex will be stable and consequently resist oxidation. In the case of the complex MnL, K_{MnL} has to be larger than $10^{13.0}$. To explain the simultaneous precipitation of ferric and manganese hydroxides K_{FeL} should be larger than $10^{14.7}$, whereas K_{MnL} should not be allowed to exceed $10^{13.0}$. Only in that case will the conditions for the simultaneous oxidation of ferrous and manganous compounds approach each other.

If the ligands also participate in the reduction-oxidation processes it becomes difficult to predict what will happen although this problem can be solved.

A third possibility might be the formation of impure Mn(II), Mn(III), and Mn(IV) oxides or their hydrates. E.g. Mn(II) may be replaced by Fe(III) and other polyvalent ions. Some of the Mn(IV) may be replaced by Fe(III), and so on (Ponnamperuma, 1969). If these non-stoichiometric oxides of variable composition have lower free energies of formation than their ideal counterparts, as was experienced by the author mentioned, the field of dominance of soluble Mn(II) species will be narrowed considerably, thus approaching that of soluble Fe(II) species (see also Part II, Chapter 4).

A fourth possibility might be found in a rapidly fluctuating groundwater table combined with different oxidation rates of manganous and ferrous ions. If the oxidation rate of ferrous ions is slower than that of manganous ions, a simultaneous precipitation of the oxides or hydroxides is very well possible, but as far as known, little if anything has been published on this. In fact, the problem of the reaction rates interferes seriously in stability studies. E.g., it is known that siderite is only found in old and never in young paddy soils, although the environment in paddy soils is favourable for its formation; the formation rate of siderite, however, seems to be so slow that it only appears after a considerable period of time (see Chapter 4 of this Part). In spite of this difficulty, a thermodynamic examination of the soil forming processes is very useful, as it predicts the result of these processes, if the circumstances remain more or less constant.

The reduction of ferric iron may be achieved either by anaerobic microorganisms able to transform Fe^{3+} directly into Fe^{2+}, or by reducing organic microbial decomposition products such as polyhydroxy carboxylic acids and polyphenols. It seems that in soils the latter process is most important (Kumura et al., 1963; Oades, 1963). Polyhydroxy carboxylic acids are frequently found in aqueous extracts of soils (see Chapter 4, Part I), such as gallic acid, protocatechuic acid, and others. Taking protocatechuic acid as a model substance for describing the function of soil organic matter in reduction processes, the following half-cell has to be examined:

$$\rightleftharpoons \qquad + 2H^+ + 2e \;-------------------------(62)$$

If the acid in the reduced state is indicated with H_3Red and in the oxidized state with HOx, (62) can be written as:

$H_3Red \rightleftharpoons HOx + 2H^+ + 2e$,

or, as it behaves also as an acid, as

$$Red^{3-} \rightleftharpoons Ox^- + 2e \;-----------------------------\; (63)$$

The redox-potential of this half-cell is given by:

$$E_{h63} = 0.88 + 0.03 \lg \frac{[ox]}{[red]} + 0.03 \lg \alpha_H \;-----------------\; (63a)$$

where [ox] is the sum of the activities of all species of the oxidized acid, [red] that of all species of the reduced acid, and α_H is a function, where all effects of dissociation and H ions are joined.

Without entering into details, some explanatory notes are necessary. If the soil solution is dilute, [red] and [ox] represent the sum of the molal concentrations of the reduced species and oxidized species of the acid, respectively. We then have: $[red] = [H_3Red] + [H_2Red^-] + [HRed^{2-}] + [Red^{3-}]$, and $[ox] = [HOx] + [Ox^-]$. These concentrations can be expressed as functions of $[Red^{3-}]$ and $[Ox^-]$ if all dissociation constants are known. The ratio $\dfrac{[Ox^-]}{[Red^{3-}]}$ in the expression for E_{h63} can be replaced by $\dfrac{[ox]}{[red]}$ multiplied with a certain factor. If it is assumed that the dissociation constant of HOx is equal to the first dissociation constant of H_3Red, which is permitted for all practical purposes, we obtain:

$$\alpha_H = \frac{[H^+]^3 + [H^+]^2\, K_{a1} + [H^+]\, K_{a1}\, K_{a2} + K_{a1}\, K_{a2}\, K_{a3}}{K_{a1} + [H^+]}$$

The negative logarithms of the acid H_3Red are: $pK_{a1} = 4.49 \pm 0.00$, $pK_{a2} = 9.13 \pm 0.01$, and $pK_{a3} = 11.32 \pm 0.05$ (Van Schuylenborgh, 1966). Consequently, at pH5, 6 and 7 the values of α_H are, respectively: 10^{-10}, 10^{-12}, and 10^{-14}. Ball and Chen (1933) determined E_{63}^0 experimentally and found a value of 0.88 V.

446

To decide whether or not protocatechuic acid is able to reduce oxygen and/or ferric iron, the standard redox-potential of half-cell (63) has to be compared with those of (16), (40), (39) and (61), and, if it is wanted to include metastable $Fe(OH)_3(a, s)$, with:

$$Fe^{2+} + 3H_2O \rightleftharpoons Fe(OH)_3(a, s) + 3H^+ + e \quad - - - - - - - - - - - - - - - \quad (64)$$
$$E_{h64} = 1.06 - 0.06lg\,[Fe^{2+}] - 0.18pH \quad - - - - - - - - - - - - - - - - - \quad (64a)$$

It may be concluded that protocatechuic acid is able to reduce oxygen, magnetite, and amorphous ferric hydroxide, and unable to reduce goethite and lepidocrocite under the standard conditions (25° C, 1 atm. total pressure, and unit activity of all dissolved species). However, as the reducing capacity of protocatechuic acid is strongly dependent on pH (function α_H), it is possible that at pH values higher than zero the acid will reduce goethite and lepidocrocite too. To investigate this possibility it is necessary to construct voltaic cells with (63) and each of the other half-cells. At equilibrium of the sets of two half-cells, the total voltage of the cells is zero, i.e. the potentials of the half-cells are equal. It is then possible to calculate the equilibrium constants. The values at pH 7 are: $lgK_{63/16} = 51.3$; $lgK_{63/40} = 19.3$; $lgK_{63/39} = 8.3$; $lgK_{63/61} = 13.3$; and $lgK_{63/64} = 20.0$.

The reactions needed for calculating the above given equilibrium constants are:

$$O_2(g) + 4H^+ + 2Red^{3-} \rightleftharpoons Ox^- + 2H_2O \quad - - - - - - - - - - - - - - - - - \quad (63/16)$$
$$Fe_3O_4(s) + 8H^+ + Red^{3-} \rightleftharpoons Ox^- + 3Fe^{2+} + 4H_2O \quad - - - - - - - - - - \quad (63/40)$$
$$2\alpha(\gamma)\text{-}FeOOH(s) + 6H^+ + Red^{3-} \rightleftharpoons Ox^- + 2Fe^+ + 4H_2O \quad - - - - - - - - \quad (63/39$$
$$\text{or } 60)$$
$$2Fe(OH)_3(a,s) + 6H^+ + Red^{3-} \rightleftharpoons Ox^- + 2Fe^{2+} + 6H_2O \quad - - - - - - - - - - \quad (63/64)$$

At equilibrium of (63/16), $E_{h63} = E_{h16}$. Thus:

$$0.88 + 0.03lg\frac{[ox]}{[red]} + 0.03lg\alpha_H = 1.23 + 0.015lg\varsigma O_2 + 0.06lg\,[H^+]$$

Rearranging results in;

$$lg\frac{[ox]^2}{[red]^2\,\varsigma O_2\,[H^+]^4} = \frac{0.35}{0.015} - 2lg_H = 23.3 - 2lg\alpha_H$$

The equilibrium constant for reaction (63/16) is;

$$lgK_{63/16} = lg\frac{[ox]^2}{[red]^2\,\varsigma O_2\,[H^+]^4} \quad - \quad (63/16a)$$

Hence

$$lgK_{63/16} = 23.3 - 2lg\alpha_H \quad - \quad (63/16b)$$

As soils with excess of water tend to establish a pH between 5 and 8 (see fig. III.16), the pH value of 7 is selected for computing the equilibrium constants. Relation (63/16) then becomes $lgK_{63/61} = 51.3$

The constants of the other reactions were calculated similarly and the results given above.

From these values it can be concluded that oxygen is most readily reduced, followed by ferric hydroxide, magnetite, and finally by lepidocrocite and goethite. Setting up a similar calculation for the reduction of the most stable mineral of the manganese oxides, pyrolusite, the $lgK_{63/49}$ value is found to be 26.3. This means that the most stable manganese oxide is even more readily reduced than the least stable ferric hydroxide. It points once again to the importance of the formation of metastable

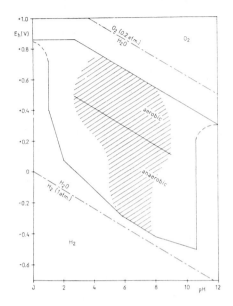

FIG. III.16. *E_h–pH characteristics of natural media (large, outlined area) and of soils (hatched area). After Baas Becking et al., 1960. The boundary between aerobic and anaerobic conditions at $E_h = 0.65$–0.06 pH (Pearsall, 1938)*

ferric oxides and hydroxides in those cases where reduction-oxidation processes are important soil forming processes, such as in plinthization.

It is understandable that very low partial oxygen pressures have to exist in order to reduce ferric iron. Pearsall (1938) placed the boundary between 'aerobic' and 'anaerobic' conditions at $E_h = 0.65 - 0.06$pH, which agrees fairly well with the results of work by Michard (1967) and theoretical considerations of Sato (1960). At pH 7, the E_h value equals or is smaller than 0.23 V. Hence:

$$1.23 + 0.015 \lg_{\varsigma} O_2 - 0.06 \text{pH} \leqslant 0.23$$

or

$\lg_{\varsigma} O_2 \leqslant -39$ and $_{\varsigma} O_2 \leqslant 10^{-39}$ atm.

Such low partial oxygen pressures are of course only possible in closed systems. The latter can be realized in the wet season, when the wet surface of the soil cuts the subsoil off from the atmosphere, as the diffusion of gases in water is much slower than in the gas phase (diffusion coefficient of O_2 in the gas phase is approximately 0.2 cm^2 sec^{-1} and in water 2×10^{-5} cm^2 sec^{-1} under conditions of 1 atm. total pressure and approximately $25°$ C). We will attempt to argue that under conditions of sufficient moisture in the surface or sub-surface soil partial O_2 pressures in the subsoil can be obtained low enough to reduce ferric to ferrous iron.

In the rainy season biological activity in the surface soil is extremely intense, especially in tropical rainforests. This results in high CO_2 and low O_2 contents of soil air. Several authors (Leather, 1915; Vine et al, 1942; Boynton and Compton, 1944) have shown that O_2 concentrations of 0% may occur in the soil air (see Chapter 1, Part I); Yamagushi et al. (1967) measured in columns of a sandy soil O_2 concentrations as low as 3% at 65 cm depth and Greenwood and Compton (1967) measured O_2 concentrations of 0 ml/ml soil air at some depth in soil columns under laboratory conditions of $30°$ C. A percentage of zero or an amount of 0 ml/ml means of course the lowest O_2 concentration that can be measured. At present, concentrations of 0.1 mg O_2/l gas are measurable; here a concentration of 1mg O_2/l will be taken as likely to occur over a considerable length of time in the sub-surface soil. The partial O_2 pressure is then 0.76×10^{-3} atm. at a total pressure of 1 atm. and $25°$ C. As 31.6 ml O_2 is dissolved in 1 l of water at $25°$ C and $\varsigma O_2 = 1$ atm. (Weast and Selby, 1966–1967), the amount of O_2 dissolved in 1 l of water at $\varsigma O_2 = 0.76 \times 10^{-3}$ atm. is equal to 2.40×10^{-2} ml of O_2; this is 0.985×10^{-6} mol. O_2 per liter water. Assuming the foregoing quantitative estimation to be correct, water, penetrating in the wet season into the subsoil, would contain 0.985×10^{-6} moles of oxygen in 1 litre. This amount has to be reduced to zero; according to equation (63/16) an amount of at least $2 \times 0.985 \times 10^{-6}$ mol.l^{-1} of protocatechuic acid is needed, corresponding with an amount of 0.3 mg per 1 l of moisture. It is quite imaginable that such amounts are present even at great depths.

The realization of the above-mentioned mechanism is only possible if there is somewhere in the profile a layer which is either completely saturated with water or where the air-filled pores and capillaries do not form a continuous system but are blocked by water and consequently the replenishment of the subsoil with air cannot take place in the gas phase. The presence of a water-saturated layer is likely to occur as a textural B horizon is formed in the first stages of laterization and signs of pseudogley formation can be observed in the profile, which implies the presence of an impervious layer. Assume the thickness of this layer to be 10 cm or assume that the pathlength of the oxygen through the water phase is 10 cm. The problem then is to calculate the time needed for O_2 to penetrate this barrier, if the O_2 concentration in the soil above is 1 mg l^{-1}. The diffusion equation (Fick's law) is:

$$f_g = -D_g \frac{\delta C}{\delta x} \text{ (mg cm}^{-2} \text{ sec}^{-1}) \quad - \quad (65)$$

where f_g is the flux which is equal to vC, v being the velocity of motion (cm sec^{-1}) and C the concentration (mg cm^{-3}), D_g is the diffusion constant (cm^{2}sec^{-1}) of O_2 in the soil-layer and $\dfrac{\delta C}{\delta x}$ the concentration gradient (mg cm^{-4}).

The diffusion coefficient, D_o, of O_2 in water is 2.6×10^{-5} cm^2 sec^{-1} (Kolthoff and Miller, 1941)[1] D_g is related to D_o by:

$$D_g = \frac{D_o \beta (1 - \gamma)}{\theta} \quad - \quad (66)$$

where β is the fraction of the water-filled pores per cm^2 of soil available for diffusion, γ a parameter for the reaction rate of O_2 with the soil during diffusion, and θ the tortuosity factor. We shall assume: $\beta = 0.4$; $\gamma = 0$ (no reaction of O_2 with the soil) and $\theta = \sqrt{2}$. Then, according to (66): $D_g = \dfrac{0.4 \times 2.6 \times 10^{-5}}{\sqrt{2}} = 0.7 \times 10^{-5}$ cm^2

sec^{-1}. In our case $\dfrac{\delta C}{\delta x} = 10^{-4}$ mg cm^{-4}. Hence, according to (65):

[1] In fact, Kolthoff and Miller (1941) determined the diffusion coefficient of O_2 in an aqueous solution of 0.1 M KNO$_3$. It will be assumed that the diffusion of O_2 is not hindered by electrolytes.

$$v = \frac{0.7 \times 10^{-5} \times 10^{-4}}{10^{-3}} = 0.7 \times 10^{-6} \, \text{cm sec}^{-1}.$$

This is $0.7 \times 864 \times 10^{-4}$ cm day^{-1} or roughly: 0.06 cm day^{-1}. Therefore, to penetrate 10 cm of water-saturated soil a time is needed of 167 days. This time is long enough to allow reduction processes to be completed. Of course this is a very hypothetical view of the problem but it shows that locally strong reducing conditions may occur if only small quantities of reductants are present.

LITERATURE CITED

BAAS BECKING, L.G.M., KAPLAN, I.R. and MOORE, D. 1960 Limits of the natural environment in terms of pH and oxidation-reduction potentials. *J. Geol.*, 68: 243–284.
BALL, E.G. and CHEN, T-T. 1933 Studies on oxidation-reduction: XX Epinephrine and related compounds. *J. biol. Chem.*, 102: 691–719.
BERNER, R.A. 1969 Goethite stability and the origin of red beds. *Geochim. Cosmochim. Acta*, 33: 267–273.
BLOOMFIELD, C. 1957 The possible significance of polyphenols in soil formation. *J. Sci. Food Agric.*, 8: 389–392.
— 1959 Mobilization of iron in podzol soils by aqueous leaf extracts. *Chem. Ind.*, No. 9: 259–260.
BOUMA, J., PONS, L.J. and VAN SCHUYLENBORGH, J. 1968 On soil genesis in temperate humid climate. VI. The formation of a glossudalf in loess (silt loam). *Neth. J. agric. Sci.*, 16: 58–70.
BOYNTON, B. and COMPTON, O.C. 1944 Normal seasonal changes of oxygen and carbon dioxide percentages in gas from the larger pores of three orchard subsoils. *Soil Sci.*, 57: 107–117.
BRICKER, O. 1965 Some stability relations in the system $Mn\text{-}O_2\text{-}H_2O$ at $25°C$ and one atmosphere total pressure. *Am. Min.*, 50: 1296–1354.
GARRELS, R.M. and CHRIST, CH.L. 1965 Solutions, minerals, and equilibria. *New York*.
GASTUCHE, M.C., BRUGGENWERT, T. and MORTLAND, M.M. 1964 Crystallization of mixed iron and aluminium gels. *Soil Sci.*, 98: 281–290.
GAYER, K.H. and WOONTNER, L. 1956 The solubility of ferrous hydroxide and ferric hydroxide in acidic and basic media at $25°C$. *J. Phys. Chem.*, 60: 1569–1571.
GREENWOOD, D.J. and GOODMAN, D. 1967 Direct measurements of the distribution of oxygen in soil aggregates and in columns of fine soil crumbs. *J. Soil Sci.*, 18: 182–196.
IRVING, H. and WILLIAMS, R.J.P. 1948 Order of stability of metal complexes. *Nature*, 162: 746–747.
KELLEY, K.K. 1962 Heats and free-energies of formation of anhydrous silicates. *U.S. Bur. Mines*, R.I. 5901.
KOLTHOFF, I.M. and MILLER, C.S. 1941 The reduction of oxygen at the dropping mercury electrode. *J. Am. Chem. Soc.*, 63: 1013–1017.
KRAUSKOPF, K.B. 1967 Introduction to geochemistry. *New York*.
KUMURA, T., TAKAI, T. and ISHIKAWA, K. 1963 Microbial reduction mechanism of ferrous iron in paddy soils. I. *Soil Sci. & Pl. Nutr.*, 9: 171–175.
LATIMER, W.M. 1964 Oxidation potentials. 2nd Ed., 6th printing. *Englewood Cliffs*.
LEATHER, J.W. 1915 Soil temperatures. *Mem. Dept. Agr. India (Chem. Ser.)*, IV, 2 : 19–49.
MAH, A.D. 1960 Thermodynamic properties of manganese and its componds. *U.S. Bur. Mines*, R.I. 5600.

450

MICHARD, G. 1967 Significance of redox potentials in natural waters. Conditions for applications of E_h-pH diagrams. *Min. Deposita*, 2: 34–37 (*Chem. Abstr.* 68: 33045).

OADES, J. M. 1963 The nature and distribution of iron compounds in soils. *Soils and Fert.*, 28: 69–80.

PEARSALL, W. H. 1938 The soil complex in relation to plant communities I. Oxidation-reduction potentials in soils. *J. Ecol.*, 26: 180–193.

ROBIE, R. A. and WALDBAUM, D. R. 1968 Thermodynamic properties of minerals and related substances at 298.15°K (25.0°C) and one atmosphere pressure and at higher temperatures. *Geol. Survey Bull.*, 1259.

PONNAMPERUMA, F. N., LOY, T. A. and TIANCO, E. M. 1969 Redox equilibria in flooded soils. II. The manganese oxide systems. *Soil Sci.*, 108 : 48–57.

SATO, M. 1960 Oxidation of sulfide ore bodies. I. Geochemical environments in terms of E_h and pH. *Econ. Geol.*, 55: 928–962.

SCHELLMANN, W. 1959 Experimentelle Untersuchungen über die sedimentäre Bildung von Goethit und Hämatit. *Chem. d. Erde*, 20: 104–135.

SCHMALZ, F. 1959 A note on the system Fe_2O_3-H_2O. *J. Geophys. Res.*, 64; 575–579.

SCHWERTMANN, U. 1959 Über die Synthese definierter Eisenoxide unter verschiedenen Bedingungen. *Z. anorg. allg. Chem.*, 298: 337–348.

— 1965 Zur Goethit- und Hematitbildung aus amorphen Eisen (III)-hydroxid. 2. Mitteilung. *Z. Pflern. Düung. Bodenk.*, 108: 37–45.

— 1966 Die Bildung von Goethit und Hämatit in Böden und Sedimenten. *Proc. Int. Clay Conf.*, I: 159–165.

TAYLOR, R. M. and GRADEY, A. M. 1967 The influence of ionic environment on the nature of iron oxides in soils. *J. Soil Sci.*, 18: 341–348.

VAN SCHUYLENBORGH, J. 1966 The dissociation constants of mono- and polyhydroxy benzoic acids. *Unpublished.*

— and BRUGGENWERT, M. G. M. 1965 On soil genesis in temperate humid climate. V. The formation of the 'albic' and 'spodic' horizon. *Neth. J. agric. Sci.*, 13: 267–279.

VINE, H., THOMPSON, H. A. and HARDY, F. 1942 Studies on aeration of cacao soils in Trinidad. II. Soil-air composition. *Trop. Agric. Trin.*, 19: 215–223.

WEAST, R. C. and SELBY, S. M. 1966–1967 Handbook of Chemistry and Physics. 47th Ed. *Cleveland.*

YAMAGUSHI, M., FLOCKER, W. J. and HOWARD, F. D. 1967 Soil atmosphere as influenced by temperature and moisture. *Soil Sci. Soc. Am. Proc.*, 31: 164–167.

CHAPTER 3

COMPLEX FORMATION, CHELUVIATION AND CHILLUVIATION

3.1. COMPLEX FORMATION

In recent times much attention has been paid to the formation of complexes of iron and aluminium with organic compounds (a.o. Bloomfield, 1957, 1959; Coulson et al., 1960; Malcolm and McCracken, 1968). The organic compounds (generally called ligands when forming complexes) can be very simple (Jones and Willcox, 1929; Gallagher, 1942/43; Gallagher and Walsh, 1944/45) or more complex (Schnitzer and Desjardins, 1962). Polyphenols and benzoic acids are important representatives of the first group and the so-called fulvic acids of the latter group. For details on complex formation reference is made to Mortensen (1963) and Lehman (1963), but some characteristics of complex formation and the importance of the knowledge of the magnitude of the formation or stability constants will be discussed here.

A complex will be defined as a particle that is formed by association of two or more simpler particles that can exist in solution, solvated or otherwise. The composing particles can be molecules or ions and can also be complexes themselves. They can be positively or negatively charged or carry no charge. It is essential that not only an electrostatic bond occurs between an electron donor and an acceptor. In our case those complexes are important where a metal or a proton is the electron acceptor. If solvation is neglected the complex in an equilibrium mixture of metal ions and ligands in aqueous solution can be represented by the general formula

$$M_x H_j L_y (OH)_z^{(xv + j - yw - z)+}$$

where M is the metal with charge $v+$, L the ligand with charge $w-$. This hydroxo complex is x-nuclear. The ligand can be 1-, 2-, or polydentate depending on whether 1-, 2-, or more atoms per ligand act as coordinating atom. If this polydentate ligand is bound to one central atom by two or more 'dents', the complex is called a chelate.

In soils there are indications of the occurrence of 1- to 6- nuclear complexes (Schnitzer and Skinner, 1963 a and b). The complexes are nearly always chelates as the ligands have generally more than one coordinating atom. The chelates are generally very stable, especially if the chelate ring is small. If the chelate ring is large or shows tension, so that the chelate effect provides a small contribution to the stability, the chance on the formation of poly-nuclear complexes increases. Attention will be confined to metal complexes with the metal as central ion, binding one or more ligands coordinatively and to the Brønsted acids, where one or more protons are bound to one ligand. So we consider the following formations:

$$M^{+v} + yL^{-w} \rightleftharpoons ML_y^{(v-yw)+} \quad - \quad (67)$$

and

$$jH^+ + L^{-w} \rightleftharpoons H_jL^{(j-w)-} \quad - - - - - - - - - - - - - - - - - - \quad (68)$$

Equilibrium (67) is characterized by the so-called formation or stability constant, K_{ML_y}:

$$K_{ML_y} = \frac{[ML_y]}{[M][L]^y} \quad - \quad (67a)$$

where brackets denote activity and where the charges are omitted for the sake of convenience. Equilibrium (68) is in the same way characterized by K_{H_jL}:

$$K_{H_jL} = \frac{[H_jL]}{[H]^j[L]} \quad - \quad (68a)$$

In nearly all cases L^{-w} does not begin to appear in quantity until above pH = 9, so that the reaction between a metallic salt and a solution of the acid H_wL, may be represented by:

$$M^{+v} + yH_jL^{(j-w)-} \rightleftharpoons ML_y^{(v-yw)+} + yjH^+ \quad - - - - - - - - - - - - \quad (69)$$

$$K = \frac{[ML_y][H]^{yj}}{[M][H_jL]^y} = \frac{[ML_y][H]^{yj}[L]^y}{[M][H_jL]^y[L]^y}$$

$$= K_{ML_y}/K_{H_jL}^y \quad - \quad (69a)$$

Generally, total concentrations rather than activities are known in a complexing system, so it may be of importance to transfer (69a) into terms of concentrations. The result is:

$$K = \frac{\gamma_{ML_y}\,\gamma_H^{yj}}{\gamma_M\,\gamma_{H_jL}^y} K_{C\,ML_y}/K_{C\,H_jL}^y = \gamma_C\,K_{C\,ML_y}/K_{C\,H_jL}^y \quad - - - - - - - - \quad (69b)$$

where K is the thermodynamic equilibrium constant (only dependent on temperature), K_c the equilibrium constant (dependent on temperature and concentration), and γ_C a parameter composed of the activity coefficients of the different species present (dependent on temperature and ionic strength).

The activity coefficients can be calculated, if the ionic strength, I, of the solution can be estimated. The ionic strength is equal to half the sum of the products of the concentration (c_i) of all species present and the square of their charges (z_i); thus,

$$I = \tfrac{1}{2} \sum_i c_i z_i^2$$

The activity coefficient, γ_i, can be found from the equation:

$$-\lg\gamma_i = \frac{Az_i^2\sqrt{I}}{1+a_iB\sqrt{I}} - CI$$

where A = 0.509 and B = 3.29 × 10^7 for dilute aqueous solutions and 25° C; a_i is the effective ionic radius (cm). Values for a_i can be found in Kielland (1937). Just as a_i, the parameter C must be determined experimentally. For most geological purposes, the following somewhat simplified formula can be used:

$$-lg\gamma_i = A z_i^2 \left(\frac{\sqrt{I}}{I + \sqrt{I}} \right) - 0.2\, I$$

For other methods (e.g. the mean salt method) to estimate the activity coefficients the reader is referred to Garrels and Christ (1965: Chapter 2).

It is evident that the free-energy change of reaction in complex formation is a function of the pH. A measure of this free-energy change of reaction is provided by the 'apparent formation constant', $(K_{ML'_y})_H$, specific for the particular H-ion concentration of the solution. It is defined as:

$$(K_{ML'_y})_H = \frac{(ML_y)}{(M)(L')_H^y} \; \text{-----------------------} \quad (67b)$$

where $(L')_H$ denotes the total concentration (at the specified H-ion concentration) of the complexing agent that is not bound to the metal. Hence,

$$(L')_H = (L) + (HL) + (H_2L) + \ldots\ldots (H_jL) + \ldots\ldots (H_wL) = \overset{w}{\underset{j=0}{\Sigma}} (H_jL) \quad (70)$$

If the formation constants of all acid species are known all concentrations can be expressed as function of (L), and (70) becomes:

$$(L')_H = (L) + (H) K_{HL}(L) + (H)^2 K_{H_2L}(L) + \ldots (H)^j K_{H_jL}(L) + \ldots\ldots$$

$$(H)^w K_{H_wL}(L) =$$

$$= (L)\{1 + (H)K_{HL} + (H)^2K_{H_2L} + \ldots\ldots (H)^jK_{H_jL} + \ldots\ldots (H)^wK_{H_wL}\} =$$

$$= (L)\{1 + \overset{w}{\underset{j=1}{\Sigma}} (H)^jK_{H_jL}\} = \alpha_H(L) \; \text{------------------} \quad (70a)$$

Combining (70a) with (67b), we obtain:

$$(K_{ML'_y})_H = K_{C\,ML_y} \times \alpha_H^y$$

3.2. CHELUVIATION

The kinds of organic substances that have the ability to form complexes with metals are manifold. The ill-defined 'fulvic acids' seem to be especially active in this respect. Apart from these acids, simpler ones have been identified (see Chapter 4, Part I). As simple free amino-acids have not been found in soil extracts, although they do occur in extracts of fresh leaves (Muir et al., 1964), we shall restrict our discussion to the hydroxy and phenolic acids, in particular because Schnitzer and Skinner (1965) showed that carboxyls and phenolic hydroxyls especially participate in organo-metallic reactions.

The most interesting study on the action of 'fulvic acids' was made by Schnitzer and co-workers. Schnitzer and Desjardins (1962) succeeded in preparing an organic matter fraction from the B_h horizon of a Podzol, that was pure enough (although still a mixture) to allow the determination of a mean molecular weight. The number-average molecular weight of this preparation was 670. Ultimate and functional group analysis showed it possible to give this fraction the molecular formula of $C_{21}H_{12}(COOH)_6$ $(OH)_5(CO)_2$. Complex formation studies (Schnitzer and Skinner, 1936 a and b) revealed that iron and aluminium formed 1 to 6-nuclear complexes with it, while the complexes became increasingly water-insoluble as more metal was complexed. We shall elaborate this further on p. 457.

Of the simpler substances oxalic, citric, malic, shikimic, mono-, di-, and trihydrozy-benzoic acids are of importance. Only few of these acids are studied in respect to their reaction with iron and aluminium. Ferric iron forms with citric acid a 1 : 1 complex. Warner and Weber (1953) determined the stability constant and found 10^{25} for the reaction:

$$Fe^{3+} + L^{4-} \rightleftharpoons FeL^- \qquad \text{(citric acid: } H_4L\text{)}$$

at a ionic strength of 0.1 Ml^{-1}. The thermodynamic stability constant is therefore $10^{27.9}$ when using the simplified formula on p. 453 for calculating the activity coefficients.

The hydroxy acid most studied is p-hydroxybenzoic acid (Bertin-Batsch, 1952; Van Schuylenborg and Bruggenwert, 1965). The latter authors found that ferric iron formed two complexes with the acid (H_2L), viz. FeL^+ and $FeOHL$. The thermodynamic stability constants were found to be 0.26×10^{13} and 0.27×10^{12}, respectively. It was rather surprising to find that aluminium formed an insoluble, well-crystallized compound of the composition $AlOHL.2H_2O$. The solubility product, $K_{so} = [Al^{3+}] [OH^-]$ $[L^{2-}]$, was 0.15×10^{-20}, the consequences of which will be discussed later (see p. 457).

With the aid of the data given it is possible to calculate the range of concentrations of iron species at varying pH values, if the soil solution contains a certain amount of the mentioned acids and if free ferric hydroxide is present in some form. Suppose the soil solution contains $10^{-4}Ml^{-1}$ of citric acid and all concentrations are low enough to put activities equal to concentrations. Then, from the relation:

$$(acid)_t = (FeL^-) + (H_4L) + (H_3L^-) + (H_2L^{2-}) + (HL^{3-}) + (L^{4-})$$

(L^{4-}) can be calculated as function of $(acid)_t–(FeL^-)$ if the formation constants of the different acid species are known. These are: $lgK_{H_4L} = 30.20$; $lgK_{H_3L} = 27.16$; $lgK_{H_2L} = 22.40$; and $lgK_{HL} = 16.00$ (Bates and Pinching, 1949; Warner and Weber, 1953) in the case of citric acid. When (L^{4-}) is thus computed, (FeL^-) can be derived from the above given relation. The total ferric-iron concentration can be obtained from the relation: $(Fe)_t = (FeL^-) + (Fe^{3+}) + (FeOH^{2+}) + (Fe(OH)_3^0)$, if the hydrolytic constants for the hydroxy-iron species are known (see table III.5, Chapter 2 of this Part).

In the case of p-hydroxybenzoic acid the equations are:

$$(acid)_t = (FeL^+) + (FeOHL) + (H_2L) + (HL^-) + (L^{2-}).$$

where $lgK_{H_2L} = 13.78$ and $lgK_{HL} = 9.35$ (Van Schuylenborgh and Bruggenwert, 1965), and $(Fe)_t = (FeL^+) + (FeOHL) + (Fe^{3+}) + (FeOH^{2+}) + (Fe(OH)_3^0)$.

The results of the calculations are summarized in table III.6. It is evident that the iron complex with citric acid is much stabler than the iron complex with p-hydroxy-benzoic acid. If these values are compared with the $Fe(OH)_3^0$-concentration of solutions in equilibrium with amorphous ferric hydroxide, being $10^{-6.54}$ Ml^{-1} or $0.232 \times$

TABLE III.6. *Total iron concentration in the systems* $Fe(OH)_3(a,s)-10^{-4}Ml^{-1}$ *citric acid* (H_4L) *and* $10^{-4}Ml^{-1}$ *p-hydroxybenzoic acid* (H_2L), *repectively, at* $25°C$, *1 atm. pressure and different pH values*

	pH4	pH5	pH6
H_4L: $(Fe)_t$ Ml^{-1}	0.101×10^{-3}	0.100×10^{-3}	0.100×10^{-3}
$(Fe_2O_3)_t$ gl^{-1}	0.807×10^{-2}	0.800×10^{-2}	0.800×10^{-2}
H_2L: $(Fe)_t$ Ml^{-1}	0.141×10^{-4}	0.181×10^{-5}	0.826×10^{-5}
$(Fe_2O_3)_t$ gl^{-1}	0.113×10^{-2}	0.145×10^{-3}	0.661×10^{-4}

10^{-4} g Fe_2O_3/l, it is evident, that the presence of such acids as discussed above contributes greatly to the mobility of iron oxides. Moreover, the citric-iron complex is practically independent of pH, indicating that cheluviation (migration of iron-chelates from the A horizon into the subsoil) is not necessarily restricted to low pH-values. If the complexes are sufficiently strong, podzol formation can be expected even at slightly acid or neutral conditions. In fact, podzols are sometimes found under such circumstances (Gallagher and Walsh, 1943/44).

So far, attention has been focused on ligands that do not possess the ability to reduce ferric-iron. However, as soon as aromatic acids possess more than two hydroxyls, they may reduce ferric-iron to ferrous-iron if the conditions are favourable (pH not too low, see Chapter 2 of this Part, p. 445). After reduction the ferrous-iron can be complexed. The simultaneous reduction and chelation has been reported by many investigators (a.o. Bloomfield, 1957; Coulson et al., 1960 b). The process can be illustrated schematically when considering gallic acid, which is a decomposition product of tannin. Gallic acid may deliver two electrons upon oxidation, ferric-iron acting as electron-acceptor:

$Fe(OH)_3$ (a, s) $+ e \rightleftharpoons Fe^{2+} + 3OH^-$

If the acid in its oxidized state is stable, the ferrous-iron may be chelated in the following way:

or may be complexed by other ligands. This process is probably responsible for the fact that the ferrous-iron content in profiles is practically always highest in the upper horizon, which is richest in organic matter.

It is beyond doubt a fact that iron can only be mobilized when there is a possibility of complex formation. The next step in the study of the process of cheluviation would be a study of the eluviation rate. However, exact data would then be required about the quantity of rain actually penetrating and percolating the soil. Information is then needed about evapotranspiration of the vegetation, the surface run-off of water and the amount of water intercepted by vegetation and evaporated directly from the leaves. Thorough knowledge of these factors is not available however and consequently estimation of soil forming rates is impossible. It would be worthwile to undertake such studies.

3.3. CHILLUVIATION

The compounds rendered soluble by complex formation are transported into the soil and are deposited somewhere in the subsoil. Several mechanisms can be responsible for this. One mechanism is the hydrolysis of the chelates or complexes. The degree of hydrolysis depends on the formation constants of the complexes, the solubility products of the hydroxides of the complexed metals and the pH level. The hydrolysis reaction may be represented by the following stepwise reactions:

$$ML_y^{(v-yw)+} + OH^- \rightleftharpoons MOHL_y^{(v-yw-1)+}$$
$$MOHL_y^{(v-yw-1)} + OH^- \rightleftharpoons M(OH)_2L_y^{(v-yw-2)+}$$
$$\vdots$$
$$M(OH)_{v-1}L_y^{(1-yw)} + OH^- \rightleftharpoons M(OH)_v(s) + yL^{w-} \text{ -- -- -- -- -- -- -- -- } (71)$$

The equilibrium constant, in this case called hydrolysis constant, K_h, is formulated:

$$K_{h\,ML_y} = \frac{[L]^y}{[ML_y][OH]^v} \text{ -- -- -- -- -- -- -- -- -- -- -- -- -- } (71a)$$

Multiplying with the metal-ion activity, $[M]$, results in:

$$K_{h\,ML_y} = \frac{[L]^y[M]}{[ML_y][M][OH]^v}$$
$$= \frac{1}{K_{ML_y}K_{so}} \text{ -- -- -- -- -- -- -- -- -- -- -- -- -- -- } (71b)$$

where K_{so} is the thermodynamic solubility product of the hydroxide. If the constant is larger than one (see reaction 71), the chelate is hydrolysed and only stable in acid media; if it is smaller than one, the metal complex is stable also in neutral and slightly alkaline media.

As there is generally a pH-gradient in the soil, it is very well understandable that the complexes formed in the surface horizons are partly hydrolysed deeper in the soil thus leading to deposition of iron oxides.

A second mechanism of iron deposition may be the biological attack and decomposition of the ligand. However, none of these two processes can account for the accumulation of organic matter in subsurface horizons such as in podzols, as in the first case the ligand is set free and drains away and in the latter the ligand is destroyed.

Organic-matter accumulation can be understood if the dissolved organic acids, penetrating with the rainwater into the soil, are able to form insoluble compounds with some metal ion. In the case of p-hydroxybenzoic acid this happens with aluminium. This mechanism could be very important in those profiles where the iron-accumulation horizon is more or less compact and offers a certain resistance to water percolation. The result is that a dense mass of fine roots is formed just above this horizon as water is here readily available. It can be imagined that in this zone also the concentration of organic acids is high because of the decay of the roots with the subsequent increased possibility of precipitation of aluminium. In this way the formation of podzols, more specifically of Humods that have a B_h horizon which shows the highest aluminium content, can be explained. If the pH of the B_h is low, so that iron chelates are not hydrolysed, iron is not accumulated in this horizon, but lower in the profile where pH values are high enough. In other cases it is very understandable that the conditions in the B_h are also favourable for hydrolysis of iron chelates, with the subsequent formation of Orthods.

The formation of Orthods or in other words the formation of podzol profiles with accumulation of iron and aluminium oxide and of organic matter in the B_h horizon, can also be explained if we take into account the investigations of Schnitzer and Skinner (1963 a and b), who found that the organic-matter fraction identified by them was able to complex up to six atoms of iron and aluminium, while the complexes become at the same time increasingly insoluble as more metal was complexed. It is imaginable that organic acids penetrating with the rainwater into the soil gradually take up iron and aluminium on their way downwards, become increasingly 'saturated', and precipitate at a certain depth. If this is true there has to be a relation between the free iron and aluminium content of the parent material, the rate of leaching and the depth of deposition. This was sometimes actually observed (Van Schuylenborgh, 1962). The occurrence of giant podzols in the tropics can be either the result of the high rate of leaching or the extreme poorness in free iron and aluminium.

The following mechanism may also explain the formation of the spodic horizon. It is possible that, initially, mobilization of iron and aluminium is achieved by the most simple organic acids, as organic-matter decomposition is still rapid. As these simple acids are generally soluble and mobile themselves, they could cause considerable movement of iron and aluminium hydroxide. When growing older the conditions for a rapid decomposition of organic-matter deteriorate and more condensed and polymerized organic substances may be formed; these may migrate in colloidal state and may precipitate on the previously deposited iron and aluminium hydroxides, thus forming the B_h horizon. The latter process was suggested by Bloomfield (1953), by Martin and Reeve (1960), and by Martin (1960).

Finally, the suggestion has been made that the substances deposited in the B horizon lose their mobility by repeated drying of the profile (Bloomfield, 1956); consequently, these become stabilized and fixed in their position. Although this process could occur, it is thought to be unimportant in the formation of the discussed podzol profiles, as the climate under which these are formed is very humid and dessiccation of the profile certainly does not occur.

458

LITERATURE CITED

BATES, R.G. and PINCHING, G.D. 1949 Resolution of the dissociation constants of citric acid at 0° to 50°, and determination of certain related thermodynamic functions. *J. Am. Chem. Soc.*, 71: 1274–1283.

BERTIN-BATSCH, C. 1952 Etude par des méthodes variées de quelques complexes organiques de l'ion ferrique. *Ann. Chem. (France)*, 7: 481–525.

BLOOMFIELD, C. 1953 Sesquioxide immobilization and clay movement in podzolic soils. *Nature*, 172: 958.

— 1956 The experimental production of podzolization. *Trans. 6th Int. Cong. Soil Sci.*, E: 21–23.

— 1957 The possible significance of polyphenols in soil formation. *J. Sci. Food Agric.*, 8: 389–392.

— 1959 Mobilization of iron in podzol soils by aqueous leaf extracts. *Chem. Ind.*, No. 9: 259–260.

COULSON, C.B., DAVIES, R.J. and LEWIS, D.A. 1960a Polyphenols in plant humus, and soil. I. Polyphenols of leaves, litter, and superficial humus from mull and mor sites. *J. Soil Sci.*, 11: 20–29.

—,— and — 1960b Polyphenols in plant, humus, and soil. II. Reduction and transport by polyphenols of iron in modal soil columns. *J. Soil Sci.*, 11: 30–45.

GALLAGHER, P.H. 1942/43 The mobile colloidal humus of podzolic soils and its relationship to the process of podzolization. *Proc. Roy. Irish Acad.*, 48B: 213–229.

— and WALSH, TH. 1943/44 The solubility of soil constituents in oxalic acid as an index of the effects of weathering. *Proc. Roy. Irish Acad.*, 49B: 1–27.

GARRELS, R.M. and CHRIST, CH.L. 1965 Solutions, minerals and equilibria. *New York*.

JONES, H.T. and WILLCOX, J.S. 1929 Studies in soil genesis I. *J. Soc. Chem. Ind.*, 48: 304T–309T.

KIELLAND, J. 1937 Individual activity coefficients of ions in aqueous solutions. *J. Amer. Chem. Soc.*, 59: 1675–1678.

LEHMAN, D.S. 1963 Some principles of chelation chemistry. *Soil Sci. Soc. Am. Proc.*, 27: 167–170.

MALCOLM, R.L. and McCRACKEN, R.J. 1968 Canopy drip: A source of mobile organic matter for mobilization of iron and aluminium. *Soil Sci. Soc. Am. Proc.*, 32: 834–838.

MARTIN, A.E. 1960 Chemical studies of podzolic illuvial horizons. V. Flocculation of humus by ferric and ferrous iron and by nickel. *J. Soil Sci.*, 11: 382–394.

— and REEVE, R. 1960 Chemical studies of podzolic illuvial horizons. IV. The flocculation of humus by aluminium. *J. Soil Sci.*, 11: 369–381.

MORTENSEN, J.L. 1963 Complexing of metals by soil organic matter. *Soil Sci. Soc. Am. Proc.*, 27: 179–186.

MUIR, J.W., MORRISON, R.I., BOWN, C.J. and LOGAN, J. 1964 The mobilization of iron by aqueous extracts of plants. I. Composition of the amino-acid and organic-acid fractions of an aqueous extract of pine needles. *J. Soil Sci.*, 15: 220–225.

SCHITZER, M. and DESJARDIN, J.G. 1962 Molecular and equivalent weights of the organic matter of a podzol. *Soil Sci. Soc. Am. Proc.*, 26: 362–365.

— and SKINNER, S.I.M. 1963a Organic-metallic interactions in soils: 1. Reactions between number of metal ions and the organic matter of a Podzol B_h-horizon. *Soil Sci.*, 96 86–94.

— and — 1963b Organo-metallic interactions in soils. 2. Reactions between different forms of iron and alluminium and the organic matter of a Podzol B_h-horizon. *Soil Sci.*, 96: 181–187.

— and — 1965 Organo-metallic interactions in soils. 4. Carboxyl and hydroxyl groups in organic matter and metal retention. *Soil Sci.*, 99: 278–284.

VAN SCHUYLENBORGH, J. 1962 On soil genesis in temperate humid climate. I. Some soil groups in the Netherlands. *Neth. J. agric. Sci.*, 10: 127–144.

— and BRUGGENWERT, M. G. M. 1965 On soil genesis in temperate humid climate. V. The formation of the 'albic' and 'spodic' horizon. *Neth. J. agric. Sci.*, 13 : 267–279.

WARNER, R.C. and WEBER, I. 1953 The cupric and ferric citrate complexes. *J. Am. Chem. Soc.*, 75: 5086–5094.

CHAPTER 4

CLAY MIGRATION
(argeluviation)
AND ACCUMULATION
(argilluviation)

As clay migration results generally in the formation of the argillic horizon, it is necessary to investigate the reasons why clay becomes mobile, why it becomes immobile somewhere in the profile and how the transportation is achieved. A review has been written by McKeague and Arnaud (1969) and some details will be discussed in the following.

The 7th Approximation (supplement March 1967) gives a satisfactory statement of the formation of the argillic horizons, although it does not go into details. It was stated that clay movement: 1) has not yet been reported in the soils of the youngest landscapes; 2) occurs more frequently under forest than under grass vegetation in the same landscape; and 3) in soils subjected to climates with pronounced dry seasons (Brewer and Haldane, 1957; Buol and Hole, 1961; Müller, 1963; Dijkerman et al., 1967; Wright and Foss, 1968). From these facts it can be concluded that the formation of the argillic horizon is a time consuming process, and that vegetation and climate have something to do with it. The 7th Approximation continues as follows:

'Wetting of a dry soil seems to lead to disruption of the fabric and to dispersion of clay. Once dispersed, the clay moves with the percolating water and stops where the percolating water stops. Water percolating in non-capillary voids commonly is stopped by capillary withdrawal into the soil fabric. During this withdrawal the clay is filtered out and deposited on the walls of the non-capillary voids. This explains why illuvial clays are so commonly plastered on the ped faces and on the walls of pores. Such a mechanism for clay movement and deposition is favoured in several ways by a seasonal moisture deficit: Firstly, as mentioned above, wetting a dry soil favours the dispersion of clay; secondly, on drying, cracks form in which percolation of gravitational water or water held with low tension can take place; thirdly, the halting of percolating water by capillary withdrawal is favoured by the strong tendency for dry soil to take up moisture.'

'Water ordinarily does not remain in the non-capillary voids; rather, it will move into and be transported through material having pores of capillary size. Movement of water in non-capillary voids occurs only if the rate of water addition exceeds the capillary conductivity of the soil. As conditions for water percolation in large voids do not usually prevail, clay movement and deposition are likely to be infrequent and sporadic. Thus, a long period of time usually is necessary before the cumulative effect of clay movement becomes readily discernible.'

'Capillarity can have still more to do with the downward movement of water (as well as into the peds). If a lower soil horizon is considerably coarser in texture, capillaries are broken and the water tends to hang in the fine capillaries above. As the water evaporates or is withdrawn by roots, suspended or dissolved materials are left. This action even accentuates the original differences in fineness of capillaries.'

Hence, one of the prerequisites for clay movement is that the clay particles become peptised or dispersed[1] and that there are pores or cracks sufficiently wide to allow rapid water movement. The former can be achieved by lowering the electrolyte content of the soil solution, e.g. by heavy downpours. This lowering of the electrolyte content of the solution results in an increase of the double layer thickness (see table III.7); consequently, the electrical repulsing forces between the particles exceed the specific (attraction) Van der Waals-London forces and the particles are dispersed and are then mobile. The latter seems to occur if the pores or cracks are at least 20μ wide (Schlichting and Blume, 1961; Blume, 1964).

The decrease of the electrolyte content of the soil solution is the result of continual weathering and leaching of the soil; the process leads to the acidification of the surface layers. The stabilizing Ca^{2+} ions are leached down and replaced by H^+ ions. This process happens when the soil pH decreases from 7 to 5 and during this process the clay is very liable to peptise (Schlichting and Blume, 1961; Schwertmann, 1965). At increasing acidification (pH values lowering to 4 and 3), the surface of the clay particles becomes unstable and increasingly saturated with H^+ ions, which results in the loosening of Al from the lattice into the electrical double layer. Hence, aluminium ions are the dominant counter-ions in acid soils. These trivalent counter-ions have a strong flocculating power (see p. 462) and the clay becomes flocculated again. Consequently, acid soils do not show clay migration as easily as moderately acid soils. An example is formed by profile 18. This profile has a textural B horizon, but the clay coatings cannot be observed in thin sections as distinct linings of ped faces (see also: Nettleton et al., 1969). They occur mostly as papules in the soil fabric as a result of disruption by shrinkage and swelling and/or by biological activity. It has to be concluded that under the present day conditions no clay migration occurs in the profile. This is very well possible, as the pH values are very low and Al saturation very high (table II.60). The clay is not mobile in its present state (Slager and Van Schuylenborgh, 1970).

Some additional notes on the stability and instability of suspensions in reference to the conclusions drawn in the previous paragraph, are necessary, although for exact details the reader should refer to the books of Verwey and Overbeek (1948) and of Van Olphen (1963).

In a suspension of electrically charged particles there are four forces acting upon the particles. Firstly, electrical repulsing forces if the particles have charges of the same sign; the magnitude of this force depends on the structure of the diffuse counter-ion atmosphere (electrical double layer) surrounding the particles and the distance between them. Secondly, the specific attraction forces, the Van der Waals-London forces which are practically independent of charge, but are dependent upon the distance between the particles. Thirdly, water molecules collide continually with the particles, because the water molecules are in continual thermal motion.

---

[1] Dijkerman et al. (1967) suggest, however, that also flocculated clays give rise to the formation of clay skins, especially with respect to the sieving (filtration) aspect.

Fourthly, gravity causes the particles to settle, which takes a considerable time if the suspension is stable.

The repulsion forces are inversely proportional to the square of the distance between the particles. The closer the particles the greater the repulsing force. The magnitude of this force depends, as already stated above, upon the structure and thickness of the double layer. If this structure can be correlated with the Gouy theory for flat surfaces, the thickness of the double layer can be calculated as function of the electrolyte concentration, if the charge density of the particles is known. The result of such a calculation is given in table III.7 for particles with a charge density of 11.7 microcoulombs cm^{-2}. If we suppose the thickness of a platy clay particle to be 10^{-5} to 2×10^{-5} cm, the thickness of the double layer is 5 to 10 times the thickness of the clay particle.

TABLE III.7. *Effect of concentration of 1–1 and 2–2 valent salts on the thickness of the double layer of a clay particle with a surface charge of 11.7 microcoulomb cm^{-2}, according to the Gouy theory* (after Van Olphen, 1963)

conc. eq l^{-1}	1–1 salt		2–2 salt	
	$1/k$	φ_0	$1/k$	φ_0
10^{-5}	10^{-5}	355	0.5×10^{-5}	178
10^{-3}	10^{-5}	240	0.5×10^{-5}	120
10^{-1}	10^{-5}	130	0.5×10^{-5}	65

$1/k$ = double layer thickness in cm; φ_0 = surface potential in mV.

The specific Van der Waals-London attraction forces are inversely proportional to the cube of the distance between platy particles. Close proximity of the particles will therefore be necessary to allow the attraction forces to exceed the repulsion forces. This approach needs to be at least 10^{-7} cm (Verwey and Overbeek, 1948). This condition is more difficult to fulfill in 1–1 electrolytes than in 2–2 or 2–1 electrolytes at corresponding concentrations. Consequently clay particles with predominantly divalent cations as counter-ions are flocculated, even if their concentration in the solution is rather low, whereas particles with predominantly monovalent ions as counter-ions are only flocculated if the concentration of these monovelent cations in the solution is high. In the case of 3–1 electrolytes the flocculating power will be highest. The following orders of magnitude of the flocculation values are observed: 25–150 mmoles l^{-1} for monovalent ions, 0.5–2.0 mmoles l^{-1} for divalent ions, and 0.01–0.1 mmoles l^{-1} for trivalent ions (Van Olphen, 1963).

In the discussion of the profiles, used in Part II, we stated and proved that in most cases of formation of an argillic horizon, kaolinite is more readily leached than the 2 : 1 layer minerals. This can probably be explained in the following way. The stability of aggregates or floccules of colloidal particles is the result of the bond that is formed by the adsorbed cations between adjacent particles, which has to be added to the Van der Waals-London forces. The firstly adsorbed cations act like bridges between the charge centres of the colloidal particles (Troelstra, 1941). The stronger the bond clay surface – cation – clay surface the stabler the aggregate or floccule. The strength of this bond is influenced by the charge density of the colloidal particles and the charge of the cations.

The higher the charge density and the higher cations' charge the greater the stability of the floccules. As the charge density of kaolinitic particles is much smaller than of montmorillonitic ones, the aggregates formed by kaolinite are weaker than those of montmorillonite, if the binding cation is the same. This was actually shown by Van Schuylenborgh (1947): aggregates prepared of kaolinite and sand were much less resistant to the impact of water drops as well as to a pure mechanical force than aggregates prepared of montmorillonite and sand under comparable conditions. Consequently, kaolinite particles will be more easily washed down than montmorillonite ones. Also montmorillonitic particles may swell considerably and thus stick in the pores and even clog them.

In the foregoing (p. 461) it was emphasized that clay migration only occurred if the exchange sites of clay had been partially desaturated. However, clay migration can also be observed in calcareous materials (De Meester and Van Schuylenborgh, 1966). This could be partially attributed to the fact that the soil is locally decalcified (Blume, 1964) and from these decalcified spots clay can migrate if the further conditions for clay movement are favourable. On the other hand we have definite proof that also clay and even the calcite particles can move in calcareous materials; the climatic conditions, however, have to be completely dry periods alternating with wet periods and the rains have to start suddenly and be downpours. In other words, arid tropical climates are favourable.

The mechanism of clay migration can be described as follows. At the end of the dry period deep cracks are present in the soil, so that conditions for free water movement are favourable. In calcareous materials there exists a close relationship between the calcium and hydrogen ion activity in the soil solution and the partial CO_2 pressure in soil air. From the reaction:

$$CaCO_3 (s: calcite) + 2H^+ \rightleftharpoons Ca^{2+} + CO_2(g) + H_2O \quad - - - - - - - - - - - \quad (72)$$

can be calculated (using the values of the standard free-energies of formation listed by Robie and Waldbaum (1968)) that

$$lg [Ca^{2+}] = 9.8 - 2pH - lg \varsigma CO_2 \quad - \quad (72a)$$

at 25° C and 1 atm. total pressure, where ςCO_2 is the partial CO_2 pressure in atmospheres.

At the end of a dry period it can be stated that the biological activity of the surface soil is reduced to the minimum and consequently ςCO_2 in the soil air is equal to ςCO_2 of the atmosphere, viz. $10^{-3.52}$ atm. Relation (72a) becomes then:

$$lg [Ca^{2+}] = 13.3 - 2pH \quad - \quad (72b)$$

When the rains start there exists in the first hours certainly no equilibrium between the solid calcite and the solution. Consequently $[Ca^{2+}]$ will be much lower than required by equation (72a) and, as ςCO_2 will not be raised in these first hours, the pH value of the surface soil will be very high. Actually, pH values of dry samples of calcareous soils measured immediately after suspending in water are very high and values of 10 and higher are usual. The effect of the temporarily exceptionally high pH values is that the surface potential of the clay particles increases considerably. This is caused by the fact $\geqslant$SiOH and $>$AlOH groups of the clay particles dissociate, as the dissociation constants of these hydroxyls vary approximately between 10^{-8} and 10^{-10}.

The result of the increased surface charge and the low $[Ca^{2+}]$ is that the possibility of

464

deflocculation and consequently clay migration cannot be excluded under these conditions. Actually, soils where calcic and argillic horizons occur simultaneously, are recognized in arid areas. The 7th Approximation (supplement March 1967) places these soils in the Argid suborder of the Aridisols.

LITERATURE CITED

BLUME, H.-P. 1964 Zum Mechanismus der Tonverlagerung. *Trans. 9th Int. Cong. Soil Sci.*, V: 715–722.

BREWER, R. and HALDANE, A.D. 1957 Preliminary experiments in the development of clay orientation in soils. *Soil Sci.*, 84: 301.

BUOL, S.W. and HOLE, F.D. 1961 Clay skin genesis in Wisconsin soils. *Soil Sci. Soc. Am. Proc.*, 25: 377–379.

DE MEESTER, T. and VAN SCHUYLENBORGH, J. 1966 Genesis and morphology of reddish brown coloured soils of the Konya Basin, Anatolia. *Trans. Conf. Medit. Soils (Madrid):* 365–373.

DIJKERMAN, J.C., CLINE, M.G. and OLSON, G.W. 1967 Properties and genesis of textural subsoil lamellae. *Soil Sci.*, 104: 7–16.

MCKEAGUE, J.A. and ARNAUD, R.J.ST. 1969 Pedotranslocation: eluviation-illuviation in soils during the Quaternary. *Soil Sci.*, 107: 428–434.

MULLER, E.H. 1963 Die Bildungsbedingungen von Braunerden und Parabraunerden sowie die Möglichkeiten ihrer Meliorierung. *Z. Pflern. Düng. Bodenk.*, 103: 112–128.

NETTLETON, W.D., FLACH, K.W. and BRASHER, B.R. 1969 Argillic horizons without clay skins. *Soil Sci. Soc. Am. Proc.*, 33: 121–125.

ROBIE, R. A. and WALDBAUM, D. R. 1968 Thermodynamic properties of minerals and related substances at 298.15°K (25.0°C) and one atmosphere (1.013 bars) pressure and at higher temperatures. *Geol. Survey Bull. 1259*: pp. 256.

SCHLICHTING, E. and BLUME, H.-P. 1961a Das typische Bodenprofil auf jungpleistozänen Geschiebemergel in der westbaltischen Klimaprovinz und sein grundsätzliche Bedeutung. *Z. Pflern. Düng. Bodenk.*, 95: 193–208.

— and — 1961b Art und Ausmasz der Veränderungen des Tonmineralbestandes typischer Böden aus jungpleistozänen Geschiebemergel und ihrer Horizonte. *Z. Pflern. Düng. Bodenk.*, 95: 227–239.

SCHWERTMANN, U. 1965 Austauschbare Kationen und Dispersität von Tonen. *Mitt. deutsch. bodenk. Ges.*, 4: 129–130.

SLAGER, S. and VAN SCHUYLENBORGH, J. 1970 Morphology and geochemistry of three clay soils of a tropical coastal plain (Surinam). *Agric. Res. Rep.* 734 : pp. 34.

SOIL SURVEY STAFF, U.S.A. 1967 Supplement to soil classification system (7th Approximation). *U.S. Dept. Agric.*

TROELSTRA, S.A. 1941 Uitvlokking en omlading. *Thesis Utrecht.*

VAN OLPHEN, H. 1963 An introduction to clay colloid chemistry. *New York.*

VAN SCHUYLENBORGH, J. 1947 A study on soil structure. *Thesis Wageningen.*

VERWEY, E.J.W. and OVERBEEK, J.TH.G. 1948 Theory of the stability of lyophobic colloids. *New York.*

WRIGHT, W.R. and FOSS, J.E. 1968 Movement of silt-sized particles in sand columns. *Soil Sci. Soc. Am. Proc.*, 32: 446–448.

CHAPTER 5

THE BEHAVIOUR OF TITANIA

In the discussion of the profiles (Part II) it was shown that the titania content of the soil increases considerably during continuous weathering and soil formation. In a few instances however, it decreased or remained constant. It is very difficult, if possible at all, to explain the latter phenomenon, but some relevant remarks should be made about it.

If the stabilities of the various possible Ti-oxides are considered as functions of the partial oxygen pressure, cO_2, the following equilibria have to be examined:

$$Ti + \tfrac{1}{2} O_2 \rightleftharpoons TiO \qquad lgK = -\tfrac{1}{2} lg\, cO_2 \qquad lg\, cO_2 = -171.4------- \tag{73}$$

$$2TiO + \tfrac{1}{2} O_2 \rightleftharpoons Ti_2O_3 \qquad lgK = -\tfrac{1}{2} lg\, cO_2 \qquad lg\, cO_2 = -159.0 ------- \tag{74}$$

$$Ti_2O_3 + \tfrac{1}{2} O_2 \rightleftharpoons 2TiO_2 \qquad lgK = -\tfrac{1}{2} lg\, cO_2 \qquad lg\, cO_2 = -121.6 ------- \tag{75}$$

(The equilibrium constants were calculated from standard free-energy of formation values listed by Garrels and Christ, 1965, and by Robie and Waldbaum, 1968).

As the lower limit of water stability is situated at a partial oxygen pressure of $10^{-83.1}$, only TiO_2 (rutile) can occur stably in water. So if a Ti-bearing mineral weathers, TiO_2 will be one of the products. Thermochemical values of the minerals perovskite ($CaTiO_3$), geikielite ($MgTiO_3$), sphene ($CaTiSiO_5$), and ilmenite ($FeTiO_3$) are known. The weathering into rutile can be represented by the following equations:

$$CaTiO_3(s) + 2H^+ \rightleftharpoons Ca^{2+} + TiO_2(s) + H_2O ------------------ \tag{76}$$
$$\Delta F_r^o = -25.0\ kcal$$

$$MgTiO_3(s) + 2H^+ \rightleftharpoons Mg^{2+} + TiO_2(s) + H_2O --------------- \tag{77}$$
$$\Delta F_r^o = -23,4\ kcal$$

$$CaTiSiO_5(s) + H_2O + 2H^+ \rightleftharpoons Ca^{2+} + TiO_2(s) + H_4SiO_4 --------- \tag{78}$$
$$\Delta F_r^o = -12.6\ kcal$$

$$FeTiO_3(s) + H_2O \rightleftharpoons Fe_3O_4(s) + TiO_2(s) + 2H^+ + 2e ----------- \tag{79}$$
$$E_h = 0.15 - 0.06\,pH \tag{79a}$$

Reactions (76), (77), and (78) all have strongly negative free-energy changes of reaction (calculated from the thermochemical values cited by Robie and Waldbaum, 1968), indicating that they easily weather to TiO_2 in contact with water. The oxidation of ilmenite shows that it is only stable under strongly reducing conditions at pH values of 5 to 8.

Several natural silicates contain Ti in their lattices at high temperatures. At low temperature, however, Ti does not fit in the lattice any longer and segregates as tiny rutile needles in the minerals. Upon weathering of these minerals one of the products will be rutile. So it is necessary to examine the solubility of titania. Two hydrates of this oxide are known, $TiO_2.H_2O$ and $TiO_2.2H_2O$. A roughly calculated standard free-energy of formation value of this monohydrate, $TiO(OH)_2$, is known, -253 kcal mol^{-1} (Latimer, 1964). This hydrate dissolves to:

$$TiO(OH)_2 \rightleftharpoons TiO^{2+} + 2OH^- \quad - \quad (80)$$

The solubility product, calculated from the free-energy data, listed by Latimer (1964), is:

$$K_{so} = [TiO^{2+}][OH^-]^2 = 10^{-29} \quad - - - - - - - - - - - - - - - - - - - \quad (80a)$$

In the cases where titania is mobile it is only slight. So, the value of 10^{-7} will be chosen as the boundary for the immobility of the solid. Hence, at pH value of 3, titania is slightly mobile. This is an extremely low pH value but it could have occurred during the formation of profile 3 in Chapter I of Part II.

In the discussion of this profile it was emphasized that strongly reducing conditions must have existed during its formation. It would be imaginable that the reduction of TiO^{2+} to Ti^{3+} could have increased the mobility of titania. According to:

$$Ti^{3+} + H_2O \rightleftharpoons TiO^{2+} + 2H^+ + e \quad - - - - - - - - - - - - - - - - - \quad (81)$$

the redox-potential is:

$$E_h = E° - 0.12\ pH + 0.06\ lg\ \frac{[TiO^{2+}]}{[Ti^{3+}]} \quad - - - - - - - - - - - - - - - \quad (81a)$$

From the free-energy data, listed by Latimer (1964), the value of E° is calculated to be

$0.10V$. At $\dfrac{[TiO^{2+}]}{[Ti^{3+}]} = 1$, (81a) turns into:

$$E_h = 0.10 - 0.12\ pH \quad - \quad (81b)$$

Combining these data into an E_h–pH diagram, fig. III. 17 is obtained.

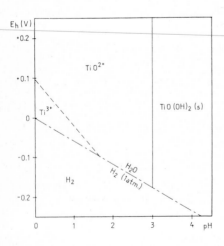

FIG. III.17. *The solubility of TiO(OH)$_2$ as function of E_h and pH at 25°C and 1 atm. pressure*

Evidently, Ti^{3+} cannot contribute to the solubility of $TiO(OH)_2$. Another factor which might stimulate dissolution of titania is the formation of organic complexes. Little is known about the occurrence of organic titanium complexes so that in certain instances the problem of the mobility of titania remains unsolved.

LITERATURE CITED

GARRELS, R.M. and CHRIST, CH.L. 1965 Solutions, minerals, and equilibria. *New York.*
LATIMER, W.M. 1964 Oxidation potentials. 2nd Ed., 6th printing. *Englewood Cliffs, N.J.*
ROBIE, R.A. and WALDBAUM, D.R. 1968 Thermodynamic properties of minerals and related substances at 298.15°K (25.0°C) and one atmosphere (1.013 bars) pressure and at higher temperatures. *Geol. Survey Bull. 1259:* pp. 256.

AUTHORS INDEX

GEOGRAPHIC INDEX

476

SUBJECT INDEX